y

Edited by
Mervyn Richardson

VCH

Distribution:

VCH, P.O. Box 10 11 61, D-69451 Weinheim, Federal Republic of Germany

Switzerland: VCH, P.O. Box, CH-4020 Basel, Switzerland

United Kingdom and Ireland: VCH, 8 Wellington Court, Cambridge CB1 1HZ, United Kingdom

USA and Canada: VCH, 220 East 23rd Street, New York, NY 10010-4606, USA

Japan: VCH, Eikow Building, 10-9 Hongo 1-chome, Bunkyo-ku, Tokyo 113, Japan

ISBN 3-527-28630-6 (VCH Verlagsgesellschaft) ISBN 1-56081-815-8 (VCH Publishers)

# Chemical Safety

## International Reference Manual

Edited by
Mervyn Richardson

VCH Weinheim · New York · Basel · Cambridge · Tokyo

Mervyn Richardson
Birch Assessment Services
for Information on Chemicals
6 Birch Drive
Maple Cross
Rickmansworth
Herts WD3 2UL, UK



Published jointly by
VCH Verlagsgesellschaft, Weinheim (Federal Republic of Germany)
VCH Publishers, New York, NY (USA)

Editorial Director: Dr. Don Emerson

Library of Congress Card No. applied for
A catalogue record for this book is available from the British Library

Die Deutsche Bibliothek – CIP-Einheitsaufnahme
**Chemical safety:** international reference manual / ed. by Mervyn Richardson. –
Weinheim ; New York ; Basel ; Cambridge ; Tokyo :
VCH, 1994
ISBN 3-527-28630-6 (Weinheim ...)
ISBN 1-56081-815-8 (New York)
NE: Richardson, Mervyn [Hrsg.]



Printed on acid-free and low chlorine paper


Printing: Strauss Offsetdruck GmbH, D-69509 Mörlenbach
Bookbinding: NB, D-64630 Heppenheim

Printed in the Federal Republic of Germany

WINDSOR CASTLE

All life and all the earth's inorganic components are locked into a series of chemical reactions. Into this immensely complicated inter-dependent system, humanity has added its own share of problems by devising and using an ever-growing range of chemicals for an ever-growing variety of purposes.

It is now becoming only too obvious that, although these chemicals may have served their purpose admirably, many of them have also had quite unexpected and unwanted side-effects. Furthermore, it has become apparent that there are also any number of human activities, that were never suspected of having any long-term chemical consequences. The release, over many years, of toxic substances and inadvertent pollutants have together created serious problems for the future health of our planet. This chain of disquieting events poses an urgent challenge to the chemical industry and research workers throughout the world.

I warmly welcome the publication of this book for demonstrating the innumerable ways in which chemicals can cause damage, and for showing how these damaging effects can be prevented or controlled.

Philip

# Preface

Mervyn Richardson

The subject of chemical safety is one which affects us all. We are now totally dependent on chemicals: agrochemicals, pharmaceuticals, colorants for aesthetic purposes, etc; the list is almost endless.

What is now essential is to derive the knowledge to decide the safety of these substances and to answer the question — *how safe is safe enough?* The costs entailed in producing a risk-free society would be so great that few benefits would remain; and, the concept of zero risk means that one has a desire to live for ever.

This book leads the reader from the basic concepts in information retrieval, through hazard and risk assessment and risk management, to the all-important topic of chemical safety and legal aspects.

For us to continue to inhabit the Earth, the only planet currently we are able to utilize, or rather ravage, we have to appreciate more fully the safety of chemicals which are vital to our wellbeing, and that of the animals, plants, bacteria, etc. on which we all depend, and which in turn depend on the air, land and water environments. Having seen at first hand in Croatia how warfare is affecting the aggressed, the aggressor and the innocent, I have come to realise that it is vital that politicians, diplomats, and not least the media, inform the global population of the consequences to all of this unwarranted and unnecessary aggression. However, every disadvantage leads to an advantage — the former highly inefficient and polluting chemical industries can now be replaced by those involving high-efficiency, clean, low-waste techniques.

Following the United Nations conference on Environment and Development held in Rio de Janeiro, June 1992, many countries have begun to develop objectives for environmental sustainability.

As chemicals have become the keystone of modern society; chemicals and chemists have to lead the way to a sustainable future. The earth has finite resources but many natural resources are renewable and the potential to utilise these has to be exploited. Previously, an adequate level of sustainability has been found only after decreased production. Today, it is vital that we confront the challenge and meet the goals without any compromise of the ability of future generations to meet their needs.

In the earlier publication *Reproductive Toxicology*, the effects of chemicals on the environment causing reproductive defects, congenital malformations, especially in Central and Eastern Europe, were described by many authors. In the past year further occurrences of mortality exceeding birth rate have been noted, especially in the Commonwealth of Independent States.

In order to sustain, and more objectively, to improve upon the ability of human, natural and mixed systems to withstand and adapt to endogenous or exogenous changes, ideally indefinitely, much greater chemical safety assessment is essential.

Even more so in times of recession, chemists and indeed other industrialists have to be aware that promotion of a good environmental image and sustainability is a requirement for their bankers, insurers, suppliers, shareholders, neighbours, and customers; coupled with pragmatic and demonstrable procedures for the assessment and management of chemical safety.

Chemical safety can never be perfect, and it is vital to assess *how safe is safe enough?*. We, the present generation, must be able to pass on to the next generation a world in a fit state and not one spoilt by unwarranted chemical contamination. Only by this means will it be possible to maintain public health and social and economic welfare at a high level. The road to sustainability is a long, difficult and a tortuous one, but in a world of over 11 million chemicals the first steps must be taken now. *Chemical Safety* outlines the fundamental steps that are necessary. The contribution from its 65 authors drawn from a wealth of experience and eminence in 20 countries — from many ethnic, social and professional backgrounds illustrate both problems and successes, lead the way forward to enable future generations to exist among the chemicals on which we depend. Data included in this volume includes information from Central and Eastern Europe either not previously published or quoted in 'grey' literature in those countries and languages. The manual refers to environments and related aspects in 85 countries.

Our future can be summed up in the words of an Inuit from the tribes of Northern Canada: *I want to cause constructive damage to the status quo*.

As is common with multi-author works, there is some overlap between chapters, but these have been reduced to a minimum by editing, except where it was considered that overlap would enhance the subject matter.

The editor is indebted to the publisher for support, in particular to Dr. Don Emerson, and is greatly appreciative to Pauline Sim of Gascoigne Secretarial Services of High Wycombe, who both retyped the whole book and generally attended to all administrative matters. I also express my most sincere thanks to my wife, Beryl, for general support and who so patiently tolerated my working on this book, the mountains of paper and telephone calls, and for her assistance in the final proofreading and comments to this Preface and to the Epilogue.

Mervyn Richardson
Birch Assessment Services for Information on Chemicals (BASIC)
6 Birch Drive, Maple Cross, Rickmansworth, Hertfordshire WD3 2UL, England.

*'The environmental threats facing the world are so great and so universal that no country, or group of countries, can hope to tackle them alone. They compel us to act together as a world community. They require us to forge a global partnership'.*

Mostaka K. Tolba, Executive Director, United Nations Environment Programme, October 1992.

# Table of Contents

## List of Contributors

Marija Alaćević, Faculty of Food Technology and Biotechnology, Laboratory of Biology and Microbial Genetics, University of Zagreb, Kršnjavoga 25, 41000 Zagreb, Croatia.

Margarita Barkiene, Centre for Environmental Medicine, Lithuanian Ministry of Health, Didžioji st 22, 2104 Vilnius, Lithuania.

Maja Blanuša, Institute for Medical Research and Occupational Health, University of Zagreb, Ksaverska, C.2, POB 291, 41001 Zagreb, Croatia.

Anthony Bulich, Microbics Corporation, 2232 Rutherford Road, Carlsbad, CA 92008, United States of America.

Marlissa A. Campbell, 6 Lovel Road, Chalfont St Peter, Buckinghamshire SL9 9NN, England.

Anne Cowie, Vital Information Ltd, 8 Leighton Road, Linslade, Leighton Buzzard, LU7 7LF, England

Andrew E. Czeizel, Department of Human Genetics & Teratology, National Institute of Hygiene, WHO Collaborating Centre, Gyáti Utca 2-6, H-1097 Budapest, Hungary.

Judith Deschamps, Department of the Environment, Room P3/008D, 2 Marsham Street, London SW1P 3EB

J-M Devos, European Chemical Industrial Council (CEFIC), Avenue E. van Nieuwenhuyse 4, Bte 1, 1160 Brussels, Belgium.

Morrell N. Draper, EDINTOX, Heriot-Watt University, Riccarton, Edinburgh EH14 4AS, Scotland.

Vlasta Drevenkar, Institute for Medical Research and Occupational Health, University of Zagreb, Ksaverska cesta 2, POB 291, 41001 Zagreb, Croatia.

John H. Duffus, EDINTOX, Heriot-Watt University, Riccarton, Edinburgh EH14 4AS, Scotland.

Marja Ekroos, European Chemical Industrial Council (CEFIC), Avenue E. van Nieuwenhuyse 4, Bte 1, 1160 Brussels, Belgium.

Khoja Nepesovich Evzhanov, The Institute of Chemistry of the Academy of Sciences of Turkmenistan, 744012, Ashgabat, Sovetskikh Pogranichnikov str, 92, Turkmenistan.

Sanja Fingler, Institute for Medical Research and Occupational Health, University of Zagreb, Ksaverska cesta, POB 291, 41001 Zagreb, Croatia.

Jasna Franekić, Faculty of Food Technology and Biotechnology, Laboratory of Biology and Microbial Genetics, University of Zagreb, Kršnjavoga 25, 41000 Zagreb, Croatia.

Zlatko Fröbe, Institute for Medical Research and Occupational Health, University of Zagreb, Ksaverska cesta 2, POB 291, 41001 Zagreb, Croatia.

Sharolta Gundy, Department of Human Genetics & Teratology, National Institute of Hygiene, WHO Collaborating Centre, Gyáti Utca 2-6, H-1097 Budapest, Hungary.

Oya Gürel, Department of Environmental Engineering, Dokuz Eylüc University, Faculty of Engineering, Bornova 35100, Izmir, Turkey.

H. Paul A. Illing, Health & Safety Executive, Magdalen House, Stanley Precinct, Bootle, Merseyside L20 3QZ, England.

Costas Ioannides, School of Biological Sciences, University of Surrey, Guildford, Surrey GU2 5XH, England.

Don Isenberg, Microbics Corporation, 2232 Rutherford Road, Carlsbad, CA 92008, United States of America.

Farhat N. Jaffery, Ecotoxicology Division, Industrial Toxicology Research Centre, Lucknow U.P. 226001, India.

Genadijus Jonauskas, Centre for Environmental Medicine, Lithunian Ministry of Health, Didžioji st 22, 2024 Vilnius, Lithuania.

Aga Mamedovich Khojamamedov, Centre of Environmental Medicine, Academy of Sciences of Turkmenistan, 744012, Ashgabat, Sovetskikh Pogranichnikov str, 92, Turkmenistan.

Derek J. Knight, SafePharm Laboratories Ltd., PO Box No. 45, Derby DE1 2BT, England.

Blanka Krauthacker, Institute for Medical Research and Occupational Health, University of Zagreb, Ksaverska cesta 2, POB 291, 41001 Zagreb, Croatia.

Prabhu Kulkarni, Loctite International, New Business Development - Europe, Tallaght Business Park, Whitestown, Tallaght, Dublin 24, Ireland

Yuri Kundiev, Academy of Sciences of the Ukraine, Institute for Occupational Health, WHO Collaborating Centre, 75 Saksagansky Street, 2520033 Kiev, Ukraine.

David F.V. Lewis, School of Biological Sciences, University of Surrey, Guildford, Surrey GU2 5XH, England.

Shen Li, Scientific Information, CAPM, Chinese Academy of Preventive Medicine, WHO Collaborating Centre, 10 Tian Tan XI Li, Beijing, China

Jenö Major, Department of Human Genetics & Teratology, National Institute of Hygiene, WHO Collaborating Centre, Gyáti Utca 2-6, H-1097 Budapest, Hungary.

Slobodan P. Miko, Mining-Geology-Petrology Engineering Faculty, Zagreb University, Picrottijeva 6, 41000 Zagreb, Croatia.

Herbert Motschi, ETAD, Clarastrasse 4, CH-4005 Basel, Switzerland.

Aysen Müezzinoğlu, Department of Environmental Engineering, Dokuz Eylüc University, Faculty of Engineering, Bornova 35100, Izmir, Turkey.

Devika Nag, Department of Neurology, King George's Medical College, Lucknow 226001, U.P. India.

Ksenija Namjesnik, Mining-Geology-Petrology Engineering Faculty, Zagreb University, Picrottijeva 6, 41000 Zagreb, Croatia.

Brendon J. Nangle, Loctite International, New Business Development - Europe, Tallaght Business Park, Whitestown, Tallaght, Dublin 24, Ireland

Mustafa Odabaşi, Department of Environmental Engineering, Dokuz Eylüc University, Faculty of Engineering, Bornova 35100, Izmir, Turkey.

Ladislav Palinkaš, Mining-Geology-Petrology Engineering Faculty, Zagreb University, Picrottijeva 6, 41000 Zagreb, Croatia.

Sheila Pantry, Sheila Pantry Associates, 85 The Meadows, Todwick, Sheffield S31 0JG, England

Dražena Papeš, Faculty of Food Technology and Biotechnology, Laboratory of Biology and Microbial Genetics, University of Zagreb, Kršnjavoga 25, 41000 Zagreb, Croatia.

Dennis, V. Parke, School of Biological Sciences, University of Surrey, Guildford, Surrey GU2 5XH, England.

Peter Pembleton, Industrial & Technological Information Section, United Nations Industrial Development Organization, Vienna International Centre, PO Box 300, A-1400 Vienna, Austria.

Simon Pirc, Faculty of Natural Sciences and Technology, University of Ljubljana, Aškerčeva 20, 61000 Ljubljana, Slovenia.

Jelena Pompe-Gotal, Veterinary Faculty, Zagreb University, Heinzelova 55, 41000 Zagreb, Croatia.

Julius Ptashekas, Centre of Environmental Medicine, Lithuanian Ministry of Health, Didžioji 22, 2024 Vilnius, Lithuania.

Elsa Reiner, Institute for Medical Research and Occupational Health, University of Zagreb, Ksaverska cesta 2, POB 291, 41001 Zagreb, Croatia.

Mervyn Richardson, BASIC, 6 Birch Drive, Maple Cross, Rickmansworth, WD3 2UL, Hertfordshire, England.

Boris L. Rubenchik, Head of Laboratory of Ecology, R.E. Kavetsky Institute for Experimental Pathology, Oncology and Radiobiology, Academy of Sciences of Ukraine 45 Vasikovskaya str., 252022, Kiev-22, Ukraine.

Dr. Motako Saito, Mitsubishi-kasei Institute of Toxicological and Environmental Sciences, 1000 Kamoshida-cho, Midori-ku, Yokohama 227, Japan.

William Seddon-Brown, European Government Affairs, Waste Management International, Avenue de Tervuren 13-B, 1040 Brussels, Belgium

Tadayoshi Shigeoka, Mitsubishi-kasei Institute of Toxicological and Environmental Sciences, 1000 Kamoshida-cho, Midori-ku, Yokohama 227, Japan.

Garislav Shkolenok, United Nations Environment Programme, International Register of Potentially Toxic Chemicals, Case Postale 356, 15 Chemin des Anémones, CH-1219 Châtelaine, Geneva, Switzerland.

Nerida Smith, The National Toxicology Group, Medical School, University of Otago, PO Box 913, Dunedin, New Zealand.

Emil Srebočan, Veterinary Faculty, Zagreb University, Heinzelova 55, 41000 Zagreb, Croatia.

Eva Susanszky, Department of Human Genetics & Teratology, National Institute of Hygiene, WHO Collaborating Centre, Gyáti Utca 2-6, H-1097 Budapest, Hungary.

Wayne Temple, The National Toxicology Group, Medical School, University of Otago, PO Box 913, Dunedin, New Zealand.

Harri Vainio, Unit of Carcinogen Identification and Evaluation, International Agency for Research on Cancer, World Health Organization, 150 Cours Albert Thomas, 69372-Lyon, Cedex 08, France.

Mihaela Vasilescu, Institute of Hygiene & Public Health, Department of Environmental Hygiene, Str. Dr. Leonte 1-3, 76256 Bucharest, Romania.

Tatjana Vergieva, Department of Toxicology, Institute of Hygiene and Occupational Health, D. Nestorov 15, Sofia 1431, Bulgaria.

Nabil Watfa, Occupational Safety & Health Branch, Working Conditions/Environment Department, International Labour Office, 4 Route des Morillons, CH-1211 Geneva 22 Switzerland.

Julian Wilbourn, International Agency for Research on Cancer, World Health Organization, 150 Cours Albert Thomas, 69372-Lyon, Cedex 08, France.

Dr. Kituo Yoshida, Mitsubishi-kasei Institute of Toxicological and Environmental Sciences, 1000 Kamoshida-cho, Midori-ku, Yokohama 227, Japan.

Skirmante Zhlabyte, Centre of Environmental Medicine, Lithuanian Ministry of Health, Didžioji St. 22, 2104 Vilnius, Lithuania.

# 1. Global Chemical Pollution — The UNEP View

Garislav Shkolenok

## 1.1 Introduction

Our modern society is irrevocably dependent on chemicals. Over the past decades chemicals have been developed, manufactured and used in increasing numbers and amounts by a steadily growing number of industries, both in developed and developing countries. At present more than 100,000 of 11 million known chemical substances are traded internationally and about 1000 new ones are introduced into commerce each year. As nations develop their industrial activities, the production and use of chemicals rise in parallel to the standard of living and the consequent increase in life expectancy. Though chemicals have made possible many of the benefits which modern society enjoys, they are also among the chief pollutants of the human environment, as substantial quantities of a wide variety of chemicals are released to the air, water and land from the above-mentioned activities.

Many of the major global problems existing today stem from the introduction of chemical substances into a media in which they may result in harm to human health and the environment. In certain instances seeking a solution to the problem, or the use of alternative substances, may involve the introduction of 'new' chemicals into the environment, the long-term effects of which may still be unknown. In this connection, in the last 2 decades concern over acute health effects has broadened to include such chronic effects as birth defects, genetic and neurological disorders and cancer.

The need for adequate information to assess the potential hazards posed by chemicals has become clearly recognized. Further knowledge about the amounts of production of particular chemicals, pattern of their use, properties and effects on man, biological systems and the environment; as well as their distribution and transformation in the environment is required. This information is an essential basis for environmentally sound management of chemicals.

## 1.2 UNEP Approach

The United Nations Environment Programme (UNEP) addresses the challenge of chemicals in the environment on several levels: mainly through the International Register of Potentially Toxic Chemicals (IRPTC) — part of the Earthwatch programme, through the International Programme on Chemical Safety (IPCS), which was set up jointly by UNEP, the International Labour Office (ILO), and the World Health Organization (WHO) in 1980, and through its work on agrochemicals, etc. (See also chapter by Watfa.)

Due to the magnitude of the problem, careful selection should be made of chemicals which need to be managed in the first instance. Therefore, such chemicals, should be of global concern, considered as those which prevail widely in the environment in significant quantities as a result of their transport through air, water and foodchains; or, because they are present in commodities or traded internationally on a large scale [1]. Chemicals of global environmental significance also include those that have regional or local significance, but that appear so frequently as to cause common concern in a large number of countries. Fortunately, exposure to most chemicals is rather limited, as most are used in very small amounts: some 1500 cover over 95% of total world production.

An activity to reveal global chemical pollution was launched by UNEP in 1981, when at its 9th session, the Governing Council of UNEP recognized that a list of selected environmentally dangerous chemical substances that are harmful at the global level should be prepared.

It was also recognized that such a review could be of policy importance for governments and that special attention should be paid to promoting public awareness of the possible environmental hazards of such chemicals, in order that measures could be adopted to prevent serious impacts. The ultimate goal was to provide risk management advice to governments and others, through fostering of integrated life cycle management and pollution prevention and control approaches for chemicals. At the same international level, the list was intended to be incorporated into the framework of Earthwatch, the global environmental assessment programme, in order to reflect priorities, for example, for monitoring under the Global Environment Monitoring System (GEMS).

## 1.3 List of Selected Environmentally Harmful Chemical Substances, Processes and Phenomena of Global Significance

To meet this requirement such a list was prepared by UNEP and has been continuously updated with the assistance of expert groups and circulated among governments, international organizations, industry and non-governmental organizations for action and comments.

The original list, which was supposed to be short, has undergone various changes: from being originally a 'list' of dangerous chemicals, it moved on to consider the 'processes' involved in the production, use and disposal of chemicals. It moved further, by the very logic of its purpose, to consider the phenomena involved throughout those processes, in recognition of the need for an integrated approach in dealing with impacts and remedies, and finally, it was called the 'List of Selected Environmentally Harmful Chemical Substances, Processes and Phenomena of Global Significance' [2]. In addition, as recommended by an expert consultation held in early 1990, specific monographs on a number of carefully selected industrial and environmental processes and phenomena of global significance in which chemicals play a major role were prepared and, subsequently, peer reviewed by an expert consultation in early 1991, and their executive summaries with recommendations put together in a report by the Executive Director of UNEP to its Governing Council in the same year.

## 1.4 Chemical Pollution: A Global Overview

The extended chapters of these executive summaries made up the body of a publication entitled 'Chemical Pollution: a Global Overview', which was issued by the International Register of Potentially Toxic Chemicals (IRPTC), Geneva, and the Global Environment Monitoring System's Monitoring and Assessment Research Centre (GEMS/MARC), London, in mid-1992 with the financial support of the Ministry of Housing, Physical Planning and Environment of the Netherlands.

This monograph reflects the need for a holistic approach to the problem, rather than the original idea of listing hazardous chemicals and their properties and impacts, and gives a clear assessment of the risks that chemicals present at the global level, as presently understood by the scientific community.

From the outset, it became apparent that certain chemicals contribute to pollution in several problem areas and also that some of these processes or phenomena are interconnected.

Seven themes were covered:

i) Pollution due to industrial chemicals;

ii) Air pollution;

iii) Acidification;

iv) Pollution due to agricultural activities;

v) Eutrophication;

vi) Oil pollution; and,

vii) Solid wastes disposal.

Certain problems involving chemicals such as those related to climatic change and the depletion of the ozone layer are not covered as they are already the subject of substantial concern and careful consideration, and are being specifically addressed by UNEP and others. Pollution by infectious biological material and radiation has not been included in the list.

In the publication, a description of the process or phenomenon given for each of the themes is followed by a discussion of its impact on humans and the environment and a set of control measures. To conclude, recommendations are made with regard to each category.

**Table 1.1** **Reported concentrations of mercury, cadmium and lead in surface layers of nearshore sediments (mg kg$^{-1}$ dry weight) [5]**

| Region/country | Location | Mercury | Cadmium | Lead |
|---|---|---|---|---|
| **Africa** | | | | |
| Côte d'Ivoire | North-east Atlantic | 0.004-2.3 | | 7-250 |
| Nigeria | North-east Atlantic | 0.04-0.16 | 1.84-2.8 | 48-87 |
| West Africa | North-east Atlantic | 0.002-1.4 | 0.1-2.8 | 2-87 |
| **North America** | | | | |
| Bermuda | North-west Atlantic | | <0.25-0.99 | 6.4-230 |
| Canada | North-west Atlantic | 0.61±0.33 | 0.10-0.47 | |
| Costa Rica | North-east Pacific | 0.022±0.029 | 0.12±0.08 | 5.3±3.0 |
| Mexico | North-west Atlantic | | 0.1-2.4 | 10-91 |
| Trinidad | North-west Atlantic | | 0.05-4.5 | 6.7-29 |
| USA | Puget Sound | 0.276 | 0.367 | 43.8 |
| | Southern California Bight[a] | 0.13-4.4 | 0.4-140 | 10-540 |
| | Southern California Bight[a] | | 1.1-6.0 | 32-130 |
| | New York Bight | 0.12-4.9 | <0.47-9.6 | 5-270 |
| | South Carolina | | 0.01-0.46 | 0.3-30 |
| **South America** | | | | |
| Argentina | South-west Atlantic | | 0.24-0.44 | 5.3-19.9 |
| Brazil | South-west Atlantic | 0.2-1.4 | 0.3-1.3 | 15-70 |
| Chile | South-east Pacific | 0.11-0.49 | 1.05-9.16 | 8.6-7.4 |
| **Asia** | | | | |
| China | North-west Pacific | | | 21.6±3.8 |
| India | Bay of Bengal | 0.95-5.3 | | |
| | Bombay | 0.038-0.08 | 10±2 | 48±7 |
| | Cauvery Estuary | 0.118 | 1.85 | 38 |
| | Karwar | 0.05-1.32 | | |
| Iraq | Gulf | | 0.14-0.23 | 5.6-25.6 |
| Israel | Mediterranean | 0.2-0.5 | | 15-28 |
| Japan | Minimata Bay | 23.5-32.4 | | |
| | Seto Inland Sea | | 0.14-0.88 | 14-43 |
| Jordan | Red Sea | | 2-18 | 83-225 |
| Korea | North-west Pacific | | | 25-120 |
| Kuwait | Gulf | | 0.75-3.0 | 10-40 |
| Malaysia | North-west Pacific | | ND-1.21 | 6.5-32 |
| Oman | Gulf | 0.012-0.023 | 2.5-4.7 | 49-63 |
| Philippines | North-west Pacific | | 0.0005-0.11 | |
| Thailand | North-west Pacific | | 0.1-0.4 | 11-18 |

**Table 1.1 (continued)**

| Region/country | Location | Mercury | Cadmium | Lead |
|---|---|---|---|---|
| **Europe** | | | | |
| France | North-east Atlantic | 0.08-0.12 | 0.15-0.21 | 31-45 |
| Greece | Saronikos Gulf | 0.3-10 | | |
| | Thermaikos | | 0.2-5.1 | 18-246 |
| Ireland | Irish Sea | 0.07-3.3 | | |
| Italy | Adriatic Sea | <0.1-16.9 | <0.05-5.6 | 5.3-96 |
| | Bay of Naples | 0.1-1.75 | 5-200 | |
| | Ligurian Sea | | 0.3-7.0 | 36-180 |
| | Sicily[a] | 0.03-2.0 | | 7.5-20 |
| | Sicily[a] | | 2.5-4.6 | 4.5-17 |
| Portugal | Tagus Estuary | 0.02-9.4 | | |
| Spain | Mediterranean | 0.06-16.5 | 0.03-4.0 | 4.8-550 |
| England | Plymouth Estuary | 0.02-2.6 | | |
| **Oceania** | | | | |
| Australia | Albany | | 0.26-7.6 | 13-180 |
| | Darwin | | 0.8-3.1 | 18.3-91 |
| | Port Phillip Bay | | 0.15-9.9 | 4.6-180 |
| New Zealand | Auckland | | | 98-247 |
| | Estuaries and harbours | | | 43±19 |
| | Fjords and sounds | | | 35±10 |
| | Manukau Harbour | | | 98-247 |

[a] Data from different references. Data presented here represent a compilation of data from a number of different published sources. Full details of which are given in the source document. Consequently data are not strictly comparable between locations.

### 1.4.1 Pollution Due to Industrial Chemicals

The following chemicals or groups of chemicals are considered in the chapter on *pollution due to industrial chemicals:*

i) Heavy metals and metalloids, including lead, mercury, cadmium, and arsenic; and,

ii) Aromatic polychlorinated compounds, including PCBs, polychlorobenzenes, pentachlorophenol, selected *p*-dioxins, etc.

In addition, in connection with a description of selected uses of chemicals, wood preservatives, flame-retardant chemicals, washing powders, and detergents, are highlighted as being most important.

Besides data on annual production and/or use of the above mentioned chemicals in the world, information and data are presented regarding health and environmental effects of the chemicals, routes of exposure, transformation in the environment, etc.

As an important source of information, the United Nations Environment Programme Environmental Data Report [4] prepared by GEMS/MARC in cooperation with the World Resources Institute, Washington, DC, and the United Kingdom's Department of the Environment, is referenced in the chapter. As an example of data from the latter UNEP report, concentrations of mercury, cadmium, and lead in surface layers of nearshore sediments are presented in Table 1.1.

### 1.4.2 Air Pollution

In this chapter, sources, occurrence, distribution and processes of pollutants are described. In particular, data on emissions of carbon dioxide, sulfur dioxide, nitric oxide, nitrogen dioxide, etc. are presented, and global and regional impact as well as impact on plants and materials is summarized.

Results of the 1989 European forest damage survey according to defoliation of sample trees are presented (Figure 1.1) for illustration of air pollution impact on plants.

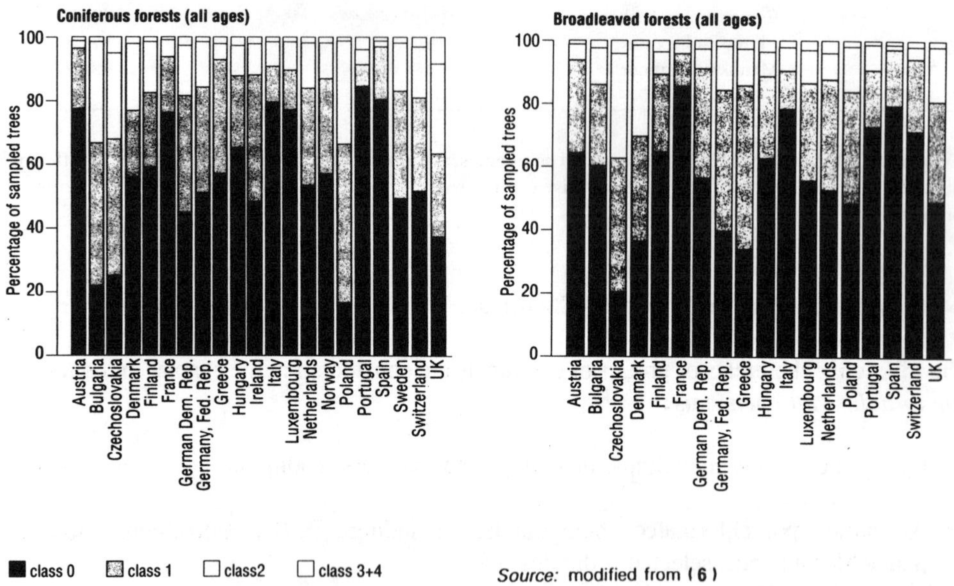


*Source:* modified from (6)

**Figure 1.1** **Results of the 1989 European forest damage survey expressed as a percentage distribution of sample trees according to defoliation [6]**

Existing control strategies reviewed in this chapter include *inter alia* references to the UN-ECE 1979 Convention on Long-range Transboundary Air Pollution and the related Protocols concerning the reduction/control of sulfur and nitrogen oxides emissions or their transboundary fluxes [7]. In addition, research and monitoring priorities as well as legislative and policy priorities and control methods are presented in the recommendations section.

### 1.4.3 Acidification

Pollution due to acidification also constitutes a separate chapter. Sources of this type of pollution and various naturally occurring processes in the atmosphere and soil, as well as aquatic processes, are summarized. When reviewing environmental impacts, terrestrial, aquatic effects, impact on both human health and structures and materials are in focus. Of particular importance is a brief summary of international agreements and emission and pollution effects control measures introduced in certain countries.

It is recommended that predictive modelling should be actively continued and expanded as this will allow the evaluation of proposed control measures, whilst maintenance and development of integrated monitoring programmes will enable the effects of implemented control measures to be assessed. Future control strategies should focus not only on the reduction of sulfur and nitrogen oxides emissions but also on the decrease of atmospheric oxidant concentrations. The effects of $NH_4^+$ in acidification processes are likely to increase in importance. Similarly, the role of nitrogen release during sewage treatment, the application of sewage sludges and fertilizer is in need of further clarification.

### 1.4.4 Pollution Due to Agricultural Activities

This review includes direct pollution due to intensification of agriculture by introducing fertilizers, pesticides, etc., and parallel growing of the amount of agricultural wastes, as well as indirect pollution as a resulting from deforestation, soil degradation, desertification, and erosion. The exploitation of wetlands and energy farming are also highlighted in the chapter.

Energy farming can be considered as an agricultural activity which may be highly beneficial for man and the environment, being theoretically an attractive, alternative to fossil energy consumption. Several energy farming projects are described in this connection.

It is concluded that due to strong mutual dependency of agriculture and environment, the integration of environmental aspects in agricultural projects is urgently needed. As recommended sustainable agricultural development, taking into consideration long-term productivity over short-term benefits should be encouraged world-wide.

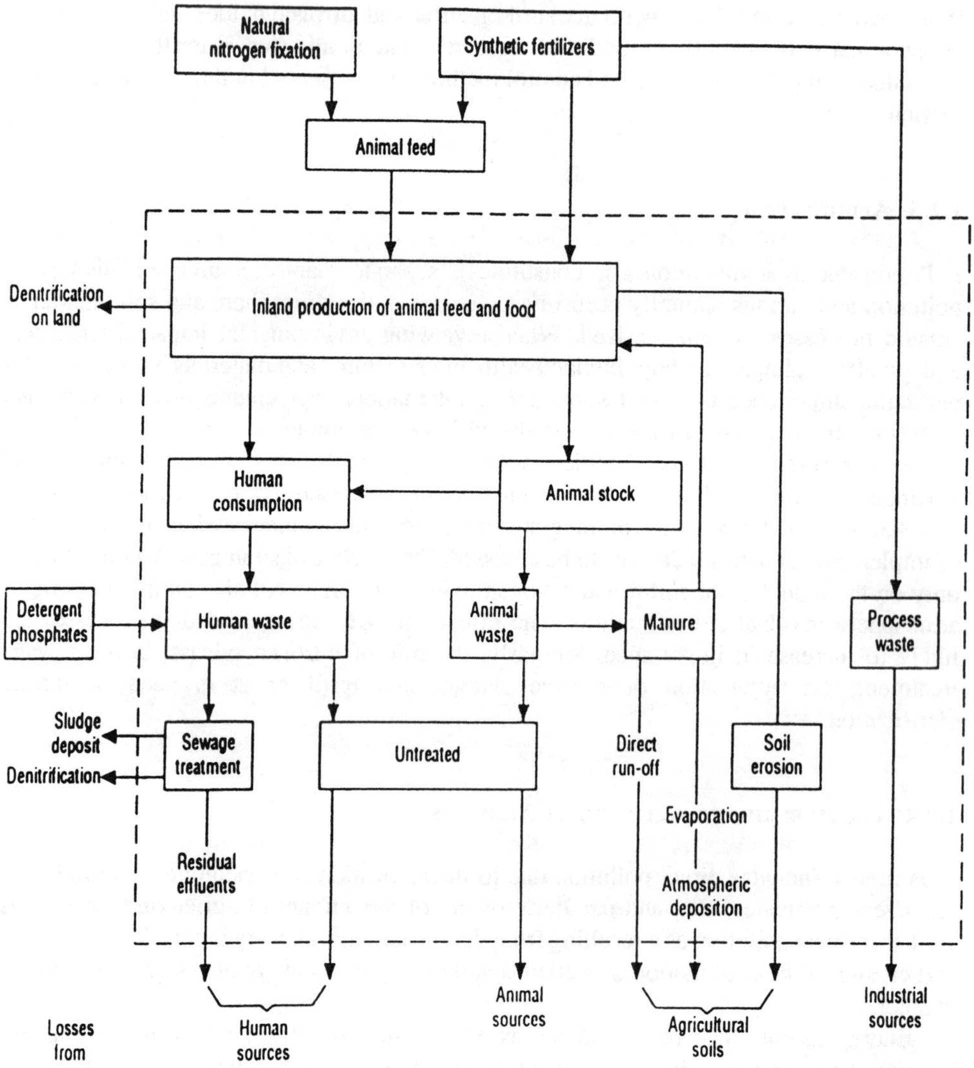


**Figure 1.2** **Regional nutrient balance with external inputs and losses that may contribute to eutrophication [3]**

### 1.4.5 Eutrophication

In this chapter, a brief review of the process occurring in various types of watercourses is presented as a typical result of nutrient imbalances at several levels. Human and industrial sources as well as disturbed biochemical cycles are briefly studied as the cause of such imbalances. In this context, Figure 1.2 provides a scheme of the regional nutrient balance with external input and losses that may contribute to eutrophication [3]. In the section of recommendations regarding actions to stop further proliferation of eutrophication various measures are proposed, *eg*, tertiary treatment of domestic sewage, proper sludge treatment and disposal, landfill and incineration for nutrient recycling, etc.

### 1.4.6 Oil Pollution

Petroleum has become a leading contaminant in prevalence and quantity in many environments, but especially the ocean. Of the 3.2 billion tonnes of oil produced $a^{-1}$, approximately 1 in 1000 or 3.2 million tonnes enter the marine environment each year. In addition, the use of fossil fuels contributes to the increase in greenhouse gases and global climate change. In the chapter on oil pollution inland and marine sources and occurrences are reviewed, along with environmental impacts including various biological effects, effects and polar and tropical ecosystems. Control strategies covering prevention, clean-up, monitoring and research are followed by concrete recommendations.

### 1.4.7 Solid Waste Disposal

It has been estimated that in the European Community alone approximately 2200 million tonnes of waste are generated annually. Estimates of hazardous waste arising in the European Community vary from 17 million tonnes to 70-80 million tonnes, depending on the interpretation of the definition of hazardous wastes in Directive 78/319/EEC [8]. Municipal wastes and consumer wastes, litter, sewage sludges and dredged spoils, agricultural wastes, demolition and construction wastes, mining and quarrying wastes, industrial wastes and hazardous wastes are the categories of wastes considered in the chapter. Impact of wastes and wastes disposal methods on humans and the environment is described in various aspects.

This chapter refers *inter alia* to the Basel Convention on the Control of Transboundary Movements of Hazardous Wastes and their Disposal providing a framework for the control of movement of wastes and prevention of further incidents of their illegal exports [9], and the London Dumping Convention [10] which controls the sea disposal of wastes, and the Oslo Convention [11] covering the north-east Atlantic, the North Sea, and the Baltic Sea.

## 1.5 Recent Activities

A recent consultation convened in Geneva in January 1993 reviewed the use made of the UNEP list and made recommendations for possible further work in light of that review. The experts considered that the work of UNEP in general and of IRPTC in particular, in close cooperation with other United Nations and inter-governmental organizations, as well as governments and non-governmental organizations (NGOs), had contributed over the years to encouraging developments leading to improved chemical safety.

The implementation of Agenda 21, in particular chapter 19 on the 'Environmentally Sound Management of Toxic and Dangerous Products' and the references to aspects of chemical pollution in its other chapters, also requires a broader approach to the assessment of chemical risks than that embodied in the original UNEP list [1].

At the expert consultation, it was concluded that it would seem appropriate to build on the experience accumulated in the preparation of the UNEP list and to broaden its mandate, in response to Agenda 21, to become the mechanism for the preparation of assessments of chemicals, including hazardous chemicals, the global risks they represent to humans and the environment, and the possible means of managing those risks, including early warning, where possible, of problems which may be caused by those chemicals. Any assessments should also support the community's right to know and include the improvement of databases for holding scientific data, including emission inventories.

It was agreed upon that the current approach for the preparation of the List should be further expanded to constitute periodical assessment of critical chemical issues at the global level and become a regular publication of UNEP in the context of the Earthwatch process.

It was proposed that due consideration should be given by UNEP and IRPTC, in particular, to the production of different publications and reports addressing various issues of chemical safety, for example, life cycle management of chemicals; risk reduction for specific chemicals, including the use of currently available clean technology; and methods to prevent accidental discharges of hazardous chemicals. The reports could also include new issues and themes for future assessment, such as biogeochemicals cycles of pollutants, interdependence of pollution problems at the global level, environmental advantages and disadvantages of biotechnology, and biological and environmental indicators of chemical pollution.

The 17th session of the Governing Council held in Nairobi, Kenya, in May 1993 considered the report of the Executive Director, in particular the recommendations made on proposals for an update of the List and requested the Executive Director to follow up on these recommendations.

## 1.6 Recommendations

It was recommended that the List should be replaced by an assessment, every 4 years, of chemicals issues that are critical at the global level; work should be initiated on preparation of the different documents as indicated above; a summary of major issues related to chemicals emanating from the above assessment work should be incorporated into the newly proposed Executive Director's statement on the environment, as appropriate [12].

Each of the above mentioned documents and reports will include action-oriented elements addressed to decision makers at the national level, as well as guidelines suitable for the participation of industry, NGOs and the general public.

## 1.7 References


[1] Earth Summit, Agenda 21, The United Nations programme of Action from Rio, New York, UN Department of Public Information, 1993.

[2] IRPTC Bulletin, 1993, **12**, (1), 6.

[3] *Chemical Pollution: a Global Overview*, United Nations Environment Programme, Geneva, 1992.

[4] United Nations Environment Programme, Environmental Data Report, 3rd Edition, Basel Blackwell, Oxford, 1991.

[5] Fawler, S.W., *Marine Environ. Res.*, 1990, **39**, (1), 64.

[6] UN-ECE/UNEP-GEMS 1990 Forest Damage and Air Pollution: Report of the 1989 Forest Damage Survey in Europe, prepared by the Programme Coordinating Centres with the assistance of the United Nations Environment Programme, Nairobi, and the Secretariat of the UN-Economic Commission for Europe, Geneva.

[7] UN-ECE 1987 Effects and Control of Transboundary Air Pollution, Air Pollution Studies 4, United Nations, New York, and the UN-Economic Commission for Europe, Geneva.

[8] EEC Directive 78/319/EEC, *Off. J. Euro. Commun.*, Brussels, 1978.

[9] Basel Convention on the Control of Transboundary Movements of Hazardous Wastes and their Disposal, Final Act, UNEP, Nairobi, 1989.

[10] Convention on the Prevention of Marine Pollution by Dumping of Wastes and Other Matter, (as amended), London, Mexico City, Moscow, (Washington), 1972.

[11] Convention for the Prevention of Marine Pollution by Dumping from Ships and Aircraft, (as amended), Oslo, 1972.

[12] Governing Council of UNEP, 17th Session, Decision 17/15 of 21 May 1993, UNEP, Nairobi, 1993.

# 2. Principles of Risk Assessment and Risk Management for Chemicals

H. Paul A. Illing

## 2.1 Introduction

Safety, taken here to include health and to refer to both humans and the environment, is the practical certainty that damage will not result from the manufacture, use or disposal of a chemical. In order to achieve safety it is necessary to assess, evaluate and manage risk.

This chapter describes some of the main principles of that assessment, evaluation and management process. Risks can arise at all stages of the cycle of production, use and disposal of a chemical substance. The chapter will concentrate on the risks arising from substances, but these risks are not independent from those relating to processes. *Sustainable development* policies are likely to encourage the use of biotechnological approaches to manufacturing chemicals. Therefore, the chapter will include risk assessment for organisms involved in biotechnological processes.

The subject of risk assessment is complex. There have been many different terms used and it is important to appreciate alternative views on the scope of the subject and the definitions used in risk assessment. Before examining principles it is first necessary to define hazard, harm and risk.

## 2.2 Hazard, Harm and Risk

In 1983 an important report [1] appeared which defined hazard and risk. It emanated from the United Kingdom's Royal Society, and resulted from a study group concerned with risk assessment for engineering and health risks. Definitions of hazard and risk were further elaborated by a Working Party of the United Kingdom's Institution of Chemical Engineers [2] in a document published in 1985 and by a re-formed Royal Society Study Group in 1992 [3]. Both of these bodies included environmental risk in their considerations, although the Royal Society Study Group only defined environmental risk in their second report.

*Hazard* was defined by the Royal Society Study Group as: 'the situation that in particular circumstances could lead to *harm*';

*Harm* as: 'loss to a human being (or a human population) consequent on *damage*'; and,

*Damage* as: 'the loss of inherent quality suffered by an entity (physical or biological).'

In the second report, the Royal Society Study Group called an *environmental hazard*: 'an event, or continuing process, which, if realized, will lead to circumstances having the potential to degrade, directly or indirectly, the quality of the environment in the short or longer term'.

The Working Party of the Institution of Chemical Engineers developed a single definition of *hazard* which covered all of this material: 'a physical situation with a potential for human injury, damage to property, damage to the environment or some combination of these'.

The Institution also developed definitions for a chemical hazard and a major hazard. It called a *chemical hazard*: 'a hazard involving chemicals or processes which may realize its potential through fire, explosion, toxic or corrosive effects'; and, a *major hazard* as: 'an imprecise term for a larger scale chemical hazard, especially one which may be realized through an acute event'.

Typically, for chemical substances the hazard is due to the presence of the substance in an appropriate physical form. Harm includes deleterious effects on human health (whether mediated directly or via the environment). By extension to individual organisms, populations, communities, ecosystems and the biosphere, harm also includes deleterious effects on the environment. Hazard, therefore, depends on the properties of the substance and the way in which the substance interacts with the organism, either directly or indirectly.

To the Royal Society Study Groups, *risk* is: 'the probability that a particular adverse event occurs during a stated period of time or results from a particular challenge'.

This was extended to: 'the likelihood of a specific undesired effect occurring within a specified time or in specified circumstances' by the Institution of Chemical Engineers Working Party, who continued: 'it may be either a frequency (the number of events occurring in unit time) or a probability (the probability of a specified event following a prior event), depending on circumstances'.

A recent American publication [4] called *risk*: 'the possibility of suffering harm from a hazard'; and, in R v. Board of Trustees of the Science Museum [5], the English Court of Appeal held that *risk* meant: 'a possible source of danger'; and it was not necessary to prove that the agent (in this case *Legionella pneumonophilia*) was present.

Therefore, risk needs a potential for exposure, either as a consequence of an event (usually called an accident) or as incidental exposure occurring in a consequence of the methods and procedures used during manufacturing, use or disposal.

Risk needs to be considered in the context of the individual and that of a society (or population). *Individual risk* is: 'the frequency at which an individual may be expected to sustain a given level of harm from the realization of specified hazards'; and, *societal risk* is 'the relationship between frequency and the number of people suffering from a specified level of harm in a given population from the realization of specified hazards'.

Human risk is often considered both in terms of *individual risk* (which is independent of population density) and *societal risk* (which depends on the size of the population at risk and therefore considers the population contained in a geographical area). Both individual and societal risk are important when examining the potential for accidental exposures, individual risk is the usual form considered when dealing with anticipatable human exposure. Most non-human environmental risks are considered mainly in terms of effects on populations and communities, *ie*, in terms similar to human societal risk;

individual risk becomes important mainly when rare species or valuable organisms are at risk.

## 2.3 Risk Assessment and Risk Management

Risk assessment was not defined by the Royal Society Study Group. The Institution of Chemical Engineers Working Party defined *risk assessment* as: 'the quantitative evaluation of the likelihood of undesired events and the likelihood of harm or damage being caused together with the value judgements made concerning the significance of the results'.

The Royal Society Study Group divided risk assessment into risk estimation and risk evaluation.

*Risk estimation* included:

i) Identification of the outcomes;

ii) Estimation of the magnitude of the associated consequences of these outcomes; and,

iii) The estimation of the probabilities of these outcomes.

If this approach is couched in engineering terms, the outcome is the release of hazardous substance and the consequence is the fire, the explosion, or the toxic or corrosive effect. In these circumstances, the probability of the outcome is defined by such matters as likelihood of a failure and size and dispersion pattern of the release.

The alternative view, usually adopted by biologists and physicians is to consider the outcome in terms of a probability of the end effect, *ie,* the ill-health consequence, occurring as a result of the exposure. The exposure is considered in terms of amount of substance to which the organism is exposed, not in terms of how that amount came to be present. This view prevails in the work of the US National Research Council Committee [6], the World Health Organization (WHO) [7], and the United Kingdom's Committee on Carcinogenicity [8] approaches to risk assessment. In engineering terminology this uncertainty in defining the likelihood of the harm occurring is part of the uncertainty in defining the hazard.

The 'engineers' approach is more obviously appropriate in the case of accidental releases (especially if they are major releases), the 'biologists' relates better to incidental continuing or frequent exposure(s).

Although terminology varies slightly between sources, the 3 sources concerned with biological effects each identify essentially the same 4 stages in the process of risk assessment for chemicals (Table 2.1). A fourth source [4] of US Governmental origin, provides additional stages which extend the exposure assessment to allow for the differences between engineering and biological approaches to risk assessment, although it is aimed primarily at societal risk as it includes population density in the exposure assessment.

for landscape page table 2.1

**Table 2.1** **Definitions of the stages of risk assessment for health effects**

| RS/IChemE [1-3] | Cohrssen/Covello [4] | NRC [6] |
|---|---|---|
| | | **Hazard identification**<br>Determining whether an agent can cause an increase in the incidence of an effect, *eg*, a health condition. |
| Estimation of the magnitude and associated consequence (explosion, fire, toxic effect, corrosion) of the outcomes | **Dose-response assessment**<br>Provides quantitative data on the specific amounts of a risk agent that may reach the organs or tissue of exposed individuals or populations and attempts to estimate the percentage of the exposed populations that might be harmed or injured and, where relevant, the characteristics of such populations (for example, sensitive subgroups such as children or the elderly). | **Dose-response assessment**<br>Characterizing the relationship between dose of an agent administered or received and the incidence of an adverse effect. |
| | **Exposure assessment**<br>Provides quantitative data on individuals, populations, or ecosystems that are, or may be, exposed to a risk agent; the concentrations of the risk agent; and the duration and other characteristics of exposures. | **Exposure assessment**<br>Measuring or estimating the intensity, frequency, and duration of exposure to an agent. |
| Identification of outcome and estimation of the probabilities of these outcomes. | **Source-release assessment**<br>Estimates the amounts, frequencies, and locations of the introduction, release, or escape of risk agents (*eg*, toxic chemicals) from specific sources (*eg*, manufacturing plants) into occupational, residential, or outdoor environments. | |
| **Risk estimate** | **Risk characterization**<br>Integrates the results of the previous steps into a risk statement that includes one or more quantitative estimates of of risk. | **Risk characterization**<br>Estimating the incidence of an effect under the conditions of exposure described in the exposure assessment. |

for landscape page table 2.1 (cont)

| WHO [7] | DH-COC [8] |
|---|---|
| **Hazard identification**<br>Identifying the environment agent of concern, its adverse effects, target populations, and conditions of exposure | **Hazard identification**<br>By review of toxicity data, the results of toxicity testing, and any knowledge of effects on human health |
| **Risk characterization**<br>Describing the different potential health effects of the hazard and quantifying the dose effect and dose-response relationships in a general scientific sense. | **Hazard evaluation**<br>By determination of factors including the dose-response relationship, potency, species variation in susceptibility mechanism of toxicity. |
| **Exposure assessment**<br>Quantifying exposure (dose) in a specific population based on measuring emissions, environmental levels, biological monitoring etc. | **Exposure evaluation**<br>By estimation (or modelling) of probable human exposure, routes of entry and levels of potential exposure. |
| **Risk estimation**<br>The process of combining the risk characterization, dose-response relationships, and exposure estimates to quantify the risks in a specific population. | **Risk estimation**<br>By combination of the animal and/or human toxicity data, with or without mathematical modelling, and an evaluation of any human exposure so that an estimate can be made of the likelihood (or magnitude) of any human health effects which may occur. |

The process of risk assessment differs for manufacturing processes involving microorganisms in order to take into account the ability of the organisms to multiply (or die) and to adapt and produce toxins. One scheme (the 'Brenner' scheme) uses access, expression and damage as the 3 headings under which the risks for microorganisms can be assessed [9].

To the Royal Society Study Group [1] *risk evaluation* is: 'the complex process of determining the **significance or value** of the identified hazards and estimated risks to those concerned or affected by the decision.'

Sociological and political considerations are involved at this stage, as well as scientific principles, and it lies at the interface between risk assessment and risk management. Although the Royal Society Study Group placed risk evaluation with risk assessment, the WHO and the US National Research Council placed it as the initial stage of risk management. Cohrssen and Covello [4] described *risk management* thus: 'Risk management uses the information from the risk assessment (risk estimate) — along with the information about technical resources; social, economic and political values; and control or response options — to determine what action to take to reduce or eliminate a risk.'

The Royal Society Study Group called *risk management:* 'the taking of decisions concerning risks and their subsequent implementation.'

The Institution of Chemical Engineers [2] uses the term *loss prevention*: 'A systematic approach to preventing accidents or minimizing their effects. The activities may be associated with financial loss or safety issues.'

The last definition is very clearly aimed at the technical and economic issues involved in risk management for accidents and does not include consideration of the management of anticipatable exposure or the social or political values in the judgements undertaken. As these latter values are important to the way in which risk management is conducted, we will examine how they might be incorporated into the evaluation process. In the next sections we will examine firstly risk assessment, then, as a separate stage, risk evaluation, and finally risk management (including loss prevention).

### 2.3.1 Risk Assessment

Risk assessment for chemicals can be divided into a number of areas. Hazard identification and, for biological effects, dose response determination are required to establish that a hazard exists. If a substance or process is hazardous, then an exposure assessment is required to establish the nature and type of risk. Dependent on the type of exposure that is being examined, it may also be necessary to consider sources of potential exposure and dispersion patterns for released substances.

#### 2.3.1.1 Identification of Consequences

Identifying the potential harm of an agent may involve all or any of observation, experimental work, information retrieval and deductive work based on physicochemical parameters and structure activity relationships. Hazard identification and dose-response assessment is relatively easy for physical effects (fire, explosion) and can be much more difficult for biological effects. This is because of the problems in interpreting the information identifying harm to humans or the environment. The relationship between cause and effect is usually apparent with the physical agents as the effect (maiming or premature death) normally occurs within a short time of an initiating event. It may be far less obvious for biological effects and be detected only through experimental or epidemiological studies. Ideally biological effects should be identified predictively; frequently they have been discovered *post facto*. In order to reduce the unnecessary repetition of predictive tests, the OECD has developed internationally accepted protocols for tests on chemicals and a quality assurance system based on 'Principles of Good Laboratory Practice' and suitable national Inspection to ensure compliance.

For most human health effects, a dose-response or dose-effect curve is required. The dose-response curve is used in cases of stochastic effects, *ie*, those where the probability of occurrence depends on the dose, whereas a dose effect curve relates severity of response to dose [10]. Dose-effect curves relate to individuals and homogeneous groups best; where large inter-individual differences are apparent, the groups may best be represented by a dose-response curve using a specific point in the individual dose-effect curves as the response, even though a dose-effect curve can be described for each individual within the group. As there are homoeostatic mechanisms attached to many biological processes, thresholds and 'no adverse effect' (or response) levels can be defined for most toxic effects. However, there are circumstances, such as those relating to genotoxic carcinogenicity, where the concept of thresholds is not considered acceptable [8] and others where it cannot be defined for lack of suitable evidence.

Some health effects, *eg*, cancers, and potential environmental change, *eg*, 'holes' in the ozone layer of the earth's atmosphere, are apparent only after a latent period, which may be many years. In these circumstances it is more difficult to identify a foreshortening of life (which may be relatively small, with the death some time after the causal event), or a reduction of quality of life, and to relate that effect to cause.

The concept of extrapolation from experimental data on environmental effects to field situations is via a 'predicted no effect concentration', based on the no-effect concentrations seen in tests conducted in single species. Other data are aimed at indicating biodegradability and bioconcentration potential. Ideally, field data and actual no effect concentrations are more useful, but, because of the difficulties and expense in conducting such studies, this type of data tends to be acquired only in specific circumstances.

Evaluating the evidence of biological hazard often requires skilled scientific judgement. Procedures for assessing biological effects are set out in other parts of this book; detailed descriptions of some of the procedures involved in human health assessment and evaluation have been published elsewhere [10-13].

#### 2.3.1.2 Exposure Assessment and Risk Characterization

One way of categorizing exposure is set out in Figure 2.1. This illustrates that there are a great number of exposure scenarios. While some may be irrelevant to particular substances and processes, normally several will be applicable.

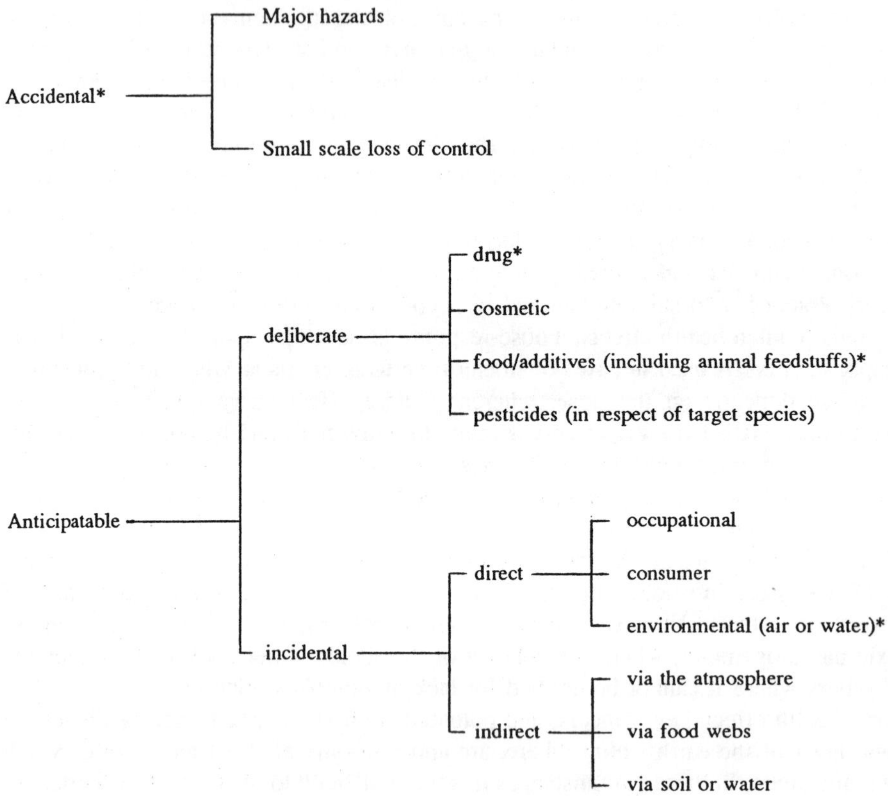


*These types of exposure are relevant to other species as well as man

**Figure 2.1** **A classification of potential exposures to chemicals**
(Reproduced with permission from 'Risk Management of Chemicals', Richardson, M.L. (Ed.), The Royal Society of Chemistry, Cambridge.

Exposure assessments may be based on measured exposure or on modelled exposure. Ideally, measured exposure is desirable, but it only becomes available with experience in use or in trials mimicking predicted use conditions. Models, often based on use or trial data for related substances or situations, may need to be employed predictively if measured data are not available.

The characteristics of the risks being examined depend on the exposure scenario. For each exposure scenario the risks are usually grouped into risks to human health and risks to the environment. In manufacture there are accidental exposures (including, when appropriate, those for major hazards), as well as incidental exposures associated with the normal operation of a process. In use, exposure may vary according to method of release (or application) and may be deliberate or incidental. A good example of variety in scenarios is that of a veterinary drug being used to treat a parasite. Here a risk assessment must cover risks to the pest (risk maximization), the animal on which the pest resides, the operator applying the drug, those manufacturing, formulating and disposing of the drug, those (humans and other species) eating meat from the animal carcass, those affected by the disposal methods, *eg*, through watercourses and into water supplies, etc. The exposure scenarios, and hence the risks change as one moves from examining production to examining use and disposal. In many cases deliberate choices can be made concerning type and level of exposure, by varying the design of the manufacturing process and associated engineering control or by selecting suitable methods of enhancing or preventing/minimizing exposure.

The risk characterization for each individual scenario, obtained from the information acquired for risk estimation may be numerical, as with quantified risk assessment, or more qualitative. The key exposures and hence the critical risk assessment elements should emerge from these data. When estimates of release frequencies and sizes and dispersion patterns are the principal aims of the risk estimation, then the overall risk assessments can be set out in numerical terms (quantified risk assessment). Apart from a small number of well studied effects, such as the cancers due to asbestos or radiation, some authorities believe that the human health data available do not allow quantitative risk assessment to be undertaken with confidence [8]. Nevertheless, others believe in carrying out the quantified risk assessments, while treating the results carefully [14]. However, the data often permit semi-quantitative assessment by expert committee and this method is frequently used when numerical methods are considered unacceptable. More recently, expert systems approaches to risk assessment have been developed [15]. Although less satisfactory than expert judgements or full quantitative risk assessment, they do provide a way of screening large numbers of substances and releasing scarce human expertise for the more critical assessments.

#### 2.3.1.3 The Special Case of Biological Agents

Because organisms have the ability to divide and multiply and to change their pathogenicity by adaption, they have to be regarded somewhat differently to chemicals. Process organisms may be derived from natural sources, but they have usually been adapted either by conventional selection and modification techniques or, in more recent times, using recombinant DNA-based procedures. Survivability in the environment is often greatly weakened during the adaption and the organisms (and cells) may die if not subject to the specialized culture conditions under which they carry out the required process. Nevertheless, consideration should be given to any potential to behave invasively to produce toxic materials or to act as pathogens.

Because of these differences, one way of examining the behaviour of these process organisms is to consider 3 aspects, access and expression (both of which may be required and relate to exposure), and damage (which relates to harm and is the consequence of the exposure). Public concern over organisms developed using recombinant DNA techniques ('genetically modified organisms') has been such that formal assessment procedures have been set out for these agents [9], although the principles are applicable more widely.

| | |
|---|---|
| TECHNICAL ASSESSMENT | Quantitative or qualitative risk assessment, which may require expert judgement. Potential for use of expert systems for preliminary assessments. |
| ⇑⇓ | |
| SOCIETAL INPUT | Process of taking into account the relevant public's perception of the risk. May include a consideration of risk and benefit and proposals concerning management. Can be conducted through 'Advisory Committees' of experts and representatives of interest groups (consensual) or through a judicial process (usually confrontational) |
| ⇑⇓ | |
| OUTCOME PROMULGATION | Legally sanctioned outcomes (*eg*, planning permission, legally enforceable standards) require governmental backing other standards (*eg*, those decided by Trade Associations and Professional Bodies) may have advisory influence. |
| ⇓ | |
| MONITORING/ ENFORCEMENT | The process of ensuring that the instigated management procedures are adhered to. |
| ⇓ | |
| RE-EVALUATION | Risk evaluation and management is an iterative process and all evaluations need re-examination in the light of experience, new knowledge or new interpretations of existing knowledge. |

**Figure 2.2** **Stages in risk evaluation and management**

### 2.3.2 Risk Evaluation

Once levels of risk associated with the manufacture, use, and disposal of a chemical or substance have been estimated, these must be set into a context and judged against criteria to determine whether and what management activity will be needed. At this point societal as well as technical judgements are being undertaken, and risks are being set against benefit. Figure 2.2 outlines the stages involved in risk evaluation and management.

Two main areas will be examined: the concepts of risk acceptability and the legislative frameworks and organizational structures for taking decisions on risk evaluation. Often the decisions taken in evaluations depend on the management procedures that are available and how effective they will be.

#### 2.3.2.1 Risk Acceptability

The Royal Society Study Group [1] suggested a regulatory process on control strategy which takes into account a cost-benefit approach to control. The scheme describes:

i) An upper limit of risk that should not be exceeded for any individual;

ii) Further control, so far as is reasonably practicable, making allowance if possible, for aversions to the higher levels of risk of detriment; and,

iii) A cut-off in the deployment of resources below some level of exposure or detriment judged to be trivial.

These levels can be described as 'unacceptable', 'tolerable', and 'broadly acceptable' risk [16].

When dealing with quantified risk assessment, these definitions need to be linked to some form of numerical value for a defined effect. It is also necessary to distinguish between individual risk and societal risk when drawing conclusions.

The effect criterion normally used for comparisons of individual risk is premature death due to the agent. In practice, this is usually those deaths easily related to a cause, *ie*, those that occurred shortly after an exposure. A risk of 1 person dying in $10^6$ exposed $a^{-1}$ (lifetime risk, statistics on an annual basis are for the whole population, *ie*, all the individuals at all stages of life and exposure) has been proposed for the boundary between 'tolerable' and 'broadly acceptable' risks [1] to the general population, with, *eg*, 1 in $10^3$ being suggested for the boundary 'unacceptable'/'tolerable' for the same population [16]. The actual choice of the appropriate criteria and numbers is a societal decision and the effect description and number chosen and the reasoning behind the choice can therefore vary. This type of mathematical approach is frequently used for major hazard risk assessment and may be used, when there is sufficient data, for stochastic effects (effects either present or absent, *eg*, cancers) following incidental exposure.

When examining societal risk, consideration has to be given both to the frequency of the event and the number of people (organisms) likely to be affected by the event. Therefore, this ties the assessment geographically as it depends on the size (and, possibly, environmental importance) of the population in the area being examined.

For major accident hazards there is a need to develop a criterion or several criteria for harm for inputting into models used to develop estimates of risk levels around the hazard. The models usually require input on the frequency, type and size of releases and the dispersion patterns that could occur. Numbers, usually in terms of a concentration-time relationship yielding the harm, are then attached to the criteria and risk isopleths (lines of equal likelihood of receiving a given level of exposure, and hence harm) are obtained. The type of harm needs to be considered carefully. A relatively severe effect (the 'dangerous dose') is used in the United Kingdom for land use planning purposes. The dangerous dose [17] is the dose which results in:

i) Severe distress to almost everyone;

ii) A substantial fraction require medical attention;

iii) Some people are serously injured, requiring prolonged treatment; or,

iv) Any highly susceptible people might be killed.

For emergency planning purposes, 3 or 4 areas can be delineated [18,19]. The boundaries for and definitions of one description of these areas is given in Table 2.2. The harm criteria are often based on evidence of acute toxicity studies as the most likely type of exposure is single, short term exposure. Acute toxicity data is often limited, and, as ethically obtained human data for serious ill-health is difficult to acquire, the whole process involves considerable uncertainties [20-21]. Nevertheless, it gives an idea of geographic areas for which careful consideration of whether a development should be allowed and the areas for which emergency planning should be undertaken.

Harm criteria for a major accident to the environment are also important. Both the built environment and the natural environment have to be considered. Major accidents can damage historic buildings or monuments, although these will be associated more with the physical consequences of the event than with chemical interactions. Damage to nature reserves, areas of natural beauty and freshwater and marine habitats, as well as groundwater and aquifer contamination all need careful examination when dealing with the natural environment. In some cases individual rare species may be sufficiently important to merit special attention. The relevant criteria for use in the United Kingdom have been published by the Department of the Environment [22].

There are a number of difficulties when examining health and environmental effects following incidental or minor accidental exposure:

i) The quality of the data available for health and environmental effects may be insufficient for numerical approaches to risk assessment;

ii) Even when quality is satisfactory, the type of data often does not lend itself to numerical approaches to risk assessment. The latter applies generally when dealing with predictive testing for toxic effects and extrapolation of data to humans; and,

iii) That most toxic effects are not stochastic.

There is a gradation of effect from mild recoverable effect through frank disease to organ failure/death. Obtaining suitable mathematical models for these effects is, therefore, difficult.

**Table 2.2** **Possible Criteria for categorizing the effect of a major release of a chemical**

| Category | Characteristics |
|---|---|
| **Death/Permanent Incapacity** | Death/Permanent Incapacity occurring either immediately or soon after exposure or a permanent loss of a necessary faculty (*eg*, blindness) resulting in serious restriction of normal social or economic activity. The possibility of surgical correction (*eg*, corneal grafting) does not affect 'permanence'. |
| **Disability** | External assistance is needed because:<br>i) Persons are disabled by exposure and cannot take actions necessary to protect themselves or escape; and/or,<br>ii) Exposed persons acquire an illness or condition;<br>• Of which the outcome or duration can be significantly modified by treatment or nursing care; or,<br>• With permanent or long-lasting residual effects including effects on the outcome of an existing or subsequent pregnancy. |
| **Discomfort** | Exposed persons may request assistance but their condition, though unpleasant and possibly amenable to symptomatic relief:<br>i) Does not produce disablement;<br>ii) Does not result in permanent or long-lasting effects; or,<br>iii) Is not modified as regards outcome and duration by treatment or nursing care. |
| **Detectability** | Exposed persons may make complaints or enquiries or may express anxiety but exposure, if perceived at all, will be perceived only by smell, taste, sight or by sensations (mild sensory irritation) which does not persist after exposure ceases. There are no direct effects of exposure on health. |

Reproduced from reference [18] by permission of the copyright holders, European Centre for Ecotoxicology and Toxicology of Chemicals, Brussels.

In theory, comparisons between dose-effect/response curves and risk boundary curves which allow for differences in acceptable frequencies for effects of varying severity could be utilized, but, in practice concepts such as the 'no adverse effect level' and safety (uncertainty) factors are used. Although attempts have been made to start a discussion on appropriate boundary values for risk estimates for non-lethal effects [23,24], consensus is absent. Thus, currently it would not be practical to use numerical values when examining for these effects.

A much simpler approach used for some assessments is to define categories of hazard or risk and to classify substances or agents and assign them to the appropriate category. Such an approach is used by, for example, the IARC for classifying carcinogens [25]. (See also chapter by Wilbourn and Vainio.) The approach may also lead to specific containment procedures for different categories of agents which might be used as process organisms, including pathogens and genetically modified organisms [26-28].

Environmental effects can be examined using studies on the toxicity, persistence and bioaccumulation for the substance in representative studies in individual species, in microcosms and in observations during field trials. Modelling of the transport and fate of the substance is also helpful. Surveys assist in providing baseline data on habitats and communities present. One aim of this exercise will be to determine how tolerant the environment in question will be at accepting the substance before some form of environmental degradation occurs.

All of the above procedures presume a knowledge of the hazards of the process or agent for which the risk is being assessed. An additional consideration often advocated in the presence of limited evidence, is 'the precautionary principle'. *In extremis*, this approach is based on the premise that until all is known about the process/compound it should not be used or, if in use and some preliminary information suggesting all might not be well emerges, the process/agent be withdrawn. Less extreme versions, include greater care in use while evidence is gathered, are frequently employed to 'feel the way forward' when there is no suitable precedent to follow. One example of this approach is in pharmaceuticals, where there is a progression from animal studies to human clinical trials of increasing size and complexity and to licensing, with, if appropriate, some form of monitored release at first.

All risk assessments need revisiting in the light of new evidence, either of harm or of risk. Thus risk assessment is an iterative process, and a 'final' assessment may well be, as one paper suggested, a myth [29].

#### 2.3.2.2 Structures for Risk Evaluation

Risk evaluation is conducted within a framework. That framework depends on societal and political considerations. Nevertheless, some general approaches can be identified, although specific details will depend on circumstances.

In the main, legislation is used to set acceptable boundaries within society. Legislation may provide for individual decisions, or may reserve decisions to some form of societal judgement at local, national or international level. In terms of chemical safety, this legislation may be connected with:

i) Where to site a plant and how to handle the risks resulting from accidental releases of chemicals at that site;

iii) Whether to allow the manufacturing process in terms of the disposal of by-products and wastes;

iii) Whether to permit the marketing of the intended products; and,

iv) Whether to allow incidental exposure to the raw materials or products during manufacture and to what extent such exposures can be tolerated or accepted.

Only in the most important cases is the actual decision taken or ratified by the national legislative body. More usually legislation is passed which sets up a decision taking structure and general framework for risk management. The appropriate body then considers the detailed technical, etc. material and comes to a decision on whether to allow the specific risk and, usually, what detailed risk management procedures should be undertaken. Alternatively, legislation may leave the legal liability with the user or transfer it from the user to the producer. In these circumstances it is the user or the producer that is the body performing a risk evaluation.

Legislation for risks due to chemicals is usually divided into a number of areas. These tend to follow governmental departmental interests fairly closely, although the divisions are, in scientific and technical terms, often artificial. Consequently, substances may need to comply with more than one set of legislation within the same country.

A societal judgement may be taken by Government after specific enquiry, as with, for example, public enquiries prior to authorization of construction or extension of nuclear or major chemical plants or of developments around them. Alternatively, the societal judgements may be delegated via ministers to specially authorized bodies which contain representatives from interested parties and experts. These bodies may, in turn, obtain professional advice from specific expert committees. The third possibility is that a technical assessment is examined by society through a judicial procedure prior to the final decision being taken.

There can be differences between countries in legislative demands for technical information. As these differences can lead to barriers to trade, considerable effort is being made to internationalize the common element, the hazard assessment, and, where possible, the risk assessment. Assessments of all the known (at a particular time) information on hazard are published by the WHO/International Labour Office (ILO)/United Nations Environment Programme (UNEP) International Programme on Chemical Safety (IPCS) as 'Environmental Health Criteria'. (See also chapter by Watfa.) In addition, prediction of the hazards for chemicals requires the performance of tests and, especially when these tests involve the use of animal models, it is being seen increasingly as unethical to perform more experiments than scientifically necessary on animals.

Risk evaluation is more difficult to internationalize as it includes a knowledge of exposure conditions, ecosystems, agricultural practices and pests, background life expectancies and causes of death and different societal judgements on the importance of various elements within a risk assessment. Nevertheless, it is being attempted by the European Community for many of the uses of chemicals. UN bodies such as the Joint (WHO/Food and Agriculture Organization (FAO), Joint Evaluation Committee on Food Additives (JECFA), and Joint (JECFA/IPCS) Meeting on Pesticide Residues (JMPR) aim to carry out evaluations for specific purposes on a wide international basis. Although possible when there is widespread consensus over the appropriate criteria, this approach is technical and may need modification when the societal judgements behind the standards are not accepted.

### 2.3.3 Risk Management

The first decision in risk management is that of allowing the use of a process of substance. One solution, if the risk is considered excessive, is to refuse to allow the building of a particular plant or the use of a specific substance. Alternatively, it may be deemed that the risks associated with a particular process or substance are sufficiently trivial not to require special management procedures. Detailed consideration of the appropriate management procedures is required if, as will most often be the case, the risk evaluation suggests that the risk from the process or substance lie somewhere between these two extremes.

There are 2 essentially different sets of circumstances which require management:

i) To deal with the consequences of loss of control (as with accidents); and,

ii) To control anticipatable exposure adequately.

#### 2.3.3.1 Accident Risks

When dealing with major accident hazards, both land use planning and emergency planning need to be considered. The former is intended to minimize risks by suitable choice of site and by ensuring developments around a site do not raise the risks to society unacceptably. The latter is aimed at ensuring that any consequences arising from the residual risks can be satisfactorily handled, *ie*, that emergency plans are in place and that the emergency services adequately prepared and briefed.

Similar principles to those for emergency planning for major accidents apply to the planning for smaller scale accidents.

#### 2.3.3.2 Anticipated Risks

Management of anticipated risks is more complex and varies according to circumstance. Controls on exposure can include restriction of outlets or uses, use of process control and/or protective equipment in combination with exposure limits, and management of wastes. Restriction of outlet and uses is typified by medicines, with requirements for prescriptions and issue only through pharmacies; occupational exposure limits, process controls and protective equipment for workplace exposure are typical occupational hygiene practices; 'integrated pollution control' (IPC), using the 'best available technique not entailing excessive cost' (BATNEEC) to control emissions and choosing the 'best practicable environmental option' (BPEO) for any discharges that remain is an approach to protecting the environment. The effectiveness of these controls can depend on attitudes as well as on equipment, and will need monitoring in order to ensure the risks are adequately contained. Monitoring should reveal whether the control measures are adequate or whether further management activity, usually leading to lower exposure and hence lower risk, is needed. Enforcement of standards may be required, and this may be performed by Government through Inspectors, or by self-policing, perhaps through professional bodies.

#### 2.3.3.3 Learning from New Information

In risk management, reaction to new information and changed opinion is essential. Thus there is a cycle of assessment, management and reassessment. In the case of incidents and accidents, lessons are often learned by careful *post facto* examination of the events. One aim of *post facto* enquiries is to learn from previous events, and, when the event is of sufficient seriousness, Governments set up official enquiries in order, *inter alia*, to determine what went wrong and how to reduce the likelihood of it happening again.

## 2.4 Conclusions

This chapter defines the process of risk assessment and risk management for chemicals and the processes used in their manufacture. Many of the ideas currently employed in describing this process are still being developed. The process itself is being examined and new methods appear. Because of the importance to society, the process of risk management has to be carried out in a manner which wins public confidence. Thus the communication of ideas and of the evidence and the conclusions reached is an essential part of the overall management of risks and how they are seen by the public. Without public confidence in the ways in which the risk management decisions are taken, technological progress will be stifled.

Only by means of adequate and satisfactory assessment and management of risk can safety of chemicals be determined. In today's society pragmatic assessments are essential in order to justify asking and answering the question 'how safe is safe enough?'

## 2.5 Disclaimer

The opinions expressed in this chapter are the author's and should not be taken as those of the Health and Safety Executive.

## 2.6 References


[1] Royal Society Study Group, *Risk Assessment*, Royal Society, London, 1983, pp. 198.

[2] Institution of Chemical Engineers Working Party, *Nomenclature for Hazard and Risk Assessment in the Process Industries*, Institution of Chemical Engineers, Rugby, England, 1985, pp. 48.

[3] Royal Society Study Group, *Risk: Analysis, Perception, Management*, Royal Society, London, 1992, pp. 201.

[4] Cohrssen, J.J. and Covello, V., *Risk Analysis: A Guide to the Principles and Methods for Analysing Health and Environmental Risks*, National Technical Information Service, Springfield, VA, USA, 1989, pp. 407.

[5] *Health and Safety Information Bulletin*, 1993 (May) **209**, 13.

[6] Committee on the Institutional Means for the Assessment of Risks to Public Health, *Risk Assessment in the Federal Government, Managing the Process*, National Academy Press, Washington, D.C., 1993, pp. 191.

[7] World Health Organization, *Control of Environmental Hazards*, WHO, Geneva, 1989, pp. 15.

[8] Committee on Carcinogenicity of Chemicals in Food, Consumer Products and the Environment. *Guidelines for the Evaluation of Chemicals for Carcinogenicity*, Reps. Health Social Subjects, 42, HMSO, London, 1991, pp. 80.

[9] Advisory Committee on Genetic Modification, *Guidelines on the Risk Assessment of Operations Involving the Contained Use of Genetically Modified Microorganisms*, ACGM/HSE/Department of the Environment Note 7, HSE, London, 1993, pp. 23.

[10] WHO/UNEP International Programme on Chemical Safety, *Guidelines on Studies in Environmental Epidemiology*, Environmental Health Criteria 27, WHO, Geneva, 1983, p. 131.

[11] WHO/UNEP International Programme on Chemical Safety, *Principles and Methods for Evaluating the Toxicity of Chemicals*, Part 1, Environmental Health Criteria 6, WHO, Geneva, 1978, pp. 272.

[12] WHO/ILO/UNEP International programme on Chemical Safety, *Principles for the Toxicological Assessment of Pesticide Residues in Food*, Environmental Health Criteria 104, WHO, Geneva, 1990, pp. 117.

[13] Illing, H.P.A., 'Industrial Toxicology', in: Croner's *Handbook of Occupational Hygiene*, 1993, Instalment 39, pp. 2.1.1-2.1.23

[14] Niemeyer, R., *Arbete och Halsa*, 1993, **15**, 53-58.

[15] United Kingdom Government/Industry Working Group, *Risk Assessment of Existing Substances*, Department of the Environment, London, 1993, pp. 69.

[16] Health and Safety Executive, *The Tolerability of Risk from Nuclear Power Stations* (revised edition), HMSO, London, 1992, pp. 61.

[17] Health and Safety Executive, *Risk Criteria for Land-Use Planning in the Vicinity of Major Industrial Hazards*, HMSO, London, 1989, pp. 32.

[18] ECETOC Technical Report No. 43, *Emergency Exposure Indices for Industrial Chemicals*, European Chemical Industry Ecology and Toxicology Centre, Brussels, 1991, pp. 69.

[19] Baxter, P.J., Davies, P.C., and Murray, V., *Brit. J. Ind. Med.*, 1989, **46**, 277-285.

[20] Turner, R.M. and Fairhurst, S., *Assessment of the Toxicity of Major Hazard Substances*, Specialist Inspector Report 21, Health and Safety Executive, London, 1989, pp. 13.

[21] Illing, H.P.A., *Human Toxicol.*, 1989, **8**, 369-374.

[22] Anon. *Interpretation of Major Accident to the Environment for the Purposes of the CIMAH Regulations,* Department of the Environment, London, 1991, pp. 13.

[23] Illing, H.P.A., *Human Exptl. Toxicol.*, 1991, **10**, 215-219.

[24] Niemeyer, R., *Arbete och Halsa*, 1993, **15**, 3-40.

[25] International Agency for Research on Cancer. *Preamble*, IARC Monographs on the Evaluation of Carcinogenic Risk to Humans, WHO, Geneva, 1991, **51**, pp. 13-33.

[26] Advisory Committee on Dangerous Pathogens, *Categorization of Pathogens According to Hazard and Categories of Containment*, Second edition, HMSO, London, 1990, pp. 68.

[27] Advisory Committee on Genetic Modification, *Laboratory Containment Facilities for Genetic Manipulation*, ACGM/HSE/DoE Note 8, HSE, London, 1988, pp. 27.

[28] Health and Safety Executive, *A Guide to the Genetically Modified Organisms (Contained Use) Regulations*, 1992, HMSO, London, pp. 50.

[29] Hart, J.W., and Jensen, N.J., *Regulatory Toxicol. Pharmacol.*, 1990, **11**, 121-131.

# 3. Information Retrieval, Validation and Interpretation

Anne Cowie and Mervyn L. Richardson

## 3.1 Introduction

Data on chemicals and their effects, whether pertaining to humans, animals, fish, invertebrates, plants, birds or bacteria, in terms of toxicology and ecotoxicology [1] are vast and often disperse in the literature. However, these data must be retrieved in order to undertake the hazard [2] and risk assessments [3] which are the early steps in making judgements entailing risk management [4] which in turn leads to the topic of this book — 'Chemical Safety'.

Access to the vast store of scientific research results contained in published and unpublished literature has vastly improved since the 1970s with the development of computer systems, both online and CD-ROM. In the 1990s the systems have become more user friendly and cheaper, making it possible to retreive selected data from the comfort of one's own desk using a personal computer. Information in journal articles, books, conference papers, newspaper articles, government reports, patents, company material safety data sheets, 'grey literature' as well as personal databases can be retrieved and manipulated using these systems. CD-ROM technology makes large quantities of data available without the complexities of telecommunications systems. In particular, they are increasingly important where they contain different types of data from a number of sources on a related theme. Similarly, data distributed on other electronic media, *eg,* magnetic tape and diskettes, have grown considerably. These sources are too numerous to mention in this chapter in detail, but are included in a number of published directories [5,6]. This chapter will concentrate on online systems, but see also chapter by Pantry.

To undertake a thorough search of the literature, it is important to use all available sources, and the assistance of specialized librarians or information scientists, as well as personal contacts should never be forgotten.

## 3.2 Online Information Sources: Toxicological and Related Data Stored in Databanks and Databases

### 3.2.1 Databanks

The toxicological profile of a chemical is a compilation of a number of reference values (properties) calculated from previous research, *eg,* $LC_{50}$, $LD_{50}$, log $P_{ow}$, melting points, boiling points, specific gravity, results from Ames tests, exposure limits, and related numeric and factual data. Databanks bring together these results plus other features, *eg,* the test parameters, either by structuring the results of each test within a record or bringing together all of the test results relating to a single chemical. Also many databanks incorporate a peer review program to verify the data prior to them being added to the existing collection, thus ensuring that the data are reliable and have been evaluated. This is of particular importance in the 1990s when, increasingly, data have been produced to accreditation schemes, such as Good Laboratory Practice, etc.

The data in these databanks are taken from previously published or unpublished material, and such databanks can be an important source of research results otherwise unavailable to the public, *eg*, that submitted for product registration purposes. Additionally, it is often a requirement on registration of a product for environmental use (*eg*, pesticides) that a Material Safety Data Sheet (MSDS) is prepared to accompany the product, outlining handling and safety procedures, toxicity to humans, plants and animals, waste disposal procedures, etc. These sheets are available directly from manufacturers. MSDSs are also compiled by organizations other than manufacturers (*eg*, regulatory bodies, trade associations, etc.), some of which are accessible through computer-based systems. Some of the online databanks containing toxicological data or MSDS data are listed in Table 3.1. Details of these and others can be found in review articles [1,7-9]. There are a number of published directories listing availability and contents of electronic databases and databanks. [5,6,10,11].

In addition, a number of standard chemical text books are now available in electronic format. For example, fundamental information on physico-chemical and related chemical properties can be found in Beilstein online for organic chemicals, Gmelin online for inorganic chemicals, and various online or hard copy versions of Dictionary of Organic Chemicals/Inorganic Chemicals, Organo-metallic chemicals, etc. produced by Chapman & Hall, London. The chemical engineer may find it useful to refer to Kirk-Othmer online. Other sources include databanks currently being developed by the International Labour Office, Geneva [12], Aldrich CD-ROM, and others. One recent print publication from The Royal Society of Chemistry, 'The Dictionary of Substances and their Effects' (DOSE) [13] should also be noted although it is only available in print format. DOSE is a multi-volume compilation of information on physico-chemical properties, ecotoxicology and toxicology, expected to include around 5000 chemicals on completion. A record from DOSE is shown in chemicals Annex 1.

**Table 3.1** **Environmental toxicology databanks**

| | |
|---|---|
| **Agrochemical Handbook** | Compiled by The Royal Society of Chemistry, U.K. Contains data on more than 750 active ingredients in chemical products used for pest control and crop protection. (To be merged with The British Crop Protection Council's Pesticide Manual from November 1994.) |
| **AQUIRE** | (Aquatic Information Retrieval). Produced by the Environmental Protection Agency, Office of Pesticides and Toxic Substances, USA. AQUIRE includes data on tests performed on freshwater and saltwater organisms. At March 1990 it contained data on over 5200 chemicals in over 104,000 different assays. |
| **BAKER** | Compiled by J.T. Baker Inc., Phillipsburg, New Jersey, USA. Contains MSDSs for around 1500 chemical substances, using guidelines of the U.S. Occupational Safety and Health Administration (OSHA). |

| | |
|---|---|
| **CCOHS-MSDS** | Compiled by the Canadian Centre for Health Services, Ontario, Canada. MSDSs for commercially available chemical substances used in the workplace. At July 1993 it contained over 85,000 MSDS from over 550 suppliers. |
| **CCRIS** | (Chemical Carcinogenesis Research Information System). Produced by the National Cancer Institute, National Institutes of Health, USA. CCRIS contains data on carcinogenicity and mutagenicity test results. At December 1991 it includes test results for 3134 chemicals. |
| **CESARS** | (Chemical Evaluation Search and Retrieval System). Compiled by Michigan State Department of Natural Resources, Michigan, USA. Contains toxicological data on around 370 chemicals of environmental concern. |
| **CHEMEST** | Compiled by Technical Database Services, New York, USA. Contains data for estimating 11 properties of pharmaceuticals and chemicals of environmental concern. |
| **CHEMINFO** | Produced by the Canadian Centre for Occupational Health and Safety, containing descriptive, health and precautionary data on pure chemicals, natural substances and chemical mixtures resulting from or used in industrial processes. |
| **CHRIS** | (Chemical Hazards Response Information System). Produced by the U.S. Coast Guard, Washington DC, USA, this databank contains information on more than 1210 chemical substances for use in water spill situations. |
| **CIDES** | (Carcinogenicity Information Database of Environmental Substances). Compiled by Technical Database Services, New York, USA. Test results on the carcinogenic and mutagenic effects of approximately 1000 substances of environmental or health concern. |
| **ECDIN** | (European Chemical Data Information Network). Produced by the Joint Research Centre, Environmental Institute of the Commission of the European Communities (CEC). ECDIN contains data on chemicals produced by human activity in such amounts as to be actually or potentially of environmental significance. At December 1991, 19,000 of the 122,400 records contained toxicological or ecological data. |
| **ENVIROFATE** | Produced by the Environmental Protection Agency, Office of Pesticides and Toxic Substances, USA. Envirofate deals with the environmental fate or behaviour of chemicals released into the environment. At January 1992 it contained information on around 800 chemicals. |
| **Environmental Fate Data Bases** | Produced by Syracuse Research Corporation, USA. Four related files contain bibliographic and numeric data on the transport and degradation of organic chemicals released into the environment. |
| **GENETOX** | (Genetic Toxicity) Produced by the Environmental Protection Agency, USA. Mutagenicity information extracted from published literature on more than 4300 chemicals. |
| **HAZARDLINE** | Compiled by Occupational Health Services, New York, USA. Contains regulatory, health and precautionary data on more than 90,000 hazardous chemicals found in the workplace. |
| **HAZINF** | (Hazardous Chemicals Information and Disposal Data Base). Compiled by the University of Alberta, Canada. Contains data on the handling and disposal of more than 220 hazardous substances. |
| **HSDB** | (Hazardous Substances Databank). Produced by the National Library of Medicine, USA. At December 1991 it contained extensive data on the toxicology and environmental effects of 4307 chemicals. |
| **INFOTOX** | Compiled by the Commission de la Sante et de la Securite du Travail du Quebec, Montreal, Canada. Contains more than 5700 MSDSs on pure and compound chemical and biological products used in industrial and commercial applications in Quebec. |
| **IRIS** | (Integrated Risk Information System). Produced by the Environmental Protection Agency, USA. Contains chemical-specific EPA health risk and regulatory information. At December 1991 data on 590 chemicals were included. |

| | |
|---|---|
| **ISHOW** | (Information System for Hazardous Organics in Water) Compiled by the Environmental Protection Agency, Emergency response Division, USA. Contains data on chemical properties of more than 5400 substances found in water. |
| **LOG P AND RELATED PARAMETERS** | Compiled by the Medicinal Chemistry Project at Pomona College, Claremont, CA, this databank contains logP values derived from the published literature for approximately 15,000 organic chemicals, plus other values which can be used to predict logP. |
| **MALLIN** | Compiled by Mallincrodt, Inc., St. Louis, USA. MSDSs for more than 1400 chemical substances used in laboratories within the electronics and other industries. |
| **NPIRS** | (National Pesticide Information Retrieval System) Compiled at Center for Environmental and Regulatory Information System (CERIS), Purdue University, West Lafayette, Indiana, USA. Includes information on around 60,000 pesticide products registered with the US Environmental Protection Agency, including MSDSs and EPA registration applications documents. |
| **OHM/TADS** | (Oils and Hazardous Materials/Technical Assistance Data System) Compiled by the U.S. Environmental Protection Agency. Data gathered from published literature on over 1400 hazardous materials with a view to providing support in the event of discharge. |
| **OHS-MSDS** | Material Safety Datasheets compiled by Occupational Health Services Inc, New York, USA. Identification, handling and hazard information on more than 85,000 chemicals. |
| **Pestline** | Compiled by Occupational Health Services Inc, New York, USA. MSDSs for around 1100 chemicals used in the manufacture of agricultural products. |
| **Phytotox** | Compiled by the University of Oklahoma, USA. Approximately 100,000 records of data extracted from published literature on the toxic effects of organic chemical substances on terrestrial vascular plants. |
| **RTECS** | (Registry of Toxic Effects of Chemical Substances). Produced by National Institute of Occupational Safety and Health (NIOSH), USA. A compilation of toxicity data for substances known to have toxic effects on humans or animals. At June 1992 it contained data on 111,390 chemical substances. |

Whilst each databank is highly structured, in most cases the information for each chemical is not complete, and searching a number of such sources may be necessary. Where there are gaps, the alternative is to scan the published bibliographic literature for research on missing aspects.

### 3.2.2 Databases

In addition to the requirement for hard data in toxicology and, perhaps even more so for ecotoxicology, it is important to keep up to date with new test procedures, test organisms, environmental impact studies, etc. Such information is published in a wide range of primary literature, and subsequently indexing a wide range of secondary indexing and abstracting sources. These indexing sources are usually compiled according to their subject which can be very broad (*eg*, BIOSIS Previews whose subject area is the whole of the life sciences), or narrow (eg the Chemical Safety NewsBase which includes material on chemical hazards at work or in the laboratory).

A number of the databases which contain items of relevance in the context of chemical safety are listed in Table 3.2, while Table 3.3 lists some of the databases specialising in occupational health and safety. Concerning regulatory information, each country has its own health and safety standards, and the regulatory authorities should be consulted regarding these regulations. However, many of the bibliographic databases listed in Table 3.4 include new developments in the regulatory field, *eg*, Chemical Business NewsBase includes relevant material from the Official Journal of the European Communities and the UNEP/IRPTC legal file (see chapter by Shkolenok). By necessity these are only a selection of the available databases, for fuller details the reader is referred to the published guides to online/electronic sources [5,9-11], and in particular the review of business and regulatory information sources by Alston [8].

**Table 3.2** **Bibliographic databases containing environmental/toxicological literature**

| | |
|---|---|
| **Agricola** | The database of the U.S. National Agriculture Library. Covers publications 1970 to date. |
| **Apilit** | Produced by American Petroleum Institute covering non-patent literature relating to the petroleum and petrochemical industry, including health, safety and environmental issues. Covers publications 1964 to date. |
| **Apipat** | Produced by the American Petroleum Institute covering patent literature relating to petroleum and petrochemical industry, including pollution control and waste disposal. Worldwide patent coverage since 1982. |
| **Aqualine** | Published by Water Research centre, U.K. Covers all commercial, technical and scientific aspects of water and wastewater industries, including water quality, sewage and sludge treatment, industrial effluent treatment, and water pollution. Covers publications 1960 to date. |
| **Aquatic Sciences and Fisheries Abstracts** | Published by United Nations Food and Agriculture Organization and Cambridge Scientific Abstracts, MD, USA. Scans primary journals, books, conference proceedings, and reports. Includes aquatic pollution and environmental quality. Covers publications 1978 to date. |
| **BioBusiness** | Published by BIOSIS, Philadelphia, USA, covers published literature, including newsletters and US patents, relating to the industrial applications and economic aspects of biological research. Includes occupational health and toxicology. Covers publications 1985 to date. |
| **BIOSIS Previews** | Published by BIOSIS, Philadelphia, USA, includes published literature back to 1970, including journals articles, conferences, reports and books as well as software and online journals. All aspects of life science research are covered. |
| **Chemicals Abstracts Online** | Produced by the American Chemical Society since 1967, including journal articles, books, conferences, reports, dissertations and patents. The authoritative source of publications on all aspects of chemistry and chemical engineering. |
| **CAB Abstracts** | Produced by CAB International, U.K., covering journals, books, theses, reports, conference proceedings and patents. Includes a broad range of agriculture and biological information. Covers publications 1972 to date. |
| **DHSS-HEF** | Published by the Department of Health, U.K. Covers chemicals in environment, pesticides, industrial chemicals, air and water pollution. Citations taken from journals, conference proceedings, government documents, grey literature etc. received by the Department of Health Library, London. Covers publications 1984 to date. |

| | |
|---|---|
| **Embase** | Published by Elsevier Science Publishers, Netherlands. Includes worldwide biomedical and pharmaceutical literature with special emphasis on European publications. Covers publications 1974 to date. |
| **Enviroline** | Published by R.R. Bowker, New York, USA. Worldwide environmental information, including management, politics, economic aspects. Sources include journals, government documents, industry reports, meeting proceedings, newspapers, etc. Covers publications 1971 to date. |
| **Environmental Bibliography** | Published by Environmental Studies Institute, Santa Barbara, CA, USA. Includes material on human ecology, atmospheric studies, water resources, etc. Covers publications 1973 to date. |
| **Medline** | Published by the National Library of Medicine, USA. Includes biomedical and medical literature. Covers publications 1966 to date. |
| **Oceanic Abstracts** | Published by Cambridge Scientific Abstracts, Bethesda, MD, USA. Includes items from journals, books, government and trade literature, relating to marine biology and marine pollution. Covers publications 1964 to date. |
| **PestDoc** | Published by Derwent Publications, U.K., covers all aspects of pesticides including chemistry, toxicology and environmental effects. Covers publications 1968 to date. |
| **Pollution Abstracts** | Published by Cambridge Scientific Abstracts, Bethesda, MD. USA. Includes all aspects of pollution including environmental quality, pesticides, wastes, etc. Covers publications 1970 to date. |
| **Riskline** | Compiled by the Kemikalieinspektionen Library, Sweden. Includes criteria documents, reports, risk assessment reports in toxicology published by such agencies as the UN Food and Agriculture Organization, US Environmental Protection Agency, National Institute for Occupational Safety and Health and International Agency for Cancer Research. Publications 1972 to date. |
| **Toxicology Abstracts** | Compiled by Cambridge Scientific Abstracts, Bethesda, MD, USA, as part of the Life Sciences Collection. Includes published literature on clinical toxicology, toxic risks in the work place and environmental toxicology. Publications 1978 to date. |
| **TOXLINE** | A compilation by the US National Library of Medicine of about 15 discrete specialist subfiles relating to different aspects of toxicology including environmental pollution, teratogens, mutagens and pesticides. Material in some of the subfiles are included in other databases. Most records date from 1965, historical material is included in some subfiles. |
| **WasteInfo** | Produced by the Waste Management Information Bureau, Harwell Laboratory, U.K. Includes international literature on non-radioactive waste management, including pollution, landfill issues, sewage, toxic and industrial wastes, waste disposal and treatment. As well as scientific research, guidelines, policies, legislation and regulations are also included. Covers publications 1973 to date. |
| **Water Resources Abstracts** | Published by US Department of the Interior, Geological Survey. Prepared from material collected by the US water research organizations in USA. Includes water quality, pollution and waste treatment. Covers publications 1968 to date. |
| **WaterNet** | Published by American Water Works Association, Denver, USA. Includes water quality, wastewater, water pollution from journals, books, government reports, handbooks, manuals, etc., covers publications 1971 to date. |

**Table 3.3** **Biblipgraphic occupational health and safety databases**

| | |
|---|---|
| **Arbline** | Compiled by the Library of the Arbetsmiljoinstitutet, Sweden. Contains citations published since 1972 to Swedish and foreign literature on occupational health and safety. |
| **Chemical Safety NewBase** | Compiled by the Royal Society of Chemistry, U.K. Contains references to worldwide literature on occupational hazards in the chemical industry and laboratories. Publications 1981 to date |
| **CIS Abstracts** | Compiled by the International Labour Office, Geneva, Switzerland. Contains worldwide literature on occupational health and safety. Covers 1972 to date. |
| **Environmental Chemistry, Health & Safety** | A compilation by The Royal Society of Chemistry, U.K., of citations to information on chemicals deemed to cause actual or potential problems to humans or the environment. Covers 1980 to date. |
| **Environmental Health News** | Compiled by Occupational Health Services Inc, New York, USA. Contains the text of news stories relating to environmental and occupational health mainly taken from USA government bodies. |
| **Health and Safety Abstracts** | Compiled by Cambridge Scientific Abstracts, Bethesda, Maryland, USA. Contains citations to safety science and hazard control literature. Covers 1982 to date. |
| **HSELine** | Compiled by the Health and Safety Executive, U.K. Contains citations to worldwide literature on occupational health and safety. Covers 1977 to date. |
| **IH&HU (Industrial Health & Hazards Update)** | Contains the complete text of Industrial Health & Hazards Update which reports on technical and legal aspects of industrial safety. Available 1984 to date. |
| **Occupational Safety and Health** | Compiled by the US National Institute for Occupational Safety and Health. Contains citations to occupational safety and health literature dating back to 1900. |

The accuracy of retrieval from these databases is dependant, amongst other factors, upon the indexing policies of the database producer. These vary considerably depending upon the target audience of the database. In the context of chemical safety, the chemicals are of course the most important aspect of the publication, however chemical nomenclature can present a major problem to online searchers. At one extreme some online records contain only the nomenclature used by the author, and to ensure complete retrieval all synonyms and possible chemical names must be entered during the online search. Searching for long complex names, or chemicals with a large number of synonyms is time consuming and requires a good understanding of the database and how it is created. In other databases records include standard indexing terms for particular classes of chemicals, *eg*, fertilisers or pesticides, thus facilitating selection of records pertaining to defined groups of chemicals. Where a limited number of chemicals are of particular significance, a list of preferred names is sometimes used to index the document irrespective of the authors's terminology. Chemical Abstracts Service Registry Numbers (CAS RNs) are numerical strings assigned by the American Chemical Society to identify precisely every chemical entity. In a similar way Enzyme Commission (EC) numbers uniquely identify enzymes, and EINECS numbers uniquely identify commercial chemical substances transported in the European Community. Such 'names' are used in an increasing number of databases to index significant chemicals and are the most accurate and efficient way of searching on online systems for particular chemicals, because their format is standard and no synonyms are required. The databases in Tables 3.1, 3.2, and 3.3 include examples of all of these types of chemical indexing. The Toxline database is a complex example of this searching problem. This file is a compilation of subfiles from a number of different parent databases, each using different indexing schemes. Some subfiles therefore contain CAS Registry or Enzyme Commission numbers, others use index terms taken from the National Library of Medicine's MeSH thesaurus, while others use different keywords taken form the original database record. Efficient searching requires a knowledge of the structure of each subfile.

Notation to describe stereochemistry, chemical formulae or chemical structure are available in some online systems, in some instances these data can be exported directly into software packages for graphical displays and further manipulation.

It should also be remembered that not every chemical mentioned in a document will be included in the online record of the secondary indexing sources described here. Space is limited in these databases, only 'significant' chemicals, techniques, methodologies, organisms etc will be included, or a maximum number of chemicals permitted in the record. This can be a significant problem when searching for toxicological information where documents review particular aspects of a large number of chemicals. For example a paper by Richardson and Bowron [14] presents a discussion of the fate of pharmaceuticals in the aquatic environment and includes an appendix containing data summaries of around 200 pharmaceuticals, including predicted water concentration and data used in making risk assessments. In the Chemical Abstracts Series Online database no chemicals were specified in the record, but the general index terms 'PHARMACEUTICALS' and 'WATER POLLUTION' were applied. In another example in the same database, the publication of a compilation by Kaiser and Palabrica [15] of some 1350 acute toxicity data of individual organic compounds using the bacterium Photobacterium phosphoreum (Microtox® test) is indexed using the terms 'TOXICITY' and 'CHEMICALS'. Such problems are now being partly overcome by the online availability of full text documents, *ie,* the complete document. Some of the databases listed in Table 3.2 include full text of the documents to which they refer. In addition the complete text of chemical journals published by the American Chemical Society, The Royal Society of Chemistry, John Wiley and Sons, VCH Verlagegesellschaft and Elsevier Science Publishers are all accessible through the STN Online service. The absence of illustrations and graphics can present a problem with this form of presentation. The online availability of the complete text of important text books has already been mentioned. (see 3.2.1.)

## 3.3 Validation of Data

Having retrieved data from either published sources or from research sponsored by one's own institution it is vital to validate the data in order to undertake any hazard assessment.

In many cases it could be found that the data are either incorrect or at the least inapplicable. Data, for example, on hepatocarcinogenicity will be of little value if one is seeking information on avian or reptile eggshell thinning or sewage works performance.

Incorrectness of data may seem surprising to the unwary, as there is a tendency to treat the written word, especially if generated by a computer, as being inherently accurate. There are three broad areas as to why this may not be so:

i) Misprints are a fact of life and will remain so despite the combined efforts of authors, editors, publishers and printers. Have not all of us at some time written μg instead of mg, or — worse ng — such errors can lead to errors of many orders of magnitude.

ii) Advancing knowledge. A journal article and a book are often partially out of date before the 'ink is dry' — this is especially true of toxicology, still a young science. Over the past 2 decades there have been enormous advances in both the interpretation of results and the methods for producing those results. The result is that some data whilst correct at the time of its origination may not be correct as we approach the end of the 20th century. Notwithstanding, the results of the older toxicological results are often invaluable but the assessor must be wary of their limitations.

iii) Incompetence — it is fair to say that some toxicological studies have and will in the future produce incorrect data. These can range from the use of impure samples where the impurities can play a greater role than the major component, the use of inappropriate test procedures, or even mistakes in the evaluation or the interpretation of the data.

## 3.4 Interpretation of Data

It is important that regulators and others interpret toxicological and particularly ecotoxicological data correctly. The public and media alike have a right to react angrily to regulations which either over- or under-estimate the hazardous significance of a substance.

In order to overcome such criticisms the most scrupulous validation of all the relevant data must be taken into consideration. This is particularly so in arriving at no-observable-effect-concentrations (NOEC), or doses or exposures where the consequences of a mistake in the decision process could be very significant. Should the criterion be set too low — irreversible damage may occur — this is now perhaps of great significance in assessing effects to the environment in Central and Eastern Europe. Alternatively, if one chooses a figure embodying too great a safety margin, heavy penalties for society which could result either in terms of over-priced products, in turn leading to non-availability of necessary formulations or articles and loss of jobs.

The whole question of assessment of hazards and risks and risk management is a complex matter outside the scope of this book, and the reader is referred to the Editor's previous works amongst others [1-4].

## 3.5 Assessment of Data

The question of the assessment of data are covered in a number of the other chapters in this book. However, the obvious has to be stressed — namely that one cannot achieve an adequate assessment if the data retrieved are inadequate, irrelevant or incorrect.

The procedures and sources outlined briefly in this chapter will serve to indicate both the problems and solutions in retrieving data for hazard assessments leading ultimately to safety in the synthesis, formulation, transportation, use and disposal of chemicals.

At the end of the day the question ***'How safe is safe enough?'*** has to be answered. Good information retrieval is one of the first stages in the process of answering this question and the scope of this book.

## 3.6 References


[1] Cowie, A., and Richardson, M.L., 'Public Sources of Data' in: *Ecotoxicology Monitoring*, Richardson, M.L. (Ed.), VCH Weinheim, 1993, pp. 37-47.

[2] *Toxic Hazard Assessment of Chemicals*, Richardson, M.L. (Ed.), The Royal Society of Chemistry, London, 1986, pp. 362.

[3] *Risk Assessment of Chemicals in the Environment*, Richardson, M.L. (Ed.), The Royal Society of Chemistry, London, 1988, pp. 580.

[4] *Risk Management of Chemicals*, The Royal Society of Chemistry, Cambridge, 1992, pp. 392.

[5] Finlay, M., and Mitchell, J., (Eds.), *The CD-ROM Directory*, TFPL, London. Updated annually.

[6] *Gale Directory of Databases*, Vol. 2 CD-ROM, Diskette, Magnetic Tape, Handheld, and batch access database products, Gale Research Inc, Washington DC. Updated semi-annually.

[7] Alston, P.G., *Database*, October 1991, pp. 34-62.

[8] Alston, P.G., *Database*, August 1992, pp. 17-35.

[9] Kidd, H. 'Information Sources for Chemistry, Agriculture and the Environment', in: *Chemistry, Agriculture and the Environment*, Richardson, M.L. (Ed.), The Royal Society of Chemistry, Cambridge, 1991. pp. 81-90.

[10] *Gale Directory of Databases, Vol. 1 Online databases.* Gale Research Inc, Washington DC. Updated semi-annually.

[11] *The Online Manual*, Cousins, J. and Robinson, L. (Eds), Blackwell Publishers, Oxford, 1992.

[12] Kogi, K., and Machida, S. 'The Chemical Safety Programme of the ILO', in: *Risk Management of Chemicals*, Richardson, M.L. (Ed.), The Royal Society of Chemistry, Cambridge, 1992. pp. 14-25.

[13] *The Dictionary of Substances and Their Effects*, Richardson, M.L. (Ed.), The Royal Society of Chemistry, Cambridge, Vol. A-B, December 1992, Vol. C, September 1993.

[14] Richardson, M.L., and Bowron J.M., *J. Pharm. Pharmacol.*, 1985, **37**, 1-12.

[15] Kaiser, K.L.E, and Palabrica, V.S. *Wat. Poll. Res. J. Can.*, 1991, **26**, (3), 1-431.

# 4. UNIDO/INTIB: An Energy and Environment Information System for Developing Countries

Peter Pembleton

## 4.1 Introduction

There are clear indications of a growing demand for environment information especially in the small- and medium-scale industry (SMI) sector in developing countries but there is a 'data gap' — between data producers (mostly in developed countries) and data users in developing countries — as well as an 'information technology and services gap' which seriously affects the industrial process in less technologically advanced countries.

This chapter explains the background and genesis of an energy and environment information programme operating in the Industrial and Technological Information Bank (INTIB), within the United Nations Industrial Development Organization (UNIDO).

It will be shown that the programme is related closely to and supportive of emerging trends and priorities in UNIDO and the international, post-Earth Summit environment movements.

## 4.2 UNIDO

The United Nations Industrial Development Organization (UNIDO), based in Vienna, Austria, is the specialized agency responsible for the promotion and acceleration of industrialization in developing countries. Through technical co-operation, policy advice, investment promotion and technical support services, UNIDO assists both governments and the private sector in developing countries to strengthen their industrial base.

As part of the re-orientation of UNIDO's activities, the new Director-General proposed 5 priority areas:

i) Strengthening of national capacity and effectiveness, particularly in human resource development;

ii) Promotion of international competitiveness in industry;

iii) More effective international industrial cooperation in the promotion of foreign investment and technology transfer as well as in regional and sub regional cooperation;

iv) Development, rehabilitation and promotion of the private sector, especially small-scale industry; and,

v) Ecologically Sustainable Industrial Development (ESID).

The objectives of the Organization's Environment Programme, which reflect the ESID concept, are as follows:

i) *'Enunciating and updating environment-related policy and programme formulation and implementation....;*

ii) *Assisting developing countries in building the technical and scientific institutional capacity to develop, absorb and diffuse pollution prevention techniques and cleaner production processes essential to making the transition to ESID;*

iii) *Assisting developing countries in the implementation of international environmental conventions and protocols related to industrial activities;*

iv) *Assisting developing countries in determining the environmental soundness of industrial technologies;*

v) *Assisting developing countries in integrating environmental considerations into their industrial strategies and policies;*

vi) *Assisting developing countries in identifying appropriate, including new, financial resources, where possible on concessional terms, that would enable them to take necessary steps to achieve ESID;*

vii) *Assisting other countries, upon request, in achieving ESID in accordance with the provisions of the UNIDO Constitution and relevant decisions of the General Conference and Industrial Development Board;*

viii) *Strengthening existing database of the United Nations Industrial Development Organization and its capacity to coordinate the dissemination of technical and policy information on ESID* [1].'

The Environment Programme is divided into 4 sub-programmes to support the above objectives, each of which have implicit, if not explicit, information requirements. At the last Industrial Development Board (IDB) meeting, the importance of information for the overall Environment Programme was underlined in a decision which stated that this governing body: *Recognizes the importance of enhancing promotion of ecologically sustainable industrial development (ESID) through undertaking, inter alia, ....information dissemination* [2].

UNIDO and its governing body, therefore, recognize that information is crucial to selecting appropriate technologies, negotiating equitable terms with suppliers of equipment, 'know-how' and services, and achieving an effective transfer of technology for developing countries.

Also, the increasing importance of information in UNIDO's activities is mirrored clearly in the transformation of industry from an energy-intensive and materials-based productive process to an increasingly flexible information- or knowledge-based activity with corresponding changes in the patterns of global productivity. In the final analysis, long-term growth of productivity is related to the introduction, dissemination and use of information in technical and organizational innovations. Thus the developing countries should be given every opportunity to strengthen their national capabilities to select, acquire, adapt and apply foreign technologies, as well as to merge them effectively with their own indigenous technologies. Therefore, investment in sound information is investment in future productivity gains.

UNIDO's Environment Programme includes many activities for which information is required as a support tool or as an output. In order to achieve the various objectives in a coordinated manner, an information programme was developed, the foundation of which is the utilization of existing sources of information wherever feasible, and exploitation of the Organization's comparative advantage — *ie*, the corporate knowledge of industry worldwide gained from the technical and administrative areas of the Organization.

Technical assistance projects implemented by UNIDO number around 2,000 $a^{-1}$, valued at between US$ 130-150 million. About 10% of these are completely environment related (the total number of environment projects has been steadily increasing over the last 5 years and this trend is continuing), while the majority of the remainder reflect varying levels of environmental concern. All projects must undergo an appraisal process which has a built-in assessment of the environmental aspects.

Several hundred experts and consulting agencies are hired for these projects and there are over 400 professional headquarters staff dealing with the full range of industrial activity in all developing countries of the world. This alone represents a massive fund of knowledge which can be drawn upon in any UNIDO information programme.

## 4.3 Industrial and Technological Information Bank (INTIB)

The objectives of UNIDO's information programme are to collect, monitor, analyze and disseminate industrial statistics, industrial investment information and industrial technological information. This not only supports technical co-operation project development by providing relevant statistical and technical data, but also contributes substantive expertise on information technologies. Together with studies and research, information delivery also supports industrial promotion activities at the national, regional and interregional levels.

The Industrial and Technological Information Bank (INTIB), formed in 1979, is specifically responsible for the third of the above areas of information. INTIB: '*aims at assisting developing countries to meet their specific information requirements and thus contribute to the proper selection of technologies and equipment in selected industrial sectors, through the establishment of regional, sub regional, national and sectoral networks providing information on advanced and appropriate technologies, new uses of existing technologies, new developments and their possible adaptation to local needs*' [3].

INTIB functions as a specialized service to coordinate the collection, packaging and dissemination of information, and thus facilitates the transfer of industrial information to developing countries. Under this mandate it must achieve 5 principal objectives:

i) Handling and servicing of industrial inquiries through the Industrial Inquiry Service to help develop and promote information sources and users;

ii) Current awareness building and dissemination of information through a number of periodical and non-periodical publications to provide various levels of access to computerized sources of industrial and technological information;

iii) Capacity-building in national industrial information centres and services in developing countries, through advisory missions, publication of guidelines, training and technical assistance programmes;

iv) Assistance in the development of decentralized information networks; and,

v) Assistance to developing countries in adopting and utilizing modern and effective methods of information processing.

INTIB is an information clearinghouse and comprehensive information service that provides information products both to users within UNIDO and other UN agencies, and to non-UN users. INTIB makes use of a system of mainframe and PC stored and accessed databases, UNIDO in-house experts and a network of national, regional and sectoral focal points that aid both the sourcing and dissemination of information.

INTIB uses a combination of information delivery mechanisms that includes direct supply of information to end-users in developing countries, and delivery through a worldwide, decentralized network. This network includes 4 Regional and almost 80 National Focal Points (RFPs and NFPs, the latter designated by agreement with national governments), and nodes or sectoral network centres cooperating on an informal basis.

In relation to INTIB's sectoral activities, an energy and environment information programme was initiated in 1987, assisted through special financial contributions made to UNIDO by the governments of Sweden and Norway as part of their support to the environmental re-orientation of UNIDO.

## 4.4 The Environment Information Programme

The underlying premise of this programme is that >90% of the information required for improved environmental management is extant — *ie*, it is possible to find appropriate information, given a few basic criteria, the major one being that of 'know-who' or 'know-where', before one comes to the question of information utilization or 'know-how'.

The 'know-how' part of the equation consists of INTIB's strategy to gain access to and consolidate (*ie*, repackage) information on industry and the environment obtained from different sources, with the objective of producing a range of products for dissemination through a variety of media. Computerized conversion and output procedures are needed in order to collate the data in a standard format and to produce value-added information products. 'Know-how' is also a much-used term related to the technology transfer process, of which information collection, repackaging and delivery form the first steps.

The prime objectives are thus:

i) To know what information sources exist;

ii) To assess their content relative to the requirements of the programme;

iii) To gain access to major sources (in other than on-line mode);

iv) To convert the latter information to a common format;

v) To 'tap' UNIDO's institutional knowledge;

vi) To merge and repackage portions of information from the various sources; and,

vii) To disseminate these packages, utilizing various media, mechanisms and intermediaries.

A typical by-product of such an on-going effort is an information bulletin about what is happening both inside and outside the Organization and about where information may be obtained. Such a bulletin was one of the first items to be produced under the programme — the 40th monthly issue of the Environmental Awareness Bulletin (EAB) has recently been released. The EAB was conceived as an in-house awareness tool and will be re-tooled for external requirements in the course of the programme's development.

The information programme draws upon UNIDO's activities carried out under its Environment Programme (outlined above) and on clearing house activities using existing environmental information from various national and international sources. The programme has already developed a range of printed and PC-based information products and has led to an extension of the INTIB network through the addition of special distribution centres.

### 4.4.1 Information Sources

The first task required in developing the programme was to initiate an inventory of existing sources of industrially-oriented information (the 'know-who' and 'know-where'), covering a variety of elements — from basic printed matter, through institutions, experts and computerized sources, to technology descriptions and vendors. Initial references for this undertaking were extracted from existing data bases and other electronic media, reformatted, merged and repackaged before being further processed.

Some of this information collected was made available as the printed *Industry and Environment: A Guide to Sources of Information* (see below). Continuous follow-up of contacts made during day-to-day work and correspondence, recorded through a computer application, ensure that the information is expanded upon and kept updated, as it is planned to issue the *Guide* at regular intervals.

The computer application (Figure 4.1) is a standardized, multi-purpose, relational data base which works at the PC-level with built in routines for data validation. The application is utilized in several units of UNIDO and is linked to a mainframe data base, where all the information is merged into a system of databases which support the programme and the Organization's environment-related activities.

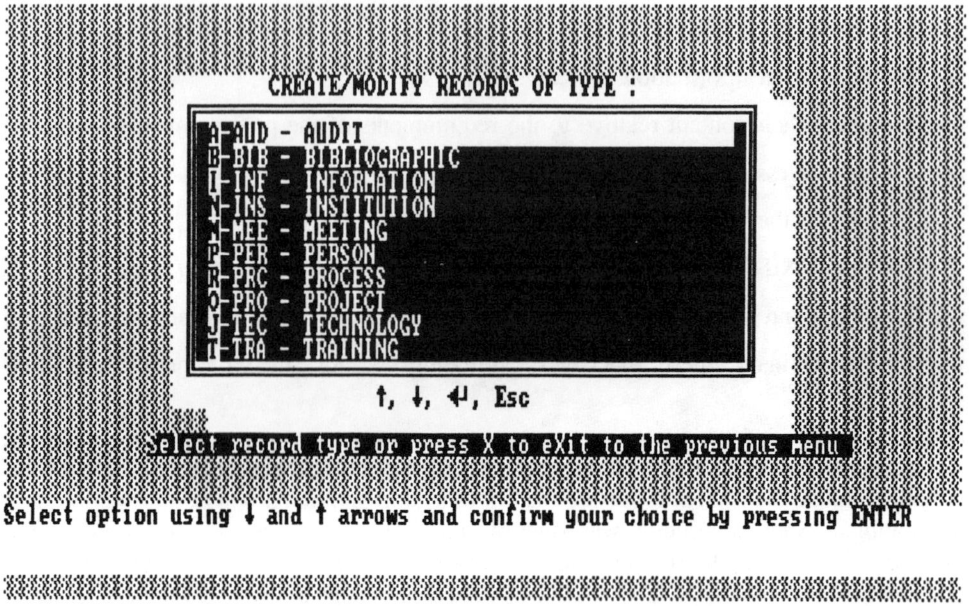


**Figure 4.1** **The computer application: record types**

As can be seen in Figure 4.1, the application contains 11 record types which are a mixture of referral (*eg*, bibliographic references, experts, institutions) and technical (*eg*, industrial processes, technologies and wastes) information.

These record types are augmented by a mailing and correspondence sub-system which allow the registration of customers, together with their interests in INTIB products and services.

The application was recently made available for use in those UNIDO projects and project countries with an environmental information component requiring decentralized information collection. It has already been installed in regional information centres in India and Chile, a national one in Mozambique and in the UN Economic Commission for Europe (UN ECE).

One of the objectives of the programme is to have a standardized computer application as the hub of an integrated system of both internal (UNIDO) and external (non-UNIDO) data bases relevant to industry and environment.

Access to a number of major international data bases dealing with some sectors of industry has already been assured with conversion procedures prepared to load monthly update tapes. Over 250,000 external records have been added to the system of data bases on UNIDO's mainframe since 1990. Around 10% of these deal specifically with environmental issues in those industrial sectors.

Smaller sources of information (*ie*, up to 1000 data items) have also been obtained to assist in the preparation of special products and negotiations are continually underway with a view to gaining access to additional information sources. All of the data obtained from these latter sources cover environmental issues in industry.

### 4.4.2 Products

In 1990 a number of INTIB products were completed and several new activities, which will lead to additional products in the coming years, were initiated. The term 'product' has gained a new meaning for INTIB in recent years, as activities must become market-oriented in the sense that some outputs will be prepared for the commercial markets in both developed and developing countries, in an attempt at income generation to offset the costs of the information programme.

One of the first products to be generated from the programme, is the reference work entitled *Industry and Environment: A Guide to Sources of Information* [4]. The *Guide* contains over 800 references to a variety of information sources, including national, regional and international organizations, as well as basic bibliographic references, commercially available data bases and audio-visual material. The *Guide* contains a subject index and a methodology in English, French, Spanish and German, explaining how to obtain information on the environmental implications of industrial processes. As mentioned above, collection of such information is a continuous process which may never be declared complete, either in a sectoral or a geographical sense. For this reason the *Guide* was conceived as an indicator only, of where further information on industry and environment in general may be obtained. The main users of such information were expected to be in developing countries.

Another product, Micro-METADEX$^{PLUS}$, was developed by UNIDO on the basis of a license agreement with Materials Information (ASM International of the USA and the Institute of Materials of the United Kingdom). This is a PC-based package available at regular market rates in developed countries and at special rates for developing countries. Micro-METADEX$^{PLUS}$ contains information from the world's leading metallurgical data base (METADEX), designed for use in a decentralized information environment, thereby extending the potential user community.

This is especially important for information clients in developing countries who, for a number of reasons, are unable to use remote data access facilities. Future plans for the PC-package are to include data obtained from other data sources available to the programme — special information sets (packages) on specific environmental topics, *inter alia* recycling, energy conservation, effluent control, would then be available over a range of industrial sectors or sub-sectors.

The *Energy and Environment Series* (formerly the *INECA Journal*) is an abstract journal compiled by INTIB from a variety of information sources (including commercial ones such as METADEX, Engineered Materials Abstracts and Materials Business File) with combined subject, author and corporate author indexes. The *Series* is issued quarterly, focusing on special themes. Numbers 1 and 2 have already been released on energy conservation and effluent control respectively. A pre-*Series* number covered recycling and further issues in 1993 will deal with hazardous waste management and industrial safety.

Data for over half of the *Series*' content is made available through INTIB's agreement with Materials Information, which was originally negotiated in 1989 and renewed in 1992, together with a special extension to cover the co-publication of this *Series*.

Despite advances in electronic communication and data transfer media, the programme is likely to concentrate on more traditional methods of distribution for the major information items in the near future, as the programme is now addressing the distribution component of the information transfer equation.

## 4.5 The Energy and Environment Information System (EEIS) Project

### 4.5.1 Background Study

INTIB commissioned a study of the energy and environment information situation in relation to small- and medium-scale industries (SMIs) in developing countries in 1991. The Terms of Reference for this study required *inter alia* an analysis of:

i) Existing international information services, mechanisms and products, with a specific concentration on technological information required for Environmentally Sustainable Industrial Development (ESID);

ii) Appropriate and cost-effective methods and mechanisms to bring the required information to the SMI target group;

iii) Appropriate promotional channels, including issues of sensitization of the target group;

iv) Suitable information brokers and vendors working in or toward this target group, which could assist in the dissemination of the information; and,

v) UNIDO/INTIB services in light of the above.

The study was awarded to Environmental Resources Limited (ERL), which undertook an indicative survey of information systems and requirements using a mix of country studies, telephone interviews and mailed questionnaires. The questions asked attempted to find out the supply of information in the countries reviewed, covering *inter alia*;

i) Information systems or data bases, located in or accessible from the country, which deal with industry and environmental issues;

ii) Awareness of sources of information used by SMIs;

iii) Usage of any external (*ie*, to the organization) data bases, information systems or host networks;

iv) National data gathering, sourcing and information services provided;

v) Types of information covered by existing services together with sources of requests — *ie*, customer profile;

vi) Forms of dissemination, distribution and promotion;

vii) Commercial (if any) aspects of the information service;

viii) If SMIs use non in-house information systems;

ix) Existing or potential demand for an EEIS targeted at SMIs;

x) What drives (or acts as a constraint on) this demand;

xii) Type of energy and environment information required;

xiii) Industry sectors with a particular need for an EEIS;

xiv) Expressed needs by individuals, companies or organizations, for an EEIS;

xv) The language in which such a service could or should be provided;

xvi) The willingness to pay for such a system and the most suitable modalities;

xvii) The most effective contact points for such a service;

xviii) The most efficient forms of communication between EEIS distribution points and the client group; and,

xix) The most effective ways of marketing the EEIS.

The report was finalized early in 1992, long before the Earth Summit agreed to Agenda 21, and the conclusions and resulting programme of action are explained in this Section.

The study concluded that there is a definite gap in the information flow to this target group and UNIDO/INTIB has put the Energy and Environment Information System (EEIS) project in place to address this problem.

The study further concluded that there are few systems that hold such information, that those that do, do not target SMIs in developing countries, and that other industrial information systems may reach end-users in developing countries, but not in the SMI sector.

On the other hand, there are clear indications of growing demand for environment information in the SMI sector in developing countries — there is therefore a gap between supply and demand.

Factors contributing to the 'data gap' between data producers and data users in developing countries are related to the location of many of these commercially-oriented information systems in the North or in international agencies. The former frequently require full-cost recovery for their systems, thus excluding the SMI sector in developing countries, and indeed any concentration on developing countries as such. The latter often have supply-led systems, set up on the basis of available information, rather than information needs, and consequently little thought is given to making this information relevant to end-users.

In particular, the following factors contribute to this information gap:

i) Information provided concerns advanced Northern technologies rather than those appropriate to conditions and financial resources in the South;

ii) Even where information systems target users in developing countries, these are either large corporations, consultants or researchers at universities or research institutes which may have advanced communication capabilities. The use of advanced technologies and information systems for information transfer does not take into account the limited communication and data handling capabilities in the SMI sector in developing countries, and therefore restricts their access;

iii) SMIs in developing countries rarely place monetary value on information, and are, therefore, unattractive targets for commercially-run systems;

iv) The commercial hosts that carry the bulk of data bases in the North do not target developing countries. Therefore there is a widespread ignorance in SMIs in developing countries as to the existence of data bases, and methods of accessing them;

v) While SMIs in developing countries are generally ignorant of the available information resources, data base owners are ignorant of the potential usefulness of the information they hold to SMIs in developing countries;

vi) SMIs recognize the need for environmental and energy information, but are rarely able to articulate this need. Any information system will therefore require an educational as well as an informative approach. Few information system operators have attempted to undertake this task; and,

vii) Poor telecommunications in many developing countries and low computer literacy in SMIs act as physical and psychological barriers to effective information and technology transfer. Few information systems function by means of local contact points and of dissemination methods appropriate to local needs, and even fewer systems have recognized the educational role they must play in creating the market they intend to serve. No existing information system is based on the needs and resources of SMIs.

UNIDO has a unique opportunity to contribute to bridging this gap. INTIB has broad experience of global industrial information transfer to developing countries. The data bases that are currently being assembled and utilized and UNIDO's expertise in disseminating information to developing countries, are valuable foundations for a demand-led system that aims to facilitate information and technology transfer to end-users in developing countries, with a strong emphasis on SMIs. These capabilities can be employed to further not only North-South information transfer, but also South-South and South-North transfer.

### 4.5.2 The EEIS Program

INTIB's environmental information strategy for the next few years will specifically address the needs of SMIs in developing countries, while continuing a broader programme of collection and dissemination.

The key issues that the strategy intends to tackle in order to achieve this objective are:

i) Development or continuation of products that meet the real demand for such a service, in qualitative and quantitative terms;

ii) Use of highest-impact mechanisms for distribution, promotion and commercialization of the system; and,

iii) Identification of lowest-cost sources of information that yield maximum economies of scale.

The proposed strategy will be based on seven broad elements:

i) Target group — identification of an SMI clientele with a real need for an environment information service;

ii) Product — development of an information product range tailored to SMI needs, with varying levels of content and formats;

iii) Sourcing — continued development of agreements with information sponsors to reduce data collection and preparation costs;

iv) Distribution — development and maintenance of a decentralized mechanism for information distribution;

v) Dissemination mechanisms — application of the most cost-effective methods of information packaging, which will also be those appropriate to SMIs;

vi) Promotion — sensitization of information intermediaries and end-users, as well as regulatory authorities through a variety of fora and media; and,

vii) Pricing and cost recovery — development of a variety of price schemes for the different levels of information, keeping in mind the economic constraints many end-users are likely to encounter.

### 4.5.3 The EEIS in Action

The objective of the Energy and Environment Information System (EEIS) programme is to test the establishment of sustainable, cost-effective mechanisms for management of industrial environment information targeted to SMIs within developing countries. The

EEIS follows a strategy that first identifies a key institution which has a proven capability in information management and an existing information programme (including staff and budget) as well as the ability to function as an information service to industry in the national context. Such a centre is the project's main liaison for the system in that country and is designated the Primary Contact Point (PCP).

It is one of the chief responsibilities of the Primary Contact Point to help build the EEIS network within the country by identifying and entering into working arrangements with between 10 and 15 other organizations which have direct association with SMIs. Such organizations could *inter alia* include trade associations, Chambers of Commerce, local administrative offices and environmental consulting companies.

These Secondary Contact Points (SCPs) have access to the information products and services made available from UNIDO/INTIB through the PCP and have the responsibility to assist their member SMIs and entrepreneurs to make use of the information, as appropriate. In this way, the network is built.

It is envisaged that existing and emerging national institutions which are responsible for the SMI sectors will, through this project, develop cost-effective mechanisms for the capacity-building support necessary to address the issues of information provision for environmental awareness and improved industrial response to pollution prevention. As each country's institutional structure varies, country studies are an essential first stage of the strategy. Pilot activities within the countries are conducted according to pre-set terms of reference and contractual obligations, together with the application of a number of criteria for evaluation of the various components of the system.

Financial support for pilot surveys in 4 developing countries — one in each geographical region — was provided from project funds. The interest aroused during the programme's initial study, however, indicated that a broader geographical coverage was needed in the pilot activities. Currently 21 additional institutions (7 in Latin America, 8 in Africa, 2 in Asia and 4 in Eastern Europe) have expressed interest in undertaking preparatory country surveys at their own cost.

The institutions that have been involved or expressed their interest in this first step of the strategy are from:

**Africa**: Botswana, Ethiopia, Kenya, Mozambique, Nigeria, Sudan, Tanzania, Zambia, and Zimbabwe;

**Latin America and the Caribbean**: Argentina, Bolivia, Brazil, Cuba, Ecuador, Jamaica, Peru, and Venezuela;

**Asia & Pacific**: India, Indonesia, and Thailand

**Eastern Europe**: Czech Republic, Hungary, Poland, Russian Federation, and the Slovak Republic

Four scheduled studies (Hungary, Peru, Thailand and Zimbabwe) and one additional study (Ecuador) have been completed to date. Terms of Reference for the functioning of a national EEIS in Hungary have been agreed upon and activities commenced in June 1993. Negotiations are currently underway with candidate PCPs in the other 4 countries.

For several other countries, surveys are in various stages of preparation and it is expected that their input will be completed by the end of 1993. Figure 4.2 indicates the present levels of interest or involvement in the EEIS in the above countries.

The EEIS will provide a number of key services including the institution of high-impact mechanisms for commercialization, distribution and promotion of information which correspond to each participating country's capabilities in disseminating information. It is therefore crucial for the success of the EEIS that each participating country has an effective PCP.

The EEIS will be a non-profit venture, but will operate on a fee-paying basis. At the same time, the System is conceived to complement, and not to compete with, existing national and international initiatives.

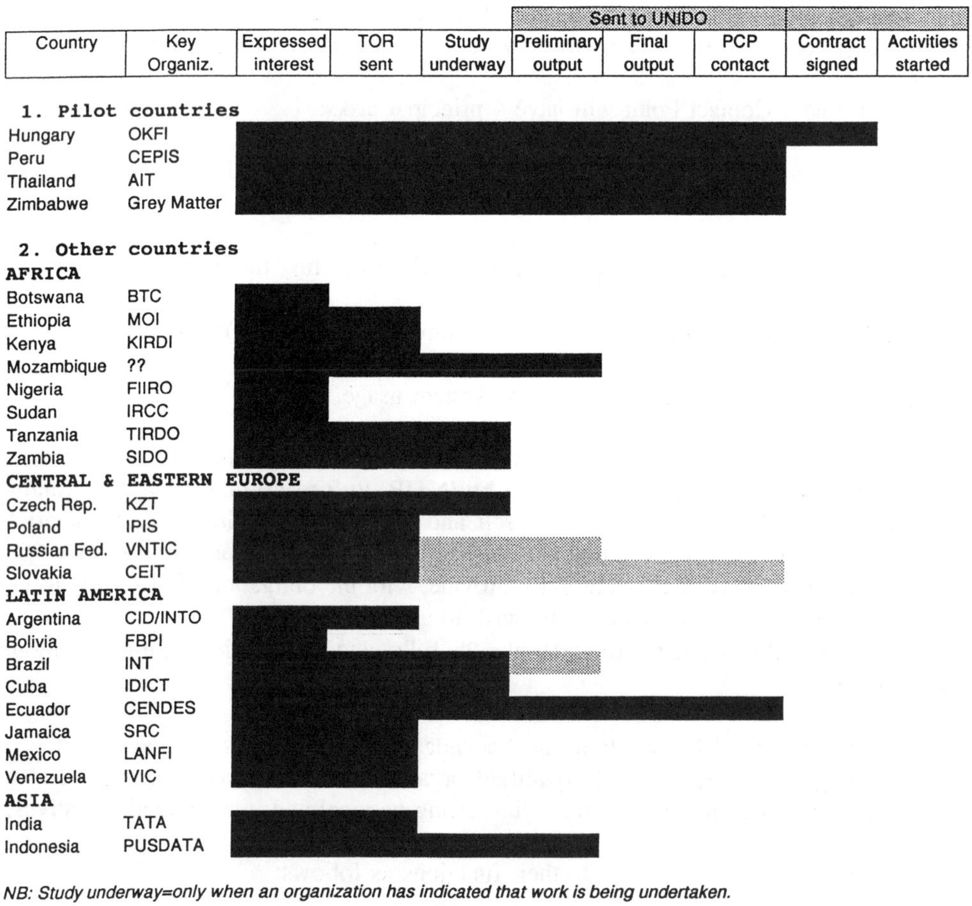


*NB: Study underway=only when an organization has indicated that work is being undertaken. However, this can also be assumed for most of the 'TOR sent' organizations.*

**Figure 4.2** **Status of Energy and Environment Information System (EEIS), September 1993**

### 4.5.4 Primary Contact Point (PCP)

Upon completion of the country surveys, the relationship of INTIB and the PCP will be governed by a Memorandum of Understanding (MoU) and by Terms of Reference (TOR).

The PCP will be the most important node in each country for the process of disseminating energy and environment information to small- and medium-scale industries and to other end users to whom this information is of interest.

The PCP will hold relevant parts of the UNIDO data bases so that most queries to the system can be answered in-country (in the long-term, it is not expected that the PCP will need to forward more than 20% of queries to INTIB in Vienna). Telecommunications infrastructure permitting, the PCP will also have electronic (*eg*, E-mail) links to Vienna.

The PCP will provide this information on a commercial basis. In addition to disseminating the information, it will monitor usage of the system, coordinate the network, coordinate marketing and promotion and administer the commercial side of the system. In exchange for services, INTIB will provide relevant datasets, logistical and marketing support.

The Primary Contact Point will have 4 principal tasks:

i) Providing an information service based on the data and other information materials provided by UNIDO and available to it from other sources;

ii) Establishing and coordinating a network for disseminating the information;

iii) Marketing and promoting the system (*eg*, through the network); and,

iv) Monitoring and reporting to INTIB on system usage.

It will be the principal task of the PCP to provide an information and query service based, *inter alia*, on the datasets provided by INTIB, to forward queries not answerable in-house to UNIDO in Vienna, and to sell and distribute other information materials produced by UNIDO. It is proposed that the PCP integrate this information service with other information services they currently provide, with the obligation of allowing access to all intermediaries and end-users who wish to use the EEIS.

The PCP will be expected to undertake the following tasks with regard to setting up the network:

i) Recruit at least 10 institutions as Secondary Contact Points (SCPs)-the PCP is encouraged to recruit suitably qualified organizations as network members and to operate the EEIS in conjunction with existing national and international initiatives;

ii) Instruct network members as to their functions as follows:

- To actively promote the system;
- To generate queries from their customer base; and,
- To act as an intermediary between PCP and end-users;

iii) Ensure effective communication channels between the PCP and the SCPs so that queries from end-users can be promptly serviced; and,

iv) Work out a detailed set of requirements and contractual obligations with SCPs.

With regard to operating and coordinating the network as a dynamic and functional system, the PCP will be expected to undertake the following:

i) Prompt delivery of responses to queries forwarded by SCPs;

ii) Provision of promotion and marketing material to SCPs;

iii) Regular meetings of representatives of SCPs;

iv) Monitoring of the 'performance' of SCPs, based on the pre-set criteria; and,

v) Regular review of the activity status of SCPs, with a view to enhancing the effectiveness of the EEIS by dropping passive SCPs from the network and including new organizations with an interest in participation.

The PCP will be the coordination point for the national marketing and promotion of the EEIS. It will need to actively promote the EEIS and may need to provide a back-up function to promotional activities by network members.

In this respect, the main PCP tasks are as follows:

i) Identification of low-cost but high-impact promotional channels for the EEIS, including printed media, broadcasting media, electronic media and presentation of the EEIS at conferences and seminars;

ii) Development and implementation of a promotional and marketing strategy appropriate to national conditions. This strategy should be developed in close consultation with the SCPs, and should be implemented making maximum use of SCP resources and activities in order to create economies of scale and minimize costs to the PCP;

iii) Distribution of promotional materials produced by INTIB, translating into the national language(s) where appropriate;

iv) Production of promotional materials in the national language(s), either based on existing INTIB material or produced independently;

v) Monitoring the effectiveness of promotional materials and channels and readjustment to the marketing strategy based on regular reviews of the monitoring results--it is important that the effectiveness of the EEIS be assessed on a regular basis, therefore the PCP should undertake to monitor and account for the use of the data provided by INTIB both by network members and end-users. Usage reports will trigger reviews of the system and adjustments where necessary; and,

vi) The main objective of EEIS is to give maximum usage to the data provided by INTIB. However, there are high costs involved in setting up a dissemination network. The system should therefore be partly self-financing by selling or subsidizing EEIS information products and services. In addition, PCPs should strive to recover costs incurred in setting up and operating the system. This would be by charging end-users for the provision of information. SMIs and other users of the system are therefore expected to pay for the information provided to them.

An assessment of appropriate pricing levels, preferred charging structures and payment mechanisms will be undertaken within the first 6 months following the signing of the MoU. Based on this assessment, experience gained during the first 6 months, as well as discussions with SMIs, existing and potential SCPs and existing providers of information to SMIs and other end-users, adjustments to the pricing strategy will probably be necessary.

### 4.5.5 Secondary Contact Points (SCPs)

In order to increase the outreach of EEIS information, it will be necessary to put into place a dissemination network of Secondary Contact Points (SCPs) which will be the principal interface of INTIB/EEIS with the end-users. While there should be no barrier to end-users interacting directly with the PCP, staffing levels and the focus of the PCP mandate are likely to act as a constraint on the dissemination range of the EEIS. It is therefore thought that the number of potential users can be significantly increased by creating a network of secondary organizations.

Each country will have a network of 10-15 SCPs (distribution nodes) which will generate, collect and forward requests to the PCP. SCPs are not expected to hold INTIB/EEIS information unless specifically agreed to by the PCP, but to serve primarily as intermediaries. This network should consist of organizations that are in contact with SMIs and other industries.

Two aspects are of particular importance:

i) SCPs are expected to play a pro-active role in promoting usage of the system. Statistics will be collected on SCP activities so as to measure the relative success of the venture. Existing communication channels with potential end-users (*eg*, newsletters, electronic bulletin boards, seminars) can become low-cost promotional channels for the EEIS. The PCP should not itself incur costs in using these channels; and,

ii) SCPs should be chosen with a view to achieving economies of scale in reaching potential end-users, *eg*, through membership lists of industry and trade associations.

Network members could, *inter alia*, be chosen from amongst the following types of organization:

i) Active trade and industry associations — introduction of new enhanced services to their existing membership will increase the visibility and attractiveness of the association, and their standing as sector representative;

ii) Technology transfer and industrial productivity centres — serving as the distribution node for the EEIS will be an additional resource and will enhance their effectiveness;

iii) Information centres — taking on distribution of the EEIS will strengthen their existing services and boost their client base;

iv) Local enterprise agencies — SCP status will increase their credibility with local enterprises and enable them to meet a demand they cannot presently meet;

v) Enforcement agencies — charged with enforcing compliance with environmental regulations, they might be interested also in providing positive advice to industry on how to achieve compliance targets;

vi) Technical and research institutions and universities; and,

vii) Consulting companies and other industrial oriented organizations with a membership or clientele already interested in industrial energy or environmental issues.

## 4.6 The International Perspective

### 4.6.1 The UNIDO Conference on Ecologically Sustainable Industrial Development

In October 1991, UNIDO convened the Ministerial Conference on Ecologically Sustainable Industrial Development (ESID), in Copenhagen, Denmark. This Conference was a milestone for the Environment Programme of the Organization and a major input, from the industry perspective, to the United Nations Conference on Environment and Development (UNCED).

The conclusions and recommendations from the ESID Conference were incorporated into the Environment Programme (mentioned at the beginning of the chapter) and are reflected in the objectives listed there. Most of these need information to a varying extent and INTIB's environment information programme is the main instrument which provides the required support, either as inputs or means of disseminating the results.

Two concise pamphlets were prepared after the ESID Conference which explain the concept in more detail [5,6].

The ESID concept — *ie*, process change and 'cleaner production' — has become the cornerstone of UNIDO's Environment Programme and was subsequently endorsed in Agenda 21.

### 4.6.2 Agenda 21

*The objective of the United Nations Conference on Environment and Development (UNCED), held in Rio de Janeiro, Brazil, 3 to 14 June 1992, was to agree on a sustainable future course of development that would reconcile the growing development requirements of the world's population with the environmental resources on which they are based* [7].

Two years of extensive negotiations preceded the Conference and the Government representatives at UNCED were able to adopt wide-reaching recommendations for a global move to sustainable development. The result is Agenda 21, widely accepted as the basis for international action into the next century.

Agenda 21 has 4 sections:

- Section I — Social and economic dimensions;
- Section II — Conservation and management of resources for development;
- Section III — Strengthening the role of major groups; and,
- Section IV — Means of implementation.

There are 40 chapters divided among the 4 sections.

The United Nations system, as well as the international community, was called upon to support the objectives of the Agenda:

i) *'All agencies of the United Nations system have a key role to play in the implementation of Agenda 21 within their respective competence* [8];

ii) *All relevant agencies, organizations and programmes of the United Nations system should adopt concrete programmes for the implementation of Agenda 21* [9];

iii) '*... all United Nations specialized agencies...may consider ways of strengthening and adjusting activities and programmes in line with Agenda 21, in particular, regarding projects for sustainable development* [10].'

The chapters of Agenda 21 which have been accorded high priority within UNIDO, in accordance with the Organization's comparative advantage as well as its existing mandate are as follows:

i) Integrating environment and development in decision-making (chapter 8);

ii) Protection of the atmosphere (chapter 9);

iii) Environmentally sound management of biotechnology (chapter 16);

iv) Protection of the oceans...(chapter 17);

v) Protection of...freshwater resources (chapter 18);

vi) Environmentally sound management of toxic chemicals... (chapter 19);

vii) Environmentally sound management of hazardous wastes... (chapter 20);

viii) Environmentally sound management of solid wastes... (chapter 21);

ix) Global action towards sustainable and equitable development (chapter 24);

x) Strengthening the role of business and industry (chapter 30);

xi) Environmentally sound technology, cooperation and capacity-building (chapter 34);

xii) National mechanisms and international cooperation for capacity-building in developing countries (chapter 37); and,

xiii) Information for decision-making (chapter 40).

All of the above-mentioned chapters of Agenda 21 mention the need for provision of information and data, while chapter 34 acknowledges that this is an integral part of the technology transfer process. All chapters have at least one section addressing the information needs within that particular sector or activity, while most contain multiple references to this aspect of the different programme areas. It has been stated that Agenda 21 is an information programme.

One of the four dimensions of the UNIDO response to Agenda 21 will be based on:

*Assessing, monitoring and disseminating industry-related information (global, regional and national levels)* [11].

This dimension will be supported by 2 major programme instruments--studies and research and information services — which are considered to be the basis for interventions at the remaining 3 levels, *viz:*

i) Support to policy formulation and negotiations;

ii) Implementation of operational activities in the field; and,

iii) Investment-related activities.

### 4.6.3 Capacity 21

One of the key issues associated with Agenda 21, excepting the concept of sustainable development, concerns what is known as capacity-building.

The reader will be aware of the term 'capacity' several times in this chapter, and perhaps elsewhere in literature related to the development process. The idea of capacity-building in itself is nothing new for the UN system and its specialized agencies.

Indeed, the whole basis of the Energy and Environment Information System (EEIS), is to support the national capacity to effectively deliver required information to the industrial sector.

Since UNCED, an attempt is being made by the UN system to generate additional financial resources to support the objectives of Agenda 21, under the umbrella of the Capacity 21 programme, with the stated aim of:

> *Sustaining the momentum of Agenda 21, the Earth Summit's agenda for sustainable development* [12].

In this pamphlet, The United Nations Development Programme (UNDP) has defined capacity-building as follows:

> *....the process and means for national governments and local communities to develop the skills and expertise needed to manage their environment and natural resources in a sustainable manner. Capacity is embodied in human resources, institutions, and an enabling environment...* [12].

Again, objectives which are reflected in the EEIS strategy.

When one looks into the details of the Capacity 21 programme, it is evident that environmental information is considered basic to the concept — within the 6 steps proposed by UNDP for the implementation of their programme, 2 make specific reference to the need for networks. Information and data collection are among the tools recommended for institutional and policy support.

### 4.6.4 The Sustainable Development Network (SDN)

One of the mechanisms proposed under UNDP's Capacity 21 programme, is the creation of Sustainable Development Networks (SDNs) within each participating country:

> *...in order to ensure maximum level information sharing among all 'stakeholders' in society (government, private sector, NGOs, community-based groups)* [12].

The underlying ideas are in many ways parallel to INTIB's EEIS strategy, *inter alia*:

i) *'To facilitate freer and more rapid access to information for users in developing countries to move towards the goal of sustainable development;*

ii) *To encourage increased communication about sustainable development across locations, borders, regions, sectors of economy, etc.; and,*

iii) *To enhance the capacity of national institutions to meet their own needs for information on sustainable development* [13].'

Again, many of the objectives and, in this case even the proposed means and criteria for assessment, are parallel to those of the EEIS. UNDP has since proposed that pilot SDNs be established to test out the concept and several countries have already requested to be involved. At the same time, sectoral SDNs have been suggested as valuable adjuncts and INTIB considers the EEIS approach to be just such a case, as industrial aspects of sustainable development have not received much attention under the Capacity 21 programme and UNIDO is the lead agency within the UN for this aspect of development.

## 4.7 Other International Initiatives

There are several major subject-specific areas of international concern, reflected in Agenda 21 and in some cases pre-dating the Earth Summit. Many of these have industrial implications and those which are of major importance to UNIDO are mentioned in the section on Agenda 21.

Three key areas currently addressed by UNIDO are:

i) The Montreal Protocol — phase out all ozone depleting substances (ODS), especially CFCs;

ii) The Basel Convention — dealing with the transborder movement of hazardous wastes; and,

iii) The International Programme on Chemical Safety — sound management of toxic chemicals.

Needless to say, activities in all 3 areas both generate and require huge amounts of information. Therefore, the INTIB environment information programme will be an integral part of the project and programme outputs and activities. Indeed, any future programme areas in which UNIDO becomes involved on the basis of its comparative advantage, will benefit from the integrated approach to information management and dissemination mentioned in this chapter.

## 4.8 Disclaimer

The views expressed in this chapter are those of the author and do not necessarily reflect the views of UNIDO.

## 4.9 References

[1] United Nations Industrial Development Organization (UNIDO), Industrial Development Board (IDB), UNIDO-IDB-10/17.

[2] United Nations Industrial Development Organization (UNIDO), Industrial Development Board (IDB), UNIDO-IDB.11/L.14.

[3] United Nations Industrial Development Organization (UNIDO), UNIDO Budget 1992-93.

[4] Industry and Environment: A Guide to Sources of Information, United Nations Industrial Development Organization, Vienna, 1991, ISBN 3-924754-17-9.

[5] Blueprint for Clean Industry (Conclusions and Recommendations of the ESID Ministerial Conference)--UNIDO-PI/111/Rev. 1.

[6] Serving Development by Saving the Environment--UNIDO-PI/112/Rev. 1.

[7] United Nations Industrial Development Organization (UNIDO), Industrial Development Board (IDB), UNIDO-IDB.10/32.

[8] Earth Summit: Agenda 21 — The United Nations Programme of Action from Rio, United Nations, New York, April 1993, ISBN 92-1-100509-4, Chapter 38, para. 38.4, p. 274.

[9] *ibid.* Chapter 38, para. 38.8(b), p. 275.

[10] *ibid.* Chapter 38, para. 38.28, pp. 278-279.

[11] United Nations Industrial Development Organization (UNIDO), Industrial Development Board (IDB), UNIDO-IDB.IO/32.

[12] United Nations Development Programme (UNDP), UNDP pamphlet on Capacity 21. Contact: Capacity 21 Coordinator, Environment and Natural Resources Group, One United Nations Plaza, New York, NY 10017.

[13] Background paper for UNDP workshop on SDN, September 1992. Contact: The Director, Sustainable Development Network, One United Nations Plaza, New York, NY 10017.

# 5. International and National Governmental Information Activities Concerning the Environmental Effects on Chemicals

Judith Deschamps

## 5.1 Introduction

Many and varied information activities sponsored by governments, both national and international, are concerned with the environmental effects and safety of chemical substances. In addition, a significant number of information sources are of value particularly when a comprehensive risk analysis has to be undertaken. This chapter considers governmental work in the United Kingdom, to a lesser extent in the United States, and overseas (with emphasis being placed on that performed by international bodies).

## 5.2 International

The activities described in this section are sponsored by the United Nations (notably UNEP, the United Nations Environment Programme), OECD (the Organization for Economic Cooperation and Development) and the Commission of the European Communities. The services mentioned provide access to much unpublished or grey literature and to individual expertise in addition to giving details of conventionally published material.

### 5.2.1 United Nations Environment Programme

UNEP was established as a result of the Stockholm Conference of 1972 which was the first world-wide attempt to deal with environmental problems (for a general account of UNEP's work see chapter by Shkolenok). It was intended to act as a catalyst for other United Nations activities since other bodies, such as the Food and Agriculture Organization, existed already.

In 1992 a successor conference, the United Nations Conference on Environment and Development (UNCED), was held in Rio de Janeiro. It considered progress since Stockholm in order to chart the way ahead. Its theme was sustainable development and it was held under the auspices of the United Nations Development Programme (UNDP). The UN Commission for Sustainable Development emerged from this meeting. Additionally, UNEP was given a strengthened role.

#### 5.2.1.1 The International Register of Potentially Toxic Chemicals

This UNEP service which started work in 1976 has a databank which holds information on a large number of chemical substances. It covers areas such as mammalian (including human) and ecotoxicity, waste management, biodegradation, and analytical methods. IRPTC also has information on regulations, legislation and standards from selected UN countries and international bodies. This *Legal File*, which was last published in 1987, is being updated at the time of writing (1993). Each record contains full details of relevant documentation. The *Legal File* can also be accessed through the European Communities database, ECDIN (see below). IRPTC also works through a network of National Correspondents and cooperates with a number of key organisations in order to update its databank,

IRPTC cooperates with the Commonwealth of Independent States Committee for Science and Technology and its successor body to produce an extensive series of monographs which *review the scientific literature in Russian on selected hazardous chemicals*. Many titles deal with pesticides. A small number of specialised publications have been produced as a result of this cooperation, for example, *Long Term Effects of Chemicals* and *Principles of Pesticide Toxicology*.

### 5.2.2 International Programme on Chemical Safety (IPCS)

IPCS is a joint programme of UNEP, the International Labour Office and the World Health Organization. (See also chapter by Watfa.) It considers the effects of chemicals on humans and on the environment, works on guidelines on exposure limits and methods for studying toxicity, and brings together the information needed for dealing with chemical accidents. It has published over a considerable period a very extensive series of monographs, *Environmental Health Criteria* which has a companion series of *Health and Safety Guides*. The Programme is also issuing, in association with the European Communities, a number of series of *International Chemical Safety Cards* which are intended for use in the workplace.

IRPTC contributes to the *Computerized Listing of Chemicals being Tested for Toxic Effects* (CCTTE) which is updated periodically. CCTTE is arranged by chemical name and lists work in progress together with details of the research workers and their organizations. It also contains details of recently completed reviews. Data is exchanged with OECD's EXICHEM (see below and chapter by Duffus and Draper).

### 5.2.3 International Agency for Research on Cancer (IARC)

IARC publications are a result of a programme initiated in 1969 to evaluate the carcinogenic risk of individual chemicals to humans (mixtures of chemicals, and other agents were added to the programme at a later stage). Groups of international experts assist in the preparation of monographs, critical reviews and other evaluative documents.

The *IARC Monographs on the Evaluation of Carcinogenic Risks to Humans*, now a very extensive series covering such topics as industrial chemicals and dyes, and man-made mineral fibers and radon, represent the first step in carcinogenic risk assessment. All relevant information, both published and unpublished, is examined in order to assess the strength of available evidence. An important use of the *Monographs* is to indicate where additional research effort is needed. (See also chapter by Wilbourn and Vainio.)

Other series which have been produced by IARC are *Information Bulletin on the Survey of Chemicals Being Tested for Carcinogenicity, Environmental Carcinogens. Methods of Analysis and Exposure Measurements, Scientific Publications* and *Technical Reports.*

### 5.2.4 Industry and Environment Programme Activity Centre (IE/PAC)

This UNEP body was set up shortly after the Stockholm Conference. It aims to bring government and industry together to cooperate in reducing the adverse effects of industrial operations on the environment. It has set up a database, the *Industry and Environment File*, which holds among other items information on pollution and abatement control technologies and associated costs. It links into key organisations in specific industries such as pulp and paper, petroleum, and aluminium extraction and production. It publishes reports on individual industries. IE/PAC does not offer an online information service, but uses a wide range of resources to respond to enquiries.

The Centre produces a newsletter, *Industry and Environment*; each issue focuses on a specific area, for example low- and non-waste technology, recycling and recovery in the metals industry, and solvents. It also issues guidelines for emergency awareness and preparedness and cooperates with OECD, ILO, EC and others as a partner in UNEP's APELL (Awareness and Preparedness at a Local Level) Programme.

Further examples of its publications include Technical Reports on:

i) Hazardous waste: Policies and strategies training manual (1992);

ii) Hazards identification in the local community (1992);

iii) Environmental management of nickel production (1993); and,

iv) Cleaner production worldwide (1993).

### 5.2.5 INFOTERRA (International Environmental Information System)

This service differs from such activities as IRPTC and IE/PAC in that it covers the wider environmental area and operates on the referral principle; *ie*, it refers users to information sources and to subject experts. Since it provides access to a great deal of material which is not formally published, INFOTERRA can be a valuable source of information on chemicals and the environment. Many of the participating organisations have expertise in chemical-related topics, *eg*, pollution and waste disposal. It is particularly suitable for multi-disciplinary topics and hence will be of value when a risk assessment has to take account of a wide range of factors.

INFOTERRA has 2 main components:

i) The *International Directory* which contains descriptions of information sources worldwide including government bodies, research organizations, academic institutions and private consultants; and,

ii) A network of National Focal Points from the vast majority of UN countries.

Each national contact has links with and is aware of local information sources. A network of Regional Service Centres covers many areas of the world.

The System also has a number of Special Sectoral (subject) Sources who provide substantive information, particularly to developing countries. Examples, in addition to IRPTC and IE/PAC, are the Waste Management Information Bureau at Harwell, England, and the Environmental Sanitation Information Centre in Thailand.

### 5.2.6 United Nations Directory of Banned Products

This publication, now in its 4th edition (1991), is worthy of a separate mention since it contains information concerning restrictive regulatory measures taken by over 90 national governments on over 600 individual chemicals and chemical products. Its full title is, *Consolidated list of products whose consumption and/or sale have been banned, withdrawn or severely restricted or not approved by governments* — the short title is *Products banned.*

*Products banned* is a collaborative exercise. WHO collects, screens and processes the information relating to government's regulatory measures on pharmaceuticals, and on the health related and environmental reasons for these measures. UNEP/IRPTC performs a similar function for chemical products and the United Nations coordinates the inputs, incorporates other available data, collects and reviews the commercial data, and edits, translates and publishes the directory which is a substantial volume of approaching 800 pages.

The directory is the only updated compendium of its kind with a global perspective. It is of great value to governments world-wide, health and environment authorities, legal experts, those who import and export chemicals, information workers and many others.

### 5.2.7 United Nations Centre for Urgent Environmental Assistance (UNCUEA)

This evolving body has headquarters in Geneva and works together with industry, national contact points and other agencies such as IRPTC and OECD to help provide rapid responses to environmental emergencies. It is developing a register of national capabilities and selected experts.

### 5.2.8 International Labour Office (ILO)

ILO is the UN body which is responsible for the protection of workers' health and safety (see also chapter by Watfa). It works closely with UNEP. Examples of its many publications are *Chemical Safety Data Sheets*, *Codes of Practice*, *Manuals*, and *Technical Guides*. A key work is the *Encyclopedia of Occupational Health and Safety*; it contains much information on chemical topics.

### 5.2.9 Summary of United Nations Programmes used to Manage Chemicals

- Those that deal with 1 aspect only. Examples are IARC's (*qv*) assessment of carcinogenic risk or the development of recommendations by the UN Committee of Experts on the Transport of Dangerous Goods.

- Those that deal with chemicals that pollute the environment or contaminate consumer goods (including food), *eg* The International Maritime Organization's work on marine pollution control and that of the Codex Alimentarius Commission.

- Those that deal with several aspects of management of specific chemicals or groups of chemicals. An example is the FAO Code of Conduct on the Distribution and Use of Pesticides.

- Large-scale international programmes on the management of the whole range of chemicals, *eg*, ILO/UNEP/WHO in IPCS (see above) and the OECD Special Programme for the Control of Chemicals.

- Cross-cutting activities concerned with technical cooperation and information dissemination such as IRPTC, and training carried out by UN specialised agencies.

- Programmes with a wider subject coverage which include information about chemical substances, *eg*, INFOTERRA.

## 5.3 Organisation for Economic Cooperation and Development (OECD)

### 5.3.1 EXICHEM

OECD operates a programme for chemicals control and risk reduction [1]. Within this programme it coordinates a database, EXICHEM containing details of work on existing chemicals. EXICHEM is produced as a printed version and is also available on diskette. The database can be used, together with other records of ongoing work, both to avoid duplication and to identify possible contacts for cooperative exercises.

### 5.3.2 Work on High Production Volume Chemicals

This work is aimed at filling gaps in data on chemicals that are considered likely to have adverse effects. Lead countries are assigned the responsibility of coordinating work on named substances. Practical work is carried out where data cannot be traced. Results are used to prepare *Screening Information Data Sheets* (SIDS). The information obtained is also supplied to IRPTC.

## 5.4 European Communities

### 5.4.1 Environmental Chemicals Data and Information Network (ECDIN)

ECDIN is the online equivalent of a chemical handbook. The main data categories covered by the publicly-available implementation (which is accessible via the DIMDI host) are:

i) Physico-chemical properties;

ii) Production and Use;

iii) Legislation and Rules (supplied by IRPTC);

iv) Occupational Health and Safety;

v) Toxicity;

vi) Concentration and Fate in the Environment;

vii) Waste Management (also provided by IRPTC); and,

viii) Detection Methods

Many categories are broken down into a number of sub-files, such as effects on soil microorganisms and aquatic bioaccumulation. Basic information is given for a very large number of substances, but the numbers included in specific files and sub-files vary considerably. ECDIN also operates the online version of EINECS, the European Inventory of Existing Commercial Chemical Substances.

### 5.4.2 European Chemical Inventory Database (EUCLID)

EUCLID is operated by the European Chemicals Bureau which, in turn is part of the EC Joint Research Centre's Environmental Institute. This newly-established database will receive, process and store all the data submitted by industry in accordance with existing Chemicals Regulations. The Bureau will use data in EUCLID to harmonise procedures for priority setting and risk assessment of existing chemicals. From 1994 the Bureau will also be in charge of information exchange between Member States, third countries and UNEP/FAO as well as monitoring the export and import of potentially hazardous chemicals.

### 5.4.3 Community R&D Information Service (CORDIS)

This recently-established, multi-component database is available through ECHO, the European Communities Host. It holds details of Community Research and Technological (RTD) activities, especially those included in the EC's R&D Framework Programme. Details of reports listed in *European Abstracts* (EABS) form part of CORDIS in addition to being available in printed format.

### 5.4.4 System for Information on Grey Literature in Europe (SIGLE)

SIGLE is a grey literature database which contains records from 1981 to date. It covers all subject areas but much technical information is included. The United Kingdom input is made by the British Library and is the online equivalent of *British Reports, Translations and Theses*. SIGLE is also available as a CD-ROM from Silver-Platter.

## 5.5 United States of America

The United States government produces many publications which will assist those assessing risks associated with chemical substances. The most important way in which details of publications are made known is through the US National Technical Information Service (NTIS) which produces *Government Reports Announcements and Index*, a fortnightly listing of abstracts of reports [2]. NTIS also publishes a series of weekly *Abstract Newsletters* on topics such as chemistry, and environmental pollution and control.

The US Environmental Protection Agency (USEPA) issues a number of guides to its publications and information services. The following reports and report series are also of value:

i) Toxicological Profiles (Agency for Toxic Substances and Disease Registry, and USEPA);

ii) Pesticides Fact Sheets (USEPA);

iii) Ambient Water Quality Criteria (USEPA);

iv) Drinking Water Health Advisories (USEPA); and,

v) Fact Sheet: National Primary Drinking Water Standards (USEPA). (See also chapter by Campbell.)

## 5.6 Sources of United Kingdom Government Information

### 5.6.1 Her Majesty's Inspectorate of Pollution

Key series issued by the Inspectorate to give guidance to industry and others are:

i) *Chief Inspectors' Guidance to Inspectors, Industry Sector Guidance Notes.* These deal with specific industrial sectors and are in the process of being replaced by a number of *Process Guidance Notes.* Current titles include individual notes covering the metal, mineral and chemical industries;

ii) *Process Guidance Notes.* These are arranged in the following sectors:

- Fuel and Power
- Waste Disposal and Recycling
- Mineral Industry
- Chemical Industry;

iii) *Technical Guidance Notes* which are divided into:

- Monitoring
- Discharges

(an example of this series is, *Guidelines on discharge stack heights for polluting emissions*);

iv) *Best Practicable Means Papers* were first issued some years ago but remain valid until replaced by other series, examples include:

- Chemical incineration works
- Chemical fertilizer works
- Hydrochloric acid works; and,

v) *General Guidance Notes* (Guidance on Local Authority Air Pollution Control)

HMIP publishes an extensive series of *Research Reports.* Selected titles in the context of risk assessment are:

- Chemical modelling studies in support of HMIP probabilistic risk assessment (1990).

- The use of expert judgement in risk assessment.
- Procedures for the elicitation of expert judgement in the probabilistic risk analysis on radioactive waste repositories: An overview.

### 5.6.2 Department of the Environment

i) *Waste Management Papers.* This series which has several titles dating back to 1976 is currently being expanded both with new titles and updates of existing titles (some of these are out of print at present). Recent titles include:

- Landfilling completion (1992)
- The control of landfilling gas — A Technical Memorandum on the monitoring and control of landfill gas (1991);

ii) *Interdepartmental Committee on the Redevelopment of Contaminated Land.* The Committee issues a number of *Guidance Notes*, 2 examples are:

- Notes on the fire hazards of contaminated land (2nd edition 1986)
- Asbestos on contaminated sites (2nd edition 1990); and,

iii) Royal Commission on Environmental Pollution. The Commission which has provided advice to government on key environmental topics since 1970 publishes a series of definitive reports which are in effect state of the art reviews. Recent examples are:

- The release of genetically engineered organisms to the environment (1989)
- Incineration of waste (1993).

## 5.7 Conclusion

It is clear from the details given above that a very large number of information activities and services world-wide are of potential value in performing a comprehensive risk assessment of the environmental effects of chemical substances.

It is also true that international bodies are cooperating to an increasing degree, often of necessity because of the cost of 'going it alone'.

The range of services available includes those which give access direct to specialists via referral networks such as INFOTERRA; peer-reviewed distillations of existing information, for example many IARC publications; databases where several sources have been used to bring together a collection of relevant data (ECDIN is a good example of this approach); and, bibliographic records which give details of grey as well as conventionally-published literature and include information on, for example current research.

A final thought is that although the effort involved in making use of such a wide range of information sources is considerable, the end result where a truly comprehensive review is appropriate may well justify the time and expense when compared with the true cost of not having the information needed.

## 5.8 References

[1] *International Environment Reporter*, June 1990, pp. 263-70.
[2] Auger, C.P., in: *Information Sources in Grey Literature*, London, Bowker-Saur, 1990.

# 6. Accessing Health and Safety Information

Sheila Pantry

## 6.1 Introducing Occupational Safety and Health (OSH) Information

### 6.1.1 What is Information?

Information is vital to today's society; it is needed in every walk of life, but none more so than in the occupational safety and health (OSH) field. The term information has so many interpretations. For the OSH information seeker and provider it can appear in many forms and be presented in many different ways.

OSH information will be found in: legislation; codes of practice; research results; journals and newsletters; films and videos; guidance and advice; encyclopedias and handbooks; books, reports and pamphlets; datasheets; standard specifications; translations; microfiche documents; computer databases and databanks; compact disc read only memory (CD-ROM); floppy discs; software programs; organizations including insurance companies; associations and federations; and, training organizations and courses.

OSH information is in a fast moving area which is constantly being updated and has no country or language boundaries. Therefore, anyone working in any industry or in a commercial enterprise needs to be aware that today's information is probably, somewhere in the world, being updated.

Some of the impetus to update the information base comes from the constant development of the legislation, particularly in technologically advanced countries where new industries, production systems, machines and new chemicals are constantly being introduced. Alongside this, novel and sometimes exciting ways of presenting information to the user have developed and are continuing to develop.

### 6.1.2 Who Needs this Information?

There is a growing awareness of occupational safety and health matters because there is an increased knowledge of possible effects on the health of the workforce from the industrial processes. Wherever their working environment may be — in the air, at sea, in transport, factories, offices, workshops, farms, mines, quarries, educational establishments, retail, hotel and catering trades, construction engineering — the workers and their employers need to know the latest developments surrounding their particular industry. There is also an increase in general interest in all things to do with personal health and the effects of the environment.

Many people, if not everyone, needs information at some time regarding their own working conditions. With the introduction of legislation, a wide spectrum of people will need OSH information, such as: inspectors; doctors and nurses; engineers from all disciplines; chemists and biochemists; scientists and technicians; lawyers and administrators; consultants and specialists; educators, organizations, federations; institutes and trade and industry associations; representatives on behalf of their members; health and safety representatives; health and safety managers and officers; unions; journalists, editors and the various media representatives; governmental agencies and departments; and, international organizations.

### 6.1.3 Authoritative Information

There is a need for OSH information to be authoritative and most of all, validated (see also chapter by Cowie and Richardson). Authoritative information will come from sources or organizations known to have the necessary expertise. There is an increasingly worrying trend that information is being produced which does not appear to have been validated. Examples include:

i) Measurements quoted are not checked and abbreviations used can be wrong, such as the use of 'm' instead of 'mm' (metres instead of millimeters);

ii) The decimal point printed in the wrong place when quoting an exposure limit;

iii) The wrong chemical name used; and,

iv) Illustrations showing the wrong practice.

### 6.1.4 Problems with OSH Information

Having indicated that there are vast amounts of information in the world on occupational safety and health, there are areas where information is sparse or not collected together in a readily accessible format. To save the information seeker time the following points should be noted:

i) **Legislation.** In the United Kingdom all OSH legislation is readily available but there is no central database of worldwide legislation. Some efforts are being made to improve this situation in that the University of Salford, European Occupational health and Safety Law Unit has now a comprehensive collection which is being made into a database;

ii) **Statistics.** It cannot be assumed that any 2 countries work from the same base points, consequently collections from different countries cannot easily be used for comparative studies;

iii) **Ergonomics.** Whilst many databases include information on ergonomics no one database brings the information available from worldwide sources together. The best source is the printed abstracting journal 'Ergonomics Abstracts';

iv) **Research.** Again there is no comprehensive source of information on research on occupational health, safety and hygiene being carried out in the world. There are numerous journals and databases containing the results of research and research programmes. The French Institut National de Recherche et de Sécurité pour la Prévention des Accidents du Travail et des Maladies Professionnels (INRS) has a database but it does not contain all known OSH research;

v) **Films and Videos.** It is recognized that films and videos on OSH subjects do help to get the message across in an easy and understandable way. Unfortunately, there is not a comprehensive database of films and videos, although new titles appear in a never ending stream. The International Labour Office Health and Safety Centre in Geneva has attempted to collect knowledge of the available material in the CISDOC database (see also chapter by Watfa). Some countries such as the United Kingdom, do produce catalogues of films and videos including new issues as they appear; and,

vi) **Duplication of effort.** In many countries simple, easy to understand booklets and information sheets are produced at great expense on popular topics when the same material has been produced elsewhere at an earlier date. Again there is no 'one stop' source or database of this type of material which would give the information seeker quick access, and possibly save a lot of unnecessary expense.

### 6.2 Legislation

**General.** Health, safety and hygiene regulation provision exists in varying degrees of complexity in the majority of countries. The International Labour Office, the European Communities and the USA have predominance on health and safety matters, particularly in the use of chemicals. Legislative information can be obtained from a number of sources. For national legislation apply to the competent national authority. Universities with law faculties may also be able to provide information. In addition, the University of Salford in the United Kingdom has a complete collection of European countries health and safety law, both pre- and post-European Communities Directives. Salford has also a growing collection of other countries' legal information. Information sources giving details of legislation, interpretations, updating services exist.

**International Labour Office (ILO).** The ILO, created in 1919, has over the years endeavoured to set standards for workers' protection and to provide practical information. Many of the ILO Conventions and Recommendations are concerned with safety, health and conditions of work (see also chapter by Watfa).

**European Communities.** For copies of European legislation, apply to the European Documentation Centres set up by the European Community which are located in major cities throughout Europe. The Office of Official Publications of the European Communities also maintains a database CELEX of all Community law.

**European Community — Form of Council acts.** For EC and Euratom matters, Council acts may take the following forms: Regulations, Directives, Recommendations and Opinions:

i) Regulations are general in scope, binding in their entirety and directly applicable in all Member States. These must be published in the Official Journal and, unless otherwise provided therein, enter into force 20 days after publication;

ii) Directives are binding on the Member States to which they are addressed as regards the results to be achieved, but leave national authorities the power to decide the form and the means. These take effect upon notification to the parties concerned;

iii) Decisions, which may be addressed to a Member State, to an undertaking or to an individual, are binding in their entirety on the parties named therein; and,

iv) Recommendations and opinions are not binding.

Apart from instruments having legal effects which are expressly mentioned on the Treaties, the Council adopts decisions on general matters and resolutions; the scope of such instruments is determined in each individual case.

**Health and Safety Legislation in the United Kingdom.** The health and safety regulatory provisions fall into 4 categories. There are Acts of Parliament which may be extended and developed by Regulations, both of which may be illustrated by Codes of Practice, Guidance Notes, and authorized and approved lists.

**Acts of Parliament.** The most important Act is the Health and Safety at Work etc Act 1974; there are other similar occupational health and safety statutes such as the Factories Act 1961 which must also be observed.

**Regulations.** Parliament, when law making, often only lays down broad duties while at the same time enabling regulations to be made to cover the situations referred to in the general legislation. The Health and Safety at Work etc Act (HASAWA) specifies only the most general duties and leaves all the detail to subsequent regulatory control by the Secretary of State. These regulations are known as Statutory Instruments, and are numbered chronologically. Lists of Statutory Instruments, pre- and post-HASAWA are available free of charge from the Health and Safety Executive's public enquiry point.

**Codes of Practice.** Within the parent Act there is provision for the creation of 'official' codes of practice for the guidance of those who have to work within the framework of the law. These codes of practice are mandatory and must be complied with unless an equally satisfactory method of complying with the law can be proved.

**Guidance Notes.** Guidance Notes are published from time to time by the enforcing agencies. They are not mandatory, neither do they hold evidential significance such as codes of practice enjoy. However, they are useful documents referring to individual tasks or operations, and are widely used in the United Kingdom.

**Authorised and Approved Lists.** These are authorised and approved by the Health and Safety Commission and are issued from time to time.

### 6.2.1 Administration and Enforcement Authorities

The Health and Safety at Work etc Act established 2 bodies, the Health and Safety Commission (HSC) and the Health and Safety Executive (HSE).

#### 6.2.1.1 Health and Safety Commission

The Commission, established in October 1974, is in practice responsible to the Secretary of State for Employment for taking appropriate steps to secure the health, safety and welfare of people at work, and to protect the public generally against risks to health and safety arising out of work situations. A Chairman is appointed by the Secretary of State for Employment. The membership of the Commission (6 or up to 9 members) includes representatives of employers, trade unions, local authorities, and other interested bodies and provides a forum for the development of policies in the field of health and safety at work. The Commission organizes widespread consultation on all aspects of health and safety and is advised by a number of Advisory Committees and working parties, as well as by the expertise and committees of its executive arm, the Health and Safety Executive. The Commission is responsible for the legislation and codes of practice.

In respect of consultation, the Commission and the HSE work closely with representatives of the Confederation of British Industry (CBI), the Trades Union Congress (TUC), Local Authorities (LAs), and other interested bodies. The CBI is an independent non-party political body financed entirely by industry and commerce, existing to ensure Government understands the needs and problems of the British business. The TUC is a permanent association of Trade Unions, which functions as a forum for the discussion of issues of common interest. The General Council of the TUC is thus able to represent the Trade Union movement on national policy making bodies. LAs have been designated enforcement authorities under Section 18(2) of the HASAWA and certain premises are allocated to them for enforcement purposes by the Health and Safety (Enforcing Authority) Regulations 1989 as amended.

#### 6.2.1.2 Health and Safety Executive

The Health and Safety Executive is the operating arm of the Commission. Its dual role is to exercise on behalf of the Commission such of its functions as the Commission directs and to make adequate arrangements for the enforcement of the relevant health and safety legislation under the 1974 Act.

The structure of the Health and Safety Executive includes the 3 person Executive (*ie*, the body which constitutes HSE in the strict legal sense), the Management Board, the Board of Chief Inspectors, and the various policy, operating and services divisions. At HSC's request, the Executive has undertaken the task of reviewing all the relevant health and safety legislation and guidance material and, as necessary, making proposals for modifying, extending and updating it. The aim is to achieve a corpus of standardized and integrated laws, codes of practice and guidance to meet all current and foreseeable needs.

HSC/HSE also promotes the furtherance of safety training and work closely with industry bodies, other Government agencies and departments and the Industrial Training Boards and lead bodies, in association with the Commission's Industry Advisory Committees. Occupational health officers, nurses and environmental specialists offer further guidance to organizations.

HSE officials represent United Kingdom interests in health and safety matters throughout the international field. HSE involvement is primarily with the European Community and includes representation on working groups establishing common standards and practices.

### 6.2.2 Agency Agreements

A number of formal agreements have been made by the HSC with government departments and other bodies for them to perform functions on behalf of HSC/HSE under HASAWA. Conversely, HSE may act for other departments under similar agreements. Further information on the current agencies can be obtained from Public Enquiry Point.

### 6.2.3 Local Authorities

The responsibility for enforcing the legislation is in the main divided between HSE and the Local Authorities Environmental Health Departments, depending largely on the nature of the work and the premises on which the work is being carried out. Note the Health and Safety (Enforcing Authority) Regulation 1989.

### 6.2.4 Guides to Legislation

A number of publications which will assist in understanding the implications of the law on health and safety at work are published.

### 6.2.5 European and United Kingdom Legislation

Before the Single European act was ratified on 1 July 1987 there was no specific provision in the Treaty of Rome for health and safety measures. Directives on health and safety were adopted under Article 100, a general provision concerned with the establishment of the Common Market, *ie*, the removal of trade barriers. Some of these Article 100 directives cover worker protection from toxic substances, such as the 'Hazardous Agents' Framework Directive (80/1107/EEC), covering chemical, physical and biological substances and its subsidiary Directives on Lead and Asbestos. These were implemented in the United Kingdom by the Control of Substances Hazardous to Health (COSHH) Regulations, the Control of Lead at Work (CLAW) Regulations, the Control of Asbestos at Work (CAW) Regulations, and their associated ACoPS (see chapters by Campbell, Knight, Kulkarni and Nangle).

### 6.2.6 The Safety Framework Directive (83/391/EEC)

The main provisions are:

i) Applies to all sectors of work activity;

ii) The employers assignment of primary responsibility for employees' health and safety; and,

iii) The setting of general principles for employers such as:

- Assessing workplace risks and introducing appropriate preventative measures;
- Development of a coherent overall prevention policy;
- Adapting work to the individual;
- Cooperation between employers;
- The designation of competent personnel to take charge of health and safety activities, or the use of competent outside services;
- The provision of first aid, fire precautions and emergency arrangements;
- The provision by employers of training and information for employees and consultation of their representatives; and,
- The requirement for employees to take care of their own and others safety and to cooperate with their employer.

It was decided that a set of free standing Regulations will be used to implement the main elements of this Directive. There will be no need to alter COSHH, CLAW, and CAW, but the relevant ACoPs will need amending to cross reference any changes to other Regulations.

### 6.2.7 Article 100A Directives

Article 100A is primarily concerned with measures needed to create the Single European Market by the end of 1992; these measures are largely concerned in turn with the free movement of goods within the 'common market'. Barriers to free movement arise because individual countries see fit to place restrictions on the sale (or importation) of products and many of the restrictions relate to health and safety, *eg*, how toxic substances are to be labelled, standards for equipment so as to prevent injury in use, etc. It follows, therefore, that many of the Article 100A Directives have a direct impact on the control of toxic substances in the workplace, and HSE is, where appropriate, closely involved in their negotiation.

An important note is that for product requirements set by Article 100A Directives, Member States cannot set more stringent requirements (since they would otherwise be creating a 'non-tariff barrier to trade' which was what the Directive sought to remove). This of course contrasts with Article 100A Directive requirements which only set minimum standards and member states may apply more stringent measures.

### 6.2.8 Other Directives

In addition to the Framework Directive (above), there are a number of 'individual' (*ie*, more specific) Directives. The following have been adopted:

i) The Workplace Directive, 89/654/EEC [1];

ii) The Use of Work Equipment Directive, 89/655/EEC [2];

iii) The Use of Personal Protective Equipment (PPE) Directive, 89/656/EEC [3];

iv) The Manual Handling of Loads Directive, 90/269/EEC [4];

v) The Display Screen Equipment (VDUs) Directive, 90/270/EEC [5];

vi) The Carcinogens Directive, 90/394/EEC [6];

vii) The Biological Agents Directive, 90/679/EEC [7];

viii) The Asbestos (Amendment) Directive, 91/382/EEC [8]; and,

ix) The Temporary Workers Directive, 92/57/EEC [9].

## 6.3 Associations, Organizations, Libraries and Information Services

Many associations, organizations, libraries and information services concerned with health, safety and the environment are available for public access throughout the United Kingdom and elsewhere. Their existence may not be well known, but further details can be obtained from the author.

## 6.4 Booklists, Bibliographies, Encyclopedia, Yearbooks and Guides

### 6.4.1 Bibliographies and Booklists

Booklists, reading lists, dictionaries, encyclopedias,, and bibliographies are usually compiled to enable the user to work systematically through a list of references, usually on a specific topic.

These lists of references can be very selective, so check the introduction or the list of sources quoted. Often there is no statement of search strategy, so a check must be of the dates of the references found to ensure that the latest information is included. If the list appears to be selective, then if a comprehensive search is needed, other sources such as magazines, handbooks, textbooks, other organizations and computerized services must be used.

### 6.4.2 Publishers Lists

Extremely useful sources of information are the lists produced by publishers. These are usually very informative, giving details of each publication and are usually available free of charge. Well known health and safety publishers such as Chapman and Hall, Butterworth, VCH, etc. may be approached.

### 6.4.3 Encyclopedias, Year Books and Guides

Various year books and guides are issues by organizations and these are very handy reference books. Some of the more relevant include: Encyclopedia of Occupational Health and Safety; The Environmental Health Yearbook; Health and Safety Directory; The Industrial Safety Yearbook; The Industrial, Safety (Protective Equipment) Manufacturers Association (ISPEMA); British Safety Council Buyers Guide to Safety Equipment; The Health and Safety Marketguide; The Health and Safety Officers Reference and Buyers Guide; and, The Royal Society for the Prevention of Accidents (RoSPA).

## 6.5 Journals

A journal is one of the terms used to describe publications issued at usually regular intervals, each issue being numbered and dated. They may appear weekly, monthly, bi-monthly, quarterly, or annually. Other terms used for journals include magazines, periodicals, or serials. They normally contain a variety of individual items from several sources. Some examples of different types of journals are:

i) Serious general interest, *eg*, New Scientist;

ii) Technical or professional society, containing news, advertisements and articles of interest to their members, *eg*, Safety and Health Practitioner;

iii) Learned, specialist type containing articles by scientists and others reporting the results of their work and experiments, *eg*, Journal of Hazardous Materials;

iv) Foreign language, *eg*, Chemie Ingenieur Technik; or,

v) Trade journals, *eg*, Chemistry and Industry.

### 6.5.1 Identifying and Locating Journals

There are so many journals of various kinds today (estimates vary from 80,000 to 200,000 worldwide) that numerous guides exist to help in identifying the one needed. These range from alphabetical lists of journals currently published to more detailed information in others. Some examples are as follows: Willings Press Guide; Current British Journals; Ulrich's International Periodicals Directory.

The HSE/IS produces annually a list of over 1600 titles taken within its Information Service entitled 'Health and Safety Executive Information Service Current Periodicals List'. This lists the current title, former title(s), and frequency of publication. A companion volume entitled 'Subject Index to the HSE Current Periodical List' gives under an alphabetical subject heading a list of relevant magazines. Both are available free of charge from the Health and Safety Executive, Information Centre, Broad Lane, Sheffield S3 7HQ, England.

## 6.6 Reports, Pamphlets, Books and Translations

Up to date information which has been validated is essential in the management of health and safety. Books can easily become dated so the user must be constantly aware that the information given may have been superseded by new knowledge. However, in most health and safety information collections a number of basic texts will be needed.

Items can be filed on shelves in the following ways without any further indexing:

i) By first author's name;

ii) By subject; or,

iii) By subject and then by author.

### 6.6.1 Translations

As searches are carried out for OSH information, some of the references found may be in languages other than English but which may have been translated. Many organizations need to have translations made of articles in periodicals, reports and even chapters of books. The Health and Safety Executive Information Service is a prolific source of translations, producing about 700+ $a^{-1}$. These translations are all deposited with the British

Library Document Supply Centre (BLDSC), Boston Spa, Wetherby, Yorkshire LS23 7BQ, England, be borrowed. It is worth asking BLDSC if a translation has been made before embarking on the expensive task of having a document translated. Many government departments, agencies and other organizations deposit copies at BLDSC.

The translations produced by the HSE Information Service are included in HSELINE, HSE's publicly available database. In addition HSELINE contains references to translations which have been acquired from other organizations, such as the US National Institute of Occupational Health (NIOSH) and the Canadian Centre for Occupational Health and Safety (CCOHS). HSE issues free of charge a quarterly 'Translation Bulletin' listing all the new translations which are available for sale. The translations are priced at a fraction of the original. Anyone wishing to receive the free 'Translation Bulletin' should wrote to HSE Information Service, Languages Unit, Harper Hill, Buxton, Derbyshire, England (see also chapter by Cowie and Richardson).

There is also a database 'World Translations Index' (WTI) which records translations of literature in all fields of science and technology. It corresponds to the publication 'World Transindex'. Translations covered are those from all languages into Western languages and those from other Western languages into French, Spanish and Portuguese. World Translation Index is available on the European Space Agency Information Service. The database is updated monthly and is produced by the International Translation Centre, Delft, The Netherlands, and the Institut d'Information Scientifique et Technique, Centre National de la Recherche Scientifique, Paris, France.

### 6.6.2 Translations of Standard Specifications

For exporting, there is a need to ensure that products meet the requirements of relevant standards and regulations of a particular country, the British Standards Institution Technical Help to Exporters (BSI/THE), Linford Wood, Milton Keynes, MK14 6LE, England should be contacted. They have a Translations Service which holds over 12,000 English translations of standards and regulations. If a document has not been translated BSI/THE will translate from any language into English at a reasonable cost.

## 6.7 Computerized Services

OSH information seekers should be aware that many of the printed paper versions of catalogues, indexes and abstracts to the literature are also available on computers throughout the world. It is not now necessary to spend many hours travelling to sources of information, checking manually through periodicals, etc., or worse, not being able to access the information at all. These facilities have been outlined in the chapter by Cowie and Richardson.

## 6.8 Chemical and Materials Safety Datasheets (MSDS)

Since the enactment of the Control of Substances Hazardous to Health Regulations 1989, anyone intending to work with such substances must carry out a risk assessment before beginning the work. To do this effectively it is necessary to know the hazards associated with the substances being used; manufacturers are obliged by law to produce MSDSs which give essential information about their products (see also chapters by Cowie and Richardson, Campbell, Knight, and Kulkarni and Nangle and others).

In addition to commercial sources, United Kingdom suppliers must provide information on the substances which they produce and/or sell as required under Section 6 of the Health and Safety at Work etc Act 1974.

## 6.9 Standard Specifications

Standard specifications are very important sources of chemical and occupational health and safety information. Most countries have a standardization body which prepares, organizes and promulgates national standards. It is usually the national standardization body which is represented on international bodies for standardization, thus ensuring harmonization and cooperation of action. The standards produced are usually listed in an annual catalog, which is updated by a monthly newsletter or journal. Very often the catalog will be computerized and available either online or on a compact disc read only memory (CD-ROM).

There are some standards available full text on CD-ROM. In the United Kingdom, the HSELINE database, OSHROM CD-ROM, OSH-UK CD-ROM list references to standards. British Standards are available full text in the Technical Indexes CD-ROM service; likewise the BSI catalog is available online as BSI Standardline, and on PERINORM CD-ROM.

## 6.10 Audiovisual Resources

Films and videos are an important way of highlighting accidents and malpractices in the working environment. A number of organizations in the United Kingdom produce films and videos on a regular basis. Many 'Open Learning' courses use videos as part of the training aids. Health and safety magazines review and list new films and videos.

## 6.11 Microfiche Services

i) Barbour Health and Safety Microfile, Barbour Index Ltd., New Lodge, Drift Road, Windsor, Berkshire, S14 4RQ, England, has been set up to provide vital reference information for safety officers, representatives, inspectors, and all others responsible for complying with or administrating the Health and Safety at Work etc Act 1974; and,

ii) Chadwyck-Healey Service. Another useful service started in 1980 is the Catalogue of British Official Publications not Published by HMSO, produced by Chadwyck-Healey Ltd., 20 Newmarket Road, Cambridge, CB4 8DT, England. The catalogue is published monthly and cumulates annually, covers the publications of over 400 organizations financed or controlled completely by the British Government, which are not produced by HMSO.

## 6.12 Conclusions

This chapter outlines publicly available sources of information relating to occupational safety and health matters. In considering chemical safety, the responsible industrialist or regulator must be in a position to adopt the most pragmatic assessment of how safe is safe enough. The many sources of information referred to in this chapter will assist in this process; it must be remembered that good and adequate validation and interpretation are especially important as good quality source data.

The acquisition of good quality OSH data from sources in Western Europe, North America, etc., will be particularly important to developing countries in formulating pragmatic legislation on both health and safety and environmental issues.

Further details on sources of information can be obtained from the author.

## 6.13 References

[1] *Off. J. Eur. Commun.*, L393, 30.12.1989, p. 1.
[2] *Off. J. Eur. Commun.*, L393, 30.12.1989, p. 13.
[3] *Off. J. Eur. Commun.*, L393, 30.12.1989, p. 18.
[4] *Off. J. Eur. Commun.*, L156, 21.12.1990, p. 9.
[5] *Off. J. Eur. Commun.*, L156, 21.06.1990, p. 14.
[6] *Off. J. Eur. Commun.*, L196, 26.07.1990, p. 1.
[7] *Off. J. Eur. Commun.*, L376, 31.12.1990, p. 1.
[8] *Off. J. Eur. Commun.*, L206, 29.07.1990, p. 16.
[9] *Off. J. Eur. Commun.*, L246, 26.08.1992, p. 6.

# 7. Environmental Hazard Assessment of Chemicals

Tadayoshi Shigeoka, Kikuo Yoshida, and Hotaka Saito

## 7.1 Introduction

Various adverse effects have been found to incur environmental pollution of chemicals via their production processes, use and disposal with the advent of the development of modern chemical industry. In a few decades, pesticides and industrial chemicals such as PCBs were recognized as harmful to health of humans, wildlife or ecosystems. In 1973, the regulatory laws to confirm the hazard of a new chemical was enacted in Japan because of an unfortunate accident known as Yusho and environmental pollution, both caused by PCBs. Similar laws were enacted in the USA and the European Community (EC), a few years later.

Methodologies on the confirmation of the safety of chemicals have made progress by the Organization for Economic Cooperation and Development (OECD) internationally, *eg*, the harmonization of many similar guidelines on toxicity and other test methods, and risk assessment methods to confirm the safety of new and existing chemicals.

In environmental hazard assessment of chemicals, it is necessary to evaluate exposure and effects on humans or ecosystems, and then to perform an assessment. It consists of comparing the predicted environmental concentration (PEC) and the predicted no effect concentration (PNEC) and to make a judgement as to whether the chemical entering into environments is hazardous or not. Ultimately, risk management including regulation of chemicals is necessary if a potential hazard is predicted (see also chapter by Motschi).

In this chapter, 4 subjects are introduced focusing on recent advances and situations in Japan. Section 7.2 outlines exposure analysis or environmental fate prediction methods using mathematical models developed by us. Section 7.3 introduces assessment methods of toxic effects on humans or environmental biota, especially ecotoxicity prediction methods. Regarding prediction methods, toxicological screening methods using cultured fish cells developed by us is described in section 7.4 as an alternative method to the use of biota. For ecological risk assessment, the book written by Suter II [1] is useful to understand the recent situation or studies. In section 7.5, the present situation pertaining to the assessment of industrial chemicals in Japan is introduced with regard to the regulation system, results of new and existing chemicals assessment, and survey systems of environmental pollution.

## 7.2 Mathematical Models for Environmental Fate and Exposure of Chemicals

### 7.2.1 Introduction

Once chemicals are released into the environment, their hazards to human and environmental biota depend on the concentrations of chemicals in the environment (*ie*, dose). However, quantifying the concentration levels is very complicated, because many processes determine the environmental fate, which are specific both to the chemical and the environment. This has led to the development of mathematical models which are applied to the calculation of the chemical concentrations in the environmental media of concern under generic or site-specific conditions. Mathematical models are also used to assess and understand distribution and persistence of chemicals in the environment.

The fundamentals of mathematical models lie in the mass balance of the chemical in the environment, which is quantitatively expressed in terms of equilibrium and rate constants of the environmental fate processes. Incorporating these constants into a set of the mass balance equations, and solving these equations are complicated, so that computers are used frequently to reduce the time and cost.

As shown in Figure 7.1, the computer programs of the models principally consist of input, calculation and output requirements.

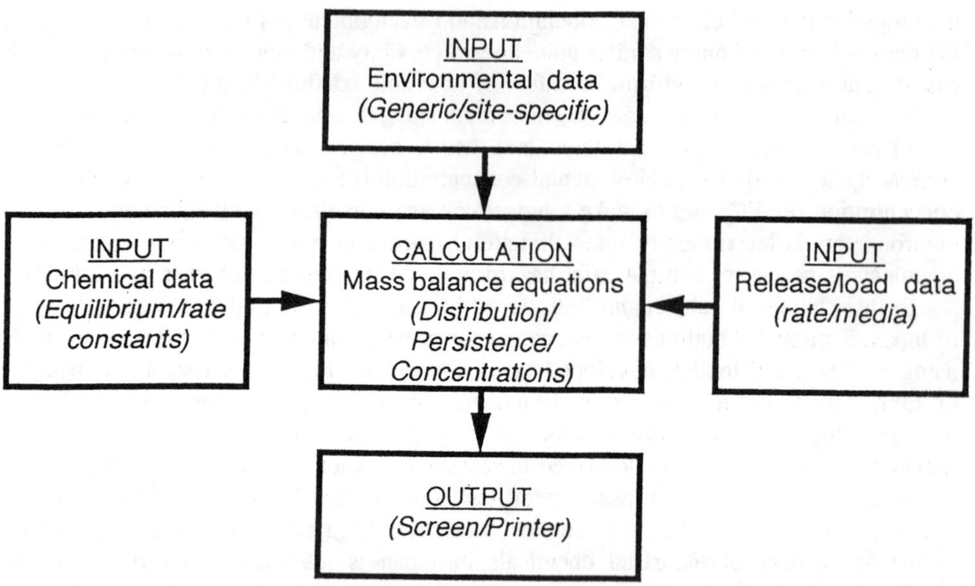


**Figure 7.1** Data processing of mathematical models

Basically, 3 types of input data are required, *ie*, chemical, environmental/meteorological and release data.

The calculation part of the computer program contains the mathematical formulae describing the environmental fate of chemicals, which are generally expressed as:

$$dMi/dt = Qi - \Sigma jAi,j - \Sigma krec \cdot Mi + \Sigma jIj,i$$

where Mi = the chemical mass in the environmental medium-*i*,
Qi = the releasing rate of the chemical into the medium-*i*
ΣjAi,j = the total mass transported and transferred from the medium-*i* to adjacent media,
ΣjIj,i = the total mass transported and transferred from adjacent media to the medium-*i*.
Σkrec·Mi = the total mass transformed by oxidation, photodegradation, hydrolysis and biodegradation, etc.

The distribution, persistence and concentrations of chemicals in the environment are evaluated by those procedures which are based on mass balance equations.

The evaluated results are displayed on a computer screen and printed out by a printer (output).

Many types of mathematical models have been developed to evaluate the fate and exposure of chemicals in the environment. These models are categorized in various ways, *eg*, based on the environmental media in concern, *ie*, single-medium and multi-media models.

Multi-media models can assess simultaneously the fate of chemicals in the environment consisting of multi-media such as air, water, soil, sediment, etc. Many users are interested in these models, because most of the chemicals released into the environment can transport between the environmental media.

### 7.2.2 Application of Mathematical Models

We have developed a number of multi-media models based on our original idea, and validated their predictability for evaluating environmental fate and exposure [2-9]. In our models, it is assumed that the environment consists of phases which are composed of several homogenous compartments. Also, the models assume that rates of intraphase transfer processes are faster than those of interphase transfer, transport and transformation processes (local equilibrium).

In this section, we introduce examples of the application of our multi-media models, MNSEM and MAC for evaluating the environmental fate of organic chemicals under generic and site-specific conditions in Japan.

Multi-Phase Non-Steady State Equilibrium Model (MNSEM) is designed to:

i) Estimate releasing rates of organic chemicals into air, water and soil;

ii) Evaluate environmental fate and concentrations of chemicals which are continuously released into air, water, and soil;

iii) Calculate clearance time (defined as the time required to reduce 90% of the steady state chemical mass, in case of termination of continuous chemical releases; and,

iv) Estimate human exposure doses through several pathways.

This model can describe the environmental fate and exposure of a given chemical by the user specifying nationwide or regional environments consisting of air, water, soil and sediment phases. MNSEM requires data on the chemical, environments, and releases, as shown in Table 7.1. Annually-averaged environmental data are usually used for the initial environmental fate and exposure assessment of chemicals. However, reliability of model application would impair considerably, when predicted environmental fate and exposure are significantly different from those observed in the real environment.

For validation of applicability of our models to the Japanese environment, we calculated environmental concentrations of a number of chemicals, and compared the calculated concentrations with monitoring data conducted by the Environment Agency of Japan [3,5,9].

The Environment Agency has been conducting successive investigations concerning the situation of persistence of chemicals in Japan since 1974, and the details of investigations are outlined in section 7.5.

The Agency measured concentrations of 700 chemicals in air, water, sediment, and/or aquatic biota. About 35% of the measured chemicals were detected in environmental media. However, most of the detected chemicals were detectable locally in Japan [10].

As an example of model validation, Figure 7.2 shows the comparison of the calculated concentrations of the following 5 chemicals with medians of their concentration measured in February, August and November at most of the monitoring points shown in Figure 7.3 [11]. The selected chemicals are manufactured in high quantities in Japan and detected widely in Japan on an annual basis: acetaldehyde, aniline, chlorobenzene, carbon tetrachloride, di-n-butyl phthalate (DBP).

The Student's t-test of correlation coefficient showed that the calculated concentrations were statistically correlated with the measured concentrations ($p=0.05$). Furthermore, Student's t-test of slope and intercept showed that slope and intercept were not significantly different from 1.0 and 0, respectively.

Also, the MNSEM model is applicable to the calculation of human exposure doses of chemicals through inhalation of ambient air and ingestion of drinking water, milk, meat, fish, and vegetation. Table 7.2 shows comparisons between the calculated and the measured daily exposure doses of carbon tetrachloride, trichloroethylene and tetrachloroethylene [9]. The calculated and measured doses through inhalation of air and ingestion of drinking water and foods were in the same order of magnitude, but the former doses were slightly higher than those calculated by MNSEM. As the exposure doses were measured at 8 large cities in Japan, hence these differences are reasonable.

**Table 7.1** **Input data required in MNSEM calculation**

| Data category | Data elements | Specifications of data |
|---|---|---|
| **Chemical** | molecular weight | g $mol^{-1}$ |
| | water solubility | mg $l^{-1}$ |
| | vapor pressure | mmHg |
| | log $K_{ow}$ | — |
| | organic carbon sorption constant | l $kg^{-1}$ |
| | bioconcentration factor | l $kg^{-1}$ |
| | oxidation | $cm^3$ $molecule^{-1}$ $sec^{-1}$ |
| | aqueous phase photodegradation | $d^{-1}$ |
| | hydrolysis | $M^{-1}$ $sec^{-1}$ |
| | biodegradation | l $cell^{-1}$ $d^{-1}$ |
| **Environment** | temperature | ° C |
| — air phase | volume | $m^3$ |
| | interphase area | $m^2$ |
| | OH radical | molecules $cm^{-3}$ |
| | wind velocity | m $sec^{-1}$ |
| | annual precipitation | mm $a^{-1}$ |
| | number of rainy days | — |
| — water phase | volume | $m^3$ |
| | interphase area | $m^2$ |
| | advection rate constant | $d^{-1}$ |
| | photolysis activity index | — |
| | pH | — |
| | active microorganisms | cell $l^{-1}$ |
| | suspended solids (SS) | mg $l^{-1}$ |
| | settling of SS | m $d^{-1}$ |
| | aquatic biota | mg $l^{-1}$ |
| — soil phase | volume | $m^3$ |
| | interphase area | $m^2$ |
| | soil-air/soil-water fraction | — |
| | soil-solid density | kg $m^{-3}$ |
| | pH | — |
| | organic carbon content | % |
| | active microorganisms | cell $kg^{-1}$ |
| — sediment phase | volume | $m^3$ |
| | interphase area | $m^2$ |
| | porosity | — |
| | pH | — |
| | solid density | kg $m^{-3}$ |
| | organic carbon content | % |
| | active microorganisms | cell $kg^{-1}$ |
| **Release** | annual production quantity | tonne $a^{-1}$ |
| | emission factors for opened use patterns | — |

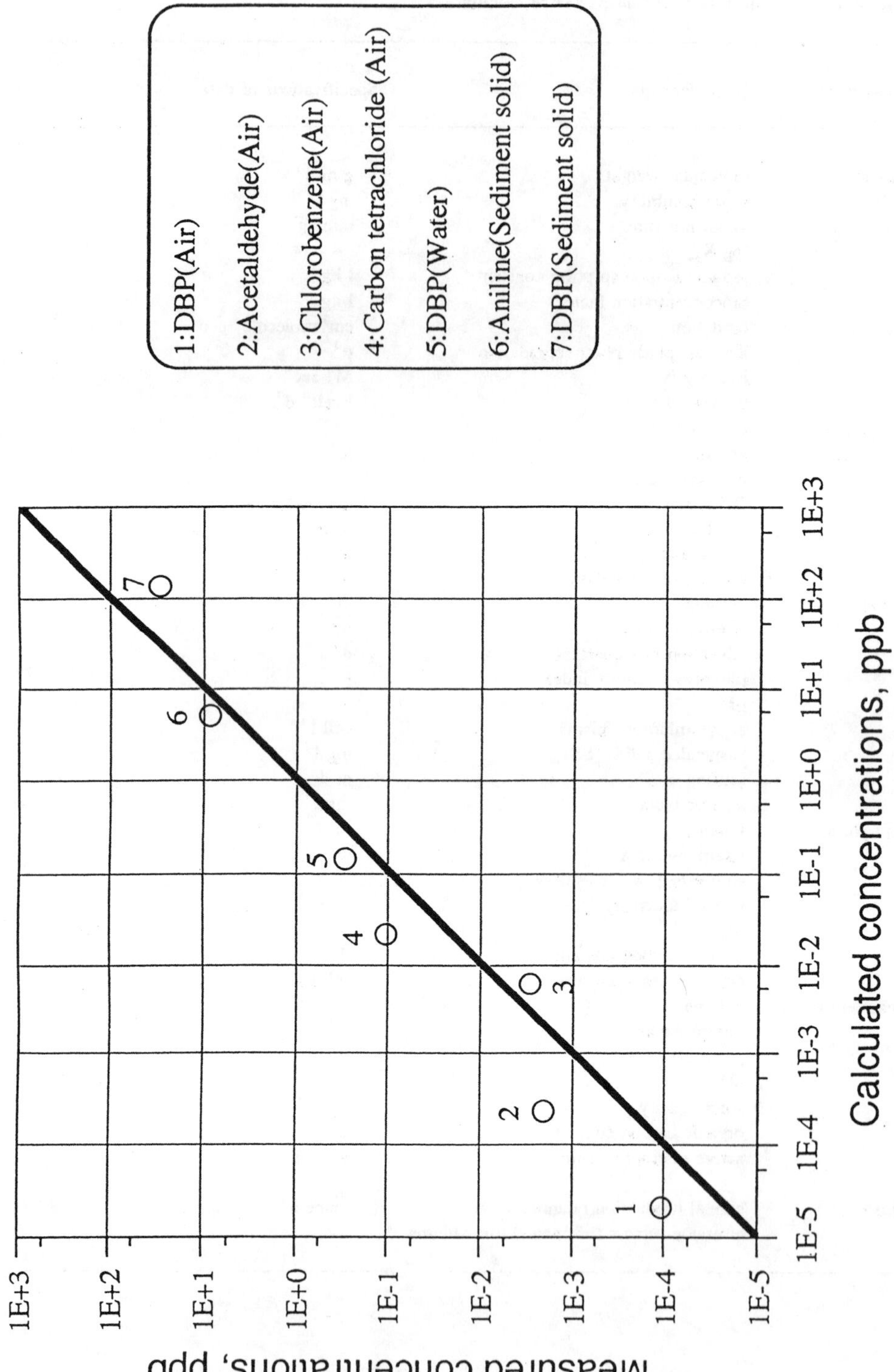


**Figure 7.2** Comparisons of calculated and measured concentrations

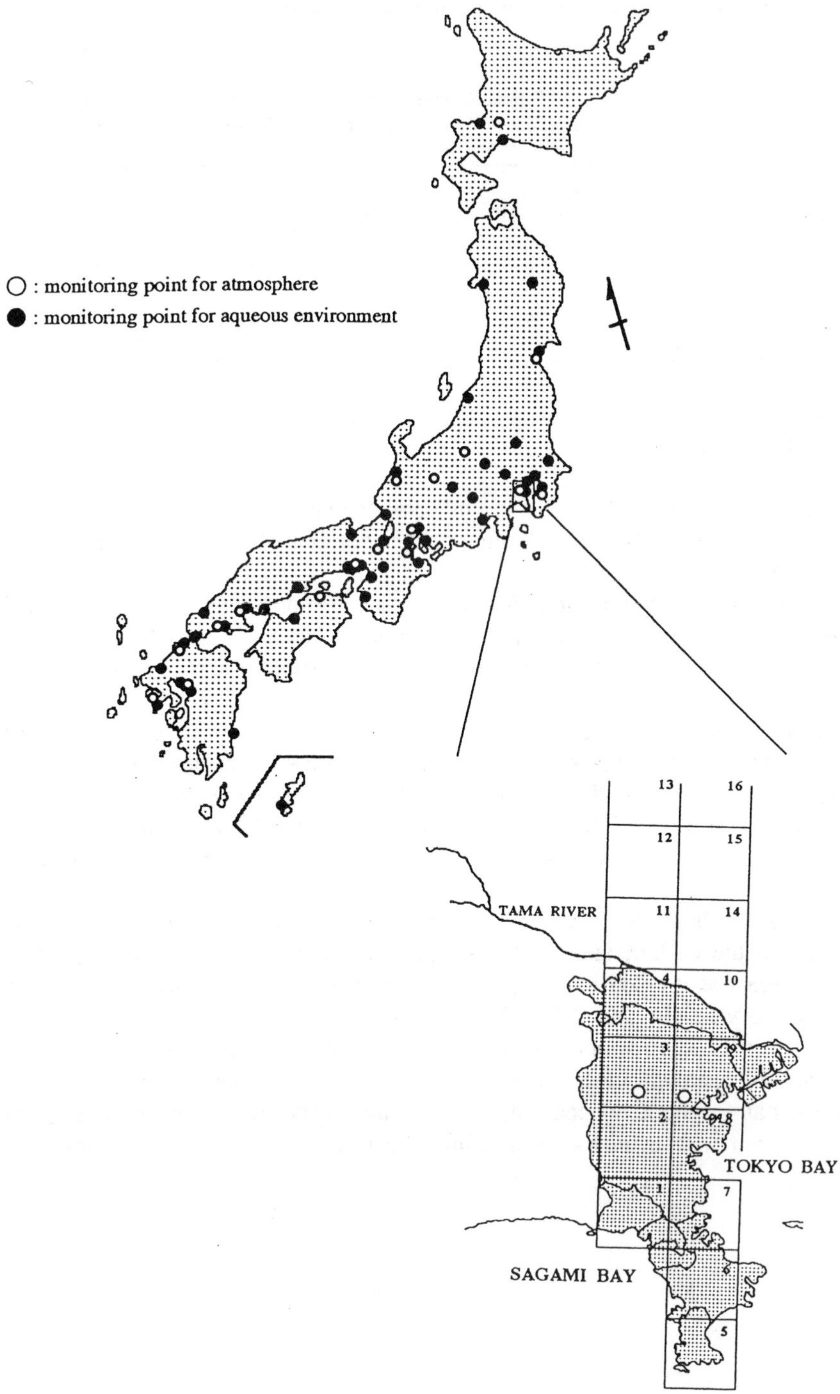


**Figure 7.3** **Monitoring points selected by the Environment Agency, Japan**

**Table 7.2** **Comparison of estimated exposure dose with measured dose**

| Chemical | Estimated dose, µg $d^{-1}$ | | Measured dose*, µg $d^{-1}$ | |
|---|---|---|---|---|
| | Inhalation** | Ingestion | Inhalation | Ingestion |
| Carbon tetrachloride | 4.61 | 0.16 | 7.7 | <0.1 |
| Trichloroethylene | 8.67 | 0.58 | 8.2 | <0.1 |
| Tetrachloroethylene | 6.39 | 0.79 | 21.0 | 0.84 |

*Average in 8 urban areas
**Dose based on 15 $m^3$ $d^{-1}$ of breathing rate

These results suggested that MNSEM is applicable to evaluate environmental fate and exposure of chemicals in the Japanese environment under annually-averaged nationwide conditions.

Monthly Averaged Concentration Model (MAC) is designed to evaluate the environmental fate and human exposure of chemicals released into the terrestrial environment consisting of air and soil phases under monthly averaged site-specific conditions.

MAC requires the same type of input data as MNSEM. However, monthly averaged and site-specific data on meteorology, environment, and releases are used to assess the environmental fate and exposure of chemicals. The MAC model divides the terrestrial area into several homogenous boxes. The different boxes are connected through advection and dispersion processes. This model can be linked with an aquatic environmental fate model, SAFECAS [4,6].

The MAC model has been applied to evaluation of fate and exposure of 1,4-dichlorobenzene in the eastern area of the Kanagawa Prefecture [8]. As illustrated in Figure 7.3, this area was divided into 16 boxes 10 km in length, 10 km in width, 100 m atmospheric boundary height, and 0.2 m depth of soil phase.

Boxes numbered 11 to 16 which were not included in the Kanagawa Prefecture were used to calculate the chemical mass transported to the eastern Kanagawa area.

The evaluated atmospheric concentrations of 1,4-dichlorobenzene were found to be in reasonable agreement with available monitoring data within a factor of 3, as shown in Figure 7.4.

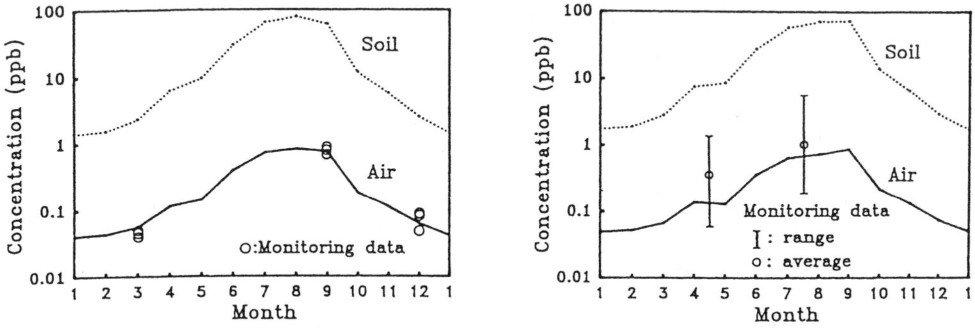


**Figure 7.4** Concentration-time profiles of 1,4-dichlorobenzene in the eastern Kanagawa area

### 7.2.3 Application

In the hazard assessment of chemicals released into the environment, it is important to evaluate the environmental concentrations of chemicals. Predicted environmental concentrations (PEC) are compared with toxicity data of environmental organisms. Thus, environmental fate models are becoming a valuable tool for the assessment of the potential hazard of chemicals, especially new chemical substances.

We demonstrated the successful application of mathematical models to generic and site-specific environments. For the assessment of chemical fate at a specific location, models require suitable and relevant data. However, local situations are complicated and available data concerning the environment and release are usually limited.

Conversely, models require more generic environment and release data for screening the evaluation of the chemical fate in regional and nationwide environments.

In all cases, uncertainty is in the source assessment in which release rate and duration of chemicals are assessed. If users can obtain these types of data more easily, mathematical models will become increasingly powerful approaches.

## 7.3 Assessment Methods of the Toxic Effects of Chemicals

### 7.3.1 Evaluation Methods of Ecotoxicity

Chemicals which enter the environments may have harmful effects on human or environmental biota, especially aquatic organisms, depending on both their concentration and their toxicity (see Annex 1) In assessment of the effects, consideration needs to be given to both direct exposure of chemicals in environmental media and intake of contaminated foodstuffs by bioconcentration or biomagnification via foodchains. In this section, the evaluation methods for aquatic ecotoxicity, especially alternative *in vitro* toxicity are briefly described.

Generally, ecotoxicity test methods are classified as follows:

i) Short-term (acute) tests with single-species;

ii) Long-term (chronic) tests with single-species;

iii) Tests with multi-species systems (ecosystem such as microcosm or mesocosm); and,

iv) Tests with *in vitro* systems (*eg*, cultured cell or tissues).

At present, reliable test methods for the effects of chemicals on whole ecosystems (iii above) are not yet established when compared to i) and ii) above, which are the test methods using single species and adopted in existing OECD guidelines [12]. The *in vitro* toxicity test methods (iv above) have been developed as an alternative toxicity test method using bacteria or cultured cells instead of biota because of animal welfare, convenience and cost saving.

Chemicals may affect both the function and the structure of the biotic section of an ecosystem. In this respect, the ecologically functional distinction between producers, consumers, and decomposers is important when considering environmental hazards. In the OECD guidelines, green algae is selected as a producer, *Daphnia* as primary consumer, and fish as secondary consumer. In ecological risk assessments, the minimum data set at the acute or chronic level should be 3 studies on at least 2 taxonomic groups, while at the ecosystem level one carefully conducted study on an appropriate species or communities should be sufficient.

Adverse or harmful effects will occur if measured or predicted environmental concentration (PEC) in various environmental media such as water, soil, sediment and the atmosphere is higher than predicted no effect concentrations (PNEC, or maximum tolerable concentration MTC) based on the above ecotoxicity test results. PNEC values combine the ecotoxicity data with an assessment factor (AF). Data from short-term studies in the laboratory generally need large AFs (100-1000 are applied to the lowest $L(E)C_{50}$); data from long-term laboratory studies or ecosystem field studies need smaller AFs (usually 10 applied to the lowest no observable effect levels (NOEL).

### 7.3.2 Alternative Toxicity Test Methods

Recently, alternative toxicity test methods using bacteria or cultured cells instead of biota itself have been developed for the purposes of animal welfare, convenience, cost saving and screening of hazardous chemicals.

A chemical's toxicity to bacteria may be used to estimate the toxicity to higher organisms such as fish if a relationship has been established between the toxic responses of the 2 organisms. As testing in higher organisms is significantly more costly and time consuming, preliminary determinations of toxicity based on bacterial testing can be advantageous. Microtox® is a standardized toxicity test using instrumentation and supplies including the marine luminescent bacterium *Photobacterium phosphoreum*, from the Microbics Corp. (CA, USA) (see chapter by Isenberg and Bulich). This is a quick, easy and reproducible test method. Therefore, it can be of great value if the toxicity values can be related to toxicity to aquatic organisms. Good correlations were found between the Microtox, other bacteria, and the fathead minnow [14].

A new *in vitro* genotoxicity assay has been developed by the Microbics Corp. This assay, known by the trade name of Mutatox® assay, is a convenient method to detect DNA-damaging substances (genotoxins) by measuring light emissions from an isolated dark mutant strain of *Photobacterium phosphoreum*. The Mutatox assay compares favorably in sensitivity with the Ames test, and it is easier and more rapid to perform [15]. As a toxicity estimation method, one convenient assay method was developed and uses cultured fish cells; this is introduced in section 7.4.

Furthermore, quantitative structure-activity relationships (QSAR) methods were developed for screening and cost saving purposes using chemical structure and physical-chemical properties. The US Environmental Protection Agency (EPA) already uses QSAR for aquatic toxicity assessment of new chemicals based on the aquatic toxicity data base known as AQUIRE. The US EPA has been accumulating an enormous amount of toxicity data on aquatic biota for many years, and at present, AQUIRE has 104,000 toxicity test results on 5200 substances using various aquatic biota and the software is available in the USA to sort such toxicity data by microcomputer [16].

### 7.3.3 Application

In ecological effects assessment, there are many problems involved, *eg*, it is often observed that laboratory test data over estimate more commonly than underestimate toxicity, because laboratory toxicity tests are conducted in filtered water of low suspended solids (*eg*, soil particles) and low organic matter content, which play an important role in natural environments. Therefore, test methods including multi-species and simulating environmental conditions, *ie*, more sophisticated ecosystems or field test methods should be developed for determination of more reliable assessment factors (AFs), in spite of its difficulties. It will be necessary to develop both aquatic toxicology methods and terrestrial or sediment ecotoxicology.

Recently, on an administrative basis in the USA, EC, and other countries, emphasis in environmental protection is shifting from attention to human health to a more balanced consideration of human and ecological health. The U.S. EPA published *Framework for Ecological Risk Assessment*, in 1992 [17] and it describes identification of the problems and selection of appropriate endpoints in ecological risk assessment which were more difficult than for human risk assessment. Recently the OECD prepared guidance documents for aquatic effect assessments, and ECETOC (European Centre for Ecotoxicology and Toxicology of Chemicals) published *Environmental Hazard Assessment of Chemicals* [18]. These publications are very useful when considering environmental risk assessments.

## 7.4 Fish Cytotoxicity Assay

The use of fish cell lines has received some attention as a screening tool for assessment of chemical risks and as a tool for detecting pollutants in aquatic environments [14-21]. However, cytotoxicity studies using fish cells are much less in use than those using mammalian cells. Advantages and disadvantages of cytotoxicity assays with cultured fish cells have recently been reviewed by Babich and Borenfreund [20,21]. In this section, recent advances of cytotoxicity assays with fish cells are introduced, referring mainly to our studies.

### 7.4.1 Advantages of Cytotoxicity Assays with Fish Cells

The advantages of cytotoxicity assays are that they can provide data more rapidly, precisely, and are more humane than *in vivo* toxicity tests. In addition, several toxicological endpoints developed for mammalian cells can be applied to fish cells, such as dye exclusion with trypan blue, dye retention with neutral red, leakage of enzymes such as lactate dehydrogenase, or release of $^{51}Cr$, uptake of $^{3}H$-uridine, cell attachment to a substratum, cell replication, and colony formation [20]. Thus, established methodologies for mammalian cells can easily be adapted to assays with fish cells. Moreover, poikilothermic fish cell lines can be maintained over a wide temperature range. Fathead minnow epithelioid (FHM) cells multiply over a wide temperature range of 0 to 36 °C with maximum growth at about 34 °C [22]. Goldfish fibroblast (GFS) cells can be cultured at 15 to 37 °C [23]. Hence, fish cells are useful for the cyto- and genotoxicity studies under various environmental temperature conditions. Additionally, fish cells derived from marine species may be useful for detection of marine pollutants and for investigation of the effects of chemicals on marine organisms by addition of appropriate amount of sodium chloride (*eg*, +0.07 M) to the medium [24].

### 7.4.2 *In Vivo/In Vitro* relationships

The cytotoxicity of chemicals to rainbow trout RTG-2 cells, bluegill sunfish BF-S cells, fathead minnow FHM cells, and goldfish GFS cells are in good agreement with the fish acute toxicities ($LC_{50}$s) (Table 7.3). Judging from our recent work [25-27], the fish acute $LC_{50}$s of unspecific narcotic chemicals (*eg*, alcohols and benzenes), polar narcotic chemicals (*eg*, phenols and anilines), reactive aliphatic aldehydes (except for formaldehyde), and specific acting chemicals, except for some pesticides (*eg*, carbamates) can be predicted from their cytotoxicity. Babich *et al* [29], describes how fish acute $LC_{50}$s for inorganic metals except for an anionic hexavalent chromium salts can be predicted from their cytotoxicity data. From extensive research on metabolism and toxic mechanism (*eg*, interaction with biomolecules) of these outliers, cytotoxicity assays using fish cells can be modified further, and adapted to predict *in vivo* responses.

**Table 7.3** **Correlation of *in vivo* fish acute toxicity ($LC_{50}$) with *in vitro* cytotoxicity to cultured fish cells**

| Cell | Fish | n | r | References |
|---|---|---|---|---|
| GFS[a] | Guppy | 38[c] | 0.95 | [23] |
| | Fathead minnow | 27[c] | 0.95 | [23] |
| | Guppy | 9[d] | 0.92 | [24] |
| | Carp | 34[e] | 0.85 | [25] |
| FHM[a] | Golden orfe | 50[f] | 0.89 | [26] |
| BF-2[a] | | 7[g] | 0.83 | [27] |
| | Bluegill | 4[h] | -0.42 | [27] |
| | | 12[i] | 0.98 | [28] |
| RTG-2[b] | Rainbow trout | 12[j] | 0.92 | [29] |

n = the number of data; r = the correlation coefficient;
a = neutral red uptake assay; b = cell attachment assay;
c = alcohols, benzenes, phenols, anilines, etc.; d = aldehydes excluding formaldehyde;
e = pesticides; f = alcohols, acids, ketones, esters, etc.;
g = cationic metals; h = anionic metals; i = phenols, toluene, j = phenols.

### 7.4.3 Relationships with Physicochemical Properties

The sequence of the cytotoxicity of organic chemicals are directly correlated with their lipophilicity (*eg*, logarithm 1-octanol/water partition coefficient; $\log P_{ow}$ [20,21,24-26,31]. In our work [26], the midpoint cytotoxicity values of 109 organic chemicals (*eg*, alcohols, aromatics, phenols, pesticides, etc.) to goldfish GFS cells as determined by the neutral red assay correlate well with $\log P_{ow}$. In particular, the cytotoxicity of unspecific and polar narcotic types of chemicals to GFS cells can be predicted from $\log P_{ow}$ reliably. A linear relationship between the cytotoxicity of unspecific narcotics and their $\log P_{ow}$ shows a minimum baseline cytotoxicity compared with those of the polar narcotics, reactive chemicals and specifically acting chemicals. Similar quantitative structure-activity relationships (QSARs) are noted in the fish acute toxicity $LC_{50}$s of organic chemicals [32]. Thus, fish cell cytotoxicity assays will be useful for the generation of QSARs, which depend on a replicable and reliable biological database.

### 7.4.4 Problems and Prospects

Whilst fish cytotoxicity assays have some advantages over the ecotoxicology described above, there are some problems. The complexity of interactions that take occur *in vivo*, *eg*, absorption, distribution, metabolism and excretion, cannot as yet be approximated by *in vitro* tests. In addition, although most cytotoxicity tests with fish cells measure cell viability, these assays are less sensitive than fish acute toxicity tests. More sensitive indicators of cell health will also be needed.

Consequently, cytotoxicity assays with fish cells will serve to screen and prioritize chemical substances and to generate computer-based QSARs to a significant extent, even if such assays cannot produce the full information necessary to make definitive regulatory decisions. In the future, fish cytotoxicity studies should be applied increasingly to screening of hazardous chemicals, and also the detection of pollution in the environment, and evaluation of the synergistic and antagonistic interactions between combinations of chemicals. These approach, in conjunction with toxicological and biotechnological development, will elucidate the applicabilities and limitations of fish cytotoxicity assays as an alternative method.

## 7.5 Hazard Assessment of Chemicals in Japan

In 1968, the Kanemi Yusho accident occurred in the western part of Japan, and this was caused by the intake of PCB-contaminated rice oil. Thousands of people suffered from the illness caused by PCB and its highly toxic derivatives, polychlorodibenzofurans (PCDF) in the rice oil. PCB used as a heating medium leaked from a pin-hole in the tubings of the oil manufacturing plant and contaminated the rice oil. Furthermore, PCB contamination of the natural environment and biota was evident based on the many research works since Jensen, (the Swedish scientist), reported his findings in 1966 [33], that PCBs contaminated birds.

As a result of this accident and the affects caused by PCBs, in Japan, the *Law Concerning the Examination and Regulation of Manufacture, etc, of Chemical Substances*, (commonly known as *Chemical Substances Control Law*) was enacted in October 1973, and enforced in April 1974. This was the first law in the world to regulate chemical substances and is aimed at the hazard evaluation of chemicals to human health via the environment. Under this law, new chemical substances are examined prior to manufacture or import from their toxicity to humans via the environment, *ie*, by inhalation of ambient air, ingestion of drinking water and foods, including fish, meat and vegetables. Currently, this is different from the U.S. and EC regulations, as this law does not include assessment with regard to the toxic effects on environmental biota such as daphnid, algae, etc.

The protection of workers' health from hazard caused by exposure to chemicals, the *Industrial Safety and Health Law* requires that the information on the hazards of new chemical substances necessitate mutagenicity test results for registration following its 1979 amendment.

### 7.5.1 Hazard Assessment of New Chemicals

A flow scheme of the Chemical Substances Control Law of Japan is shown in Figure 7.5. This law is under the jurisdiction of the Ministry of International Trade and Industry (MITI), principally for biodegradation and bioaccumulation, the Ministry of Health and Welfare (MHW) for toxicity and the Environment Agency (EA) for environmental pollution. The Japanese law has adopted a tier system for hazard assessment and puts emphasis on the persistence of chemicals in the environment, which is the reason for testing the biodegradability initially. This is different from the regulatory system used in the U.S. and the EC. The second tier consists of 2 phases, the evaluation of the bioaccumulation property and toxicity screening of the chemical. Hence, measurement of partition coefficient or a bioaccumulation test will be required to be performed at first phase if a chemical is persistent. Then, at the second phase, toxicity screening tests are performed to examine the possibility of chronic toxicity to humans if the chemical is of low bioaccumulation. This second phase was added to the original law by the 1986 amendment (enforcement; 1987), resulting from a case of groundwater pollution caused by trichloroethylene and tetrachloroethylene used as washing solvents. Thus, chemical substances which are not bioaccumulative but persistent in the environment and possibly chronically toxic or cause mutation in genes are *Designated Chemical Substances*, and the quantity of their manufacture or import are supervised.

The third tier is the evaluation of the chronic toxicity if a chemical is highly accumulative.

Consequently, new chemical substances are assessed when they do not lend themselves easily to chemical changes to inorganic elements, (*ie*, complete mineralization) by natural effects, especially by microorganism (*ie*, not easily biodegradable), or have the property to easily accumulate in biological organisms (*ie*, bioaccumulation), and have the danger of being harmful to human health when exposed for long time periods (*ie*, chronic toxicity). The manufacture, import and use of chemical substances incurring properties similar to PCBs are regulated (essentially inhibited) as *Class I Specified Chemical Substances.*

Standard test methods adopted in Japan are described in the OECD testing guidelines; 301C for biodegradation (301D 'closed bottle' method for volatile substances), 305C for bioaccumulation, etc. (*qv.* Annex 2).

However, this assessment scheme is not applicable to polymeric substances with number average molecular weight ($MW_n$) >1000 and with a low content of oligomer (<1% of oligomer (MW) <1000). Polymers are recognized as being substantially safe because of their low permeability through biological membranes, and therefore are assessed by another system — the so-called Polymer Flow Scheme, which evaluates solubility and stability of the polymer in conditions close to the natural environment.

The results of assessment from the enforcement of law to the amendment, and from the amendment to present time, are shown in Table 7.4 [32], and we can find that biodegradable substances are nearly 20% of the assessed both a) and b). The substances judged as safe from the results of chronic toxicity tests were very few. This fact is attributed to high cost for chronic toxicity tests which are needed if the substance has highly bioaccumulative properties.

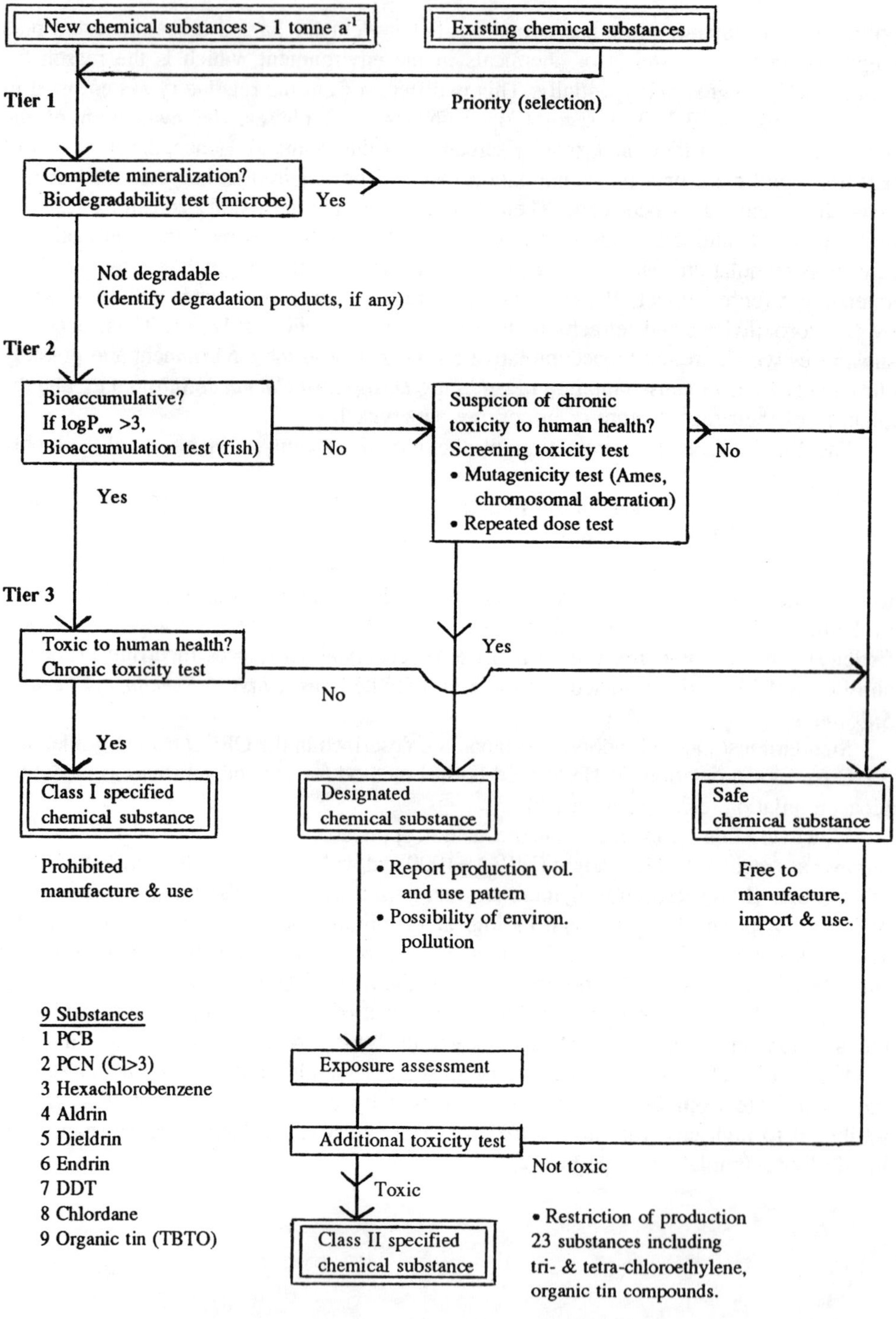


**Figure 7.5** **Flow of Chemical Substances Control Law of Japan (Enforcement: 1974, Amendment:1987)**

**Table 7.4** **Assessment results under Chemical Substances Control Law [34] (judged as safe chemical substances)**

| | | | |
|---|---|---|---|
| a) | Assessment before amendment of law (1974-1986) | | |
| | • biodegradable | 535 | 17% |
| | • low bioaccumulation (low biodegradability) | 2589 | 83% |
| | • no chronic toxicity (low biodegradability, high bioaccumulation | 8 | 0.3% |
| | Total | 3132 | 100% |
| b) | Assessment after amendment of law (1987-1992) | | |
| | • biodegradable | 211 | 19% |
| | • no suspicion of toxicity (low biodegradability, low bioaccumulation) | 774 | 68% (non-polymer 38% + polymer* 30%) |
| | • suspicion of toxicity (designated chemical substance) | 150 | 13% |
| | • no chronic toxicity (low biodegradability, high bioaccumulation) | 6 | 0.5% |
| | Total | 1141 | 100% |

*Assessed by Polymer Flow Scheme

### 7.5.2 Hazard Assessment of Existing Chemicals

Chemical substances, which were being manufactured or used commercially at the time the Chemical Substances Control Law was enacted (existing chemical substances), are not subject to the hazard assessment by chemical industry or importer. These existing chemicals are subject to government's examination for the confirmation of the hazard since the enforcement of the law and, if necessary, may be designated as Class I or II Specified Chemical Substances for regulation. Investigation and inspection with regard to biodegradation using microorganisms and bioaccumulation in fish have been conducted by the Ministry of International Trade and Industry (MITI), chronic toxicity on human health by the Ministry of Health and Welfare (MHW), and the situation of persistence in the environment by the Environment Agency. The priority of substances in performing safety tests is determined by consideration of the quantity of the substance on the market and their use. Biodegradation and bioaccumulation properties were assessed on 918 substances by the Chemicals Inspection and Testing Institute (CITI) during the period 1975 to 1992. These test results were published in 1992 under the supervision of MITI [35]. It is remarkable that all of the test data of the 918 substances were obtained using the same test method. Table 7.5 shows substances having higher BCF values (BCF >10000) of ~600 substances on which bioaccumulation tests were performed.

At present, 9 substances, namely PCBs, PCN, HCB, aldrin, dieldrin, endrin, DDT, chlordanes, and bis(tributyltin) oxide (TBTO) have been identified as Class I Specified

Chemical Substances, based on such biodegradation and bioaccumulation data and chronic toxicity data. In April 1989, trichloroethylene, tetrachloroethylene and carbon tetrachloride were designated as Class II Specified Chemical Substances, and in 1990, 7 triphenyltin compounds and 13 tributyltin compounds were designated similarly.

**Table 7.5** **Existing chemicals having bioconcentration factor (BCF) >10000**

| Chemical name | BCF |
|---|---|
| Organic chain compounds | |
| bis(n-tributyltin)oxide | 12100 |
| Monocyclic organic compounds | |
| Hexachlorobenzene | 27000 |
| N-mono(di)methylphenyl-N'-mono(di)methylphenyl-1,4-phenylenediamine | 15200 |
| 2,4,6-tri-tert-butylphenol | 23200 |
| 1,5,9-Cyclododecatriene | 14800 |
| 1,1-bis(tert-Butyldioxy)-3,3,5-trimethylcyclohexane | 13200 |
| 2,4,6-Tribromophenyl(2-methyl-2,3-dibromopropyl)ether | 31000 |
| 1,3,5-tri-tert-Butylbenzene | 36700 |
| Polycyclic organic compounds | |
| Diethylbiphenyl | 14600 |
| 4,4'-Dibromobiphenyl | 19900 |
| 1,1-bis(p-Chlorophenyl)-2,2,2-trichloroethanol | 10000 |
| Endrin | 12600 |
| Dieldrin | 14500 |
| Aldrin | 20000 |
| PCN (Cl=3-5) | 11800 |
| 3,5-di-tert-Butylbiphenyl-4-ol | 15900 |
| DDT | 24400 |
| Triisopropylnaphthalene | 14500 |
| PCB (Cl=2) | 16000 |
| PCB (Cl=3) | 20200 |
| PCB (Cl=4) | 21900 |
| Others | |
| Heptachlor | 17300 |

### 7.5.3 Investigation of Environmental Persistency of Chemicals in Japan

In relation to the Chemical Substances Control Law, the Environment Agency of Japan has been investigating the environmental pollution by chemicals, *ie*, monitoring persistent chemicals in the environment since fiscal year 1974, as a part of its Safety Inspection Program of the existing chemical substances [10]. In order to investigate 20,000 or more existing chemicals efficiently and systematically, the Environment Agency conducted the First General Inspection Survey of chemicals on environmental safety from 1979 to 1988, and data on environmental pollution by existing chemicals of toxic concern in Japan were accumulated and the methodology of the survey was developed. Since fiscal year 1989, the Second General Inspection Survey (Figure 7.6) has been conducted after improvement of the methodology based on the experiences of the First Survey. The priority of substances for the survey was determined considering the information on their toxicity, production volume, inspection results of biodegradation and bioaccumulation of existing chemicals by MITI, etc.

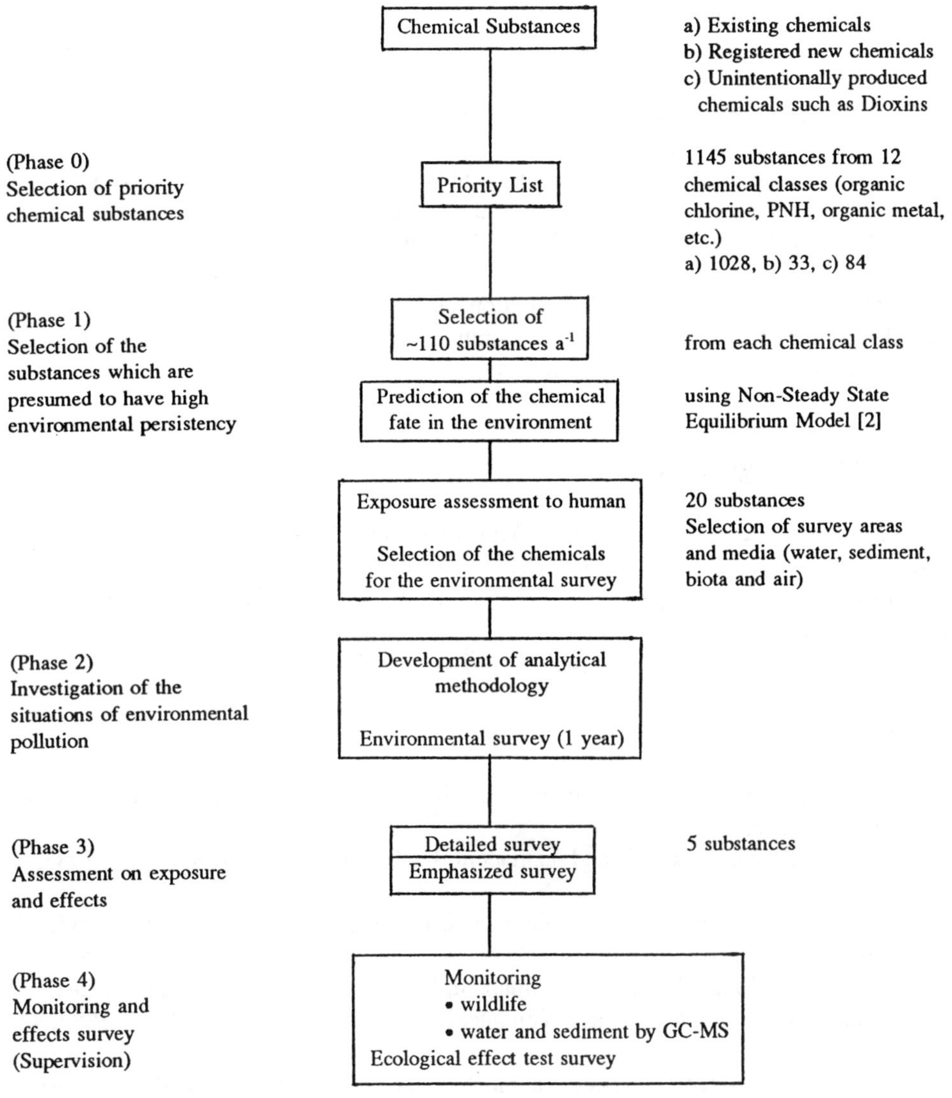


**Figure 7.6** **The system of the second general inspection survey of chemicals by the Environmental Agency of Japan**

Currently, 3 major investigations have been conducted:

i) General inspection survey of chemicals on environmental safety;

ii) Actual condition follow-up surveys of pollution by toxic chemicals; and,

iii) Examinational surveys of environmental persistency of Designated Chemical Substances.

The results of the first and the second survey have contributed to the regulation of existing chemicals as useful information for the prevention of environmental pollution.

## 7.6 Conclusion and Future Prospects

In Japan, the chemical safety problem is now moving to the third stage as a result of the assessment of chemicals performed under the regulation of the Chemical Substances Control Law of Japan, and other relevant laws during the past 2 decades. For risk reduction of chemicals, voluntary measures or actions of the chemical industries will be anticipated instead of administrative regulation, such as the preparation of Material Safety Data Sheets (MSDSs), including a consideration of the international cooperation with OECD and the UNCED Agenda 21 program.

## 7.7 Acknowledgements

The authors wish to thank Dr. S. Morita, Deputy General Manager of the Research Center of Mitsubishi Kasei Corporation, and Dr. F. Yamauchi, Senior Advisor of Mitsubishi-Kasei Institute of Toxicological and Environmental Sciences, for encouragement and valuable advice.

## 7.8 References

[1] *Ecological Risk Assessment*, Suter II, G. W., (Ed.), Lewis Publishers, Boca Laton, 1993, pp. 538.

[2] Yoshida, K., Shigeoka, T., and Yamauchi, F., *Ecotoxicol. Environ. Safety*, 1983, **7**, 179-190.

[3] Yoshida, K., Shigeoka, T., and Yamauchi, F., *Toxicol. Environ. Chem.*, 1987, **15**, 159-183.

[4] Yoshida, K., Shigeoka, T., and Yamauchi, F., *Chemosphere*, 1987, **16**, 2531-2544.

[5] Yoshida, K., Shigeoka, T., and Yamauchi, F., *Toxicol. Environ. Chem.*, 1987, **17**, 69-85.

[6] Yoshida, K., Shigeoka, T., and Yamauchi, F., *Chemosphere*, 1988, **17**, 2063-2072.

[7] Yoshida, K., *Jpn, J. Toxicol. Environ. Health*, 1989, **35**, 313-321.

[8] Yoshida, K. and Shigeoka, T., *Environ. Sci*, 1992, **5**, 33-44.

[9] Yoshida, K, *Chemosphere*, 1993, **27**, 621-630.

[10] Office of Health Study, *Chemicals in the Environment*, Environment Agency, Japan, 1991, pp. 118.
[11] Environment Agency, Japan, Comparison of Global Environmental Fate Models-Applicability of Global Models to Japanese Environment, prepared to OECD Phase 1 SIDS Initial Assessment Meeting, 1993.
[12] OECD. OECD Guidelines for Testing of Chemicals, 1981.
[13] Blum, D.J.W. and Speece, R.E., *Res. J. Wat. Pollut. Cont. Fed.*, 1991, **63**, 198-207.
[14] *Ecotoxicology Monitoring*, Richardson, M.L. (Ed.), VCH Publishers, Weinheim, 1993, pp. 384.
[15] Johnson, B.T., *Environ. Tox. Chem.*, 1992, **1**, 473-480.
[16] *SETAC NEWS*, 1993, **13**, (4), 16.
[17] U.S. EPA. *Framework for Ecological Risk Assessment*, EPA 630/R-92/001, Washington D.C., 1992.
[18] European Centre for Ecotoxicology and Toxicology of Chemicals (ECETOC), *Environmental hazard assessment of substances*, Technical Report No. 51, Brussels, Belgium, 1993, pp. 92.
[19] Shigeoka, T., Saito, H., and Yamauchi, F., *Jpn. J. Toxicol. Environ. Health*, 1987, **33**, 1-10.
[20] Babich, H. and Borenfreund, E., *Toxicity Assessment: An International Quarterly*, 1987, **2**, 119-133.
[21] Babich, H. and Borenfreund, E., *Toxic. in Vitro*, 1991, **5**, 91-100.
[22] Wolf, K. and Mann, J.A., *In Vitro*, 1980, **16**, 168-179.
[23] Saito, H., Sudo, M., Shigeoka, T., and Yamauchi, F., *Environ. Toxicol. Chem.*, 1991, **10**, 235-241.
[24] Nicholson, B.L., 'Fish cell cultures: an overview, in: *Invertebrate and Fish Tissue Culture*, Kuroda, Y., Kurstake, E., and Maramorosch, K., (Ed.), Springer-Verlag, New York, 1988, pp. 292-294.
[25] Saito, H., Koyasu, J., Yoshida, K., Shigeoka, T., and Koike, S., *Chemosphere*, 1993, **26**, 1015-1028.
[26] Saito, H., Koyasu, J., and Shigeoka, T., *Chemosphere*, 1993, (in press).
[27] Saito, H., Iwami, S., and Shigeoka, T., *Chemosphere*, 1991, **23**, 525-537.
[28] Brandao, J.C., Bohets, H.H.L., Van De Vyver, I.E., and Dierickx, P.J., *Chemosphere*, 1992, **25**, 553-562.
[29] Babich, H., Puerner, A., and Borenfreund, E., *Arch. Environ. Contam. Toxicol.*, 1986, **15**, 31-37.
[30] Babich, H. and Borenfreund, E., *Environ. Res.*, 1987, **42**, 229-237.
[31] Bols, N.C., Boliska, S.A. Dixon, D.G., Hodson, P.V., and Kaiser, K.L.E., *Toxicol.*, 1985, **6**, 147-155.
[32] Konemann, W.H. and Musch, A., *Toxicol.*, 1981, **196**, 223-228.
[33] Jensen, S., *New Sci.*, 1966, **32**, 612.
[34] Pamphlet from JETOC-MITI, 2nd seminar on the regulation of chemicals, April 16, 1993, Tokyo.
[35] Chemicals Inspection and Testing Institute (Ed.), compiled under the supervision of the Ministry of International Trade and Industry, Japan, *Biodegradation and Bioaccumulation data of Existing Chemicals based on CSCL, Japan,* JETOC, Tokyo, 1992, pp. 493.

# 8. Adverse Health Effects of Environmental Chemicals: Indian Scenario

Devika Nag and Farhat N. Jaffery

## 8.1 Introduction

Industrialization of developing countries such as India has provided several benefits to the citizens and raised the standard of living. However, the development has not been entirely free from drawbacks including environmental pollution. The Bhopal gas catastrophe of December 3, 1984, with a major loss of life and continuing adverse effects on life systems, galvanized the Government and citizens to ensure that firm control on industry by regulatory agencies is enforced in practice.

The chemical industry in India accounts for 10% of Gross National Product (GNP) and is poised for an impressive growth and performance in the coming years (Table 8.1). Many of these chemicals are hazardous and care has to be taken during their usage, storage, transportation, and disposal (Tables 8.2 and 8.3). As industrial activities have grown and population increased, unfortunately so has the pollution not only in industrial regions but even in distant rural areas. By following the development pattern of the industrialized nations, the Third World countries can learn from past pollution episodes.

However, the problem is greater in India as safety procedures and detoxification procedures advocated in developed countries are often not implemented totally. Human exposure to environmental chemicals can arise from inhalation, dermal contact, and ingestion of polluted water or food, especially those containing biomagnified toxic residues. The industrial and economic developments have changed the lifestyle of urban and rural populations considerably. This has also led to increased stress, thereby threatening health in general.

The health risks due to industrial chemicals can be direct or indirect. In the first category, exposure may be occupational due to fugitive chemicals, leading to several industrial diseases. Even though low-dose, low-duration exposure takes place, the effects are quickly noticed. However, chemicals polluting the ambient environment by chronic low-dose exposure may cause environmental diseases. Furthermore, pollutants could persist in the environment and indirectly affect human health [1]. In addition to the potential health risks during normal routine process operations, there is also a probability of chemical accidents causing massive trauma, mostly due to acute short-term, high-dose exposure and environmental pollution through toxic leakages, fire, and explosion.

**Table 8.1** Production of some leading industries [2]

| Industry | Production (thousand MT) 1989-1990 |
|---|---|
| Mining and quarrying (coal, petroleum, bauxite, chromate, copper, manganese and iron ore, limestone, dolomite) | 380427.0 |
| Heavy chemicals (Caustic soda, soda ash) | 2303.0 |
| Cement (million MT) | 46.0 |
| Iron and steel | 37056.0 |
| Non-ferrous metals (Al, Cu, Pb, Zn, Cd) | 893.0 |
| Petroleum refinery products | 487.0 |
| Wood pulp | 1000.0 |
| Major petrochemicals | |
| Thermoplastics and rubber | 501.0 |
| Synthetic fibres | 448.0 |
| Plastics and polymers | 492.0 |
| Drugs and pharmaceuticals | 41.3 |
| Agrochemicals | |
| Pesticides and insecticides | 58.0 |
| Fertilizers | 8534.0 |
| Dyestuffs | 11.7 |

**Table 8.2** Industries generating toxic chemicals [3]

| | |
|---|---|
| Asbestos manufacture | Lead acid storage battery production |
| Carbon black manufacture | Leather tanning and finishing |
| Cement manufacture | Mercury cell chloralkali plants |
| Chemical process plants | Lime manufacturing plants |
| Coal mining | Primary aluminium plants |
| Coal preparation plants | Primary zinc smelters |
| Dyestuffs (organic) plants | Offshore oil extraction |
| Electronic components production | Organic chemicals manufacture |
| Electroplating | Paint formulation |
| Explosive manufacture | Pesticide manufacture |
| Ferroalloy manufacture | Pesticide formulations |
| Fertilizer manufacture | Petroleum refineries |
| Thermal power plants | Petrochemical complexes |
| Glass fiber processing plants | Pharmaceuticals manufacture |
| Inorganic chemicals manufacture | Plastics and synthetic fiber manufacture |
| Chlorine production | Printing industries |
| Hydrofluoric acid plants | Pulp, paper and craft paper manufacture |
| Nitric acid plants | Rubber manufacture and processing |
| Sulfuric acid plants | Soap and detergent manufacture |
| Boric acid production | Sugar processing and refining |
| Antimony oxide production | Textile manufacture |
| Iron and steel manufacture | Timber processing plywood |

**Table 8.3** **Selected list of toxic chemicals to be controlled [3]**

| Chemical | Use | Hazard |
|---|---|---|
| Acrylonitrile | Acrylic fibers/synthetic rubber<br>Pesticides/Unani medicines[a]/glass | Highly toxic/carcinogenic/teratogenic<br>Toxic/dermatitis/muscular paralysis/damage to liver and kidney/possibly carcinogenic and teratogenic |
| Asbestos | Roofing/insulation/air conditioning conduits/plastics/fiber/paper | Carcinogenic to workers and even family members |
| Benzene | Octane number of gasoline/manufacture of many chemicals | Leukemia/chromosomal damage in exposed workers/behaviour changes |
| Beryllium | Aerospace industry/ceramic parts/ household appliances | Fatal lung disease/heart and lung toxicity |
| Cadmium | Electroplating/plastics/pigments/ superphosphate fertilizers | Kidney damage/emphysema/possibly carcinogenic, teratogenic, and mutagenic |
| Chlorinated organics (DDT, BHC, etc.) | Pesticides/fumigants | Depression of central nervous system/ possibly carcinogenic |
| Chromates | Tanning/paints/pigments/corrosion inhibition/fungicides | Skin ulcers/kidney inflammation/possibly carcinogenic/toxic to fish |
| Lead | Pipes/storage batteries/paints/ printing/plastics/gasoline additive | Intoxicant/neurotoxic/affects blood system |
| Manganese | Mining/welding/dry cell battery/ ferromanganese | Neurotoxic/damage to reproductive system |
| Mercury | Chloralkali cells/fungicides/ pharmaceuticals | Nerve damage/kidney damage |
| Polychlorobiphenyls | Transformers/insulation of electricity | Possibly carcinogenic/nerve, skin and liver damage |
| Sulfur dioxide | Sugar/bleaching agent/coal-based power stations | Irritation to eyes and respiratory system |
| Urea | Fertilizer | Bronchial problems/kidney damage |
| Vinyl chloride | Plastics/organic compounds synthesis | Systemically toxic/carcinogenic |

[a]An indigenous system of medicine practiced in India and derived from Persian sources.

## 8.2 Health Hazards

In addition to intrinsic toxicity, the risks of certain chemicals vary widely depending on the person's genetic inheritance, his or her power of resistance, nutritional and overall health status. Irreversible damage may be inflicted upon living organisms by the long term effects of toxic chemicals. Acute effects lead to immediate death surpassing major long-term issues, the effects of which may appear many years after the exposure.

There is also a possibility that the exposed person may not be the individual exposed to that chemical, but his or her future progeny may suffer through the mutagenic action of chemicals in the environment.

Assessment of chemical risks in the Indian context and anticipatory action for abatement by regulatory agencies have been taken up as follows:

i) Air pollution;

ii) Water pollution;

iii) Food contaminants; and,

iv) Occupational hazards.

### 8.2.1 Air Pollutants

The geography, demography, socio-economic profile, climate and topography of a region are among factors which will determine formation and distribution of pollutants and ultimately effects on the environment and/or human health. Exposure may vary greatly depending upon the location and activity of the individual. In addition to industrial pollutants in India, respiratory diseases have been associated with the use of smoky fuels, especially in rural and weaker sections of the society. Several studies have shown that women cooking with solid fuel (cow-dung cakes, coal, wood) stoves may be exposed to concentrations of respirable particulate matter, polynucleic aromatic hydrocarbons, *eg*, benzo[a]pyrene, carbon monoxide, and formaldehyde which may exceed ambient and guideline levels by several orders of magnitude. This can result in cardiovascular, neurobehavioral damage, and other toxic effects.

The increased mortality, morbidity and deficits in pulmonary function associated with sulfur dioxide and suspended particulate matter (SPM) are widely documented. Sulfur dioxide alone can cause severe effects in the form of bronchoconstriction, chemical bronchitis and tracheitis [4]. Sulfur dioxide and nitrogen oxides, the 2 main offenders, emanate from heavy industries especially coal-based. Electrical generating plants, industrial boilers, large smelters and motor vehicles release oxides of nitrogen and sulfur into the atmosphere. Fortunately, the sulfur content of Indian coal is low (0.3-0.5%), and therefore, the resulting sulfur dioxide produced is of concern only in the vicinity of low chimneys [5].

In India, the industrial and domestic sectors are the major contributors to air pollution emission followed by the transport (Table 8.4).

**Table 8.4** **Total emissions in major cities of India (1990-1991)**

| Cities | Industrial % | Transportation % | Domestic % |
|---|---|---|---|
| Calcutta | 72 | 20 | 8 |
| Bombay | 54 | 42 | 4 |
| Delhi | 29 | 63 | 8 |

The increase in auto emissions between 1970-1971 and 2000-2001 is estimated to be 73%. The problem is exacerbated by the relatively high numbers of old and poorly maintained vehicles which produce proportionally more $NO_2$ [6]. Estimates on the potential lead released in Delhi, Bombay and Calcutta based on petrol consumption indicate that approximately 103, 91, and 50 metric tonnes of lead will pollute the above cities, respectively, by the year 2000. The observations on existing status of roadside lead levels ranked Calcutta (1.0-16 μg $m^{-3}$) the highest polluted city followed by Bombay (0.2-14 μg $m^{-3}$), and Delhi (0.2-1.8 μg $m^{-3}$), against the WHO recommended ambient air quality criteria value of 0.5 μg $m^{-3}$ [7]. These data indicate that the urban population is exposed to high concentrations of potential carcinogenic agents, *eg*, fluoranthene, pyrene, benzo(a)anthracene, benzo(b)fluoranthene, and benzo[a]pyrene. The most studied species of PAH is benzo[a]pyrene (BaP). Indoor BaP concentrations of 4 μg $m^{-3}$ have been observed in India due to cooking with biomass fuels [4]. Wood burning is a major source of PAH and $CO_2$ in developing countries [8]. Tobacco smoke and unvented gas cooking may increase indoor $NO_2$ concentration to unacceptably high levels [4].

A hydrocarbon and lubricating oil manufacturing company, located in the center of Calcutta city was emitting noxious fumes into the atmosphere causing burning of eyes, conjunctivitis and eczema-like illnesses among the local residents. The company produced light liquid paraffin, white oil and sodium sulfonate [9].

Exposure to airborne lead from motor vehicles using leaded petrol has been the subject of a great deal of scientific debate. Old vehicles with poor emission control are allowed to travel freely on the Indian roads. Currently, there is no effort towards providing lead-free petrol in India, whereas in all major cities of the industrialized nations strict emission controls are enforced. The use of 'cleaner' fuels [10] has led to declining emissions in recent years. In India, the lead content in petrol has increased with a rise in the octane number from 83 to 87 since 1983.

Polluted urban air can and has aggravated chronic bronchitis, chronic obstructive ventilatory disease, pulmonary emphysema, and bronchial asthma [11]. The incidence of pulmonary tuberculosis is high in the major cities of India, and air pollution can retard recovery despite adequate therapy. A study of 130 traffic constables, 60 bus drivers and 20 auto mechanics in Madras, who constantly inhaled lead polluted air, recorded that these people had a high frequency of respiratory abnormalities. 61.38% of the bus drivers,

52.3% of traffic policemen, and 72.2% of the workshop personnel had severe to moderate respiratory morbidity. The study also indicated that the pulmonary abnormalities were irreversible in the case of middle-aged men. Among the exposed groups, workshop personnel were found to have the highest blood lead concentrations, followed by bus drivers and traffic policemen [12]. In children, raised intracranial tension and cognitive defects have been recorded at Lucknow [13].

### 8.2.2 Water Pollution

Industrial and sewage discharges initiated a story of ever increasing water pollution, commencing with low dissolved oxygen in rivers and increasing towards graver problems in an approximately sequential manner, *ie*, oxygen balance, eutrophication, heavy metals, acidification, organic micropollutants, nitrates, and ground water contamination. Chemical pollutants of diverse natures derived from industrial and agricultural wastes are increasingly finding their way into the water supply systems. The combined wastewater flow from large paper mills averaged 200 $m^3$ $tonne^{-1}$ [7]. The pollution load in terms of suspended solids and biological oxygen demand (BOD) were in the range of 109-280 and 54-179 kg $tonne^{-1}$, respectively. The effluents discharged from Kanpur tanneries in Uttar Pradesh have not only polluted the Ganges river, but also the groundwater. Very high levels of chromium have been found in the groundwater by the People's Science Institute, Dehradun, during the post-monsoon period [12].

The Industrial Toxicology Research Centre (ITRC) has conducted regular monitoring of the water quality of Ganges River for selected heavy metals and organochlorine pesticides. The levels of iron and manganese exceeded WHO limits at all the sampling sites, where as the levels of cadmium, chromate, lead, and mercury were higher only at a few points. DDT, BHC and endosulfan were generally found to exceed their respective EPA criteria (Table 8.5).

An analysis of water samples of one of the tributaries of Brahmini in Orissa indicated high levels of fluoride [14]. The Damodar catchment, particularly the segment from Giddi in Bihar to Durgapur in West Bengal has about 50 major industries with many medium- and small-scale adjuncts. About 6 million $m^3$ of untreated industrial waste effluent, and 50.5 million $m^3$ of domestic wastewater is discharged daily. Hence, the river from Giddi to Durgapur has become unfit for use by humans or for animals [15].

In the Kuttanad, Vembanad and Periyar estuaries in Kerala, industrial and agricultural pollution has initiated major environmental problems including an increased incidence of water-related diseases, aquatic weed growth, and bioaccumulation of toxic residues in human beings [12].

In some of the villages of Unnao district, U.P., where a number of villagers were found to be suffering from paraplegia, it was found that the well and pond waters had a very high concentration of manganese [5]. Exposure to manganese mines in Maharashtra have caused psychiatric disorders, basal ganglia disorders, in addition to Parkinsonian-like syndromes [13].

**Table 8.5** **Concentration range of pesticides and metals from different locations in Ganga (1989-1990)**

| Site | Pesticides | | | Metals | | | | | |
|---|---|---|---|---|---|---|---|---|---|
| | DDT $\mu g\ l^{-1}$ | BHC $\mu g\ l^{-1}$ | Endosulfan $\mu g\ l^{-1}$ | Cd $mg\ l^{-1}$ | Cr $mg\ l^{-1}$ | Fe $mg\ l^{-1}$ | Pb $mg\ l^{-1}$ | Mn $mg\ l^{-1}$ | Hg $mgl^{-1}$ |
| Rishikesh | ND-0.118 | ND-0.064 | ND-0.064 | ND-0.002 | - | 0.382-34.78 | - | 0.02-0.66 | - |
| Garbmukteshwar | ND-0.005 | ND-0.026 | ND-0.018 | - | - | ND-8.58 | ND-0.25 | ND-0.22 | - |
| Kannauj | ND-0.002 | ND-0.208 | ND-0.001 | - | ND-0.019 | 1.54-13.86 | ND-0.18 | 0.06-0.38 | - |
| Kanpur | ND-0.002 | ND-0.323 | ND | - | 0.01-0.04 | 0.25-12.0 | ND | 0.05-0.27 | ND |
| Allahabad | ND-0.008 | ND-0.271 | ND-0.037 | - | ND-0.22 | ND-10.32 | ND-1.85 | ND-0.38 | ND |
| Varanasi | ND-0.001 | ND-0.138 | ND | - | ND-0.35 | 0.36-13.46 | - | 0.03-0.38 | ND |
| Buxar | ND-0.006 | ND-0.152 | ND | - | ND-0.02 | ND-1.15 | ND-0.17 | ND-0.06 | ND |
| Patna | ND-0.003 | ND-0.06 | ND | - | ND-0.07 | ND-2.74 | ND-0.17 | ND-0.33 | ND |
| Bahrampur | ND-0.016 | ND-0.173 | ND-0.015 | ND-0.004 | - | ND-22.16 | - | ND-0.33 | - |
| Uluberia | ND-0.001 | ND-0.182 | ND | - | - | ND-17.16 | - | ND-0.31 | - |

ND=Not detected.
Modified from: Fourth Annual Progress Report (July 1989-June 1990) of ITRC.
Measurements on Ganga River Water Quality, Heavy Metals and Pesticides,
under Ganga Action Plan, Ministry of Environment and Forests, Government of India.

Industrial effluents in the river Kalu at Ambivali, Madhya Pradesh, contain metals (mercury, lead, copper, and cadmium) chlorides, dyestuffs, organic acids from rayon, paper mills, dyestuff factories, and chemical plants at high concentrations [12].

India, with its massive coastline of about 6000 km, has approximately 25% of the total population residing in these coastal areas. Such a large human settlement leads to an adverse influence on coastal waters due to discharge of sewage and industrial effluents. Hence, the surface waters of the Bay of Bengal have a relatively higher range of metals when compared to the Arabian sea. The coastal regions receive about 25% of fertilizers, pesticides, and synthetic detergents every year, with a concomitant increase in the levels of nutrient pool, particularly phosphates, ammonia and urea. This has led to ecological disturbances [16].

The total DDT concentration in plankton of the northern part of the west coast of India is high. The concentration of organochlorine and organophosphate pesticides in some of the fish, particularly plankton feeders, was found to be appreciable [16].

### 8.2.3 Food Contaminants

Due to the changing lifestyles in developing nations, there is an increased demand for processed food. Currently, there is a search for chemicals of value in preserving foodstuffs and for increasing their palatability. The common pollutants, contaminants and adulterants in food may be intentional or unintentional.

Non-permitted colors are used to a great extent in cereals and pulses and an appreciable proportion was detected in sugar confectionary, bakery products, ice-candy, chewing tobacco, and condiments. This illicit use of prohibited colors in foodstuffs sold in Uttar Pradesh was reported in a survey carried out by Industrial Toxicology Research Centre (ITRC) [17]. The prevalence of using non-permitted toxic colors such as Metanil yellow, Orange II, Auramine, Rhodamine B, Blue VRS, Malachite green, and others, was higher in the socio-economically poorer eastern zone [17].

Edible oils are often adulterated with synthetic fat soluble dyestuffs which is a matter of serious concern. The presence of butter yellow and allyl isothiocyanate in mustard oil was reported [17].

During the last decade, 2 major outbreaks of polyneuropathy due to tricresyl-*o*-phosphate (T*o*CP) contaminated rapeseed oil occurred in West Bengal [18]. T*o*CP is widely used in lacquers and varnishes, as a plasticizer and also in hydraulic fluid. It is known to cause polyneuritis in animals and humans, eventually leading to irreversible paralysis of limbs.

Limited and scattered surveys in India have revealed contamination of bovine milk and its products with high levels of DDT and HCH residues [19,20]. Values for the DDT complex in human milk are considerably higher than the level of this pesticide in cow's milk, by a factor of at least 250 [21].

In a survey by the Indian Council of Medical Research, a total of 186 samples of 20 brands of infant formula milk were collected from retail shops in and around Pune, Bombay, Mysore, Lucknow, and Ludhiana, and analyzed for HCH isomers and DDT-complex. Residues of total HCH and DDT-complex were detected in 175 (94.1%), and 130 (69.9%) of samples, respectively. The study also indicated high levels of metal contamination (As, Cd, Pb, Cu, and Zn) in infant formula milk [22] (see Table 8.6). These collectively cause neural dysfunction.

**Table 8.6** **Incidence and levels of contamination of pesticides and metals in infant formula (milk) samples [22]**

| Infant formula milk | No of samples | Range | ADI (mg $kg^{-1}$ b.w.) |
|---|---|---|---|
| **Pesticides** | | | |
| HCH | 186 | ND - 5.70 | 0.01 |
| DDT | 186 | ND - 4.33 | 0.02 |
| **Metals** | | | |
| As | 198 | ND - 2.26 | 0.002 |
| Cd | 198 | ND - 1.71 | 0.0067 - 0.0083 |
| Pb | 198 | ND - 3.92 | 0.025 |
| Cu | 195 | ND - 93.11 | 0.05 - 0.5* |
| Zn | 195 | 3.1 - 143.8 | 0.3-1.0* |

ADI=Admissible daily intake; ND=Not detected; b.w.=body weight; *provisional

## 8.3 Occupational Health

Based on the 1981 census, and assuming an annual growth rate of 7.1%, the Indian chemical industry is employing about 7.2 million workers who are exposed to a variety of pollutants for at least 8 h $d^{-1}$. In India, the manufacture of chemicals is undertaken by both organized sectors and the small-scale industries. Additionally, many traditional crafts such as dyeing, textile printing, leather processing, bangle making, carpet weaving, household utensils manufacture, etc., involve handling of toxic chemicals. In welding operations, whether for engineering workshops or wayside smithies, the welders are exposed to toxic metal fumes.

Among the occupational diseases, silicosis is the major cause of permanent disability and mortality. It was first reported in India from the Kolar Gold Mines (Karnataka) in 1947. Subsequently, its occurrence has been recorded periodically in various other industries, *eg*, mining (coal, mica, gold, silver, lead, zinc, manganese), pottery and ceramic, sand blasting, metal grinding, and in building and construction work. In a survey by the ITRC the incidence of silicosis in agate workers in Khambhat, Gujarat, was found to be 18.01% [5].

Asbestos is still a major menace to health in India, whilst it is restricted as a building material in many countries. The National Institute of Occupational Health studies reveal that the prevalence of lung diseases, including asbestosis, has remained >20% among asbestos factories and mine workers. The average male life span is about 40 years in Multanpur, M.P., where the major industry is of slate pencils. Mortality is due to chronic lung obstructive disease [5].

Occupational eye diseases have been reported among glass bangle workers in Firozabad. Occupational dermatitis is highly prevalent among workers in the chrome-plating industry, tanneries, textile, chemical, engineering, printing, and photographic industries. Chronic bronchitis is rampant among workers who are exposed to dust and fumes during their employment. Spraying and application of pesticides in the control of malaria, filaria and other vector-borne diseases or for pest control in agriculture is a hazardous operation involving exposure to highly toxic chemicals, and has been recorded to cause seizure disorders, subclinical peripheral neuropathy, visuomotor dysfunction, impaired short-term memory and macula degeneration [13,23,24].

Workers in viscose rayon factories have reported symptoms of indigestion, abdominal pain and hypertension. Neuropsychiatric symptoms included headache, giddiness, tremors and eye congestion. Most problems have been attributed to carbon disulfide, while hydrogen sulfide and sulfuric acid mists cause eye problems [12].

Industrial accidents, poisonings (acute) and occupational cancers are well known, but their prevalence in exact numbers in different industries is not known.

## 8.4 Accidents

India has a high rate of industrial accidents, as evident from Table 8.7. The industrial fatality rate in India is currently estimated at 0.14 per 1000 workers, which is 8 times higher than in other developing countries [25]. In 1992, ammonia gas leaking from a fertilizer plant killed about 12 workers in Panipat (fault in the suction valve). Similarly, as a result of an effluent leakage from a viscose rayon mill in Shahad, Maharashtra, 11 persons died due to failure of the power supply for 30 min, when the untreated effluent containing 10% sulfuric acid, zinc sulfate, sodium sulfate, and carbon disulfide (pH ca. 2), escaped into the nearby drain. Symptoms of illness were confined to gastrointestinal disturbance, central nervous system dysfunction, and respiratory distress. The Bhopal episode, of course, is well documented [26] and so details are not given here.

**Table 8.7** **Some recent chemical accidents in India**

| Year | City | Origin of accident | Product involved | Deaths | Injuries |
|---|---|---|---|---|---|
| 1984 | Bhopal | Leakage | MIC | 2800 | 50000 |
| 1985 | Tamilnadu | Transport | Gasoline | 60 | — |
| 1985 | Padaval | Fire | Gasoline | >43 | 82 |
| 1985 | New Delhi | Release | Sulfuric acid | 1 | 340 |
| 1988 | Jhurkully | Leakage | Sulfur dioxide | — | 500 |
| 1989 | Bhatinda | Leakage | Ammonia | — | 500 |
| 1989 | Britannia Chowk | Leakage | Chlorine | — | 200 |
| 1992 | Panipat | Leakage | Ammonia | 12 | — |
| 1993 | Agra | Water contamination | BHC | 17 | — |
| 1993 | Shahad | Leakage | $CS_2$ and $H_2SO_4$ | 11 | 123 |

## 8.5 High Risk Groups

The interaction between chemical exposure and factors within the total environment can have a profound effect on observed toxic responses. Complicating factors such as social, physiological, biological, and iatrogenic status of the individual, or physical agents, are all known to affect chemical absorption in humans. In addition, each individual or genetic subset of the population may show a unique response to the same xenobiotic stress conditions which are often encountered in occupational and environmental conditions. Physiological conditions, such as age and reproductive cycles, could also be at risk in critical groups; similarly, environmental conditions, such as extreme variations in climate, high or low ambient temperature, and humidity, need to be understood [27].

Agrochemical residues from the environment or from food could affect many diseases. Similarly, pesticide toxicity can pose abnormal situations in a sick person with alterations in the immune system function when compared to normal populations.

Immune dysfunctions may be associated with exposures to polychlorinated and polybrominated biphenyls, polycyclic aromatic hydrocarbons, hexachlorobenzene, diethylstilbestrol, pentachlorophenol pesticides, certain organometals, and a number of heavy metals, particularly when associated with the abuse of drugs.

The history of catastrophic pollution episodes has clearly indicated that the very young and the very old are affected more severely than other age groups [29.30].

Reports from Bhopal regarding abnormal babies, implying teratogenic effects of methyl isocyanate are variable. Births of babies with defects, such as closed anus, missing ears, meningocele, closed eyelids, and also substantive reports of a high proportion of spina bifida, are available [31].

In the understanding of the effects of occupational and environmental toxicants in tropical countries, variations in responses to the same toxicant under different situations must be emphasized. Parasitic infestations, chronic protein and calorie malnutrition, immunosuppressive status and undercurrent infections prevalent in many developing countries, and concurrent exposure to multiple stresses, can also cause increased health hazards [32].

Certain segments of the population may be subjected to greater exposure of certain pollutants because of their dietary habits, *eg*, fish eaters or vegetarians. Physical factors, such as posture, mechanical strain, load of additional domestic chores, longer working shifts and climatic extremes, maternity stress, malnutrition, and anemia, also lead to further misery to the female workers engaged in hazardous occupations, *eg*, cashew nut processing, pottery glazing, handloom dyeing, and the tobacco, tea and cotton industries [32]. Such problems are of specific concern to India and other developing countries.

## 8.6 Conclusions

With identification of the problems due to chemical risks, regulatory activities also have expanded in scope, jurisdiction, and execution. The various existing regulations regarding registration and licensing of chemicals, origination of hazardous industries, warehousing, and transportation, are illustrated in the review by Ray [2], the Environment (Protection) Act, 1986 and related laws, etc. The Factory Act, the Pesticide Act, and many other Acts have helped in establishing mandatory control in chemical usage. Also, the national standards set by the Indian Bureau of Standards assist in setting these limits.

The Department of Environment, Forests and Wildlife, and the Government of India, together with agencies such as the Central Board for Pollution Prevention and Control, is the major regulatory authority. Such agencies also function in other states. In addition, for specific items such as pesticides, drugs and food additives, respective ministries, *eg*, Agriculture and Health, are responsible. The Ministries of Chemicals, Labour and Industry are also involved in these programmes. In the post-Bhopal scenario, these regulatory activities are given adequate support by government, industries and the public. From the foregoing, it follows that the undesirable health and environmental effects, accompanying India's industrial and agricultural expansion programmes are being recognized at the outset, and adequate anticipatory actions are initiated along with creations of the necessary surveillance machinery and regulatory guidelines. This should lead to evaluation of a strategy for development without destruction. Such a programme should also consider the following suggestions:

i) Environmental pollution control laws could be more effectively and stringently enforced, and extended to small-scale and rural industries;

ii) Information should be encouraged between nations, among experts/professionals, state governments, and aid agencies;

iii) Methodology to link health and environmental data should be developed as a means of supporting decision making;

iv) The country should indigenously develop capabilities for environmental impact assessment and case studies through chemical and biological monitoring of pollutants and their effects. Coordinated monitoring and sampling programmes are necessary to check widespread regional pollution. Attention must be given to sources and types of pollution, modes of occurrence and spread, dynamics of transport and dispersion, and means of waste disposal;

v) Predictive environmental impact assessment could be performed by suitable models, and standard protocols should be developed;

vi) Health risks due to environmental factors such as direct exposure to pollutants, pathogens, parasites, allergens, biomagnified toxic residues, biotoxins, etc., should be evaluated in different locations, *vis a vis* health status; and,

vii) Prevention is better than cure — hence via regulation of sources, toxic pollutant loads on the environment could be effectively reduced.

It has to be born in mind that in addition to well-recognized pollution mediated health effects, other major areas that have emerged in the 1990s in the domain of environmental pollution monitoring recently in India includes ozone layer depletion, greenhouse effect, persistence of chemical species, acidic deposition, and altered biogeochemical cycles.

All these programmes need considerable infrastructure and trained human resources. Environmental consciousness and consumer awareness have been generated, and education at schools, colleges, and specialist levels, are encouraged. Research and development activities in environmental health from about 5 major and 100s of smaller institutions provide the know-how for India's environmental reforms. Furthermore , there are currently 19 agencies in India for toxicological and documentation studies of hazardous chemicals, metals and industrial waste, together with 7 regulatory agencies for hazardous chemicals and 9 organizations alone for ensuring environment protection from hazardous substances. Environmental impact and risk assessment (EIA), hazard/risk assessment, and environmental audits through computer-aided management plans are now emerging as priorities, to ensure that resources are used with maximum efficacy and residues are either recycled or recovered. In addition to government agencies, several non-governmental organizations exist, and industries have also appreciated the need for safe environments. It is hoped that these groups will benefit from the experience of developed nations and protect the health and future of the citizens of India.

## 8.7 Acknowledgements

The authors are grateful to Dr. P.N. Viswanathan, Assistant Director, and Dr. Poonam Kakkar, Scientist, ITRC, for a critical review of this chapter.

## 8.8 References


[1] Misra, V., Jaffery, F.N., and Viswanathan, P.N., *Reg. Toxicol. Pharmacol.*, 1991, **13**, 62-69.

[2] CIER's Industrial Data Book, Central Institute of Economic Research, Department of Chemicals and Petrochemicals, Government of India, New Delhi, India, 1991.

[3] Ray, P.K., 'An overview of the safety and control of pollutants and toxic chemicals in India', A National Status Report submitted to WHO, 1989.

[4] WHO. Air Quality Guidelines for Europe, WHO Regional Publications, European Series No. 23, Copenhagen, 1987.

[5] Gupta, B.N., Agarwal, S.N., Viswanathan, P.N., Chandra, S.V., and Ray, P.K., (Eds.), *Environmental Hygiene*, National Status Report for the Biological Coordination, Council of Scientific and Industrial Research, Industrial Toxicology Research Centre (ITRC), Lucknow, July, 1984.

[6] UNEP/WHO, Assessment of urban air quality, United Nations Environment Programme, Nairobi, and the World Health Organization, Geneva, 1988.

[7] NEERI, National Environmental Engineering Research Institute, Annual Report for 1991.

[8] Khalil, M.A.K. and Rasmussen, R.A., *Chemosphere*, 1990, **20**, 227-242.

[9] Bhattacharya, D., A Report in: Green File, A selection of clippings on the environment, Centre for Science and Environment, June 1993, pp. 40.

[10] UNEP, Chemical Pollution: A Global Review, A joint publication of the International Register of Potentially Toxic Chemicals and Global Environment Monitoring System's Monitoring and Assessment Research Centre, Geneva, 1992.

[11] *Casarett and Doull's Toxicology, The Basic Science of Poisons*, Amdur, N.O., Doull, J., and Klaassen, C.D., (Eds.), 4th Edition, 1991, Pergamon Press.

[12] Green File, A selection of clippings on the environment, Centre for Science and Environment, June 1993, pp. 40.

[13] Nag, D., 'Neurotoxins in the Environment — A Status Report', Ministry of Environment and Forest, New Delhi, 1986, 7-74.

[14] Patnaik, N., 'Effluent threatens Orissa's river ecology', A report in the Economic Times, New Delhi, June 6, 1993.

[15] Bhardwaj, D., 'Dirty Damodar; Bihar's river of sludge', A report, in: *The Pioneer*, New Delhi, 25th June, 1993.

[16] Jaffery, F.N., Misra, V., and Viswanathan, P.N., 'Toxicology aspects in the control of marine environment, in: *Environmental Impact on Aquatic and Terrestrial Habitat*, Agrawal, V.P., Abidi, S.A.H., Verma, G.P., Society of Biosciences, Muzaffarnagar, India, 1993, pp. 31-54.

[17] Khanna, S.K. and Das, M., *Standards India*, 1992, **6**, 43-47.

[18] Srivastava, R.C., Gupta, B.N., and Athar, M., *Indian J. Exp. Biol.*, 1988, **26**, 165-172.

[19] Tripathi, H.C., 'Organochlorine insecticide residues in agricultural and animal products in the Terai Area', MSc Thesis, Uttar Pradesh Agricultural University, Pantnagar, 1966.

[20] Kalra, R.L. and Chawla, R.P., *Proc. Indian Natl. Sci. Acad.*, **52**, (Part B), 188-204.

[21] Saxena, M.C. and Siddiqui, M.K.J., *J. Dairy Sci.*, 1982, **65**, 245.

[22] ICMR, Indian Council of Medical Research Report, 'Surveillance of food contaminants in India', 1993.

[23] Misra, U.K., Nag, D., and Misra, N.K., *Lancet*, 1982, **1**, 288.

[24] Misra, U.K., Nag, D., and Krishna Murti, C.R., *Ind. Health*, 1981, **22**, 199-206.

[25] *Chemical Industry News*, Oct. 1992, pp. 1016.

[26] Varma, D.R., 'Anatomy of the methyl isocyanate leak in Bhopal', in: *Hazard Assessment of Chemicals*, Saxena, J., (Ed.), 1987, pp. 258-279, Hemisphere Publishing Corporation, Washington.

[27] Viswanathan, P.N. and Krishna Murti, C.R., 'Effect of temperature and humidity on ecotoxicology', in: *IPCS Joint Symposia, Ecotoxicology and Climatic*, Bordeau, P., Jaines, J.A., Klein, W., and Krishna Murti, C.R., (Eds.), 1989, pp. 139-154, John Wiley and Sons, New York.

[28] Luster, M.I., Faith, R.E., and Moore, J.A., *Environ. Hlth, Perspect.*, 1978, **23**, 227-232.

[29] Gupta, B.N., Rastogi, S.K., Chandra, H., Mathur, A.K., Mathur, N., Mahendra, P.N., Pangtey, B.S., Kumar, S., Kumar, P., Seth, P.K., Dwivedi, R.S., and Ray, P.K., *Indian J. Exp. Biol.*, 1988, **26**, 149-160.

[30] Rastogi, S.K., Gupta, B.N., Husain, T., Kumar, A., Chandra, S., and Ray, P.K., *Indian J. Exp. Biol.*, 1988, **26**, 161-164.

[31] *Hazard Assessment of Chemicals*, Saxena, J., (Ed.), Hemisphere Publication Corporation, 1987, p. 5, Washington.

[32] Occupational and Environmental Health Problems of Indian Women, State-of-the-Art, Department of Science and Technology, Government of India, 1984.

# 9. Parental Occupation and Childhood Cancer

Tatjana Vergieva

## 9.1 Introduction

The peak of incidences of tumors such as Wilms' tumor, retinoblastoma and neuroblastoma in early childhood supports the hypothesis that events near the time of conception, during pregnancy, or shortly after birth may be involved in their pathogenesis. Similar hypothesis for brain tumors and leukemias in children and young adults can be proposed. Postulated (but unconfirmed) risk factors include a wide range of demographic and environmental determinants such as socio-economic status, urbanization, maternal consumption of alcohol and neural active drugs during pregnancy together with parental occupation [1]. The proposed risk factors for brain tumors in children and young people (reviewed by Preston-Martin et al. [2]) include exposure to ionising radiation *in utero* resulting from maternal pelvimetry; or in early childhood due to x-ray treatment for *tinea capitis*; birth trauma; exposure to barbiturates; or insecticides *in utero,* or in early childhood.

Much of the epidemiological evidence pertaining to parental occupational exposure as a risk factor for childhood cancer and leukemia is inconsistent or even contradictory; and this could be explained, at least for some of the data, by the different study designs, different sources of data, poor definition of the level, and period of exposure [3].

An increased risk of childhood cancer has been proposed as an association with parental exposure to pesticides, plastics, paints, and pigments. A higher risk of childhood leukemia was found in children whose parents were employed in the chemical industry, farming and agriculture, textile industry, medical and social services, painting (including spraying of paints), metal refining, manufacturing of transport equipment and machinery [4,5]. Positive associations between childhood central nervous system (CNS) tumors and parental occupations in agriculture, transportation and construction have been reported by some authors, but the findings were unconfirmed by others [4]. In addition to certain parental employment specific exposure to the following were found to indicate an excess risk of childhood cancer: metals, paints, amino compounds, aromatic and aliphatic hydrocarbons. Negative findings relating to an association with parental occupational exposure to chemicals were indicated by Gold et al. [6] who considered a case control study of brain tumors in childhood.

Most of the studies cited above have included a case control design with parental occupational data extracted from birth or death certificates, or obtained during an interview with the parents. In view of the poor approximation of the exposure status provided by an occupational title and/or the employment industry, and as specific exposures have been identified by questioning the parents, but neither validated regarding quantity nor quality, the findings must be interpreted as an epidemiological association rather than be considered as a demonstration of a causative link. The differential recall of exposure data by case and control parents may be suspected as a reason for positive results, because the affected families are more likely to report potential hazardous exposures. The contribution of a chance effect for the appearance of a positive association should also be considered in studies with multiple comparisons. The strength of the association and eventuality a consistency with later studies are in turn pointing to a possible causative inference.

On the other hand, poor data for exposure will lead to a mis-classification and would always be suspected to be associated with the introduction of non-differential bias to attenuate the odds ratios, respectively to mask an association. In addition, the small sample size would not allow a small excess of risk to be detected.

## 9.2 Paternal Occupational Exposure

Epidemiological studies which explored the hypothesis that paternal occupational exposures are associated with childhood cancer commenced at the end of the 1970s and following attempts to confirm earlier findings revealed new associations. Together with the related studies of involving case control design limitations, the inconsistency of findings, and the difficulties in defining plausibility lead to interpretational problems. This requires the results of the studies to be regarded as warranting further research.

Further cited occupational exposures and/or positions of the fathers were found to be associated with a higher risk of childhood malignancies. However, it should be emphasized that there is no single exposure to be found consistently throughout the different studies, or there to be a risk factor at a level of a statistical significance.

The positive findings of Kantor et al. [7] of a higher risk of Wilms' tumor in children of fathers who worked in lead-related occupations were not confirmed by a later study [8]. In this later study, the case fathers were found more likely to have been exposed to boron, whilst the control fathers were more likely to have encountered exposure to insecticides, acetylene, *o*-chlorobenzylidene, Oil Orange SS (1-[2-methylphenyl)azo]-2-naphthalenol), and diethylene glycol. There was no consistent pattern of an increased risk arising from paternal occupational exposure to lead or hydrocarbons found in Olshan et al.'s case control study [9]. However, certain occupations including vehicle mechanics, autobody repairmen and welders were found to indicate an elevated odds ratio of Wilms' tumor.

The paternal occupational risk factors leading to brain tumors in their children which were identified in the case control studies included: occupations classified as hydrocarbon related, occupations linked with aromatic amino and nitro compounds (exposure in the postnatal periods), paternal employment in agriculture, construction, metal industry, food and tobacco industries, electrical assembling, and installation and repair work in the machinery industry [4,10].

Concerning paternal occupational risk factors for neuroblastoma, various authors [1,11,12] have suggested that exposure to metal fumes and dusts, benzene, asbestos, or pesticides, but not ionizing or non-ionizing radiation may be related. Paternal occupational exposure to hydrocarbons and paternal employment involving contact with electromagnetic fields working as electricians or as electronics operatives may also have risk factors implications.

Hydrocarbon related occupations were found to be twice as likely for fathers of children who had malignant diseases when compared to control group fathers [13]. However, no relationship was found between paternal exposure to hydrocarbons and childhood leukemia in 2 later studies [14,15]. A significantly elevated risk of childhood leukemia was found to be associated with the father's exposure to chlorinated solvents, ethyl methyl ketone, spray paints, dyestuffs or pigments, and cutting oils [16], in addition to preconceptional exposure to wood dust, benzene, ionizing radiation, periconceptional exposure to carbon tetrachloride, trichloroethylene and radiation, and postnatal exposure to graphite and radiation [3]. Children with acute leukemia were more likely to have a father with an occupation related to meat production or selling, *ie*, butchers, charcutiers, slaughterhouse workers etc, than controls [17]. Paternal exposure to solvents, petroleum products and plastics and lead were reported to be more common for children with acute non-lymphocytic leukemia [5].

Paternal occupational exposure prior to conception to radiation at a nuclear plant near Sellafield was associated with a higher risk of childhood leukemia and non-Hodgkin's lymphoma [18]. These data conflict with the results from the project on the atomic bomb survivors in Japan [19], where the fathers were exposed to a single high dose of radiation and where the risk was not increased with the increased gonadal dose to the father. Negative findings were also reported in case control study in children whose fathers worked at the Donnreay nuclear plant [20].

The reported excess incidence of childhood leukemia in children living near a fuel processing nuclear plant located at Sellafield, England, was not confirmed for other populations living near similar plants at other locations [21]. Additionally, Cook-Mozaffari et al. [22] found an excess mortality rate due to leukemia and Hodgkins' disease in young people who lived near both existing and potential sites for nuclear power stations.

The occupation of the father rather than the mother was the principal concern in these epidemiological studies, *ie*, that the studies were focused on a preconceptional or postconceptional exposure of the father rather than on an *in utero* exposure as a result of maternal employment in hazardous workplace atmospheres. Purely circumstantial reasons would be the most probable explanation. Simply, in most cases the father is at work outside home and he is more likely to suffer exposure to hazardous factors at work. Also there is the theoretical possibility that genetic damage to the fathers' germ cells leads to a consequential malignancy in his progeny; it should be emphasized that there are limited experimental data and no definite human evidence even for exposure to radiation or strong carcinogens to support such a theory. In this context one should appreciate that during work employees are likely to be exposed to weak but not strong carcinogens, and usually these are present at very low if not negligible concentrations. As stated by Olshan et al. [9], one potential mechanism involves direct effects on the sperm DNA; see also [23]. This mechanism would be of particular value for specific exposures where such an effect was proven either in human or in experimental models. These effects would be expected *apriori* for agents which induce mutagenic activity rather than for any chemical. It would be difficult to indicate the biological plausibility pertaining to the positive association of childhood tumors with paternal occupational exposures from chemicals which are neither mutagenic nor exhibit carcinogenic activity in adults, nor are acting eventually via epigenetic mechanisms. But these are the facts relating to situations with the majority of occupational exposures considered in studies reviewed in the references cited above (Table

9.1). Few studies have considered exposures which are proven, probable or possible carcinogens for the workers themselves (Table 9.2).

**Table 9.1** **Parental exposures at work associated with childhood cancer together with an indication if they have been classified by IARC 1990 [24] as human carcinogens (group 1), probable (group 2A) or possible (group 2B) human carcinogens**

| Paternal exposure | Maternal exposure |
|---|---|
| **Industrial processes, industries, occupations** | |
| Agriculture | Food and tobacco industry: |
| Construction and transportation | — food related |
| Electrical assembly | — catering |
| Food and tobacco industry | Personal service industry: |
| Installation (general) | — beauty shops |
| Metal industry | — hairdressing |
| Meat production or sale | — personal household |
| Repairing machinery | — laundries |
| Autobody repairing | Automobile mechanic (2A* diesel gasoline exhaust) |
| Vehicle mechanics (2A* diesel gasoline exhaust) | Cleaner |
| Welders (2B* welding fumes) | Dyer (2B* textile manufacture) |
| | Gas station attendant |
| | (2A* diesel gasoline exhaust) |
| | Laundry operator |
| | Machinist |
| | Painter (1) |
| | Pharmacist |
| | Printer |
| **Chemicals and group of chemicals** | |
| Aromatic amino and nitro compounds | Metal dust |
| Asbestos (1) | Paints and pigments (1* painter) |
| Benzene (1) | Petroleum products |
| Carbon tetrachloride (2B) | Sawdust |
| Chlorinated solvents | |
| Cutting Oil | |
| Dust | |
| Graphite | |
| Hydrocarbons | |
| Lead (2A) | |
| Metal fumes (2B* welding fumes) | |
| Ethyl methyl ketone | |
| Paints, dyes or pigments (1* painter) | |
| Petroleum products | |
| Solvents | |
| Wood dust (1* furniture and cabinet making) | |

*Exposures classified by IARC as groups 1, 2A or 2B which might be relevant to those reported by the parents of children with childhood cancer, or associated with occupational conditions and/or chemicals

**Table 9.2 Human evidence for an increased risk of childhood cancer associated with parental occupational exposure to human carcinogens**

| Carcinogenic to adults (IARC 1990) (group 1) [24,25] | Carcinogenic to children of exposed father | mother |
|---|---|---|
| **Industrial processes** | | |
| Aluminium production | NS | NS |
| Auramine (manufacture) | NS | NS |
| Boot and shoe manufacture and repair | NS, PNR* solvents RNR* ethyl methyl ketone | NS,N* solvents |
| Coal gasification | NS | NS |
| Coke production | NS | NS |
| Furniture and cabinet making | NS,PNR* wood dust PNR* solvents | NS |
| Haematite mining underground with exposure to radon | NS | NS |
| Iron and steel foundry | NS,PNR* metal fumes, PNR* metal industry | NS |
| Isopropyl alcohol manufacture (strong acid process) | NS | NS |
| Magenta (manufacture) | NS | NS |
| Painter (occupation) | PNR,PNR* paints, dyes or pigments | PNR |
| Rubber industry | NS,PNR* plastics | NS,N* plastics |
| **Chemicals and group of chemicals** | | |
| Aflatoxins | NS | NS |
| 4-Aminobiphenyl | NS | NS |
| Arsenic and its compounds | NS | NS |
| Asbestos | PNR | NS |
| Benzene | PR | NS |
| Benzidine | NS | NS |
| bis(Chloromethyl)ether and chloromethyl ether (technical) | NS | NS |
| Chromium (VI) | NS | NS |
| Erionite | NS | NS |
| Mustard gas (sulfur mustard) | NS | NS |
| 2-Naphthylamine | NS | NS |
| Nickel compounds | NS | NS |
| Radon and its decay products | NS | NS |
| Talc containing asbestiform fibres | NS | NS |
| Vinyl chloride | NS | NS |

**Table 9.2** (continued)

| Carcinogenic to adults (IARC 1990) (group 1) [24,25] | Carcinogenic to children of exposed father | mother |
|---|---|---|
| **Mixtures** | | |
| Alcoholic beverages | NS | NS |
| Betel quid with tobacco | NS | NS |
| Coal-tars pitches | NS,PNR* hydro-carbons related | NS,N* coal or oil products |
| Coal tars | NS | NS,N* coal products |
| Mineral oils, untreated and mildly treated | NS,PNR* cutting oil, PNR* petroleum products | NS,PNR* petroleum products |
| Shale oils | NS | NS |
| Soots | NS | NS |
| Tobacco products, smokeless | NS,PNR* tobacco industry | NS,PNR* tobacco industry |
| Tobacco smoke | NS (occupational) | NS (occupational) |

*Presumed comparable or similar exposures

PR=Positive association in a single study or replicated in several studies
PNR=Positive association not replicated in other studies
N=Negative association or no association
NS=Not studied or not reported by the parents in a case control study

On the contrary, transplacental carcinogenesis of many chemicals is well documented in many experimental studies. Moreover, it has been proved as early as in the 1960s that much lower doses are effective for an *in utero* exposure than for an exposure in adults [26]. Also, there is adequate human evidence for carcinogenic activity of drugs and radiation following *in utero* exposure, as shown by the clinical data pertaining to diethylstilbestrol [27] and maternal x-ray pelvimetry [28].

An alternative theoretically possible mechanism of the paternal occupational contribution for an excess of childhood cancer would be a transmission of chemicals to the mother via the seminal fluid. Maternal exposure with consequent *in utero* exposure can occur theoretically from chemicals brought home as contaminants on the fathers' skin, clothing, etc, either as the parent compound or its metabolites in the fathers' expired air. For a specialist with toxicological knowledge this possibility will always remain speculative until quantitative data for specific exposures are available. This hypothesis was suggested for a paternal contribution to fetal mal-development [29]. It is difficult to accept that for events such as teratogenesis, for which there is a strong indication of the existence of a threshold negligible quantities to induce such effects. Whereas for the induction of tumors the existence of a threshold dose is disputable; such mechanisms appear to be more likely. However, the possibility of a small increase in the risk detectable at the lower end of the dose response curve would be very improbable and would require an extremely large sample population. A study on the direct exposure of the mother at the workplace to the same chemical would be much more relevant as the exposure would be at least one order higher.

A third hypothesis of the possible mechanisms for an elevated risk of childhood cancer in the progeny of chemically exposed workers would be the direct contact of newborn and young children with the chemicals brought home on the fathers' contaminated clothing. A higher sensitivity of children in the age group 0-9 years to leukemogenic and carcinogenic effect of ionising radiation is registered for atomic bomb survivors [30]. Newborn and very young animals were shown to be more sensitive to malignancies induced by chemical carcinogens [26]. Therefore, a higher sensitivity to chemical carcinogens and probably to oncogenic viruses can be expected for early childhood in humans. In favor of this hypothesis, one might refer to the findings of a significantly elevated risk of intracranial neoplasms in children of fathers who received occupational exposure to aromatic amino and nitro compounds in the postnatal period of their children's development [8,23]. A further supportive example for this hypothesis are the findings of a case control study [6] which indicated that there was a larger number of children who had brain tumors and other neoplasms of healthy children who had been exposed during early childhood to insecticides following household disinfection and possibly to viruses because of the more common contact with farm animals and sick pets. Naturally, one should not forget the possible differential reporting bias coupled with over-reporting by the case parents.

## 9.3 Maternal Occupational Exposure

Only a minority of epidemiological studies have explored the possible associations between maternal occupational exposures and an elevated risk for a child to develop a malignant disease.

An increased odds ratio has been shown for childhood leukemia in the children of mothers working as pharmacists or factory workers in a register-based case control study in Finland [31,32]. Exposure to chemicals (including paints, petroleum products and other unspecified chemicals) was reported more often by mothers of children who developed acute lymphocytic leukemia than mothers in the control groups [15]. An elevated, but not significant, relative risk was observed for occupations involving hydrocarbons including: machinists, automobile mechanics, painters, gas station attendants, laundry operators, printers, pharmacists, chemical analysts, workers in the chemical and petroleum industries, cleaners and dyers. In contrast, hydrocarbon related occupations and industries were not found to be more common among the parents of children with cancer as compared to control group children in another case control study [14]. This disagreement in the results of these 2 studies is difficult to interpret. There is evidence of diversity in the exposure conditions of the above individual occupations, both qualitatively (different chemicals) and quantitatively (different level of exposure). There is further confusion in the above study due to the authors not distinguishing maternal from paternal exposure by reference to parental exposure.

Maternal exposure to paints and pigments, metal dusts and sawdust was reported significantly more frequently by the parents of children with acute lymphocytic leukemia in a further case control study [5].

Few associations with maternal occupational factors were apparent from the numerous case control studies concerned with parental occupations. This can probably be explained by the relatively small number of women employed in occupations outside the home, and because most were women who are employed in that group of occupations with low exposure to hazardous factors. In this group, there were 52-75% of maternal jobs in the Wilkins and Sinks [8] case control study. These groupings were valid evidently for the Scandinavian countries, USA and Canada, in which the studies were undertaken. The sparseness of the study population in the individual occupational groupings permitted an odds ratio estimation for a limited number of occupational categories (in the Wilkins and Sinks [8] study, these were service, processing and benchwork) and thus accounted for the unstable risk estimates. In this study, the only maternal occupations for which the odds ratios were higher (but not statistically significant), were processing occupations and the industries involving food and tobacco.

The non-participation of women in industrial processes entailing exposures to carcinogens (group 1) seems to be the reason why they were not investigated for a possible association with childhood cancers (see Table 9.2).

Catering, cleaning and hairdressing in both preconceptional and gestational periods were maternal occupations that were associated with a higher risk for childhood leukemia and non-Hodgkin's lymphoma, in the McKinney *et al.* case control study [3]. The odds ratio for food industry related occupations was also significantly elevated. The authors evaluated critically their findings by suggesting a chance as a reason for the positive associations because of the absence of any specific range for occupations and/or exposures.

Risk of leukemia was found to be higher in children of mothers employed in personal service industries such as beauty shops, personal household or household laundries in the Lovengart et al.'s case control study [16]. There were no significant associations with specific exposures such as solvents, plastic materials, paints or pigments, oil or coal products, metals, or miscellaneous chemicals. The lack of consistency between these findings and those of other studies might be related to the lack of statistical significance of small study groups to detect a moderately elevated risk. Another possible explanation for the lack of positive association is the possible dilution of an effect relating to a misclassification of exposure. This may be due to the grouping under a title of solvents or metals, of exposure to different chemicals some, but not all, of which might have a carcinogenic potential.

An elevated risk for childhood leukemia was observed for household exposure of mothers to paints or lacquers [16]. Furthermore, an elevated risk was found for children whose parents had used pesticides at home or in the garden, or whose parents had burned incense at home.

In the case control study of Buckley et al. [5], the most consistent association with childhood acute lymphoblastic leukemia was found to be related to maternal exposure to pesticides, coupled with direct exposure to pesticides and petroleum products in the household during early childhood. The contribution of a differential reporting for the appearance of a positive association in a case control study where the exposure data generated from a self-administered questionnaire or provided by the parents during an interview; but not validated in any other manner, was a fact which should not be neglected.

As many as 3-5% of all malignancies can be attributed to sources of radiation, including medical, occupational or environmental [33]. Numerous studies [34-36] have correlated childhood leukemia with prenatal diagnostic x-ray exposure, whereas no noticeable increase in childhood cancer mortality, including leukemia was recorded in the *in utero* exposed atomic bomb survivors [19,33]. The incompleteness of the statistical records for the relevant periods, in addition to the finite number of subjects exposed *in utero*, were suggested as a possible explanation for this discrepancy [19]. Moreover, as it was demonstrated that the younger the subject at the time of the atomic bomb explosion, the greater was the risk for leukemia et al. [30], it should be anticipated that an exposure a few months before birth would also carry a similar risk [33]. The lifespan study among atomic bomb survivors indicated that the radiation induced solid cancers such as lung cancers in survivors who were exposed in the first or second decade of their life [30]. These only began to appear after the survivors attained the age at which this type of cancer is normally observable, *ie,* several decades later. For leukemia, the latent period was short, with an increased risk appearing 1-3 years after bombing. Also, the specific temporal pattern for the different radiation induced neoplasias should be considered as a possibility for environmental carcinogenesis induced by other agents. A further implication of this conclusion would be to examine the possible association between parental occupational exposures and adulthood rather than only childhood cancer.

## 9.4 Conclusions

There are a number of hypotheses on parental occupational exposures as a contribution to an increased risk of childhood cancer. These have been suggested by case control studies in the last decade. However, no consistent pattern for an increased risk associated with specific exposures has been postulated.

Despite the fact that transplacental rather than male mediated carcinogenicity of drugs and x-ray radiation has been demonstrated in human and experimental studies, research on occupational factors has been focused predominantly on paternal exposures. Circumstantial reasons instead of scientific have been postulated. More often the father — not the mother — is working outside the home and usually the father is employed where contact with occupational hazards is more common.

The association of employment and exposure with an excess risk of childhood malignancies has been observed in case control studies where the exposure status has been estimated on the basis of occupation and industry data registered in birth or death certificates. Hence, the mis-classification of exposure is a major limitation and hinders the interpretation of these findings. The exposure status is poorly ascertained both regarding level and timing of exposure, and the specificity of exposure. Furthermore, with the use of job title for an estimation of exposure a mis-classification is introduced so that the exposure status of the individual is not necessarily that of the group.

The exposure to known or suspected human carcinogens is in rare cases a matter of consideration in studies on childhood cancer and parental occupational exposure. In addition, the definitions of the industrial processes and exposures for which associations have been reported in these studies do not correspond directly for the definitions used in IARC classification [24] even when similar circumstances are considered. This hinders the comparison of the findings in children of exposed parents with those in the working population. Moreover, groups of chemicals, or trade names, or names according to their industrial use but not generic, or chemical names of the products, are used to characterize the exposure status of the parents and these cannot be identified in the IARC list of carcinogens or non-carcinogens.

The present status of knowledge in this field is far from relevant, hence one can neither incriminate nor refute the occupational causative factors for childhood cancer and leukemias. The positive associations of occupations and exposures having a higher risk could be used only in setting priorities for further research.

As a rule, all the foregoing cited studies lack a strong indication of causality:

i) The associations are weak;

ii) The findings are not replicated in further studies;

iii) No graded exposure response was demonstrated;

iv) The specificity of the association was not demonstrated (*ie*, a specific site and type of cancer after specific exposure);

v) Results from randomized trials were not available; and,

vi) Often biological plausibility was difficult to observe, etc.

The following paternal occupational exposures, jobs and industry have been indicated (without consistency through the studies) as representative of a higher risk for childhood malignancies:

i) Exposure to lead, hydrocarbons, boron, metal fumes and dusts, benzene, pesticides, asbestos, chlorinated solvents, ethyl methyl ketone, spray paints, dyestuffs and pigments, and cutting oils;

ii) Occupations with contact with aromatic and aliphatic hydrocarbons, aromatic amino and nitro compounds, metals, solvents, and petroleum products;

iii) Occupations — mechanics, autobody repairmen, and welders; and,

iv) Industries — agriculture, metal, food and tobacco, electrical assembling, installing, machinery repair, electronics, meat production or sale.

The following maternal occupational exposures, occupations and industries have been suspected as representing a risk for a childhood cancer on the small scale research in this field:

i) Exposure to paints, petroleum products, unspecified chemicals, pigments, metal dust, and sawdust;

ii) Occupations related to hydrocarbons exposure such as machine operatives, automobile mechanics, laundry operators, printers, work in chemical and petrochemical industry, cleaners, or dyers; and,

iii) Industries — food and tobacco, catering, cleaning, hairdressing, and personal services.

The human evidence for drugs and x-rays transplacental carcinogenesis coupled with the experimental evidence for a higher sensitivity of the fetus and newborns to carcinogenic chemicals are a sufficient basis to justify further research in the field of occupational developmental carcinogenesis. This study should be undertaken with the joint collaboration of chemists, epidemiologists, oncologists, and occupational health specialists. Additionally, the experience gained from atomic bomb survivors indicates the possibility that no only childhood, but adulthood types of cancer might originate *in utero*. This would imply that investigations for parental occupational risk factors, should include not only childhood cases, but adulthood cancer.

Priorities for research in occupational developmental carcinogenesis include:

i) Maternal occupational exposure to chemical, biological, and physical hazards;

ii) Exposures and occupational situations which represent a risk for carcinogenesis in the working population itself;

iii) Exposure to carcinogenic and/or mutagenic chemicals to experimental animals; and,

iv) Exposures identified as possibly increasing the risk of transplacental carcinogenesis in case control studies.

## 9.5 References

[1] Wilkins III, J.R., and Hundley, V.D., *Am. J. Epidemiol.* 1990, **131**, (6), 995-1008.

[2] Preston-Martin, S., Yu, M.C., Benton, B., and Henderson, B.E., *Cancer Res.* 1982, **42**, 5240-5245.

[3] McKinney, P.A., Alexander, F.E., Cartwright, R.A., and Parker, L., *Brit. Med. J.* 1991, **302**, 681-687.

[4] Wilkins III, J.R., and Sinks, T., *Am. J. Epidemiol.* 1990, **132**, (2), 275-292.

[5] Buckley, J.D., Robinson, L.L., Swotinsky, R., Garabrant, D.H., LeBeau, M., Manchester P., Nesbit, M.E., Odom, L., Peters, J.M., Woods, W.G., and Hammond, G.D., *Cancer Res.* 1989, **49**, 4030-4037.

[6] Gold, E., Gordis, L., Tonascia, J., and Szklo, M., *Am. J. Epidemiology* 1979, **109**, (3), 309-319.

[7] Kantor, A.F., Curnen, M.G.M., Meigs, J.W., and Flannery, J.T., *J. Epidemiol. Community Health* 1979, **33**, 253-256.

[8] Wilkins III, J.R., and Sinks, T.J., *J. Occ. Med.* 1984, **26**, (6), 427-435.

[9] Olshan, A.F., Breslow, N.E., Daling, J.R., Falletta, J.M., Grufferman, S., Robinson, L.L., Waskerwitz, M., and Hammond, G.D., *Cancer Res.* 1990, 3212-3217.

[10] Wilkins III, J.R., and Koutras, R.A., *Am. J. Ind. Med.* 1988, **14**, 299-318.

[11] Ward, E.M., A case-control study of the etiology of neuroblastoma, PhD dissertation, Philadelphia, PA, University of Pensilvania, 1983. Cited in Wilkins, J.R., and Hundley, V.D., *Am. J. Epidemiol.* 1990, **131**, (6), 985-1008.

[12] Spitz, M.R., and Johnson, C.C., *Am. J. Epidemiol.* 1985, **121**, 924-929.

[13] Fabia, J., and Thuy, T.D., *Brit. J. Prev. Soc. Med.* 1974, **28**, 98-100.

[14] Zack, M., Cannon, Sh., Loyd, D., Heath, C.W., Falletta, J.M., Jones, B., Housworth, J., and Crowley, S., *Am. J. Epidemiol.* 1980, **111**, (3), 329-336.

[15] Van Steensel-Moll, H.A., Valkenburg, H.A., and Van Zanen, G.E., *Am. J. Epidemiol.* 1985, **121**, (2), 216-224.

[16] Lowengart, R.A., Peters, J.M., Cicioni, C., Buckley, J., Bernstein, L., Preston-Martin, S., and Rappaport, E., *J. Nat. Canc. Inst.* 1987, **79**, (1), 39-45.

[17] Laval, G., and Tuyns, A.J., *Brit. J. Ind. Med.* 1988, **45**, (x), 843-844.

[18] Gardner, M.J., Snee, M.P., Hall, A.J., Powell, C.A., Downers, S., and Terrell, J.D., *Brit. Med. J.* 1990, **300**, 423-429.

[19] Yoshimito, Y., *J. Am. Med. Assoc.* 1990, **264**, (5), 596-600.

[20] Urquart, J.D., Black, R.J., Muirhead, M.J., Sharp, L., Maxwell, M., Eden, O.B., and Jones, D.A., *Brit. Med. J.* 1991, **302**, 687-692.

[21] Howe, G.R., *J. Am. Med. Assoc.* 1991, **265**, (11), 1438-1439.

[22] Cook-Mozaffari, P., Darby, S., and Doll, R., *The Lancet* 1989, (Nov. 11), 1145-1147.

[23] Gundy, S., Babosa, M., and Baki, M., 'Offsprings of Testicular Cancer Patients: A Model for Male-mediated Mutagenesis and Consequences', in: *Reproductive Toxicology*, Richardson, M.L. (Ed.), VCH Weinheim, 1993, pp. 143-151.

[24] Tomatis (Ed. in Chief), IARC Scientific Publication No. 100, *Cancer: Causes, Occurrence and Control*, WHO, IARC, Lyon, 1990.

[25] Little, J., 'Are Occupational Carcinogens Teratogenic?' in: *Reproductive Toxicology*, Richardson, M.L. (Ed.), VCH Weinheim, 1993, pp. 3-43.

[26] Druckrey, H., Preussmann, R., Ivankovic, S., and Schmäl, D., *Z. Krebsforsch* 1967, **69**, 103-201.

[27] Greenwald, P., Barlow, J.J., and Burnett, W.S., *New Engl. J. Med.* 1971, **285**, 390-392.

[28] MacMahon, B., *J. Natl. Canc. Inst.* 1962, **28**, 1173-1191.

[29] Pearn, J.A., *Med. J. Aust.* 1983, **2**, 16-20.

[30] Shimuzo, Y., Schull, W.J., and Kato, H., *J. Am. Med. Assoc.* 1990, **264**, (5), 601-604.

[31] Hemminki, K., Saloniemi, I., Salonen, T., Partanen, T., and Vainio, H., *J. Epidemiol. Community Health* 1981, **35**, 11-15.

[32] Vergieva, T., 'Adverse Effects of Environmental Chemicals on the Outcome of Human Pregnancy', in: *Reproductive Toxicology*, Richardson, M.L., (Ed.), VCH Weinheim, 1993, pp. 73-97.

[33] Boice, J.D., *J. Am. Med. Assoc.* 1990, **264** (5), 622-623.

[34] Brent, R.L., *Clin. Obstet. Gynecol.* 1983, **26**, (2), 484-510.

[35] Vos, O., *Boll. Soc. It. Biol. Sper.* (Idelson-Napoli), 1989, **LXV**-, 481-500.

[36] Bithell, J.F., and Stewart, A.M., *Brit. J. Cancer* 1975, **31**, 271-287.

# 10. Comparative Genetic Toxicity of Some Pesticides

Jasna Franekić, Dražena Papeš and Marija Alačević

## 10.1 Introduction

In the industrialized countries at least 50,000-60,000 chemicals are on the market today [1] with 500-600 new ones becoming available each year [2]. Epidemiological evidence of carcinogenicity to humans is available only for about 50 chemicals or industrial processes. More chemicals have been tested by private chemical and pharmaceutical companies in long-term experiments on rodents, but the results are not usually available to the public.

To protect ourselves from the possible danger of carcinogenicity induced by new chemicals, during the past 2 decades, it has been proposed, that short-term tests for genotoxicity and *in vitro* cell transformation be used [3]. The expectation that mutagenic activity should predict carcinogenic potential is based on the considerable level of mechanistic similarity between somatic cell mutation and carcinogenesis initiation. The conversion of a cellular proto-oncogene to an active oncogene may require as little as a single specific base substitution, as in the case of the *ras* gene [4], or a chromosome alteration, as indicated by the high degree of association between chromosome breakpoints and oncogene locations in tumor cells [5]. Epidemiological evidence suggest that 60-80% of all human cancers may be the result of lifestyle and environmental factors.

Of particular importance is the potentially hazardous effects associated with the widespread application of pesticides. These compounds are widely used in agriculture, and represent a large proportion of chemicals to which man is environmentally exposed. The acute toxic effects of pesticides are well-established, with 100000 non-fatal cases of human poisoning reported each year [6]. However, the potential long-term genetic hazard of pesticides on man cannot be ignored. Genotoxic effects have been reported for many pesticides, including carbamates, organophosphates, and chlorinated hydrocarbons.
Two major problems exist in assessing human exposure to genotoxic chemicals in the environment:

i) There is usually a long latency period (20-30 years) between the time of exposure and manifestation of the disease; and,

ii) Exposures generally involve mixtures of compounds from many different sources.

Even if individual compounds can be identified, the toxicological characteristics of the agents are unknown.

## 10.2 Genotoxicity Tests

A large number of genotoxicity tests are presently available for use in hazard evaluation. These tests detect the 2 main categories of mutations, gene mutation and chromosomal aberration, as well as indications of DNA damage. Tests to assess these endpoints can be carried out both *in vitro* and *in vivo*, with *in vivo* tests being conducted in germ cells, as well as in somatic cells. In order to asses adequately any expression of genotoxicity, a systematic approach to the selection of these tests is required.

The result of >25 years of investigation has demonstrated that sensitivity of short-term tests (the proportion of carcinogens tested which yield positive results) is generally high.

The genotoxic potential of a chemical can be assessed by using a variety of genetic endpoints both *in vitro* and *in vivo*. Two basic categories of endpoints, gene mutations and chromosomal alterations (both structural and numerical), are believed responsible for the induction of somatic (including carcinogenic) as well as heritable mutation leading to genetic disorders in offspring. There is a large variety of tests that detect these endpoints directly, or indirectly by measuring effects that are precursors of these endpoints or are indirectly related to them.

When examining the precision of short-term genotoxicity tests for predicting carcinogenicity there are 4 possible outcomes. The first 2 categories include genotoxic carcinogens and non-genotoxic non-carcinogens. For these agents, genotoxicity tests and the cancer bioassay concur. The 3rd category includes chemicals which are carcinogenic but not mutagenic [7]. It appears that there a considerable number of carcinogens that induce cancer via non-genetic mechanisms. Butterworth *et al.*, [8] reported that diethylhexyl phthalate (DEHP) is believed to induce cancer by causing hepatic hyperplasia, hypertrophy and peroxisome proliferation. The 4th category includes agents that are genotoxic in short-term tests but are negative in the rodent cancer bioassay.

## 10.3 Pesticide Hazard Assessment

The Federal Insecticide, Fungicide and Rodenticide Act (FIFRA) defines the term pesticide as any substance or mixture of substances intended for preventing, destroying, repelling, or mitigating any pest, and any substance or mixture of substances intended for use as a plant regulator, defoliant, or desiccant [9].

Exposure to pesticides may occur in a variety of different ways including worker exposure during manufacture, during transport, and exposure to residues in edible crops, soil and water. Adverse effects on man may result from the compound itself, its mammalian metabolites, plant and soil metabolites or, possibly, from breakdown products in the environment. Pesticides are often dispersed widely in the environment as stable materials, such as DDT, which may remain as virtually permanent contaminants, though at detectable concentrations. This, together with the fact that pesticides are highly biologically-active molecules, requires a fine balance to be set between the benefits of pesticides and their possible hazard to man or the environment.

Tests for mutagenicity form only a small part of the overall package of data accumulated before a pesticide is released for use. Short-term tests are usually carried out in parallel with the development of a new pesticide. Pesticides are often supplied and used in a variety of formulations and in mixtures with other pesticides. It is usual, therefore, to consider both the pure material and specific formulations, when testing pesticides and assessing the significance to toxicity data.

Through the study of pesticide effects and how they affect plants, animals, man, and the environment, many advancements have been made in the evaluation of new and old chemicals. Over the years, various scientific groups have published documents concerning the problem of evaluation. One of the most complicated areas for the understanding of pesticide effects is the field of metabolic pathways in plants, animals, and man.
Some pesticides, eg, some s-trazines, are metabolized by plant [10] or by mammalian enzymes [11,12] to mutagenic products.

Pesticides as a class contain 2 widely quoted examples of ambiguity between mutagenic activity and carcinogenicity. Dichlorvos (2,2-dichlorovinyl dimethyl phosphate), an organophosphate insecticide, and ziram (bis(dimethyldithio-carbamate)zinc), a dithiocarbamate fungicide, are confirmed bacterial mutagens [13].

## 10.4 Behaviour of Pesticides in the Environment

Ethylenebisdithiocarbamates (EBDC) including maneb, zineb, mancozeb, habam and amobam are used to control crop diseases and for mould prevention. Ethylenethiourea (ETU), a degradation and a byproduct of the manufacturing of EBDCs, is formed during their storage. ETU is present in commercial formulations of EBDC and increases during their environmental degradation and heat processing of food containing EBDC residues. Moreover, EBDC are metabolised by mammals to ETU [14]. Kurttio *et al.* [15] reported that exposure of workers to EBDCs (maneb or mancozeb) in 29 potato farms resulted in the presence of ETU in urine. The creatinine corrected concentration of ETU in urine was 11-28 mg $kg^{-1}$ creatinine 24 h after exposure ended. The estimated $t_{½}$ for eliminating ETU through the kidneys is almost 100 hours [15]. These results indicate that the measurement of ETU in urine is suitable for biological monitoring of exposure to EBDCs. ETU causes thyroid hyperplasia and pronounced alterations in the levels of thyroid hormones in serum [16] and is also known for its significant teratogenic potency [17]. Marked differences between rats and mice in acute toxicity and teratogenicity after a single dose of ETU have been observed [17].

Single oral administration of zineb is sufficient to induce transient dose-dependent modifications of xenobiotic metabolizing systems in rats and mice. Depression of aminopyrine N-dimethylase in rats, and the stimulatory effect on aniline hydroxylase in mice are also observed after treatment with ETU. Therefore, it appears likely that these effects of zineb may be related to its transformation into this metabolite. On the other hand, the depression of aniline hydroxylase in rats and of aminopyrine N-demethylase in mice are observed after zineb, but not after ETU, treatment [18]. These effects of zineb may depend on the fungicide itself, or on its transformation into other metabolites, such as ethylenebisdiisocyanato sulfide (EBIS) known to reduce aniline hydroxylase in rats. Borin *et al.* [19] showed in *in vitro* experiments that neither ETU nor EBIS but also zineb itself at high concentrations, had a significant inhibitory effect on aniline and aminopyrine metabolism in rat microsomes. Savaloinen and Pyysalo [20] reported that ETU is metabolized in mice by oxidation of the sulfur atom, with 2-imidazolin-2-yl sulfenate being the main product (Figure 10.1)

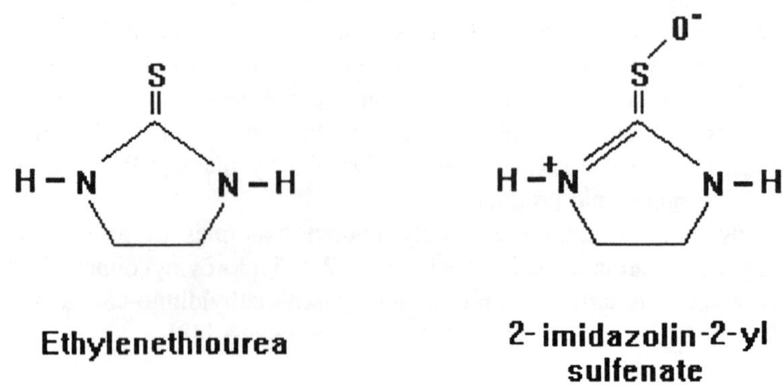


**Figure 10.1** **Formula of ethylenethiourea and 2-imidazolin-2-yl sulfenate**

In bacterial tests and in host-mediated assays 2-imidazolin-2-yl sulfenate was less mutagenic than the parent compound. It appears that the oxidation of the sulfur atom in ETU effects the molecular mechanisms responsible for the mutagenic effects of this compound [21].

Maini and Boni [22] have reported interior concentration of EBDCs during the production of EBDCs 100 times higher [23] than the highest outdoor concentrations in agriculture [22].

It has been suggested that a possible degradation scheme for metallic derivatives of EBDCs may be as follows [24].

In short-term static bioaccumulation experiments with $^{14}C$-labelled zinc ethylene-bisdithiocarbamate (zineb) and zinc dimethyldithio-carbamate (ziram) both compounds were spread rapidly through the rainbow trout (*Salmo gairdneri*) tissues [25]. For both compounds, high levels of radioactivity were recorded in the liver, gall bladder and intestinal lumen, which suggest their rapid biotransformation. Ziram, and to a lesser extent zineb and/or their degradation products, appeared to accumulate specifically in melanophores in the skin, the choroid-epithelium complex of the eye, and in the other melanin containing tissue such as the kidney. This may be attributed either to the removal of copper, the prosthetic group of phenol oxidase (tyrosinase), a metallo-enzyme involved in melanin synthesis or to the attachment to copper, by which a dithiocarbamate — enzyme complex is formed [26]. These assumptions are supported by the finding that dithiocarbamates and various thioureas are potent inhibitors of phenol oxidase.

Dithiocarbamates are selectively localized in various tissues. Autoradiography revealed a high labelling of thyroid follicles [25].

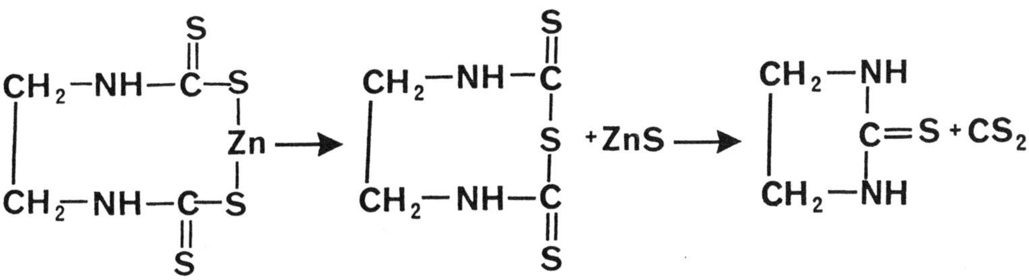

EBDC — Ethylenthiuram monosulfide — Ethylenethiourea

**Figure 10.2** **Transformation of EBDC**

## 10.5 Genotoxicity of Selected Dithiocarbamates

Dithiocarbamates (DTC) are a group of one of the most widely distributed environmental pollutants. There are conflicting results concerning the mutagenicity of ziram, thiram, zineb and ETU. Ziram (zinc-dimethyl dithiocarbamate, CAS RN 137-30-4), thiram (tetramethylthiuram disulphide, CAS RN 137-30-4) and zineb (zinc-ethylene bisdithiocarbamate, CAS RN 12122-67-7) are fungicides used currently in agricultural practice for eradication of fungal infection of tomato, rice, potato, cafe, tobacco and sugar beet [27-29]. ETU (ethylenethiourea, CAS RN 96-45-7) is the principal degradation and metabolic product of Zineb).

The determination of the genotoxic properties of these chemicals is of relevance since their residues and derivatives are known to contaminate field crops.

### 10.5.1. Ziram

Ziram has principal uses as an accelerator in the process of rubber vulcanization and as a protective foliar fungicide for fruit nuts, vines vegetables and ornamental plants. It was introduced ca. 1931 as a fungicide [30].

Ziram induced thyroid gland C-cell adenoma and lung alveolar/bronchiolar adenoma in male rats [31]. Ziram is not classifiable as to is carcinogenicity to humans.

**Table 10.1** **Genetic and related effects of ziram in selected assays**

| Test system | Result: Without exogenous metabolic system | Result: With exogenous metabolic system | Reference |
|---|---|---|---|
| ***Salmonella typhimurium*** | | | |
| TA100, reverse mutation | - | + | [33] |
| TA100, reverse mutation | + | + | [34] |
| TA100, reverse mutation | + | + | [35] |
| TA100, reverse mutation | (+) | (+) | [36] |
| TA100, reverse mutation | + | + | [27] |
| TA100, reverse mutation | + | + | [37] |
| TA1535, reverse mutation | + | + | [35] |
| TA1535, reverse mutation | - | (+) | [38] |
| TA1535, reverse mutation | - | - | [35] |
| TA1535, reverse mutation | + | + | [27] |
| TA1535, reverse mutation | + | + | [37] |
| TA98, reverse mutation | - | (+) | [33] |
| TA98, reverse mutation | + | - | [36] |
| TA98, reverse mutation | - | (+) | [38] |
| TA98, reverse mutation | - | - | [35] |
| TA98, reverse mutation | - | - | [27] |
| TA98, reverse mutation | - | - | [37] |
| TA1538, reverse mutation | - | - | [36] |
| TA1538, reverse mutation | - | - | [35] |
| TA102, reverse mutation | - | - | [27] |
| TA102, reverse mutation | - | - | [37] |
| TA104, reverse mutation | (+) | - | [37] |
| ***Saccharomyces cerevisiae*** | | | |
| D7, mitotic gene conversion | - | ND | [39] |
| D7, mitotic gene conversion | - | ND | [37] |
| D61.M, aneuploidy | - | ND | [37] |
| ***Allium ascalonicum*** | | | |
| Chromosomal aberrations | (+) | | [37] |
| Poliploidy | + | | [37] |
| Aneuploidy | + | | [37] |
| Mitotic aberrations | + | | [37] |
| Micronucleus | + | | [37] |
| Micronucleus test in mice | - (♀ and ♂) | | [27] |
| Micronucleus test in mice | | + | [32] |

+, positive results; (+), weakly positive results; -, negative results; ND, no data

Mutagenicity data for ziram, are contradictory (Table 10.1). Ziram caused DNA damage and point mutation in bacteria, and these effects were increased by the presence of exogenous metabolic systems. It induced neither gene conversion nor aneuploidy in yeast. *In vivo*, administration of Cuman L (a formulation containing 27 % ziram as the active ingredient) to Swiss mice at sublethal doses resulted in the induction in the number of micronuclei in polychromatic erythrocytes [32]. Crebelli *et al.* [27] reported that ziram, tested in a lower range of doses because of its higher toxicity, produced negative results in both sexes. The results with the *Allium* test showed that ziram induced aneugenic effects such as spindle disfunction, in anaphase lagging chromosomes, metaphase arrest and aneuploidy.

### 10.5.2. Thiram

Thiram can be combined in formulations with most fungicides and insecticides. In the USA, such products include thiram with phenylmercury, dimethyldithiocarbamate, Malachite green, thiophanate, zineb, molybdenum, vinclozolin and carboxin [40]. The major use of thiram is in rubber processing as an accelerator and vulcanizing agent. It is also used as a seed treatment to protect against fungal diseases and by foliar application for control of diseases on fruit and vegetable crops. In the USA, it was estimated that 220 tonnes of thiram (active ingredient) were used in 1981 for seed treatment [41]. Thiram can be found in the environment as a degradation product of ferbam and ziram.

The positive results obtained in microbial short-term tests of the mutagenic activity of thiram (see Table 10.2) suggest that thiram may be a hazardous agent for man.

**Table 10.2** **Genetic and related effects of thiram in selected assays**

| Test system | Result | | Reference |
|---|---|---|---|
| | Without exogenous metabolic system | With exogenous metabolic system | |
| ***Salmonella typhimurium*** | | | |
| TA100, reverse mutation | + | ND | [44] |
| TA100, reverse mutation | + | - | [35] |
| TA100, reverse mutation | + | + | [45] |
| TA100, reverse mutation | - | + | [46] |
| TA100, reverse mutation | + | + | [27] |
| TA100, reverse mutation | + | + | [37] |
| TA1535, reverse mutation | + | ND | [44] |
| TA1535, reverse mutation | (+) | - | [35] |
| TA1535, reverse mutation | + | + | [27] |
| TA1535, reverse mutation | + | + | [37] |
| TA98, reverse mutation | - | - | [44] |
| TA98, reverse mutation | - | - | [35] |

**Table 10.2** (Continued)

| Test system | Result: Without exogenous metabolic system | Result: With exogenous metabolic system | Reference |
|---|---|---|---|
| TA98, reverse mutation | - | + | [46] |
| TA98, reverse mutation | - | - | [27] |
| TA98, reverse mutation | + | + | [37] |
| TA1538, reverse mutation | - | (+) | [44] |
| TA1538, reverse mutation | - | - | [35] |
| TA1538, reverse mutation | + | + | [37] |
| TA102, reverse mutation | - | - | [27] |
| TA102, reverse mutation | - | - | [37] |
| TA104, reverse mutation | (+) | (+) | [37] |
| ***Saccharomyces cerevisiae*** | | | |
| D7, mitotic gene conversion | - | - | [37] |
| D61.M, aneuploidy | (+) | ND | [37] |
| ***Aspergillus nidulans*** | | | |
| Aneuploidy | + | ND | [47] |
| ***Hordeum vulgare*** | | | |
| Chromosomal aberrations | + | | [48] |
| ***Allium ascalonicum*** | | | |
| Chromosomal aberrations | (+) | | [37] |
| Polyploidy | + | | [37] |
| Aneuploidy | + | | [37] |
| Mitotic aberrations | + | | [37] |
| Micronucleus | + | | [37] |
| Micronucleus test in mice | + | | [49] |
| Micronucleus test in mice | + (only in ♂) | | [27] |

+, positive results; (+), weakly positive results; -, negative results; ND, no data

Thiram induced point mutation in bacteria, but data on the induction of DNA damage were conflicting. In *Aspergillus nidulans* and in *Saccharomyces cerevisiae*, thiram induced aneuploidy; both aneuploidy and chromosomal aberrations were induced in plants. It induced micronucleus formation in mouse bone marrow and in plants.

No data have been reported on the carcinogenic activity of thiram *per se* in animal models [42], but when it was administered to rats together with sodium nitrite, it caused the development of neoplasms in the nasal cavity and increased the frequency of monocytic leukaemia [43]. Thiram is not classifiable as to its carcinogenicity to humans.

### 10.5.3 Zineb

Zineb is registered for use on all cereals, various vegetables as well as for treatment of many seeds. The significance of zineb as a residue of agricultural products is enhanced by reports on toxicity of its degradation products such as ethylenethiourea.
There are relatively few data in the literature on the mutagenic activity of zineb (Table 10.3).

**Table 10.3 Genetic and related effects of zineb in selected assays**

| Test system | Result | | Reference |
|---|---|---|---|
| | Without exogenous metabolic system | With exogenous metabolic system | |
| ***Salmonella typhimurium*** | | | |
| TA100, reverse mutation | - | - | [53] |
| TA100, reverse mutation | - | - | [37] |
| TA1535, reverse mutation | - | - | [53] |
| TA97, reverse mutation | - | - | [53] |
| TA98, reverse mutation | - | - | [53] |
| TA98, reverse mutation | - | - | [37] |
| TA102, reverse mutation | - | - | [37] |
| TA104, reverse mutation | - | - | [37] |
| ***Aspergillus nidulans*** | | | |
| Aneuploidy | - | - | [54] |
| ***Saccharomyces cerevisiae*** | | | |
| D7, gene conversion | - | ND | [37] |
| D61.M, aneuploidy | + | ND | [37] |
| Micronucleus test in mice | + | | [55] |
| ***Allium cepa*** | | | |
| Micronucleus, laggards | + | | [56] |
| Binucleation | + | | [56] |
| ***Triticum aestivum*** | | | |
| Antimitotic activity | - | | [51] |

+, positive results; (+), weakly positive results; -, negative results; ND, no data

This compound gave negative results in bacterial strains of *S. typhimurium*. In the contrary, in the most tests used for detection aneuploidy the results were positive, except in *A. nidulans*. Chromosomal aberrations were found in lymphocytes of workers exposed to zineb [50].

Plant tests of antimitotic activity of pesticides, which is associated with carcinogenic, mutagenic and teratogenic effects, with zineb showed no antimitotic activity [51].
Zineb is potent teratogen inducing formation of large, wavy notochord in embryo of *Microhyla ornata* [52].

### 10.5.4 Ethylene Thiourea (ETU)

Some agents seem to be capable of increasing the tumor incidence of certain tissues in same species/strains/sexes of rodents but are non-mutagenic. These agents might be expected to be aneugens. In that case, the role of non-mammalian eukaryotic assays in screening for aneugens, is important.

Certain important carcinogens such as benzene, diethylstilbestrol (and ETU) are reported to be non-mutagenic in standard mutation assays, but are found to be involved in mitotic spindle disruption and induction of aneuploidy [57]. ETU was ineffective in increasing the frequency of mitotic crossing-over of forward mutation (Table 10.4).

We have found [37] that ETU increases aneuploidy in yeast and in *Allium* test. The observation of Crebelli *et al.* [58] in *Aspergillus* were also positive. It is likely that zineb and its metabolite ETU act differently on cell structures. In some studies, no effect on micronuclei frequency, or SCE frequency were observed with ETU.

There is sufficient evidence for the carcinogenicity of ETU in experimental animals. When administrated in the diet, ETU induced increased incidences of thyroid follicular cell carcinomas and papillary carcinomas with some metastases and liver hyperplastic nodules in rats of both sexes. There is inadequate evidence for the carcinogenicity of ETU in humans [42]. ETU is used primarily as an accelerator for vulcanizing polychloropene and polyacrylate rubbers. The primary routes of potential human exposure to ETU are inhalation, ingestion and dermal contact. Potential occupational exposure also occurs during the manufacture of formulation and application of fungicides and insecticides prepared from ETU. Residues of the compound have been found in 28 different commercial ethylenebisdithiocarbamates products [59].

**Table 10.4** **Genetic and related effects of ethylene thiourea in selected assays**

| Test system | Result: Without exogenous metabolic system | Result: With exogenous metabolic system | Reference |
|---|---|---|---|
| ***Salmonella typhimurium*** | | | |
| TA100, reverse mutation | ND | - | [60] |
| TA100, reverse mutation | - | - | [60] |
| TA100, reverse mutation | - | - | [60] |
| TA100, reverse mutation | - | - | [37] |
| TA1535, reverse mutation | - | - | [60] |
| TA1535, reverse mutation | + | + | [35] |
| TA1950, reverse mutation | + | ND | [21] |
| TA98, reverse mutation | - | - | [61] |
| TA98, reverse mutation | - | - | [37] |
| TA1538, reverse mutation | - | - | [62] |
| TA102, reverse mutation | - | - | [37] |
| TA104, reverse mutation | - | - | [37] |
| ***Aspergillus nidulans*** | | | |
| P1, gene mutation | - | ND | [58] |
| ***Saccharomyces cerevisiae*** | | | |
| D7, mitotic gene conversion | - | ND | [37] |
| ***Aspergillus nidulans*** | | | |
| P1, crossing-over | - | ND | [58] |
| P1, aneuploidy | + | ND | [58] |
| ***Saccharomyces cerevisiae*** | | | |
| D61.M, aneuploidy | + | ND | [37] |
| D6, aneuploidy | + | + | [63] |
| ***Allium ascalonicum*** | | | |
| Chromosomal aberrations | (+) | | [37] |
| Polyploidy | + | | [37] |
| Aneuploidy | + | | [37] |
| Mitotic aberrations | + | | [37] |
| Micronucleus | + | | [37] |
| Micronucleus test in mice | - | | [64) |

+, positive results; (+), weakly positive results; -, negative results; ND, no data

## 10.6 Are Dithiocarbamates Challengers of Aneuploidy?

The study of aneuploidy has been the topic of recent detailed considerations [65,66,67]. Cytogenetic analyses indicate that approximately 25 % of aborted fetuses are afflicted by trisomy and 0.5 % of live births suffer from similar genetic disorders [68]. Aneuploidy may also be involved in the development of neoplasia [69,70]. Aneuploidy represents a class of genetic changes that may have originated from alteration in non-DNA as well as DNA components of the cell. There is an increasing interest in developing assays, specially short-term tests, that are effective in detecting chromosomal malsegregation. At the present time, it is difficult to calculate the value and to compare the sensitivity of different aneuploidy test systems. The need to select a number of model chemicals to be tested in available assays is urgent. The aim of our study was to analyze some suspected spindle poisons and other substances causing mitotic chromosome malsegregation using *Saccharomyces cerevisiae* D61.M and *Allium ascalonicum.*

Many assays exist for detecting chemically induced gene mutations or chromosome aberrations. The *Salmonella*/mammalian microsome tests for gene mutations has become widely accepted as an initial and most often used test for the identification of chemicals with mutagenic activity. The standard concept of induction of genetic change are based on DNA being the major molecular target. This is certainly justified for prokaryotic organisms. The genetic apparatus of eukaryotes is more complex. The spindle apparatus is required for orderly segregation of chromatids after replication. There are a large number of carcinogens that are not mutagenic to *Salmonella.*

It is important to ascertain which chemicals increase the burden of human aneuploidy, but are not detectable in assays designed for screening of gene mutations and chromosome aberrations.

The yeast *S. cerevisiae* has been widely used for the investigation of basic genetic phenomena, including chromosome malsegregation.
The number of chemicals tested for aneuploidy in yeast is increased over the last few years [71,72,73].

In comparing results obtained in yeast of mammalian results it should be remembered that there are significant differences in cell division in fungi compared to higher eukaryotes. There are now numerous chemicals that are capable of inducing chromosomal malsegregation in various test systems involving different results.

Comparison of dithiocarbamates ziram, thiram, zineb and ETU selected on the basis of their known or suspected spindle activity (Table 10.5) showed different response in the 4 assays used. The study demonstrated that the selected dithiocarbamates assayed were able to induce aneuploidy in at least one assay. These results support the hypothesis that some carcinogens are capable of disturbing the segregation of chromosomes through their interaction with non-DNA targets.

Awareness of the increased effort in the area of the aneuploidy test development prompted the EPA to hold a workshop in 1983 to evaluate the progress of test development and to discuss mechanisms by which aneuploidy may be induced [74]. It was suggested that an in-depth analysis of existing test methodology and a critical evaluation of the results on chemicals from these tests should assist in stimulating further accurate and creative work in the area of aneuploidy test development. In general, the aneuploidy test have not been adequately validated. Certain fungal and *Drosophila* systems are available for validation, and some plant system could be made available for validation in a relatively short timescale [75]. Comparative analysis of results for dithiocarbamates (see table 10.5) suggest that evaluation of some chemicals as inducers of aneuploidy, it may be preferable to use combination of 2 or more assays (*eg*, fungal, plant and mammalian).

**Table 10.5** **Tumorigenicity and aneuploidy of dithiocarbamates**

| Substance | Micronucleus test | *Saccharomyces cerevisiae* D61.M | *Aspergillus nidulans* | *Allium ascalonicum* | Tumorigenicity |
|---|---|---|---|---|---|
| Ziram | E | - | ND | + | + |
| Thiram | + | (+) | + | + | E |
| Zineb | + | + | - | ND | + |
| ETU | - | + | + | + | + |

+ positive results; (+) weakly positive results; - negative results; (E) equivocal evidence for mutagenicity and tumorigenicity; ND no data

## 10.7 Some Conclusions resulting from these Genotoxic Studies

It can be stated that yeast, *S. cerevisiae* D61.M, can discriminate chemicals inducing only chromosome malsegregation, but not mutation (*eg*, ETU and zineb).

The yeast D61.M assay for mitotic chromosome malsegregation is presently an excellent test system as demonstrated by the good inter-laboratory reproducibility of results [73].

The mechanism by which ETU, zineb and thiram interfere with chromosome segregation has not yet been elucidated.

It is clear that the available comparative data base for induced aneuploidy in plant, in fungal and in mammalian cells are limited. The generation of such comparative data should be the major aim in genetic toxicology.

## 10.8 General Conclusions

The extensive use of pesticides in modern agriculture requires for both the compatibility of these agents in the environment, and that public health requirements should be determined in order to ensure their chemical safety.

As the fungicides are widely used in agriculture and persist for a considerable time, all types of genetic potential should be determined carefully.

Currently, few conclusion can be drawn from the relatively insufficient comparative data base for induced aneuploidy in plants, fungi and mammals. The positive results in fungal assays for induced aneuploidy during mitotic cell division can be a predictive aid for mitotic effect in mammalian cells.

Therefore, it is considered that the *Allium* assay is a useful complement to other tests for the detection of chemicals that may cause non-disjunction and other chromosomal aberrations in human populations.

## 10.9 References


[1] Bingham, E., *Ann. NY Acad. Sci.*, 1988, **534**, 1038-1041

[2] Infante, P.F., Pohl, G.K., *Teratogen. Carcinogen. Mutagen.*, 1988, **8**, 225-249

[3] Parodi, S., Taningher, M., Romano, P., Grilli, S., and Santi, L., *Teratogen. Carcinogen. Mutagen.*, 1990, **10**, 177-197

[4] Ramel, C., *Mutat. Res.*, 1986, **168**, 327-342

[5] Evans, H.J., 'The Role of Human Cytogenetics in Studies of Mutagenesis and Carcinogenesis', in: *Genetic Toxicology of Environmental Chemical*, Part A, *Basic Principles and Mechanisms of Action*, Ramel, C., Lambert, B., Magnusson, J., (Eds.) Alan R. Liss Inc., 1986, pp 41-69

[6] Plimmer, J.R., *Trends in Chemical Residues Including Reentry Considerations*, in *Pesticide Residues and Exposure*, Plimmer, J.R., (Ed.) ACS Symposium Series, American Chemical Society, Washington DC, 1982, pp 1-8

[7] Clayson, D.B., *Mutat. Res.*, 1987, **185**, 243-269.

[8] Butterworth, B.E., Bermurez, E., Smith-Oliver, T., Earle, L., Cattley, R., Martin, J., Popp, J.A., Strom, S., Jirtle, R., and Michalopoulos, A., *Carcinogen.*, 1984, **5**, 1329-1335.

[9] Dearfield, K.L., 'Use of mutagenicity data by the US Environmental Protection Agency's Office of Pesticide Programs', in: *Genetic Toxicology*, Li A.P. and Heflich R.H. (Eds.), CRC Press, Boca Raton, Florida, USA, 1991, pp. 472-484.

[10] Gentile, J.M., Gentile, G.J. and Plewa, M.J., *Mutat. Res.*, 1986, **164**, 53-58.

[11] Franekić, J., Hulina, G., Kniewald, J., and Alačević, M., *Environ. Mol. Mutagen.*, 1989, **14**(15), 62.

[12] Franekić, J., Hulina, G., Kniewald, J., and Alačević, M., *Mutat. Res.*, 1990, **234**, 284-285.

[13] Zeiger, E., Haseman, J.K., Shelby, M.D., Margolin, B.H., and Tennant, R.W., *Environ. Mol. Mutagen.*, 1990, **16**(16), 1-14.

[14] Camoni, J., Cicero, A.M., Di Muccio, A., Dommarco, R., *Med. Lav.*, 1984, **75**, 207-214.

[15] Kurttio, P., Vartiainen, T., Savolainen, K., *Br. J. Ind. Med.*, 1990, **47**, 203-206.

[16] Kurttio, P., Savolainen, K., and Tuominen, R., *Arch. Toxicol.*, 1986, **9**, 339-344.

[17] Khera, K.S., *J. Toxicol. Environ. Health.*,1984, **13**, 747-756.

[18] Meneguz, A., and Michalek, H., *Bull. Environ. Contam. Toxicol.*, 1987, **38**, 862-867.

[19] Borin, C., Periquet, A., Mitgavila, S., *Toxicol. Appl. Pharmacol.*, 1985, **81**, 460-468.

[20] Savolainen, K., and Pyysalo, H., *J. Agric. Food Chem.*, 1979, **27**, 1177-1181.

[21] Autio, K., Von Wright, A., and Pyysalo, H., *Mutat. Res.*, 1982, **106**, 27-31.

[22] Maini, P., Boni, R., *Bull. Environ. Contam. Toxicol.*, 1986, **37**, 931-937.

[23] Nilsson, C.A., Nygren, O., Sikström, E., *Chemosphere.*, 1987, **16**, 2423-2428.
[24] Ludwig, R.A., Thorn, G.D., Miller, D.M., *Can. J. Bot.*, 1954, **32**, 48.
[25] Van Leeuwen, C.J., Van Hammeren, P., Bogers, M., and Griffioen, P.S., *Toxicology*, 1986, **42**, 33-46.
[26] Wing, R.E., and Rayford, W.E., *Plat. Surf. Finish.*, 1982, **69**, 67.
[27] Crebelli, R., Zijno, A., Conti, L., Brochi, B., Leopardi, P., Marcon, F., Renzi, L., and Carere, A., *Teratogen. Carcinogen. Mutagen.*, 1992, **12**, 97-112
[28] Tripathy, N.K., Dey, L., Majhi, B., and Das, C.C., *Mutat. Res.*, 1988, **206**, 25-31.
[29] Pienkowska, M., and Zielenska, M., *Mutat. Res.*, 1990, **245**, 119-123.
[30] WHO, Dithiocarbamate Pesticides, *Ethylenethiourea and Propylenethiourea. A general Introduction* (Environmental Health Criteria 78), 1988, World Health Organization, Geneva.
[31] Ashby, Y., and Tennant, R.W., *Mutat. Res.*, 1991, **257**, 229-306.
[32] Hemavathy, K.C., and Krishna Murti, N.B., *Mutat. Res.*, 1988, **208**, 57-60.
[33] Wildeman, A.G. and Nazar, R.N., *Can. J. Cytol.*, 1982, **24**, 437-449
[34] Zeiger, E., *Cancer. Res.*, 1987, **47**, 1287-1296
[35] Moriya, M., Ohta, T., Watanabe, K., Miyazawa, T., Kato, K. and Shirasu, Y., *Mutat. Res.*, 1983, **116**, 185-216
[36] Brooks, T.M., and Meyer, A.L., *Mutat. Res.*, 1983, **124**, 129-143
[37] Franekić, J., Bratulić, N., Pavlica, M., and Papeš, D., *Mutat. Res.*, 1993, (In press)
[38] Haworth, S., Lawor, T., Mortelmans, K., Speck, W., and Zeiger, E., *Environ. Mutagen.*, 1983, **5**(1), 3-142
[39] Siebert, D., Zimmermann, F.K., and Lempre, E., *Mutat. Res.*, 1970, **10**, 533-553
[40] Meister, R.T., ed., *Farm Chemicals Handbook 90*, Willoughby, OH. Meister Publishing Company, 1990, p. C 286.
[41] Vlier, L.K., *Preliminary Quantitative Usage Analysis of Thiram*, 1982, Washington DC, Office of Pesticide Programs, US Environmental Protection Agency.
[42] IARC *Monograph on the Evaluation of the Carcinogenic Risk of Chemicals to Humans*, 1982, **28**, The Rubber Industry, International Agency for Research on Cancer, Lyon.
[43] Lijinski, W., *J. Toxicol. Environ. Health*, 1984, **13**, 609-614.
[44] Zdzienicka, M., Zielenska, M., Hryniwiez, M., Trojanowska, M., Zalejska, M., and Szymczyk, T., *Progr. Mutat. Res.*, 1981, **2**, 79-86
[45] Rannung, A., and Rannung, U., *Chem. Biol. Interact.*, 1984, **49**, 329-340
[46] Crebelli, R., Paoletti, A., Falcone, E., Aquilina, G., Fabri, G., and Carere, A., *Br. J. Ind. Med.*, 1985, **42**, 481-487
[47] Upshall, A., and Johnson, P.E., *Mutat. Res.*, 1981, **89**, 297-301
[48] George, M.K., Anlakh, K.S., and Dhesi, Y.S., *Can. J. Genet. Cytol.*, 1970, **12**, 415-419.
[49] Paschin, Y.V., and Bakhitova, L.M., *Food. Chem. Toxicol.*, 1985, **23**, 373-375.
[50] Abbrecht, R., *Cah. Nutr. Diet.*, 1979, **14**(1), 49-61.
[51] Andrzejewska-Golec, E., *Bromatol. Chem. Toksykol.*, 1981, **14**, 23-27.
[52] Ghate, H.V., *Riv. Bio.*, 1985, **78**(2), 288-291.
[53] Zeiger, E., Anderson, B., Howarth, S., Lawlor, T., Montelmans, K., *Environ. Mol. Mutagen.*, 1988, **11**(12), 1-158.
[54] Käfer, E., Scott, B.R., Dorn, G.L., and Stafford, R., *Mutat. Res.*, 1982, **98**, 1-48.

[55] Ryazanova, R.A., and Gafurova, T.V., *Gig. Sanit.*, 1980, **45**(1), 80-81.
[56] Sharma, C.B.S.R., *Mutagenesis*, 1990, **5**(2), 105-125.
[57] Waters, M.D., Bergman, H.B. and Nesnow, S., *Mutat. Res.*, 1988, **205**, 139-181
[58] Crebelli, R., Bellincampi, D., Conti, G., Conti, L., Morpurgo, G., and Carere, A., *Mutat. Res.*, 1986, **172**, 139-149.
[59] NIH Fifth Annual Report on Carcinogens, *National Institute of Health Publication, National Toxicity Program*, 89-239, 1989, pp. 155-157.
[60] IARC, *Monographs on the Evaluation of Carcinogenic Risk to Humans*, 1987, **7**, 304-306, International Agency for Research on Cancer, Lyon.
[61] Mortelmans, K., Howarth, S., Lawor, T., Speck, W., Tainer, B., and Zeiger, E., *Environ. Mutag.*, 1986, **8**(7), 1-179.
[62] Teramoto, S., Moriya, M., Kato, K., Tezuka, H., Nakamura, S., Shingu, A., and Shirasu, *Mutat. Res.*, 1977, **56**, 121-129.
[63] Parry, Y.M., and Sharp, D.C., 'The induction of mitotic aneuploidy in the yeast strain D6 by 42 coded compounds', in: *Evaluation of Short-Term Tests for Carcinogenesis, Progress in Mutation Research*, F.J. de Serres and J. Ashby (Eds.), 1981, Elsevier, New York, pp. 468-480.
[64] Kirkhart, B., 'Micronucleus test on 21 compounds', in: *Progress in Mutation Research*, De Serres, F.J., and Ashby, J. (Eds.), 1981, Vol.1, pp. 698-704.
[65] Vig, B.K., and Paweletz, N., *Mutat. Res.*, 1988, **201**, 259-269.
[66] Rédei, G.P., and Sandhu, S.S., *Mutat. Res.*, 1988, **201**, 337-348.
[67] Albertini, S., *Mutagenesis*, 1990, **5**(5), 453-459.
[68] Hassold, T.J., and Jacobs, P.A., *Annu. Rev. Genet.*, 1984, **18**, 69-97.
[69] Gudi, R., Sandhu, S.S., and Athwal, R.S., *Mutat. Res.*, 1990, **234**, 263-268.
[70] Oshimura, M., Koi, M., Ozawa, N., Sugawara, O., Lamb, P.W., and Barett, J.C., *Cancer Res.*, 1988, **48**, 1623-1632.
[71] Albertini, S., and Zimmermann, F.K., *Mutat. Res.*, 1991, **258**, 237-258.
[72] Crebelli, R., Benigni, R., Franekić, J., Conti, G., Conti, L., and Carere, A., *Mutat. Res.*, 1988, **201**, 401-411.
[73] Albertini, S., Brunner, M., and Würgler, F.E., *Environ. Mol. Mutagen.*, 1993, **21**, 180-192.
[74] Dellarco, V.L., Mavournin, K.H., and Tice, R.R., *Environ. Mutagen.*, 1985, **7**, 405-424.
[75] Pavlica, M., Papeš, D., and Nagy, B., *Mutat. Res.*, 1991, **263**, 77-81.

# 11. Intake of Organochlorine Compounds and Levels in Population Groups

Blanka Krauthacker and Elsa Reiner

## 11.1 Introduction

Organochlorine pesticides have been used in Croatia since the end of the second world war. In recent years their use has been considerably restricted but have never been banned in Croatia. During the course of industrialization chlorophenols and polychlorinated biphenyls have also emerged as organochlorine contaminants, resulting in further contamination of the biosphere by polychlorinated dibenzodioxins and polychlorinated dibenzofurans.

This chapter summarizes findings on levels of organochlorine compounds found in population groups in Croatia, and in food. A calculation of the intake of organochlorine compounds of adults and breast-fed children is given. The data are presented in tabular form together with information concerning the place and year of sampling. Until now, no review of these findings has been published in domestic or international journals.

Four groups of compounds are considered: organochlorine pesticides, polychlorinated biphenyls, polychlorinated dibenzodioxins and polychlorinated dibenzofurans. The list of compounds is given in Table 11.1.

Most measurements for organochlorine compounds have been undertaken on human serum and milk, but analysis of urine and abdominal fat has also been made. Analysis of food has concentrated on high fat-containing foods of animal origin. All analyses have been performed by gas-chromatographic techniques.

## 11.2 Levels in Human Serum and Urine

Results obtained in human serum are summarized in Table 11.2. Most data refer to samples collected in Zagreb, an industrial town of about one million inhabitants in the north-west of the country. Zabok, Bjelovar and Klakar are located in the rural north-west. Krk is an island in the northern Adriatic while Pula and Labin are on the Istria peninsula.

p,p'-DDE, the principal metabolite of DDT, was found in all serum samples. p,p'-DDT occurred less frequently and the frequency has steadily decreased over the 18 years since monitoring commenced. Analysis for PCB began in 1985 and all samples have been found to be positive. Other compounds were detected considerably less frequently. No data are available for PCDD or PCDF in either serum or urine.

**Table 11.1** List of organochlorine compounds and abbreviations used

| Compound | Abbreviation |
|---|---|
| Hexachlorocyclohexane | HCH |
| Hexachlorocyclohexane; α-isomer | α-HCH |
| Hexachlorocyclohexane: β-isomer | β-HCH |
| Hexachlorocyclohexane; γ-isomer | γ-HCH |
| Hexachlorocyclohexane; δ-isomer | δ-HCH |
| Aldrin | Aldrin |
| Dieldrin | Dieldrin |
| Endrin | Endrin |
| Heptachlor | Heptachlor |
| Heptachlor epoxide | Heptachlor epoxide |
| p,p'-DDT | p,p'-DDT |
| p,p'-DDE | p,p'-DDE |
| p,p'-DDD | p,p'-DDD |
| o,p'-DDT | o,p'-DDT |
| Pentachlorobenzene | Pentachlorobenzene |
| Hexachlorobenzene | HCB |
| Pentachlorophenol | PCP |
| 2,4-dichlorophenol | 2,4-DCP |
| 2,4,5-trichlorophenol | 2,4,5-TCP |
| 2,4,6-trichlorophenol | 2,4,6-TCP |
| 2,3,4,5-tetrachlorophenol | 2,3,4,5-TeCP |
| 2,3,4,6-tetrachlorophenol | 2,3,4,6-TeCP |
| Polychlorinated biphenyls | PCB |
| Polychlorinated dibenzodioxins | PCDD |
| 2,3,7,8-tetrachloro dibenzodioxin | 2,3,7,8-TCDD |
| 1,2,3,7,8-pentachloro dibenzodioxin | 1,2,3,7,8-PeCDD |
| 1,2,3,4,7,8-hexachloro dibenzodioxin | 1,2,3,4,7,8-HxCDD |
| 1,2,3,6,7,8-hexachloro dibenzodioxin | 1,2,3,6,7,8-HxCDD |
| 1,2,3,4,6,7,8-heptachloro dibenzodioxin | 1,2,3,4,6,7,8-HpCDD |
| Octachloro dibenzodioxin | octa-CDD |
| Polychlorinated dibenzofurans | PCDF |
| 2,3,7,8-tetrachloro dibenzofuran | 2,3,7,8-TCDF |
| 1,2,3,7,8-pentachloro dibenzofuran | 1,2,3,7,8-PeCDF |
| 2,3,4,7,8-pentachloro dibenzofuran | 2,3,4,7,8-PeCDF |
| 1,2,3,4,7,8-hexachloro dibenzofuran | 1,2,3,4,7,8-HxCDF |
| 1,2,3,6,7,8-hexachloro dibenzofuran | 1,2,3,6,7,8-HxCDF |
| 1,2,3,7,8,9-hexachloro dibenzofuran | 1,2,3,7,8,9-HxCDF |
| 2,3,4,6,7,8-hexachloro dibenzofuran | 2,3,4,6,7,8-HxCDF |
| 1,2,3,4,6,7,8-heptachloro dibenzofuran | 1,2,3,4,6,7,8-HpCDF |
| 1,2,3,4,7,8,9-heptachloro dibenzofuran | 1,2,3,4,7,8,9-HpCDF |
| Octachloro dibenzofuran | octa-CDF |

**Table 11.2** **Concentrations of organochlorine pesticides an PCB in human serum (μg l⁻¹)**

| Year/ Site | N | HCB | α-HCH | β-HCH | γ-HCH | p,p' DDE | o,p' DDT | p,p' DDD | p,p' DDT | PCB | Ref. |
|---|---|---|---|---|---|---|---|---|---|---|---|
| **Zagreb** | | | | | | | | | | | |
| 1975 * | 147 | - | 0 | - | 0 | 31 | - | 0 | 0 | - | [1,2] |
| 1976 *E | 50 | - | 0 | - | 5.5 | 59 | - | 6.8 | 8.8 | - | [3] |
| 1976 #M | 18 | - | 2.3 | 4.8 | - | 8.3 | 0.5 | 1.6 | 8.7 | - | [4] |
| 1976 #Ch | 18 | - | 2.4 | 7.4 | - | 7.0 | 1.6 | 2.2 | 5.1 | - | [4] |
| 1976-77 * | 11 | - | 0 | - | 0 | 33 | - | 0 | 0 | - | [2] |
| 1977-79 *M | 35 | - | 0 | - | 0 | 18 | - | 0 | 0 | - | [2,5] |
| 1977-79 *C | 35 | - | 0 | - | 0 | 6.3 | - | 0 | 0 | - | [5] |
| 1978-81 #M | 31 | - | 2.2 | - | 3.7 | 11.2 | 0.3 | 1.2 | 8.1 | - | [6] |
| 1978-81 #Ch | 31 | - | 3.0 | - | 6.9 | 6.4 | 1.0 | 2.4 | 3.2 | - | [6] |
| 1985 * | 15 | 1 | 0 | 0 | 0 | 7 | - | 0 | 0 | 4 | [2] |
| 1987-88 * | 24 | 0.9 | 0 | 0 | 3 | 4 | - | 0 | 0 | 3 | [2] |
| 1989-90 * | 26 | 1 | 0 | 0 | 0 | 8 | - | 0 | 0 | 8 | [2] |
| 1990 * | 32 | 0 | 0 | 0 | 0.5 | 2 | - | 0 | 0 | 8 | [2] |
| **Zabok and Bjelovar** | | | | | | | | | | | |
| 1976 #M | 27 | - | 6.8 | 13.1 | - | 13.8 | 10.7 | 5.5 | 34.4 | - | [4] |
| **Klakar** | | | | | | | | | | | |
| 1979 * | 41 | - | 0 | - | 0 | 7 | - | 0 | 0 | - | [2,3] |
| **Krk** | | | | | | | | | | | |
| 1977 * | 44 | - | 0 | - | 0 | 18 | - | 0 | 0 | - | [2,3] |
| **Pula** | | | | | | | | | | | |
| 1978-81 #M | 33 | - | 1.4 | - | 1.7 | 11.2 | 0 | 0.6 | 3.6 | - | [6] |
| 1978-81 #Ch | 33 | - | 1.9 | - | 4.9 | 6.3 | 0.9 | 2.8 | 34.3 | - | [6] |
| **Labin** | | | | | | | | | | | |
| 1989 *M | 10 | 2 | 2 | 18 | 0 | 6 | 0 | 0 | 0 | 7 | [2,7] |

N=number of analyzed samples, 0=below detection limit
*=median, #=arithmetic mean
E=occupationally exposed workers,
M=mothers, Ch=children, C=cord blood

The concentration range found for most compounds was large. Where zero concentrations are reported they refer to levels below the limits of detection. These vary depending upon the compound and methodology used. For HCB and HCH isomers it is 0.1-2 μg $l^{-1}$ and for other compounds 1-5 μg $l^{-1}$.

Breakdown of results in Table 11.2 by region shows no obvious differences. If results are compared chronologically, there is a gradual decrease in median p,p'-DDE concentrations. PCB levels have remained similar since 1985. The presence of other compounds has been too infrequent and the levels too low to observe any trend.

Three studies reported serum levels in mothers and newborn children [4,6]. The concentration of most compounds was the same or higher in children's serum than in those of their mothers. One study found lower p,p'-DDE concentrations in cord blood than maternal serum [5].

Table 11.2 contains findings on sera taken from individuals having no accidental or occupational exposure to organochlorine compounds except for one group of 50 workers employed in the pesticide industry [5]. These workers handled several pesticides including organochlorine compounds. In comparison to the non-exposed population only their median p,p'-DDE level was higher. Five studies of PCB have been conducted [2,7]. One has been on serum samples taken from workers employed in the repair and maintenance of electrical equipment [2,8]. Ten people in that group were exposed as a result of an explosion of a transformer (in Zagreb) but no increased levels of total PCB were observed.

Apart from the compounds listed in Table 11.2, Bažulić *et al.* [4] could not detect aldrin, dieldrin, endrin, heptachlor, heptachlor epoxide or δ-HCH in sera taken from the general population.

PCP levels have been reported in serum and urine samples collected in and near to Zagreb during 1987-88 [9-11]. The median serum level in 20 agricultural workers handling pesticides which did not contain PCP was 12 $\mu g\ l^{-1}$ compared with 3,5 $\mu g\ l^{-1}$ found in 15 individuals who had not been exposed to pesticides [9,10]. Urine samples of 15 agricultural workers and 6 unexposed individuals had median PCP levels 2 and 3 $\mu g\ l^{-1}$ respectively [11].

## 11.3 Levels in Human Milk and Fat Tissue

Monitoring of organochlorine pesticides in human milk began in 1976 and of PCB in 1978. Levels of PCDD and PCDF were measured only in pooled samples collected over the period 1981-87. Samples were collected from mothers living in the north-west of the country (Zagreb, Karlovac, Sisak, Zabok, and Bjelovar), the north-east (Osijek), and in the northern Adriatic area (Labin, Krk).

Results are summarized in Table 11.3. All refer to mothers having had no accidental or occupational exposure to organochlorine compounds. Mothers were breast-feeding one child only and the majority were primiparae or secundiparae. Again, zero median concentrations indicate values below the limit of detection. This ranged from 0.1-5 $\mu g\ kg^{-1}$. All samples contained p,p'-DDE and PCB. The frequency with which other compounds were found was considerably less. Observed concentration ranges were again large. One account of PCB in human milk (20 samples collected in Sisak during 1985) stated only a range of 300-2700 $\mu g\ kg^{-1}$ [12].

**Table 11.3** **Median concentrations of organochlorine pesticides and PCB in human milk (µg kg$^{-1}$ milk fat)**

| Year/ Site | N | HCB | α-HCH | β-HCH | γ-HCH | p,p' DDE | o,p' DDT | p,p' DDD | p,p' DDT | PCB | Ref. |
|---|---|---|---|---|---|---|---|---|---|---|---|
| **Zagreb** | | | | | | | | | | | |
| 1977/79 *K | 34 | - | 0 | - | 0 | 30 | - | 0 | 0 | - | [5] |
| 1977/79 * | 37 | - | 0 | - | 0 | 63 | - | 3 | 0 | - | [5] |
| 1981/82 | 50 | 210 | - | 280 | - | 1900 | - | - | 180 | 620 | [13,14] |
| 1985 | 18 | 210 | 0 | 230 | 0 | 1060 | - | 0 | 130 | 440 | Unpubl. |
| 1986/87 P | 41 | 120 | 0 | 170 | 60 | 1480 | - | 0 | 70 | 450 | Unpubl. |
| 1987/89 | 22 | 60 | 0 | 40 | 0 | 620 | - | 0 | 0 | 290 | [15] |
| 1990/91 | 30 | 20 | 0 | 40 | 0 | 450 | - | 0 | 0 | 230 | [16] |
| **Karlovac** | | | | | | | | | | | |
| 1987 | 9 | 75 | 0 | 45 | 0 | 600 | 0 | 0 | 31 | 300 | Unpubl. |
| **Sisak** | | | | | | | | | | | |
| 1988 | 9 | 36 | 0 | 59 | 0 | 633 | 0 | 0 | 0 | 431 | Unpubl. |
| **Zabok and Bjelovar** (results expressed as arithmetic mean) | | | | | | | | | | | |
| 1976 &K | 27 | - | 78 | 150 | - | 1537 | 43 | 60 | 256 | - | [4] |
| **Osijek** (results expressed as arithmetic mean) | | | | | | | | | | | |
| 1978 * | 10 | 5.9 | 0 | 9.1 | 0 | 176 | - | 6.5 | 51 | 0 | [17,18] |
| 1979 * | 10 | 4.1 | 0 | 15.0 | 0.4 | 126 | - | 0 | 12 | - | [17,18] |
| **Island Krk** | | | | | | | | | | | |
| 1986/87 | 33 | 100 | 0 | 100 | 0 | 1080 | - | 0 | 160 | 500 | [7] |
| **Labin** | | | | | | | | | | | |
| 1989 | 20 | 0 | 0 | 50 | 0 | 550 | 0 | 0 | 0 | 270 | [7] |

N=number of samples, 0=below detection limit
* = results expressed in µg kg$^{-1}$ whole milk
& = results expressed in µg kg$^{-1}$ basis not stated
P = pooled sample prepared of N individual samples
K=colostrum, Unpubl. = unpublished own data

Comparison of median concentrations, expressed in terms of milk fat, indicates no difference in levels between regions. Results of p,p'-DDE and PCB levels suggest a decreasing trend during the past 10 years. Bažulić *et al.* could not detect aldrin, dieldrin, endrin, heptachlor, heptachlor epoxide or δ-HCH in breast milk [4].

Four pools of human milk samples have been analyzed for PCDD and PCDF (Table 11.4). Both groups of compounds were invariably present. In all samples octa-CDD had the highest concentration followed by 1,2,3,4,6,7,8-HpCDD, 2,3,4,7,8-PeCDF and the sum of 1,2,3,4,7,8-HxCDD and 1,2,3,6,7,8-HxCDD.

**Table 11.4** **Concentrations of PCDD and PCDF in pooled samples of human milk (ng kg$^{-2}$ milk fat)**

| Congener | Zagreb 1981-82 N=50 | Zagreb 1985 N=17 | Zagreb 1987 N=41 | Island Krk 1986-1987 N=41 |
|---|---|---|---|---|
| **Dioxins** | | | | |
| 2,3,7,8-TCDD | <1.0 | <1.0 | 1.9 | 1.6 |
| 1,2,3,7,8-PeCDD | 4.9 | 5.8 | 2.4 | 3.0 |
| 1,2,3,4,7,8-HxCDD | 3.6 | 3.5 | 20.4 | 15.1 |
| 1,2,3,6,7,8-HxCDD | 14 | 16 | | |
| 1,2,3,7,8,9-HxCDD | <0.5 | <0.8 | 4.7 | 4.2 |
| 1,2,3,4,6,7,8-HpCDD | 28 | 29 | 14.6 | 19.8 |
| octa-CDD | 95 | 116 | 90 | 101 |
| **Furans** | | | | |
| 2,3,7,8-TCDF | <1.2 | <1.9 | <2.0 | <3.1 |
| 1,2,3,7,8-PeCDF | - | - | <0.9 | 0.9 |
| 2,3,4,7,8-PeCDF | 27 | 23 | 9.7 | 11.3 |
| 1,2,3,4,7,8-HxCDF | 3.4 | 4.0 | 3.2 | 2.6 |
| 1,2,3,6,7,8-HxCDF | 3.1 | 4.1 | 2.9 | 3.0 |
| 1,2,3,7,8,9-HxCDF | <0.2 | <0.3 | - | - |
| 2,3,4,6,7,8-HxCDF | 1.4 | 1.2 | 1.6 | 1.3 |
| 1,2,3,4,6,7,8-HpCDF | 3.4 | 3.5 | 1.9 | 2.1 |
| 1,2,3,4,7,8,9-HpCD | <0.5 | <0.8 | - | - |
| octa-CDF | <4.7 | <8.0 | - | |
| Reference | [19] | [19] | [20] | [20] |

N=number of individual samples in the pool

Levels of PCP in 10 human milk samples collected in Zagreb during 1990-91 had a median value of 5.9 µg l$^{-1}$ [16].

Only 2 studies have been conducted on organochlorine pesticide and PCB levels in abdominal fat tissue. Fifty samples collected in Zagreb (1970-71) were reported to contain α-HCH, γ-HCH, p,p'-DDE, p,p'-DDT and p,p'-DDD, but not o,p'-DDT. The reported range was 1.9-1246 µg kg$^{-1}$, with γ-HCH having the highest concentration [21]. Fifteen samples collected in Sisak during 1985-1991 contained PCB in the range 700-5200 µg kg$^{-1}$ [12]. It is not clear from these reports whether concentrations have been expressed per weight of wet tissue or weight of fat extracted.

## 11.4 Levels in Food

Mussels and fish caught along the Adriatic coast, in fresh water fish from the river Kupa and from several fish ponds lying between the rivers Sava and Drava have been examined for organochlorine compounds (Tables 11.5 and 11.6). Levels in mussels and Goby fish during 1974-75 were considerably higher than those found 10 years later in sea fish from the same area. The PCB content of fish from the river Kupa increased considerably in 1986. This may be attributed to pollution of the river caused by improper disposal of PCB waste at Bela Krajina (Slovenia). Concentrations in carp from fish ponds were measured between 1973 and 1975 (Table 11.5). No explanation has been offered for the extra-ordinarily high concentration of γ-HCH in one of the ponds in 1974.

**Table 11.5** **Concentration ranges of organochlorine pesticides and PCB in mussels and fish (μg kg$^{-1}$ wet weight)**

| Type/Year Site | N | p,p' DDE | p,p' DDD | p,p' DDT | Dieldrin | PCB | Ref. |
|---|---|---|---|---|---|---|---|
| **Sea mussels and Goby fish (1974-75)** | | | | | | | |
| Istrian coast | 27 | 0- 80 | 0- 76 | 0-135 | 0-15 | 0-520 | [22] |
| Rijeka area | 33 | 0- 86 | 0- 48 | 0-131 | 0-10 | 0-356 | [22] |
| Zadar area | 18 | 0-113 | 0- 68 | 0- 63 | 0- 4 | 0-390 | [22] |
| Island Lošinj | 29 | 0-158 | 0-870 | 0-375 | 0-13 | 0-624 | [22] |
| **Several classes of sea fish** | | | | | | | |
| Rijeka area (1983) | - | 7-10 | 1-1.5 | 8.7-12 | 0.2-0.4 | 48-79 | [23] |
| Rijeka area (1987) | - | 0-6.2 | 0-2.5 | 0-3.4 | - | 16-120 | [23] |
| **Several classes of fish from the river Kupa** | | | | | | | |
| Letovanić (1985) | 7 | 0.6-6.9 | 1.1-14 | 0.5-5.0 | 0.1-3.4 | 49-659 | [24] |
| Sisak (1986) * | 47 | - | - | - | - | 0.1-42 | [12] |
| Petrinja (1987-88) | 28 | 0.4-175 | 0.2-20.1 | 0-7.6 | 0.1-2.2 | 70-1233 | [24] |

N=number of samples, 0=below detection limit,
*=results expressed in mg kg$^{-1}$, basis not stated

**Table 11.6** **Mean (arithmetic) concentrations of organochlorine pesticides in fish samples (µg kg⁻¹, basis not stated) collected from fish ponds [25]**

| Type/Year Site | N | α-HCH | δ-HCH | p,p' DDE | o,p' DDT | p,p' DDD | p,p' DDT | Dieldrin |
|---|---|---|---|---|---|---|---|---|
| **Carp - adipose tissue (1973)** | | | | | | | | |
| Pisarovina | 11 | 1203 | 499 | 52 | 0 | 24 | 22 | 24 |
| Crna Mlaka | 13 | 489 | 128 | 75 | 0 | 38 | 32 | 15 |
| **Carp - muscle tissue (1974)** | | | | | | | | |
| Pisarovina | 20 | 213 | 128 | 180 | 14 | 43 | 83 | 106 |
| Crna Mlaka | - | 47 | 100 | 135 | 7 | 30 | 36 | 4 |
| Lipovljani | - | 123 | 126 | 369 | 0 | 219 | 44 | 31 |
| Narta | 10 | 199 | 12257 | 423 | 88 | 33 | 66 | 14 |
| **Carp - muscle tissue (1975)** | | | | | | | | |
| Pisarovina | 25 | 213 | 128 | 180 | 14 | 43 | 83 | 105 |
| Crna Mlaka | 27 | 110 | 104 | 256 | 32 | 86 | 68 | 15 |
| Lipovljani | 24 | 303 | 248 | 405 | 68 | 331 | 82 | 44 |
| Narta | 34 | 172 | 181 | 105 | 19 | 34 | 22 | 41 |

N=number of samples, 0=below detection limit

Levels of organochlorine pesticide found in samples tested by the food inspection authorities during 1985-1989 are summarized in Table 11.7. Samples were collected from food markets throughout the country. Levels of organochlorine pesticide and PCB in foods from markets in Zagreb (1985-1992) and from households in Karlovac along the river Kupa (1987) are listed in Table 11.8. Analysis of a small number of specimens from Karlovac did not indicate any increase in PCB levels following contamination of the river. All samples listed in Table 11.8 contained p,p'-DDE and the majority also PCB. The frequency with which p,p'-DDE and PCB occurred in samples listed in Tables 11.5—11.7 was not stated.

**Table 11.7** **Mean (arithmetic) concentrations of organochlorine pesticides in food samples (µg kg⁻¹ fat) collected from markets throughout the country (1985-1989)**

| Type of food | N | HCB | α-HCH | γ-HCH | DDT-complex | Ref. |
|---|---|---|---|---|---|---|
| Milk and milk products | 438 | 7 | 3 | 24 | 83 | [26] |
| Meat and meat products | 733 | 3 | 2 | 25 | 75 | [26] |
| Fish and fish products | 153 | 5 | 2 | 25 | 127 | [26] |
| Pig adipose tissue | 60 | - | 0 | 12 | 65 | [27] |
| Cow adipose tissue | 28 | - | 0 | 5 | 61 | [27] |

N=number of samples, 0-below detection limit

**Table 11.8** **Median concentrations of organochlorine pesticides and PCB in food samples (μg kg⁻¹) collected in Zagreb and Karlovac (Unpublished own data and [28])**

| Site Type/Year | N | HCB | α-HCH | β-HCH | γ-HCH | p,p' DDE | o,p' DDT | p,p' DDD | p,p' DDT | PCB |
|---|---|---|---|---|---|---|---|---|---|---|
| **Zagreb** | | | | | | | | | | |
| Cow's milk | | | | | | | | | | |
| 1985-86 | 10 | 63 | 25 | 0 | 38 | 43 | - | 0 | 0 | 108 |
| 1989 | 10 | 16 | 9 | 12 | 7 | 25 | 0 | 0 | 0 | 123 |
| 1992 | 10 | 7 | 10 | 0 | 26 | 47 | 0 | 0 | 0 | 73 |
| Butter | | | | | | | | | | |
| 1985-86 | 10 | 7 | 10 | 0 | 6 | 17 | - | 0 | 0 | 26 |
| 1989 | 10 | 7 | 3 | 5 | 1 | 16 | 0 | 0 | 0 | 28 |
| 1992 | 10 | 3 | 0 | 0 | 5 | 5 | 0 | 0 | 0 | 20 |
| Pig's fat | | | | | | | | | | |
| 1985-86 | 10 | 17 | 2 | 0 | 3 | 9 | - | 0 | 10 | 13 |
| 1989 | 10 | 6 | 0 | 3 | 12 | 4 | 4 | 3 | 3 | 17 |
| 1992 | 10 | 2 | 0 | 0 | 2 | 5 | 0 | 0 | 0 | 19 |
| Pig's fat tissue | | | | | | | | | | |
| 1985-86 | 10 | 9 | 0 | 0 | 12 | 8 | - | 0 | 6 | 14 |
| 1989 | 10 | 2 | 2 | 3 | 0 | 7 | 0 | 0 | 0 | 19 |
| 1992 | 10 | 3 | 0 | 0 | 4 | 6 | 0 | 0 | 0 | 12 |
| Hen's fat tissue | | | | | | | | | | |
| 1985-86 | 10 | 5 | 2 | 0 | 3 | 64 | - | 0 | 14 | 51 |
| 1989 | 10 | 4 | 3 | 3 | 9 | 6 | 0 | 0 | 0 | 13 |
| 1992 | 10 | 2 | 0 | 3 | 3 | 4 | 0 | 0 | 0 | 14 |
| **Karlovac** | | | | | | | | | | |
| Cow's milk | | | | | | | | | | |
| 1987 | 1 | 30 | 14 | 0 | 16 | 20 | 0 | 0 | 0 | 0 |
| Pig's fat | | | | | | | | | | |
| 1987 | 7 | 11 | 2 | 0 | 0 | 11 | 0 | 0 | 0 | 7 |

N=number of samples, 0=below detection limit

## 11.5 PCB Pattern in Human and Animal Samples

In all studies presented in this chapter the total concentration of PCB was calculated using Aroclor 1260 as standard. Comparison of the chromatograms of analyzed samples with Aroclor 1242, 1254, 1016 and 1260 indicated that Aroclor 1260 was preferred. Only data taken from references [12, 17, 22-24] have been expressed relative to other PCB standards (Aroclor 1242, Aroclor 1254, Pyralen 1500 or Clophen).

**Table 11.9** **PCB pattern in human and animal samples [29]. N=number of analyzed samples. Number of positive samples is given in parenthesis**

| $RRT_{DDE}$ | Percent of total | | | | | | | No. of Cl atoms |
|---|---|---|---|---|---|---|---|---|
| . | Human serum | Human milk | Cow milk | Cow butter | Pig fat | Pig fat tissue | Hen fat tissue | |
| 70 | 12.8 | 5.5 | 16.7 | 12.7 | 13.9 | 33.4 | 12.4 | 5 |
| | (16) | (76) | (13) | (8) | (5) | (2) | (6) | |
| 84 | 11.6 | 3.6 | 10.5 | 15.0 | 11.2 | 16.5 | 6.0 | 5 |
| | (16) | (72) | (11) | (8) | (11) | (9) | (8) | |
| 117 | 4.2 | 2.1 | 2.7 | 0 | 8.6 | 3.3 | 6.2 | 6 |
| | (9) | (10) | (8) | (0) | (6) | (5) | (2) | |
| 125 | 7.8 | 8.4 | 14.7 | 18.8 | 25.3 | 34.5 | 15.9 | 5+6 |
| | (13) | (77) | (13) | (8) | (14) | (9) | (9) | |
| 146 | 16.4 | 30.6 | 19.2 | 17.2 | 17.4 | 19.2 | 23.7 | 5+6 |
| | (16) | (78) | (13) | (10) | (13) | (6) | (8) | |
| 203 | 7.1 | 9.1 | 7.1 | 7.6 | 11.6 | 12.2 | 12.7 | 7 |
| | (15) | (770 | (7) | (4) | (15) | (5) | (9) | |
| 232+244 | 5.2 | 6.5 | 6.6 | 13.2 | 10.2 | 12.4 | 4.8 | 7 |
| | (6) | (67) | (5) | (3) | (7) | (3) | (5) | |
| 280 | 10.5 | 12.9 | 9.8 | 6.7 | 10.0 | 10.3 | 9.4 | 7 |
| | (14) | (78) | (11) | (9) | (16) | (5) | (9) | |
| 332 | 16.9 | 4.5 | 11.4 | 15.3 | 6.9 | 11.1 | 4.9 | 7 |
| | (15) | (78) | (6) | (9) | (12) | (1) | (9) | |
| 360+372 | 0 | 2.2 | 0 | 0 | 7.5 | 0 | 3.7 | 7 |
| | (0) | (17) | (0) | (0) | (4) | (0) | (2) | |
| 448 | 0 | 1.2 | 0 | 0 | 0 | 0 | 0 | 7 |
| | (0) | (3) | (0) | (0) | (0) | (0) | (0) | |
| 528 | 1.6 | 1.0 | 4.8 | 0 | 4.4 | 0 | 0.6 | 7 |
| | (1) | (19) | (2) | (0) | (5) | (0) | (1) | |
| N | 16 | 78 | 13 | 12 | 17 | 10 | 10 | |

No isomer specific analysis of PCB has been performed on any sample. However, over the period 1981 to 1987 chromatograms of some human and animal samples have been analyzed according to the Sawyer method [30] and peaks assigned relative to the retention time of DDE ($RRT_{DDE}$) (Table 11.9). Peaks 70, 84, 125, 146, 203, 280 and 332 were present in nearly all human samples, and peak 146 in most animal samples. Peaks 360+372, and 448 have not been found in any human serum sample and peak 448 in no animal sample.

## 11.6 Calculation of the Intake of Organochlorine Compounds by Adults and Breast-Fed Infants

Two reports have been published on the calculated intake of organochlorine compounds by infants being fed only with maternal milk [10,14]. Calculations have been based on the assumption that infants consume 130 g milk $kg^{-1}$ b.w. $d^{-1}$, the milk having a fat content of 3.7 % (w/w). Estimated daily intakes are given in Tables 11.10 and 11.11. Data in Table 11.10 are derived from concentrations found in milk samples collected in Zagreb during 1981-82 [14] and in Table 11.11 on samples collected in Zagreb and Labin during 1987-89 [10].

**Table 11.10** **Calculated daily intake of organochlorine compounds by breast-fed infants [14]**

| Compound | Intake (µg $kg^{-1}$ b.w. $d^{-1}$) Median | Maximum |
|---|---|---|
| HCB | 1.0 | 2.4 |
| β-HCH | 1.3 | 5.3 |
| p,p'-DDE | 9.1 | 23 |
| p,p'-DDT | 0.87 | 2.1 |
| PCB | 3.0 | 8.2 |

**Table 11.11** **Calculated daily intake of organochlorine compounds from food [10]. Zero stands for values below detection limit**

| Compound | Intake range (µg $kg^{-1}$ b.w. $d^{-1}$) | | |
|---|---|---|---|
| | Breast-fed infants | Nursing mothers | Non-nursing women |
| HCB | 0-0.5 | 0.002-1.1 | 0.002-0.7 |
| α-HCH | 0-0.2 | 0.05-1.5 | 0.03-0.7 |
| γ-HCH | 0-0.2 | 0.03-1.2 | 0.02-0.6 |
| DDT-complex | 0.7-7.4 | 0.5-2.4 | 0.2-1.2 |

Information given in Table 11.4 enables the intake of PCDD and PCDF by breast-fed infants to be estimated. The concentrations of PCDD and PCDF expressed as 2,3,7,8-TCDD toxic equivalents are 7.1, 7.3, 5.4 and 5.4 ng $kg^{-1}$ milk fat respectively for the 4 studies listed in Table 11.4. They are calculated applying the US EPA model [20]. The average intake of PCDD and PCDF by infants in European countries has been reported by the World Health Organization to be 70 pg $kg^{-1}$ b.w. $d^{-1}$, expressed in TCDD toxic equivalents [20,31]. This calculation is based upon the assumption that infants consume 120 g milk $kg^{-1}$ b.w. $d^{-1}$ and that the milk fat content is 3.5 % w/w. Applying the same criteria to the figures in Table 11.4 the average intake by infants would be 27 pg $kg^{-1}$ b.w. $d^{-1}$.

The intake of organochlorine compounds by adults has been calculated for 2 groups of women: nursing mothers (N=15), and non-nursing women of the same age (N=6) [10]. Food consumption was assessed from a survey conducted in Zagreb in 1989, where women kept a diary of their eating habits for a period of 7 days [10]. The daily intake was calculated from the concentration range of the organochlorine compounds in food [26] and is given in Table 11.11. The intake of PCB and DDT complex from fish was calculated for a population group (N=140) living along the river Kupa [24]. The consumption of fish over the years 1985-88 was assessed from questionnaires. The daily intake of PCB ranged from 0.008 to 3.55 µg $kg^{-1}$ b.w. and of the DDT-complex up to 0.158 µg $kg^{-1}$ b.w.

The acceptable daily intake (ADI) for adults suggested by the World Health Organization [32] is 20 µg $kg^{-1}$ b.w. for the DDT-complex (DDT plus metabolites) and 10 µg $kg^{-1}$ b.w. for $\gamma$-HCH. The intake reported for women [10] is considerably lower. It follows from Tables 11.10 and 11.11 that the calculated intake of the DDT-complex into infants approaches the ADI for adults, while for $\gamma$-HCH it is >50-times lower. The estimated intake of PCB by infants is about the same as the average of 4.2 µg $kg^{-1}$ b.w. $d^{-1}$ assessed by the World Health Organization for infants in European countries [31].

## 11.7 Conclusion

Organochlorine pesticides and PCB are widely distributed in human and animal tissues collected in Croatia. PCDD and PCDF are present in human milk. Measured levels are comparable to those reported for countries in Western Europe and North America. Levels of the DDT-complex appear to be decreasing gradually.

These data will form the basis for evaluating risk assessments and will also be used to assess contamination of the environment caused during the present war, particularly from PCB contained material.

## 11.8 References


[1] Reiner, E., Krauthacker, B., Stipčević, M., and Štefanac, Z., *Pestic. Monit. J.*, 1977, **11**, 54-55.

[2] Krauthacker, B., *Bull. Environ. Contam. Toxicol.*, 1993, **50**, 8-11.

[3] Krauthacker, B., Alebić-Kolbah, T., Kralj, M., Tkalčević, B., and Reiner, E., *Int. Arch. Occup. Environ. Health*, 1980, **45**, 217-220.

[4] Bažulić, D., Kipčić, D., Štampar-Plasaj, B., Jerić, J., Bujanović, V., and Juzbašić, N., *Arh. hig. rada* 1977, **29**, 125-128 (in Croatian).

[5] Krauthacker, B., Alebić-Kolbah,T., Buntić, A., Tkalčević, B., and Reiner, E., *Int. Arch. Occup. Environ. Health*, 1980, **46**, 267-273.

[6] Bažulić, D., Štampar-Plasaj, B., Bujanović, V., Stojanovski, N., Nastev, B., Rudelić, I., Sišul, N., and Žužek, A., *Bull. Environ. Contam. Toxicol.*, 1984, **32**, 265-268.

[7] Krauthacker, B., *Bull. Environ. Contam. Toxicol.*, 1991, **46**, 797-802.

[8] Krauthacker, B., *Levels of Polychlorinated Biphenyls (PCBs) in Human Blood Serum Collected from Environmentally and Occupationally Exposed Populations in Zagreb, Yugoslavia*, in: DIOXIN 90 Short Papers, Hutzinger, O., and Fiedler, H., (Eds.), Bayreuth 1990, **1**, 251-254.

[9] Krauthacker, B., *Pentachlorophenol (PCP) in the Serum of Agricultural Workers*, in: Abstracts of the 'XI Meeting of Chemists of Croatia', Zagreb 1989, 128 (in Croatian).

[10] Krauthacker, B., *Human Exposure to Organochlorine Compounds*, Report to US EPA on Project PN 770, 1990, 1-45.

[11] Vasilić, Ž., Fingler, S., and Drevenkar, V., *Frasenius J. Anal. Chem.*, 1991, **341**, 732-737.

[12] Šmit, Z., and Kodrić-Šmit, M., *Some Aspects of the Environment Contamination with Commercial Mixtures of Chlorinated Biphenyls*, in: Proceedings of the Meeting 'Ecological Danger During Exploitation of Energy Transformers and Capacitors Insulated with Askarel', Stubičke Toplice 1992, 41-47 (in Croatian).

[13] *Assessment of Human Exposure to Selected Organochlorine Compounds through Biological Monitoring*, Slorach, S.A., and Vaz, R., (Eds.), GEMS, UNEP, WHO, Swedish National Food Administration, Uppsala, 1983, 1-134.

[14] Krauthacker, B., Kralj, M., Tkalčević, B., and Reiner, E., *Int. Arch. Occup. Environ. Health*, 1986, **58**, 69-74.

[15] Votava, A., Krauthacker, B., Pokrajac, D., Goluža, I., Vlahović, I., and Raić, F., *Organochlorine Compounds in the Milk of Nursing Mothers from the Zagreb Area*, in: Booklet of Abstracts of 'Second Pediatric Alps-Adriatic Symposium', Maribor, 1990, 43.

[16] Krauthacker, B., *Human Exposure to PCDDs and PCDFs*, Report to US EPA on Project PN 958, 1993, 1-32.

[17] Kodrić-Šmit, M., *Gas Chromatographic Determination of Organochlorine Pollutants in Human Milk*, M. Sc. Thesis, University of Zagreb, 1980, 1-110 (in Croatian).

[18] Kodrić-Šmit, M., Šmit, Z., and Olie, K., *Pestic. Monit. J.*, 1980, **14**, 1-2

[19] Krauthacker, B., Reiner, E., Lindström, G., and Rappe, C., *Arh. hig. rada toksikol.*, 1989, **40**, 9-14.

[20] *Levels of PCBs, PCDDs, and PCDFs in Breast Milk,* Yrjänheikki, E.J, (Ed.), Environmental Health Series No. 34, World Health Organization Regional Office for Europe, Copenhagen 1989, 1-92.

[21] Žarković, G., Čustović-Begović, F., Adamović, V., Bauer, K., and Jan, J., *Arh. hig. rada*, 1973, **24**, 381-394 (in Croatian).

[22] Picer, M., Picer, N., and Ahel, M., *Pestic. Monit. J.*, 1978, **12**, 102-112.

[23] Šilipetar-Picer, N., *Chlorinated Insecticides and Polychlorinated Biphenyls in the Rijeka Bay Aquatorium*, Ph. D. Thesis, University of Zagreb, 1989, 1-212 (in Croatian).

[24] Perkov, S., *Daily Intake of Polychlorinated Biphenyls in Populations of the Petrinja and Sisak Region*, M. Sc. Thesis, University of Zagreb, 1990, 1-106 (in Croatian).

[25] Radaković, M., Delak, M., and Žuković, J., *Hrana i ishrana*, 1980, **21**, 187-195 (in Croatian).

[26] Kipčić, D., and Vukušić, J., *Pesticides as Contaminants of Foodstuff - Results of Latest Research in Croatia*, in: Proceedings of 'XVII Meeting of Nutritional-Sanitary Chemists', Opatija 1989, 1-7 (in Croatian).

[27] Kipčić, D., Vukušić, J., and Bešić, J., *Chlorinated Pesticides and Polychlorinated Biphenyls in Meat from the Territory of Croatia*, in: Proceedings of 'XV Meeting of Nutritional-Sanitary Chemists', Osijek 1986, 1-10 (in Croatian).

[28] Krauthacker, B., Reiner, E., Simeon, V., and Škrinjarić-Špoljar, M., *Arh. hig. rada toksikol.*, 1988, **39**, 27-31.

[29] Krauthacker, B., *PCB Pattern in Human and Animal Samples Collected in Croatia*, in: DIOXIN '92 Extended Abstracts, Tampere 1992, **9**, 119-121.

[30] Sawyer, L.D., *J. Assoc. Off. Anal. Chem.*, 1978, **61**, 272-281.

[31] *PCBs, PCDDs and PCDFs in Breast Milk: Assessment of Health Risks*, Environmental Health Series No. 29, World Health Organization Regional Office for Europe, Copenhagen 1988, 1-116.

[32] *Pesticide Residues in Food-1984 Evaluations. Report Sponsored Jointly by FAO and WHO*, FAO Plant Production and Protection Paper 62, Food and Agriculture Organization, Rome, 1985, 33-35.

# 12. Heavy Metal Dietary Intake: A European Comparison

Maja Blanuša

## 12.1 Introduction

Monitoring human food and the evaluation of daily dietary intake of toxic metals is a part of international efforts to assess the integral human exposure to various pollutants. The greatest attention is presently paid to lead, cadmium and mercury. They are released continuously into the environment, and therefore, reflect increasing levels in human food.

To ascertain whether a general population is at risk or not, it is necessary to estimate the actual dietary intake of a toxic metal by comparison with provisional tolerable weekly intakes (PTWIs) [1]. This estimation is a measure of human exposure to pollutant and thus indispensable for risk assessment.

Several international monitoring programs were initiated and coordinated by various UN agencies. In the late 1970s the joint UNEP/FAO/WHO Food Contamination Monitoring Programme was initiated with the objective to estimate the intake of chemicals via food and thus enabling the total intake of the contaminant to be estimated [2,3]. In 1985, the International Atomic Energy Agency initiated a Coordinated Research Program to obtain reliable comparative data on the average daily dietary intake of 23 elements in 15 countries among which lead, cadmium and mercury were included [4]. WHO and UNEP coordinated Human Exposure Assessment Location Studies (HEALs) as a pilot project at the beginning of 1980s. It included human exposure monitoring study for lead and cadmium which involved the sampling of duplicate diets, exposure to airborne particles, blood and faeces. Such exposure monitoring was carried out in 1988 on small groups of women in 4 countries [5].

In all of these internationally coordinated programs quality control of the methods applied in various countries was performed. Therefore, it is assumed that the results obtained are more reliable and can be compared.

This review will be focused on available literature data of concentration levels of lead, cadmium, and mercury in different food items in Croatia and in other republics of former Yugoslavia, compared to other eastern and western European countries. The evaluation of the daily dietary intake of metals in general population, obtained by different methods will be also presented compared to other countries. Although the author is aware of the high risk groups within the country population (small children and pregnant women), the data presented here apply only to adult general population, as such data from other countries are available in the literature.

The data presented for Croatia were obtained before the Serbian aggression on its territory. The areas contaminated by the damaged installations or stocks of chemicals may in future reflect higher contamination of food. This aspect should be taken into consideration in future studies. Some food monitoring measurements are in progress already.

## 12.2 Methodology

Lead, cadmium and mercury occur in food samples at low concentrations and, therefore, stringent precautious are necessary to overcome problems of contamination and inaccurate determinations. Therefore every laboratory that attempts to be engaged in trace element analysis of food, must, as a rule validate the analytical procedure by analyzing the available dietary reference material before generating new data [6]. After sampling of different food items it is generally accepted that washing of vegetables prior to analysis is undertaken normally, as is normal in culinary practice. Dry ashing procedure for lead and cadmium analysis is the preferred method of mineralization compared to wet ashing because of the possibility of lower contamination. Although reports in the literature do not describe methodology in detail, it has been found that dry ashing is adequate up to 500 °C [7]. It does not cause losses of lead or cadmium if performed in quartz, platinum or silica crucibles. Porcelain crucibles can cause losses (incorporation into porcelain) or leaching of lead [8].

Preparation of samples for total and/or inorganic mercury analysis are mostly performed in closed vessels under pressure and at lower temperatures, usually up to 140 °C [9].

The widest used methodology for analytical estimation of all 3 elements is atomic absorption spectrophotometry (AAS). Lead and cadmium can be measured either by flame (FAAS) with preconcentration or by electrothermal (ETAAS) method. For lead and cadmium analysis in food it is essential also to compensate for matrix effects, which is usually performed by continuum source background corrector and by employing the technique of standard additions [10]. Total mercury is usually measured by cold vapour atomic absorption (CVAAS) after reduction of mercury with stannous chloride for inorganic and with $SnCl_2$ + $CdCl_2$ for total mercury [11]. Over last 20 years the Magos method of inorganic and total mercury analysis has been modified and improved [12-14]. The sensitivity of the method has been significantly improved by amalgamation with gold prior to atomic absorption [15]. Methylmercury determination is performed preferably by gas chromatography [16] instead of indirect method for total and inorganic CVAAS method.

In most literature data included in this review analytical methods were validated by analyzing reference material. Due to such selection some publications from former Yugoslav republics had to be disregarded. The fact that it is not sure whether all the studies were performed with adequate quality control, the comparison of the data has to be taken with some precaution. An international quality control performed in all eastern European countries would be highly welcomed.

## 12.3 Metals Examined

### 12.3.1 Lead

Lead is widely distributed in foods, but the lead content of staple foods such as bread, vegetables, fruit and meat is generally small [17]. A main source of lead could be the lead soldered cans which was regulated by laws in most developed countries since 1972. A limit of 0.3 (beverages) to 1 (fish) mg Pb $kg^{-1}$ of food was regulated by former Yugoslav federal law in 1983. This was adjusted to regulations of other European countries which had a general limit of 1 mg Pb $kg^{-1}$ of food after 1980. Eastern European countries are limiting heavy metals in food at similar levels [18]. The combustion gases from gasoline are a significant source of lead emission in all European countries. Higher concentrations of lead in food are found in vegetation grown near heavy traffic roads in Great Britain [19,20]. This will be less important in future since developed countries have already lowered gasoline lead content and the lead free gasoline is increasingly used. The same policy will be implemented in eastern countries but with more difficulties due to economic problems, and lack of refinery facilities to produce lead low gasoline. Food contamination with lead also originates from high density centres particularly adjacent to lead smelters and heat and power generating plants. High lead levels in soil, vegetables as well as in meals were found in lead smelter region in Republic of Slovenia [21,22] even 10 years after the reduction of smelter lead air pollution. In the whole region of the former Yugoslav republics a study performed by household interviews for the period between 1984 and 1987 which revealed that the main food commodity consumed in the form of bread, pasta or other products was wheat. It formed 37%, milk 25%, vegetables 16% and meat 8% of all main food commodities consumed [23]. Whilst these food items have relatively low concentration of lead, they form the majority of food items consumed. Table 12.1 presents lead concentration data in main food commodities lately reported in some countries. Latest publication from Sweden [24] reports the decrease in lead levels (meat, fish and vegetables) compared to 1984 [25]. Although environmental contamination has reduced within last several years, this is explained by significant improvements to analytical methods. All other data from other European countries appears to be within similar same levels, but substantially higher than Sweden.

For the evaluation of daily dietary intake of lead, duplicate diet and total diet methods were presented in Table 12.2. Data were reproduced from original articles with as much information (mean, range and number of subjects or diets analyzed) as possible. While earlier reports of daily dietary lead intake of general population was generally higher, *ie*, 100 in the United Kingdom in 1982 [26], and 40 μg $d^{-1}$ $person^{-1}$ in 1989 [27] there are still in some countries rather high values, *ie*, Italy 410 [28], and Poland 282 μg $d^{-1}$ $person^{-1}$ [29]. These values are close to PTWI which amounts for lead 430 μg $day^{-1}$ $person^{-1}$. The majority of European countries fall between 25 and 120 μg. Two different methods of evaluating daily intake, duplicate diet and total diet study, indicated very similar values in most countries. In 2 European countries within the UNEP/WHO coordinated program faecal elimination of lead was measured to check the intake obtained from duplicate diet, since lead intestinal absorption is known to be very small in adults.

**Table 12.1** **Lead and cadmium concentrations in foodstuffs of some European countries (µg kg⁻¹ fresh weight)**

| Species/Country | Lead Mean | Lead Range | (n) | Cadmium Mean | Cadmium Range | (n) | Ref. |
|---|---|---|---|---|---|---|---|
| **Cabbage** | | | | | | | |
| Croatia | 19 | 9-24 | (3) | 161 | 47-283 | (3) | [47] |
| Poland | 126 | <10-1490 | (66) | 9 | 1-101 | (66) | [18] |
| Sweden | 12 | 3-27 | (24) | 4 | 1-17 | (25) | [25] |
| **Carrots** | | | | | | | |
| Croatia | 31 | 6-75 | (6) | 40 | 9-63 | (6) | [47] |
| Poland | 80 | <10-760 | (113) | 52 | <1-480 | (113) | [18] |
| Spain | 191 | 107-359 | (6) | 12 | 7-24 | (6) | [51] |
| Sweden | 5 | <5-8 | (6) | 22 | 4-48 | (6) | [24] |
| United Kingdom | 40 | 20-90 | (16) | - | | - | [27] |
| **Lettuce** | | | | | | | |
| Croatia | 39 | 19-129 | (7) | 29 | 15-58 | (6) | [47] |
| Poland | 129 | <10-620 | (29) | 25 | <1-100 | (29) | [18] |
| Spain | 178 | 117-242 | (9) | 10 | 6-15 | (9) | [51] |
| Sweden | 17 | 12-24 | (8) | 8 | 2-18 | (8) | [24] |
| **Cows milk (µg l⁻¹)** | | | | | | | |
| Croatia | 3 | 1-8 | (34) | - | | - | [48] |
| Germany | 1 | | (6) | 0.06 | | - | [52] |
| Sweden | 6 | 3-9 | (4) | 1 | 1-1 | (4) | [25] |
| **Potatoes** | | | | | | | |
| Croatia | 10 | 7-17 | (4) | 24 | 18-31 | (3) | [47] |
| Poland | 68 | <10-540 | (90) | 18 | <1-90 | (90) | [18] |
| Spain | 195 | 128-242 | (8) | 13 | 8-17 | (8) | [51] |
| Sweden | <5 | <5-7 | (8) | 17 | 8-46 | (8) | [24] |
| United Kingdom | 40 | 20-60 | (9) | - | | - | [27] |
| **Tomatoes** | | | | | | | |
| Croatia | 13 | 10,15 | (2) | 11 | 3,19 | (2) | [47] |
| Poland | 65 | <10-865 | (70) | 17 | <1-410 | (70) | [18] |
| Spain | 82 | 45-119 | (7) | 7 | <6-8 | (7) | [51] |
| Sweden | <5 | <5-7 | (2) | 2 | 1-4 | (2) | [24] |
| **Wheat, bread or cereals** | | | | | | | |
| Macedonia | - | | - | 10 | | - | [49] |
| Serbia | - | | - | 21 | 9-36 | (17) | [49] |
| Slovenia | 40 | | - | 50 | 58,41 | (2) | [49] |
| Sweden | 8 | <5-33 | (55) | 25 | 14-47 | (55) | [24] |
| **Cattle meat** | | | | | | | |
| Croatia | - | | - | - | 17-55 | (581) | [50] |
| Poland | 40 | <10-100 | (93) | 6 | <5-20 | (92) | [18] |
| Sweden | <5 | <5-8 | (34) | 1 | <1-3 | (34) | [24] |
| **Cattle kidney** | | | | | | | |
| Croatia | - | | - | - | 300-650 | | [50] |
| Poland | 210 | 40-860 | (291) | 610 | 30-3600 | (291) | [18] |
| Sweden | 79 | 5-300 | (187) | 350 | 23-6400 | (187) | [24] |
| **Cattle liver** | | | | | | | |
| Croatia | - | | - | - | 110-160 | | [50] |
| Poland | 160 | 10-910 | (290) | 120 | 5-850 | (290) | [18] |
| Sweden | 47 | 10-160 | (33) | 70 | 1-200 | (33) | [24] |

In Sweden, faecal lead elimination using the duplicate diet method were confirmed at 23 and 26 µg $d^{-1}$, in Croatia faecal elimination was substantially higher than the value obtained by duplicate diet method, 49 and 15 µg $d^{-1}$, respectively [5]. The faecal elimination method appears generally to be the more reliable method for estimation of daily intake, but less popular and widespread to assess general population exposure to lead from food intake.

**Table 12.2** **Daily dietary intake of lead and cadmium (µg $d^{-1}$ $person^{-1}$) in various European countries**

| Country/[Ref.] | | Lead Mean | Lead Range | (n) | Cadmium Mean | Cadmium Range | (n) | Method |
|---|---|---|---|---|---|---|---|---|
| **Croatia** | [53] | 15 | 6.1-37 | (17) | 8.5 | 3.5-18.6 | (17) | DD |
| | | 49 | 8.8-112 | (17) | 15 | 5.0-25 | (17) | FE |
| **Denmark** | [54] | 70 | 0-957 | (100) | 15 | 3-102 | (100) | DD |
| **Germany** | [55] | 23.2 ♂ | | (7) | 11.5 ♂ | | (7) | DD |
| | | 20.8 ♀ | | (7) | 9.7 ♀ | | (7) | DD |
| | [56] | 30.8 ♂ | | | 14.0 ♂ | | | TD |
| | | 25.2 ♀ | | | 10.9 ♀ | | | TD |
| **Hungary** | [39] | 120 | | | 5.8 | | | TD |
| **Italy** | [28] | 410 | | | 166 | | | TD |
| **Netherlands** | | | | | | | | |
| | [57] | 34 | 7-210 | (110) | 10 | 3-55 | (110 | DD |
| | [58] | 32 | 26-41 | (10) | 21 | 17-33 | (10) | TD |
| **Poland** | [29] | 281.5 | | (187) | 32.3 | | (187) | TD |
| **Spain** | [59] | 115 | | | 56 | | | DD |
| | [60] | 170 | 60-357 | (25) | 17 | 8-33 | (25) | TD |
| **Sweden** | [5] | 26 | 13-40 | (15) | 8.5 | 5.7-14 | (15) | DD |
| | | 23 | 10-40 | (15) | 8.4 | 5.5-12 | (15) | FE |
| | [61] | 27 | 15-45 | (7) | 10 | 6.2-10.7 | (7) | TD |
| | [62] | 17 | | | 12 | | | TD |
| **United** | [27] | 44 | - | | - | | - | DD |
| **Kingdom** | | - | 20-60 | | - | | - | TD |

DD=Duplicate diet method; TD=Total diet method;
FE=Faecal elimination method;
n=Number of subjects included in the DD study or number of TD analyzed

### 12.3.2 Cadmium

The largest quantity of cadmium in the environment originates from waste disposal, a further 4 major sources are: coal combustion, iron and steel production, phosphate fertilizers and zinc production. It has been estimated that cadmium transports to soils from the atmosphere and phosphate-fertilizers at the rate 9 g $ha^{-1}$ $y^{-1}$ [30]. Cadmium deposited on soil enters the plant easily, especially in acidic soils [31]. Higher levels of cadmium are accumulated in leafy vegetables. Therefore, the present acidification of soils may increase the availability of cadmium. A combination of increased cadmium levels in air and increased soil acidity may in future contribute significantly to cadmium concentrations in food [32]. Tobacco plant naturally accumulates relatively high cadmium concentrations in its leaves. As a result, this material represents an important source of exposure for smokers [33]. Biological monitoring surveys of the general population have shown that cigarette smoking can cause significant increases in the concentration of cadmium in the kidney [34,35]. Food is another principal source of cadmium in humans which contributes equally to the cadmium body burden as smoking. Cadmium in food is limited in Croatia from 0.03 in beverages to 1.5 mg $kg^{-1}$ in canned food and crabs which is similar to other European countries. Cadmium concentrations in main food items consumed in this region are shown in Table 12.1 compared to other countries. It is difficult to compare food items with very low level of cadmium because of analytical uncertainties or small number of samples analyzed. In general, it appears that Croatia and other republics of former Yugoslavia have similar levels of cadmium in main food commodities as Poland and both regions are slightly higher than Sweden (Table 12.1). Aquatic food species including fish, crabs, oysters and shrimp bioaccumulate cadmium [36]. Monitoring data for cadmium in these food items are not available in Croatian regions.

Daily dietary intake of cadmium estimated by duplicate diet and total diet method fall in general between 6 and 20 µg $d^{-1}$ $person^{-1}$ (Table 12.2). Exception is Italy with daily cadmium intake of 166 µg, which is higher than the recommended PTWI value which is 64 µg $d^{-1}$ $person^{-1}$ [28].

Faecal elimination method, again as for lead, confirmed the daily intake of cadmium obtained by duplicate diet method in Sweden. In Croatia faecal elimination method showed higher values.

### 12.3.3 Mercury

Mercury is present naturally in the earth's crust and evaporates through the action of volcanic gases and from the oceans. Main anthropogenic sources of mercury are: burning of fossil fuels, pollution of water by mine tailings and the chloralkali industry. The use of mercury is reducing but high concentrations remain present in sediments associated with the industrial mercury applications. Additionally, some mercury compounds were used in agriculture as fungicides. Mercuric salts and particularly organic mercury, are taken up readily by aquatic invertebrates. Fish also absorbs the metal and retains it in tissues, principally as methylmercury, although most of the environmental mercury to which fish are exposed is inorganic. There is an indication that bacterial action leads to methylation in aquatic systems, either in the environment or in bacteria associated with fish gills, surface, or gut [37].

It has been found that the ratio of methylmercury to total mercury of different species is approximately constant and that fish contributes to the contamination of the aquatic food chain with MeHg [38].

A significant amount of data on mercury concentration in Mediterranean fish has been collected under the UNEP Coordinated Mediterranean Pollution Monitoring and Research Programme. In general, levels of mercury were higher in fish from the Mediterranean Sea than from the Atlantic, Pacific and Indian Oceans [3]. It could be explained by the fact that active mining sites in the Mediterranean account for about 50% of the world's production of mercury.

Total mercury in food in Croatia is limited from 0.01 in beverages to 1.5 mg $kg^{-1}$ in canned fish, which is substantially higher than in other countries where the highest value for fish is 0.5 mg $kg^{-1}$ [39].

In the Central Adriatic, Croatia, a highly polluted area resulting from a chloralkali production process is Kaštela Bay, where a waste water treatment process started in 1985. Valuable studies on mercury distribution in this and other unpolluted Adriatic areas and on ratios of total to methyl mercury in sediments, mussels and fish have been carried out in 2 Institutes in Zagreb (Croatia), and Ljubljana (Slovenia) since the late 1970s [40-46]. Levels of total mercury in fish and mussels fresh or canned from Adriatic (Table 12.3) range from 28 to 339 µg $kg^{-1}$ in unpolluted areas. It is assumed that intakes of mercury through fish consumption in the general Croatian population is low because of low fish consumption. However, the population from coastal Adriatic area might be exposed to higher levels of ingested mercury. The PTWI of 300 µg of total mercury $person^{-1}$ established by the FAO/WHO in 1972 [1] might be exceeded by this population. Currently such studies have not been performed in this region.

**Table 12.3** **Total mercury in various sea food from Adriatic, Croatia (µg $kg^{-1}$ fresh weight)**

| | | Mercury Mean | Range | (n) | Ref. |
|---|---|---|---|---|---|
| Canned sardines | | 175 | 139-277 | (6) | [63] |
| Fresh fish (hake muscle) | | 218 | 100-380 | (8) | [64] |
| Mussels | MA | 28 | 10-50 | (52) | [46] |
| Fresh fish | KB | 843 | 100-6310 | (13) | [65] |
| and mussels | MA | 315 | 260-390 | (4) | |
| Mussels | NA | 246 | 58-640 | (23) | [66] |
| Oysters | NA | 339 | 163-766 | (16) | |

KB=Kaštela Bay (polluted area); MA=Middle Adriatic (unpolluted area); NA=North Adriatic

## 12.4 Conclusions

This chapter reviews data on the heavy metal contamination of various foodstuffs in Croatia and compares the results obtained with those from other European countries.

Whilst much of these data were obtained prior to the conflict, some are recent. The overall scenario is that except for mercury in the Kaštela Bay area heavy metal concentrations in foodstuffs do not exceed those in nearby countries.

At the conclusion of the conflict more monitoring will be necessary, especially to monitor foodstuffs growth near large munition explosions, *eg,* Delnice and Ogulin (see chapter by Srebočan) and for fish in the Sava and Drava rivers and crops and cattle exposed to its waters.

Only by means of good monitoring can risk assessments on known hazardous chemicals be undertaken, and hence chemical safety be managed effectively.

## 12.5 References


[1] WHO. *Evaluation of Certain Food Additives and the Contaminants Mercury, Lead and Cadmium,* Technical Report Series 505, World Health Organization, Geneva, 1972, pp. 1-31.

[2] WHO. *Guidelines for the Study of Dietary Intakes of Chemical Contaminants.* GEMS: Global Environmental Monitoring System. WHO Offset Publication No. 87, World Health Organization, Geneva, 1985, pp. 1-102.

[3] Global Environment Monitoring System, *Assessment of Chemical Contaminants in Food.* Report on the results of the UNEP/FAO/WHO programme on health-related environmental monitoring, Monitoring and Assessment Research Centre, London, 1988, pp. 1-104.

[4] Parr, R.M., Abdulla, M., Aras, N.K., Byrne, A.R., Camara-Rica, C., Finnie, S., Gharib, A.G., Ingrao, G., Iyengar, G.V., Khangi, F.A., Krishnan, S.S., Kumpulainen, J., Liu, S., Schelenz, R., Srianujata, S., Tanner, J.T., and Wolf, W., Dietary intakes of trace elements and related nutrients in eleven countries: Preliminary results from an International Atomic Energy Agency (IAEA) coordinated research programme, in: *Trace Elements in Man and Animals - TEMA 7,* Momčilović, B. (Ed.), Zagreb, Institute for Medical Research and Occupational Health, University of Zagreb, 1990, pp. 13/3-13/5.

[5] Vahter, M., and Slorach, S., *Exposure Monitoring of Lead and Cadmium. An international pilot study within the WHO/UNEP Human Exposure Assessment Location (HEAL) Programme.* Technical Report. Global Environment Monitoring System. WHO and UNEP, Nairobi, 1990, pp. 1-82.

[6] Iyengar, V., *Clin. Nutr.* 1987, **6**, 105-117.

[7] Blanuša, M., and Breški, Đ., *Talanta,* 1981, **28**, 681-684.

[8] Blanuša, M., and Breški, Đ., Contribution to resolving analytical problems of lead and cadmium determination in food and faeces, in: *Heavy Metals in the Environment,* Farmer J.G. (Ed.), CEP Consultants, Edinburgh, 1991, Vol. 1, pp. 597-600.

[9] Horvat, M., Development of methods for low level mercury analysis and application on environmental biological samples. *Dissertation* (in Slovenian). University 'E. Kardelj', Ljubljana, Slovenia, 1989, pp. 1-164.

[10] IAEA. *Elemental Analysis of Biological Materials. Current Problems and Techniques with Special Reference to Trace Elements.* Technical Reports No. 197. IAEA, Vienna, 1980, pp. 1-371.

[11] Magos, L., *Analyst*, 1971, **96**, 847-853.

[12] Farant, J.-P., Brissette, D., Moncion, L., Bigras, L., and Chartrand, A., *J. Anal. Toxicol.* 1981, **5**, 47-51.

[13] Daniels, R.S., and Wigfield, D.C., *Sci. Total Environ.* 1989, **89**, 319-323.

[14] Daniels, R.S., and Wigfield, D.C., *Sci. Total Environ.* 1989, **89**, 325-329.

[15] Horvat, M., Zvonarić, T., and Stegnar, P., *Acta Adriat.* 1987, **28**, 59-63.

[16] Horvat, M., Byrne, A.R., and May, K., *Talanta*, 1990, **37**, 207-212.

[17] Quarterman, J., Lead, in: *Trace Elements in Human and Animal Nutrition*, Fifth edition, Mertz, W., (Ed.), Orlando, Academic Press, Inc., 1986, pp. 281-307.

[18] Karlowski, K., and Wojiciechowska-Mazurek, M., Dietary Monitoring Studies on Lead and Cadmium Exposures in Poland, in: Proceedings of the Symposium on the Bioavailability and Dietary Exposure to Lead, *Chemical Speciation and Bioavailability*, 1991, **3**, 21-29.

[19] Ward, N.I., Lead contamination of the London orbital (M25) motorway (since it's opening in 1986), in: *Heavy Metals in the Environment*, Vol. II, Vernet, J.-P., (Ed.), CEP Consultants Ltd., Edinburgh, 1989, pp. 274-278.

[20] Ward, N.I., *Sci. Total Environ.* 1990, **93**, 393-401.

[21] Blanuša, M., Hršak, J., and Fugaš, M., Lead and Cadmium in Human Diet in Lead Polluted Area, in: *Environmental Contamination*, Barcelo J. (Ed.), CEP Consultants Ltd., Edinburgh, 1990, pp. 490-492.

[22] Blanuša, M., and Kostial, K., 'Dietary exposure to lead and cadmium in Yugoslavia', in: Proceedings of the Symposium Bioavailability and Dietary Exposure to Lead, *Chemical Speciation and Bioavailability*, 1991, **3**, 17-21.

[23] Božidarević, D., and Vlahović, B., *Hrana i ishrana*, 1989, **30**, 109-114.

[24] Jorhem, L., and Sundstrom, B., *J. Food. Comp. Anal.* 1993, **6** (in press)

[25] Jorhem, L., Mattson, P., and Slorach, S., *Vår Föda*, 1984, **36**, 135-208.

[26] MAFF. *Survey of Lead in Food: Second Supplementary Report*, Food Surveillance Paper No. 10, HMSO, London, 1972.

[27] MAFF. *Lead in Food: Third Supplementary Report on Lead.* Food Surveillance Paper No. 27, HMSO, London, 1989, pp. 1-66.

[28] Tomassi, G., Assessment of Exposure of Human Populations to Heavy Metals through Dietary Intakes, in: *Environmental Inorganic Chemistry*, Irgulic, K.J., and Martell, E., (Eds.), VCH Publishers, Inc., 1985, pp. 437-446.

[29] Olejnik, D., Viśniewska, J., and Walkovska, A., *Rocz. Panstw. Zag. Hig.*, 1982, **33**, 386-396.

[30] Tjell, J.C., and Christensen, T.H., Evidence of increasing cadmium contents of agricultural soils, in: *Heavy Metals in the Environment*, Vol. 2, Lekkas T.D. (Ed.), CEP Consultants Ltd., Edinburgh, 1985, pp. 391-393.

[31] Houtmeyers, J., Vanhengel, P., Steegmans, R., Demuynck, M., and Becker, B., Cadmium in soil and food crops in the surroundings of zinc smelters, in: *Heavy Metals in the Environment*, Vol. 2, Lekkas T.D. (Ed.), CEP Consultants Ltd., Edinburgh, 1985, pp. 581-583.
[32] WHO. *Air Quality Guidelines for Europe*, WHO Regional Publications, European Series No. 23, Copenhagen, WHO Regional Office for Europe, 1987, pp. 1-426.
[33] IPCS. *Environmental Health Criteria 134*, Cadmium, World Health Organization Geneva, 1992, pp. 1-280.
[34] Vahter, M., (Ed.), *Assessment of Human Exposure to Lead and Cadmium through Biological Monitoring*, Global Environmental Monitoring System (GEMS), National Swedish Institute of Environmental Medicine and Karolinska Institute, Stockholm, 1982, pp. 1-136.
[35] Blanuša, M., Kralj, Z., and Bunarević, A., *Arch. Toxicol.* 1985, **58**, 115-117.
[36] Kostial, K., Cadmium, in: *Trace Elements in Human and Animal Nutrition*, Fifth Edition, Mertz, W., (Ed.), Orlando, Academic Press Inc., 1986, pp. 319-337.
[37] IPCS. *International Programme on Chemical Safety, Environmental Health Criteria 86, Mercury - Environmental Aspects*, World Health Organization, Geneva, 1989, pp. 1-115.
[38] May, K., Stoeppler, M., and Reisinger, K., Studies in the Ratio Total Mercury/Methylmercury in the Aquatic Food Chain, in: *Carcinogenic and Mutagenic Metal Compounds 2*, Merian, E., Frei, R.W., Hardi, W., and Schlatter, C., (Eds.), Gordon and Breach Science Publishers, New York, 1987, pp. 109-115.
[39] Gorchev, H.G., *Food Laboratory Newsletter*, 1987, No. 10, 31-36.
[40] Kosta, L., Ravnik, V., Byrne, A., Štirn, J., Dermelj, M., and Stegnar, P., *J. Radioanal. Chem.* 1978, **44**, 317-332.
[41] Stegnar, P., Vukadin, I., Smodić, B., Vaskelj, A., and Prosenc, A., Trace elements in sediments in organisms from Kaštela Bay, *V.J. Etud. Pollutions*, Cagliari, CIESM, 1980, pp. 595-600.
[42] Mikac, N., Picer, M., Stegnar, P., and Tušek-Žnidarić, M., *Water Res.* 1985, **19**, 1387-1392.
[43] Mikac, N., and Picer, M., *Sci. Total Environ.* 1985, **43**, 27-39.
[44] Žutić, V., *Long-term research and pollution monitoring of the Krka Estuary and Kornati Archipelago (Adriatic Sea)*, Annual Reports 1985-87, MED POL Phase II. Center for Marine Research, 'Rudjer Bošković' Institute, Zagreb, 1987.
[45] Zvonarić, Z., Horvat, M., and Stegnar, P., Ecological cycle of mercury in the marine environment of Kaštela Bay. in: *Proc. Int. Conf. Heavy Metals in the Environment*, New Orleans, 1987, Vol. II, p. 461.
[46] Mikac, N., Kwokal, Ž., May, K., and Branica, M., *Marine Chem.* 1989, **28**, 109-126.
[47] Blanuša, M., unpublished results.
[48] Telišman, J., Pongračić, J., Čretnik, R., and Prpić-Majić, D., Lead in milk and indicators of lead absorption in cows from lead contaminated and control areas, in: *Heavy Metals in the Environment*, Vol. 1, Lekkas T.D. (Ed.), CEP Consultants Ltd., Edinburgh, 1985, pp. 417-419.
[49] Dermelj, M., Hudnik, V., Pihlar, B., Byrne, A.R., and Kosta, L., *Vest. Slov. Kem. Drus.* 1982, **29**, 307-321.
[50] Srebočan, E., Srebočan, V., and Pompe-Gotal, J., *Vet. arh.* 1991, **61**, 207-215.

[51] Zurera, G., Estrada, B., Rincon, F., and Pozo, R., *Bull. Environ. Contam. Toxicol.* 1987, **38**, 805-812.

[52] Wagley, D., Schmiedel, G., Mainka, E., and Ache, J.A., *At. Spectrom.* 1989, **10**, 106-111.

[53] Blanuša, M., Telišman, S., Hršak, J., Fugaš, M., Prpić-Majić, D., and Šarić, M., *Arh. hig. rada toksikol.* 1991, **42**, 257-266.

[54] Bro, S., Sandstrom, B., and Heydorn, K., *J. Trace Elem. Electrolytes Health Dis.* 1990, **4**, 147-155.

[55] Müller, M., Anke, M., Thiel, C., and Hartmann, E., 'Exposure of adults to lead from food, estimated by analysis and calculation - comparison of the methods', in: Eight International Symposium on Trace Elements in Man and Animals (TEMA-8), Dresden, *Book of Abstracts*, 1993, p. 30.

[56] Müller, M., Thiel, C., Anke, M., Hartman, E., and Arnhold, W., 'Cadmium intake of adults in Germany', in: Eight International Symposium on Trace Elements in Man and Animals, TEMA-8, Dresden, *Book of Abstracts*, 1993, p. 26.

[57] Ellen, G., Egmond, E., Van Loon, J.W., Sahertian, E.T., and Tolsma, K., *Food Additives and Contaminants*, 1990, **7**, 207-221.

[58] Van Dokkum, W., De Vos, R.H., Muys, Th., and Wesstra, J.A., *Brit. J. Nutr.* 1989, **61**, 7-15.

[59] Schuhmacker, M., Bosque, M.A., Domingo, J.L., and Corbella, J. *Bull. Environ. Contam. Toxicol.* 1991, **46**, 320-328.

[60] Barbera, R., Farre, R., and Lozano, A., *J. Micronutr. Anal.* 1989, **6**, 47-57.

[61] Slorach, S., Gustafsson, I.B., Jorhem, L., and Mattson, P. *Vår Föda*, 1983, **35** (suppl. 1), 1-16.

[62] Becker B.W. and Kumpulainen, *J. Brit. J. Nutr.* 1991, **66**, 151-160.

[63] Prester, Lj., Blanuša, M., and Ciganović, M., Analysis of mercury in fish from the Adriatic, Second Symposium 'Ecologically rational development of chemical technologies', Zagreb, *Book of Abstracts*, 1993, p. 410.

[64] Horvat, M., Zvonarić, T., Stegnar, P., Prosenc, A., Konda, D., Sabadin, A., 'Relation between total mercury, methylmercury and selenium in fish muscle from the Adriatic sea', in: *Heavy Metals in the Environment*, Vol. I, Vernet, J-P, (Ed.), Edinburgh, CEP Consultants Ltd., 1993, pp. 370-373.

[65] Orlov, M., Pavlov, J., Čulin, S., and Stamenković, M., Mercury and methyl-mercury contents in sea water organisms of middle Adriatic sea, in: *Heavy Metals in the Environment*, Vol. II, Farmer, J.G. (Ed.), Edinburgh, CEP Consultants, 1991, pp. 141-144.

[66] Najdek, M., and Sapunar, J., *Bull. Environ. Contam. Toxicol.* 1987, **39**, 56-62.

# 13. COMPACT and ENACT Procedures in Predicting the Formation of Reactive Intermediates by Cytochrome P450 Metabolism

Costas Ioannides, David F.V. Lewis and Dennis V. Parke

## 13.1 Introduction

For the manifestation of toxicity, a chemical must:

i) Interact with important cellular macromolecules;

ii) Impair cellular defensive mechanisms rendering the cells vulnerable;

iii) Interfere with physiological homeostasis; or,

iv) Interact with specific cellular receptors resulting in the impairment of the regulatory control of cellular function.

Most emphasis so far has been placed on the interaction of chemicals with vital cellular macromolecules. Adducts with protein, DNA and RNA resulting from the covalent interaction of chemicals with these macromolecules, have been isolated and their structures determined.

## 13.2 Generation of Reactive Intermediates

Most toxins are chemically inert, unreactive compounds, precluding interactions with cellular constituents. Indeed, if such a chemical that is a genotoxic carcinogen is mixed with DNA no interaction is apparent and no adducts are generated. How then can such compounds, totally devoid of chemical reactivity, provoke toxicity through mechanisms which necessitate covalent binding to cellular macromolecules. The answer to this enigma is that chemicals can acquire high reactivity through metabolism that occurs within the cell. Almost every chemical that gains access to the living organism is subject to some degree of metabolism, and certain chemicals are completely metabolized. The outcome of such metabolism, in almost all instances, is detoxication, by which an inactive, more polar metabolite(s) is formed, and this is readily excreted via the bile and kidney, frequently in the form of a conjugate, with endogenous substrates such as sulfate and glucuronic acid.

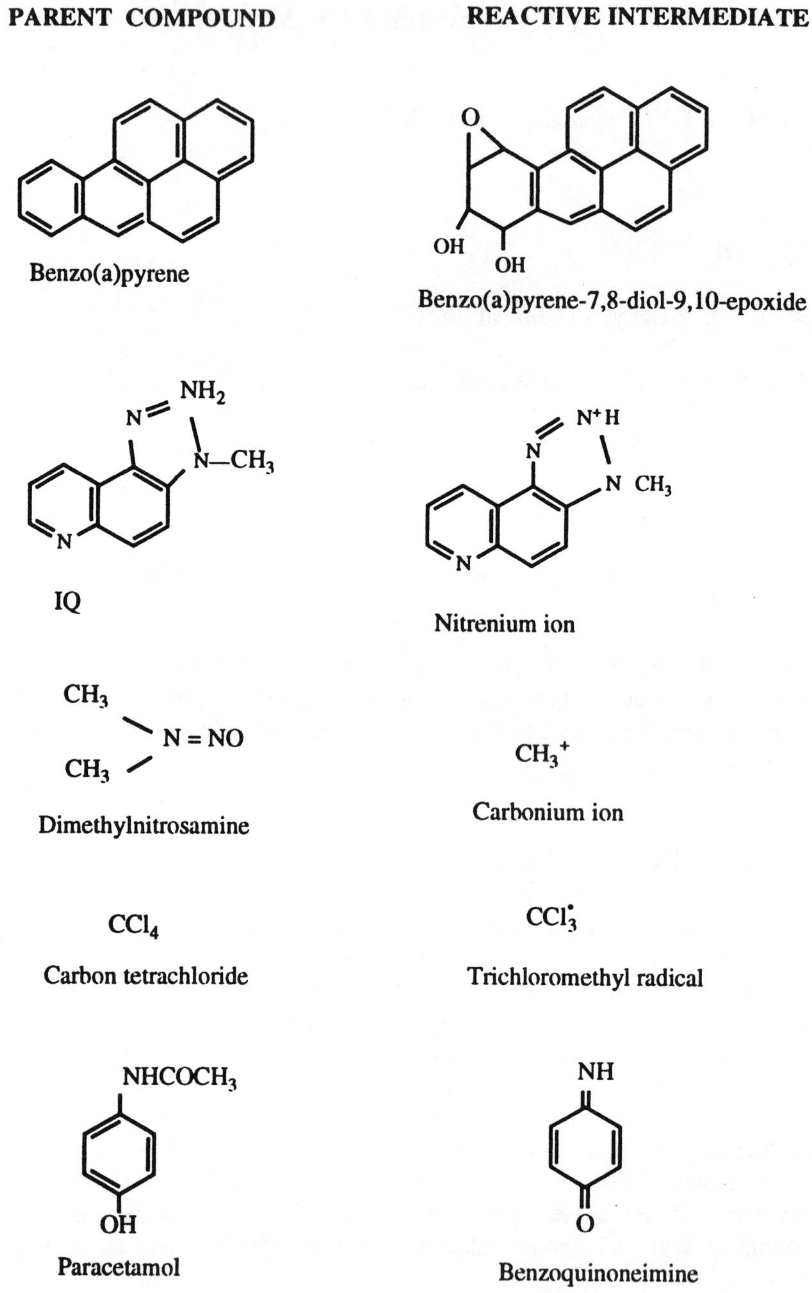


**Figure 13.1** **Toxic chemicals and their reactive intermediates**

A chemical may undergo metabolism at many sites in the molecule to produce these readily excretable, inactive metabolites that ensure the uneventful elimination of the chemical from the body. However, metabolism, almost always involving a single route, may also generate a metabolite markedly more reactive than the parent compound, and consequently potentially more toxic because of its avidity for interaction with cellular components. Such toxic metabolites, formed within the cell, can freely interact with cellular macromolecules to form adducts, impairing enzymic action, and altering the physiological function of the cell. Figure 13.1 lists some chemical toxins and their metabolically-formed reactive intermediates responsible for their toxicity. For such chemicals, toxicity and carcinogenicity are inextricably linked to their metabolism.

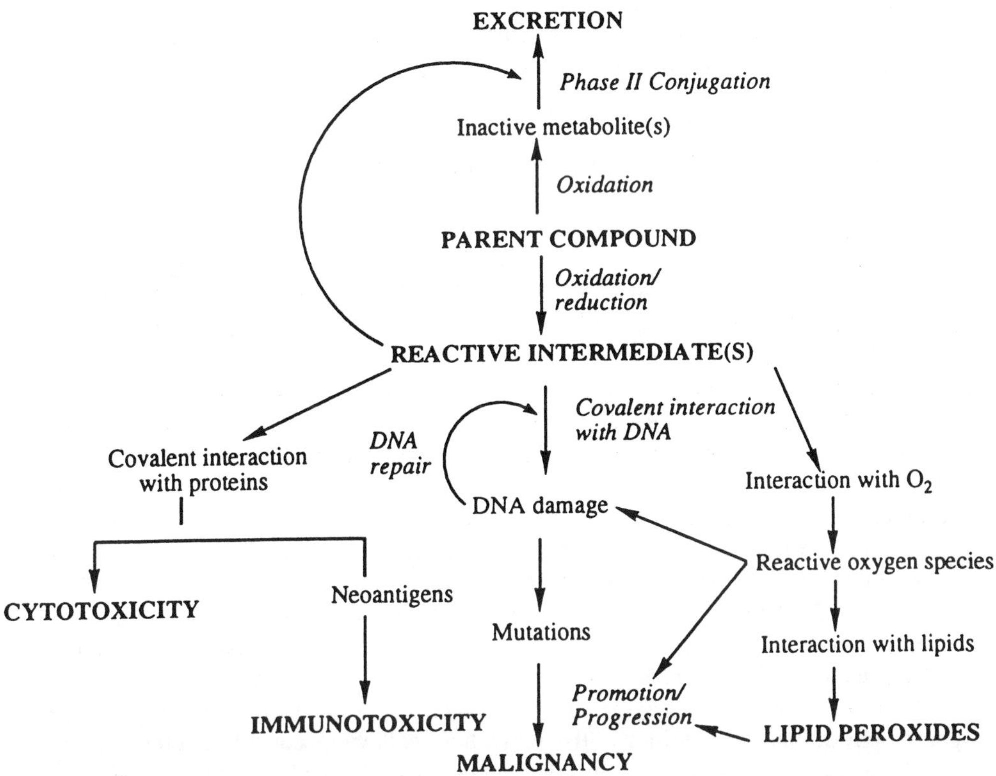


**Figure 13.2** **Schematic representation of the bioactivation of chemicals**

As chemical toxins may express their toxicity through highly reactive intermediates, generated within the exposed organism, any animal species unable to form the reactive intermediate because of a lack of the appropriate enzyme system(s), will be resistant to the chemical toxicity. The reactive intermediates may interact with DNA to form adducts which, if they escape the repair mechanisms, may be fixed giving rise to mutations and setting into motion the processes that eventually lead to tumor formation (Figure 13.2). The reactive intermediates may also interact with vital cellular proteins causing cell death. Alternatively, they may function as haptens, forming a protein with antigenic properties, eliciting immunotoxicity. An additional possible interaction of the reactive intermediates is with molecular oxygen, to form superoxide anions which can be converted to potent reactive oxygen species (ROS) such as the hydroxyl radical. These are also capable of oxidative damage of DNA leading to cancer, the formation of lipid peroxides with carcinogenic potential, and cell death by disturbing the structural integrity of the cell (Figure 13.2).

Certain chemicals possess chemical reactivity *per se*, *ie*, they are electrophiles, and can interact directly with cellular macromolecules to elicit various forms of toxicity. In this case, metabolism almost invariably leads to deactivation and attenuation of toxicity. These chemicals tend to be less toxic than those requiring metabolism because they are frequently neutralized by interactions with nucleophiles prior to reaching their site of action and/or are unable to gain entry into the cell.

## 13.3 Importance of Activation/Deactivation

Clearly, a chemical may be subject to metabolism by a number of routes, the majority of which produce inactive metabolites and are therefore deactivation pathways; however one or two may generate highly toxic metabolites and are considered activation pathways. An important and efficient cellular defensive mechanism is the neutralization of these reactive electrophiles by conjugation with endogenous nucleophiles, the tripeptide glutathione being the most prominent; in this way the cell hinders interaction between the reactive intermediate and the vital cellular structures. Perhaps it is not surprising that the cellular content of glutathione tends to be high (about 10 mM) and can only be depleted following exposure to megadoses of chemicals. However, when glutathione depletion occurs the cell becomes very vulnerable to chemical toxins. For example, the toxin bromobenzene is markedly more toxic to animals from which glutathione has been depleted as a result of starvation which impedes its synthesis from the constituent amino acids [1]. What is thus apparent is that the amount of reactive intermediates formed, and consequently the likelihood of toxicity, is governed by the rates of the competing pathways of activation and deactivation. The extent and routes of metabolism of a chemical are largely dependent on the level and nature of enzymes present in the living organism at the time of exposure. Under physiological conditions, the activation pathways constitute minor routes of metabolism and the low levels of reactive intermediates formed are effectively detoxicated by the defensive, protective mechanisms and no toxicity is apparent. Most of the routes of metabolism of a chemical lead to deactivation and usually only a single pathway of metabolism produces a deleterious reactive intermediate. However, under certain conditions the activation pathways may assume greater importance, leading to high production of reactive intermediates that overwhelms the deactivation pathways and facilitates interaction with cellular macromolecules. Such situations may occur when:

i) Saturation of the deactivation pathways directs metabolism towards the activation pathways. Such a situation may arise following exposure to high doses of chemical(s), or because an endogenous substrate, utilized in conjugation reactions, is unavailable. For example, the mild analgesic and antipyretic agent acetaminophen (paracetamol) is readily deactivated by conjugation with sulfate and glucuronic acid. Oxidation to generate a reactive quinoneimine is a minor pathway, and this reactive intermediate is readily detoxicated by interaction with glutathione, thus preventing it from interacting covalently with proteins, which leads eventually to cytotoxicity. Ingestion of large doses of acetaminophen, as occurs during suicide attempts, results in depletion of sulfate (PAPS) and glucuronic acid (UDPGA) as the rate of their utilization is higher than the rate of their synthesis. Consequently, more of the acetaminophen metabolism is directed towards the formation of the quinoneimine which now becomes a significant metabolite. This is initially detoxicated by glutathione conjugation, but as the body cannot compensate for the high rate of utilization of this tripeptide, glutathione levels decline, the protective mechanism falters and covalent interaction with proteins takes place, leading to hepatotoxicity, which can be fatal if allowed to progress. Indeed, the accepted treatment of such a condition is to supply the body with precursors of cysteine, *eg*, N-acetylcysteine, the limiting amino acid in the biosynthesis of glutathione; or,

ii) Selective induction of the enzyme system(s) catalyzing the activation pathways takes place. This may occur during exposure to chemicals acting as inducing agents [2] or during some disease syndromes, such as insulin-dependent diabetes, which are accompanied by an increase in the levels of an endogenous inducing agent, *eg*, acetone during diabetes, and/or by impairment of the regulatory control of the enzyme protein [3]. Induction of the xenobiotic metabolizing system is a common phenomenon, observed not only in animals but also in man. Such inducing agents are abundant in the environment, encountered in the air we breath and especially in the diet, being inherent to the food, *eg*, indoles and flavonoids, or contaminants generated during cooking, *eg*, polycyclic aromatic hydrocarbons. Selective induction of an activation pathway will exacerbate the toxicity/carcinogenicity of a chemical. For example, treatment of animals with ethanol potentiates the carcinogenicity of azoxymethane presumably because the alcohol preferentially stimulates activation of the azoxymethane to a methyldiazonium ion [4]. Moreover, most chemical carcinogens elicit a mutagenic response in *in vitro* short-term tests only when the enzymic activation system is derived from the livers of induced animals; no response, or very poor response, is seen when control, non-induced animals are the source of the activation system [5].

## 13.4 Cytochromes P450

Almost every enzyme system capable of metabolizing chemicals, has the potential to produce reactive intermediates. These include enzyme catalyzing oxidations, such as the cytochrome P450 mixed-function oxidases, the FAD monooxygenases, the peroxidases and prostaglandin synthetase, enzymes catalyzing reductions such as the nitroreductases and azoreductases, and phase II conjugation reactions such as O-acetylation, sulfation, glucuronylation, and glutathione conjugation.

Undoubtedly the most important enzyme system in the oxidation of chemicals, both endogenous and exogenous, is that of the cytochrome P450 oxidases. Vitamins, fatty acids, steroids and prostaglandins, as well as structurally diverse chemicals, of markedly different molecular size and shape, are subject to oxidation by this system. Although its oxidase capacity has received enormous attention, it should not be forgotten that the cytochromes P450 are capable also of catalyzing reductions, such as conversion of nitrocompounds to their hydroxylamines, and of azocompounds to their amino-components. It metabolizes small molecules such as methanol (MW=42) and large compounds such as the immunosuppressant, cyclosporin (MW=1203), planar molecules such as benzo(a)pyrene, and globular molecules such as dieldrin. Such an unprecedented, high affinity, broad substrate specificity cannot be attained by a single enzyme protein, so that it is not perhaps surprising that the cytochrome P450-dependent mixed-function oxidase system comprises hundreds of proteins each with its own characteristic substrate specificity.

The cytochromes P450 are classified into families, based strictly on their structural similarity, with no attention given to their substrate specificity. A family may contain one or more subfamilies, which in turn may comprise one or more proteins. Proteins within a family display at least 40% structural similarity, whereas between proteins within the same subfamily the structural similarity is at least 55%. The various cytochrome P450 families are denoted by the prefix CYP, followed by an arabic number representing the family, a capital letter for the subfamily, and finally another arabic number showing the individual cytochrome P450 protein. The families which are involved in the metabolism of xenobiotics are CYP1-CYP4 and their major characteristics are outlined in Table 13.1. The CYP1 family, and to a lesser extent the CYP2E subfamily, are toxicologically most important, since they are very closely associated with the production of reactive intermediates, and thus with the production of toxic responses mediated by chemicals.

**Table 13.1** **Principal characteristics of xenobiotic-metabolizing cytochromes P450**

| Family | Subfamily | Substrate characteristics | Typical substrate | Role in bio-activation | Inducibility | Other characteristics |
|---|---|---|---|---|---|---|
| CYP1 | A | Essentially planar | Ethoxyresorufin<br>Glu-P-1 | Very extensive | Very high | Induction mediated by Ah receptor, oxidises at conformationally-hindered positions |
| CYP2 | A | Endogenous steroids | Testosterone | Very limited | Yes | Catalyses specifically the 7$\alpha$-hydroxylation of steroids |
| | B | Wide specificity | Pentoxyresorufin | Limited | Very high | The 'classical' rodent proteins appear not to be expressed in humans |
| | C | Non-planar | Tolbutamide<br>Mephenytoin | None | Poor | Marked genetic polymorphism |
| | D | Basic, positively charged nitrogen and ability to form H-bonds 5-7 Å from nitrogen | Debrisoquine<br>Dextromethorphan | None | No | Marked genetic polymorphism |
| | E | Small molecular weight | p-Nitrophenol<br>Carbon tetrachloride | Yes | Yes | Propensity to generate reactive oxygen species |
| CYP3 | A | Generally large molecular weight | Erythromycin<br>Cyclosporin | Limited | Yes | Expressed in human fetus |
| CYP4 | A | Primarily endogenous arachidonic and fatty acids | Lauric acid<br>Arachidonic acid | None | Yes | Its induction is associated with peroxisomal proliferation and epigenetic carcinogenicity in rodents |

### 13.4.1 The CYP1 Family

This is one of the smallest families of the cytochromes P450, comprising a single subfamily that consists of 2 proteins. Its existence was first noted more than 2 decades ago and for this reason it has become the subject of numerous investigations, and consequently our understanding of its contribution to xenobiotic metabolism and its regulation are relatively advanced.

The structural feature of substrates of this family is that of a planar molecular configuration brought about by fused aromatic rings [6]. An additional major characteristic, which helps to distinguish it from other families, is its propensity to metabolize chemicals at sites which give rise to highly reactive electrophiles. It appears, almost always to direct the metabolism of a compound towards the formation of active metabolites, and only in a handful of cases has it been ascribed a deactivating role, *eg*, of 1,3-dinitropyrene [7] and of the food additive furylfuramide, a nitrofuran [8]. The 2 proteins that constitute this family also display some degree of substrate preference, in that CYP1A1 oxidises primarily aromatic carbon atoms whereas CYP1A2 is more closely associated with the oxidation of exocyclic nitrogens.

The 2 CYP1A proteins have been isolated from the livers of a number of animal species, purified, and shown to share extensive structural similarity and to display similar substrate specificity. The human orthologue of CYP1A2 has been isolated from liver and shown to metabolize the same substrates, and to play the same role in carcinogen activation, as the rodent proteins [9]. The human CYP1A1 has not been purified but it has been expressed in mammalian cells; like the rodent orthologue, it catalyses the oxidation of polycyclic aromatic hydrocarbons and the N-oxidation of aromatic amines [10]. This apparent similarity in substrate specificity between the human and rodent CYP1A proteins would indicate that where CYP1A is involved, toxicological data can, in principle, be extrapolated to man with more confidence. Of the cytochrome P450 proteins so far characterized, the CYP1 family appears to be the most conserved within the phylogenetic tree [11].

Although other xenobiotic-metabolizing cytochrome P450 proteins may activate a very limited number of chemicals, and at relatively low rates when compared with the CYP1 family, the latter is considered the most important in chemical carcinogenesis, and possibly also in the aetiology of human cancer, for the following reasons:

i) CYP1 is the most ubiquitous of all cytochrome P450 families. Its presence has been demonstrated in every living organism and in all tissues examined. Such ubiquity frequently implies a major role in physiological homeostasis, but in the case of the CYP1 family the natural endogenous substrates, if any, are still a matter of speculation. Recent studies have ascribed a role for it in the catabolism and elimination of bilirubin [12], and its down regulation in the adult rat has implications for its involvement in growth and tissue proliferation [2];

ii) Most chemical carcinogens are planar molecules, which presumably facilitates their intercalation with DNA. Consequently they are CYP1 substrates, which partly explains the important role that this P450 family plays in the activation of chemical carcinogens [2,13,14];

iii) The chemical carcinogens to which man is involuntarily exposed are:

- Those inherent in the environment such as polycyclic aromatic hydrocarbons, including their amino- and nitro-derivatives;
- Those present in food such as safrole and estragole; or,
- Those produced during the cooking of food such as the heterocyclic amines.

Humans are exposed to these environmental carcinogens throughout their entire lifetime, and all of these are activated primarily or exclusively by the CYP1 family. Ingestion of such CYP1-activated carcinogens is virtually unavoidable;

iv) A unique characteristic of the CYP1 family is that it oxygenates chemicals at conformationally-hindered positions. Consequently, the reactive intermediates formed are inaccessible to phase II conjugation systems, and this resistance to detoxication undoubtedly contributes to their genotoxicity by making interaction with DNA more likely, *eg*, the dihydrodiol-epoxides of polycyclic aromatic hydrocarbons, the ultimate carcinogens, *ie*, the entities that interact with DNA, are not substrates of epoxide hydrolase and are not subject to detoxication through conjugation with glutathione catalyzed by the glutathione S-transferases [2];

v) The CYP1 appears to be the most extensively conserved P450 family throughout the animal kingdom [11]. The orthologous proteins in rats, mice, rabbits, and most importantly the human proteins, share the same substrate specificity. Toxicologically this is of paramount relevance as safety evaluation studies of chemicals, metabolized by the CYP1 family, carried out in animals can be extrapolated more confidently to man, since the CYP1-catalyzed pathways of metabolism in animals will also be operative in man;

vi) Although many of the xenobiotic-metabolizing cytochrome P450 proteins may be induced in various tissues by exposure to chemical agents, no family is as susceptible to induction as the proteins of the CYP1 family. In rats a single intraperitoneal dose of as little as 50 $\mu g\ kg^{-1}$ doubles the activity of hepatic ethoxyresorufin O-deethylase, a diagnostic probe for the CYP1 family [15]. Potent inducing agents may increase CYP1 levels many fold over the low constitutive levels, with the result that this family may comprise up to 80% of the total hepatic cytochrome P450 [16]. It is inducible by a host of environmental chemicals, such as polycyclic aromatic hydrocarbons, polyhalogenated biphenyls, dioxins, heterocyclic amines, aromatic amines and plant anutrients such as flavonoids, polyhydroxy compounds, methylenedioxyphenyls, indoles, etc., so it may be inferred that human exposure to CYP1-inducing agents is ubiquitous and continuous throughout life. A number of studies have clearly illustrated that diet can induce the liver and gastrointestinal levels of CYP1. Human volunteers maintained on diets containing large amounts of cruciferous vegetables rich in indoles, or on diets of charcoal-broiled beef resulting in contamination with polycyclic aromatic hydrocarbons, metabolize the drug phenacetin, a CYP1 substrate, more readily as a result of the induction of hepatic and gastrointestinal enzymes, resulting in much lower plasma levels of the drug [17,18]. Numerous examples have been reported where CYP1 induction in animals has been associated with increased toxicity and carcinogenicity [2,19-21]. Many of these studies have exploited the murine model described by Nebert [22] employing strains of mice which are either resistant or responsive to CYP1 induction. A potentially very important observation is that responsive mice are most susceptible to polycyclic aromatic hydrocarbon-induced atherosclerosis when compared to the resistant strains [23]; furthermore, CYP1A1 has been detected in the aorta of rabbits [24]. In rats, insulin imbalance, whether hyper- or hypo-insulinemia, has been associated with an increase in hepatic CYP1A2 levels [25,26].

In man, CYP1 is inducible both in the liver and in extrahepatic tissues, such as the lung and placenta [27-31]. Induction of the CYP1 family has been demonstrated in smokers, presumably due to the polycyclic aromatic hydrocarbon content of smoke [29], or after accidental exposure to polychlorinated biphenyls [32], and even following the therapeutic administration of drugs such as omeprazole [33-35]. It is pertinent to point out at this stage that very few currently used drugs interact with the CYP1 family, at least at therapeutic doses. However, caffeine is a CYP1A2 substrate and is proving a very useful means of monitoring the activity of this isoform in man [9].

Tissue-mediated induction of CYP1 may be, at least partly, a factor in determining the target site of chemical carcinogenesis. Extensive studies in humans have established a good relationship between lung cancer and CYP1A1 levels in the lungs of smokers [36,37]. Interestingly, activation of polycyclic hydrocarbons by CYP1A appears to occur in the same part of the airways, and in the same cell types, as those in which carcinomas are encountered [37];

vii) A frequently ignored property of CYP1 inducing agents is their ability to trigger cellular growth and proliferation. It is now widely accepted that DNA damage, even if expressed in the cell progeny (initiation), is not in itself sufficient to induce a tumor, since this may undergo DNA repair. Other complex stages must follow initiation, generally and simplistically described as promotion and progression, and invoking the action of the protein kinase c enzyme cascade. The characteristic of the promotion process is rapid and uncontrolled growth, which establishes the DNA damage in perpetuity in the transformed clone of cells. Thus CYP1 inducing agents, almost invariably substrates of this enzyme, are able also to satisfy the second prerequisite for carcinogenesis (accelerated DNA replications), and consequently may be considered as *complete* carcinogens.

viii) One of the 2 CYP1 proteins, namely CYP1A1, is present in lymphocytes and has been associated, in controversial studies during the 1970s, with susceptibility to lung cancer. These studies have subsequently been confirmed using improved methodology, and have further established a relationship between human lung cancer and CYP1A1 activity in lung and lymphocytes as exemplified by the aryl hydrocarbon hydroxylase (AHH) activity [36, 38-41].

#### 13.4.1.1 CYP1 Polymorphism

Polymorphism in cytochrome P450 proteins has often been linked to human cancer risk [42,43]. In the case of the CYP1 family, such a polymorphism could help explain, at least partly, the marked difference in susceptibility to chemical carcinogens, *eg*, in smoking-induced lung cancer. Experimental evidence points to such a polymorphism, but as yet, this has not been unequivocally established, and studies carried out in different countries are sometimes contradictory [44,45]. What is of interest is that among smokers, those who contract cancer display high tissue CYP1A1 activity; only smokers expressing high CYP1A1 levels in lung were associated with a higher lung cancer risk. This indicates that induction of this enzyme in humans is also under genetic control [46]. These studies raise the possibility that genotyping for CYP1A1 polymorphism may identify the high risk subjects. Moreover, they provide a feasible explanation as to why only a fraction of smokers develop lung cancer. A link between CYP1A1 polymorphism and increased risk in tobacco-linked lung carcinoma has been reported in a Japanese cohort [44], but no relationship was evident in a Norwegian cohort [45]. CYP1A1 genotyping has been considered as a possible means to identify individuals with high cancer risk [38]. It is important also to note that a relationship has been established between breast CYP1A1 activity, as measured by the AHH assay, and survival rate in human breast cancer [47].

Marked variations have also been observed in the levels of CYP1A2, which catalyzes the activation of many amino compounds in the liver of humans, but what the implications are, has not yet been clarified [48,49]. The CYP1A2-catalyzed N-hydroxylation of carcinogenic aromatic amines also showed marked variation among human individuals 9,38,50]; however, the possibility that this reflects differences in exposure to inducing agents cannot be ruled out. CYP1A2 activity is monitored in humans by measuring the carbon dioxide exhalation following ingestion of caffeine, the 3-demethylation of which appears to be catalyzed exclusively by this enzyme protein [9].

### 13.4.2 The CYP2E Subfamily

Two unique characteristics of this subfamily are the molecular size of its substrates, which tend to be small molecular weight compounds having a molecular diameter of <6.5Å [51], and its high propensity to generate deleterious reactive oxygen species (ROS) [52,53]. CYP2E catalyzes the bioactivation of many small molecular weight carcinogens and toxins, which may not be substrates of the CYP1 family. It has been linked to the metabolism and activation of some nitrosamines [54-57], carbon tetrachloride [58,59], azoxymethane, methylazoxymethanol [60], vinyl chloride, acrylonitrile, ethyl carbamate [58], organic solvents such as acetone, dimethylsulfoxide, benzene and ethanol [61], general anaesthetics such as halothane and enflurane [59,62], and of drugs such as paracetamol (acetaminophen) [63]. Many of these substrates also induce this subfamily in the liver of rats, *eg*, ethanol, acetone, pyrazole, and the antitubercular drug isoniazid [64,65]. CYP2E is also induced in conditions resulting in hyperketonemia, such as starvation and insulin-dependent diabetes [66,67]. Of the various ketone bodies acetone appears to be the inducing agent [65]. Interestingly, CYP2E levels in peripheral lymphocytes are higher in diabetic patients [68].

The ability of CYP2E to generate ROS raises the possibility that it may have a role in the initiation and promotion of carcinogenesis. ROS are known to damage DNA and to be genotoxic, and by enhancing cellular proliferation and dysplastic growth they enhance the promotional stage of carcinogenesis, as, for example, when ethanol is administered post-initiation with nitrosamine oesophageal carcinogens [69]. An endogenous function is in the metabolism and elimination of acetone [70], and the increase in CYP2E activity observed during fasting and diabetes may be viewed as an adaptive response to eliminate excess ketone bodies.

CYP2E has been purified from human liver and has also been expressed in mammalian cells; and it appears to have similar substrate preferences to the orthologous rat and rabbit proteins [55,71,72], thus enabling the confident extrapolation of animal data to man. In common with the CYP1A subfamily, CYP2E appears also to be one of the most conserved cytochromes P450. CYP2E is inducible in man, at least by ethanol and isoniazid [73,74]. The hydroxylation of the drug chlorzoxazone has been proposed as a probe for the non-invasive determination of CYP2E activity [75].

## 13.5 COMPACT (Computer Optimized Parametric Analysis for Chemical Toxicity)

The realization that the toxicological fate of a chemical may be determined largely by the nature of the cytochrome P450 proteins with which it interacts, as this determines the site of oxidation and consequently the formation of reactive intermediates, led us to consider the possibility of devising a means by which the particular enzymic catalyst of the metabolism of a given chemical could be predicted. Since the CYP1A proteins are undoubtedly the most closely linked to chemical carcinogenesis, it was natural that they were the prime object of attention.

For a chemical to be metabolized by an enzyme, 3 prerequisites must be satisfied:

i) The chemical must be endowed with the necessary physicochemical properties that will allow it to reach the environment of the enzyme. In the case of cytochrome P450 proteins, which are embedded in lipid, some degree of lipophilicity is essential and it is perhaps not surprising that most carcinogens are lipophilic compounds;

ii) The chemical must gain access to the substrate binding site of the enzyme. In order to achieve this, it must have a certain molecular size and conformation that would allow it to enter the substrate binding site, which may not be situated on the surface of the enzyme, although certain surface residues may act as recognition sites for substrates; and,

iii) Once at the active site, the chemical must be able to interact with the enzyme in such a way as to facilitate the metabolism of the chemical.

### 13.5.1 Characteristics of CYP1 and CYP2E Substrates

The CYP1 family was one of the first to be identified and consequently extensive literature is available concerning its substrates and inhibitors, as well as its inducing agents. A computer-graphic analysis was undertaken to ascertain the molecular geometric criteria of these compounds which enable them to interact preferentially with CYP1 [6,76]. These studies revealed that the common feature of these chemicals is that they are essentially planar molecules, characterized by a high area/depth$^2$ ratio, a factor used to define planarity (Table 13.2), which accords with the fact that most chemical carcinogens identified so far, are of an aromatic nature, comprising one or more fused aromatic or heteroaromatic rings, constraining them to adopt a planar conformation. In contrast, substrates which have no affinity for CYP1A are bulky non-planar molecules with small area/depth$^2$ ratios.

**Table 13.2** **Molecular dimensions of cytochromes P450 substrates/inducers**

| Compound | Preferred cytochrome P450 family/subfamily | Area/depth$^{2*}$ |
|---|---|---|
| Benzo(a)pyrene | CYP1 | 12.0 |
| β-Naphthylamine | CYP1 | 7.9 |
| TCDD | CYP1 | 7.9 |
| Caffeine | CYP1 | 4.8 |
| Trp-P-1 | CYP1 | 8.5 |
| Phenobarbitone | CYP2B | 1.1 |
| Phenylimidazole | CYP2B | 1.6 |
| Cyclophosphamide | CYP2B | 2.2 |
| Imidazole | CYP2E | 3.6 |
| Paracetamol | CYP1/CYP2E | 4.8 |
| Isoniazid | CYP2E | 3.2 |
| Rifampicin | CYP3 | 1.3 |
| Ethylmorphine | CYP3 | 2.0 |
| Clofibrate | CYP4 | 2.0 |

*The ratio area/depth$^2$ is an index of degree of planarity; the higher it is the more planar the compound is.

How critical planarity is, and how it relates to carcinogenicity may be appreciated by considering three of the isomers of aminobiphenyl, namely, the highly carcinogenic 4-aminobiphenyl and the non-carcinogenic 2- and 3-aminobiphenyls (Table 13.3). The N-hydroxylamines, which are the proximate carcinogens of the 2- and 4-isomers are mutagenic in the Ames test, whereas of the 3 parent compounds only the 4-isomer is mutagenic in the presence of an activation system [77]. The non-carcinogenicity of 3-aminobiphenyl can be attributed to the lack of genotoxic potential of its hydroxylamine. However, what these observations further indicate is that the reason for the lack of mutagenicity of 2-aminobiphenyl is that no N-hydroxylation occurs, *ie*, in contrast to the 4-isomer, 2-aminobiphenyl is not CYP1 substrate. This is further supported by the observation that only the 4-isomer is an inducer of CYP1 proteins in the liver of rats [20]. The explanation for this marked difference in affinity for the CYP1 family by the two aminobiphenyl isomers becomes readily obvious when considering their molecular geometries (Figure 13.3). 4-Aminobiphenyl is a planar molecule with an area/depth$^2$ ratio of 7.3, whereas 2-aminobiphenyl, because of the presence of the amino group in an *ortho* position to the ring, which forms a dihedral angle of 40°, is non-planar, characterized by an area/depth$^2$ ratio of 4.1 [77]. Similar observations have been reported for tetrachlorobiphenyls [78] and dichlorobiphenyls [70], where chlorine substitution at the *ortho* positions results in loss of planarity rendering them poor inducers and substrates of the CYP1 family. Moreover, excellent correlations have been obtained between the area/depth$^2$ ratio of 10 polychlorinated biphenyls and their ability to induce CYP1A1 as exemplified by the O-deethylation of ethoxyresorufin [80].

**Table 13.3** **Carcinogenic/mutagenic characteristics and molecular shape of aminobiphenyl isomers**

| Aminobiphenyl isomer | Carcinogenicity | Mutagenicity of parent compound* | Mutagenicity of N-hydroxylamine** | Planarity index (area/depth$^2$) |
|---|---|---|---|---|
| 2-Aminobiphenyl | Non-carcinogen | Non-mutagen | Mutagen | 4.1 |
| 3-Aminobiphenyl | Non-carcinogen | Non-mutagen | Non-mutagen | 7.8 |
| 4-Aminobiphenyl | Carcinogen | Mutagen | Mutagen | 7.3 |

*Mutagenicity in the Ames test in the presence of an activation system
**Mutagenicity in the Ames test in the absence of an activation system

The same approaches have been used to define the molecular characteristics of the CYP2E subfamily, once its contribution to the activation of toxic and carcinogenic chemicals was recognized. The principal characteristic of CYP2E substrates is that they are small molecules, possessing collision diameters of <6.5Å [51]. The major substrates of CYP2E are small molecular weight organic solvents, *eg*, diethylether and ethanol, halogenated hydrocarbons, *eg*, carbon tetrachloride, short chain aliphatic nitrosamines, *eg*, dimethylnitrosamine, and generally compounds containing a single aromatic ring, *eg*, benzene, paracetamol (acetaminophen) and isoniazid.

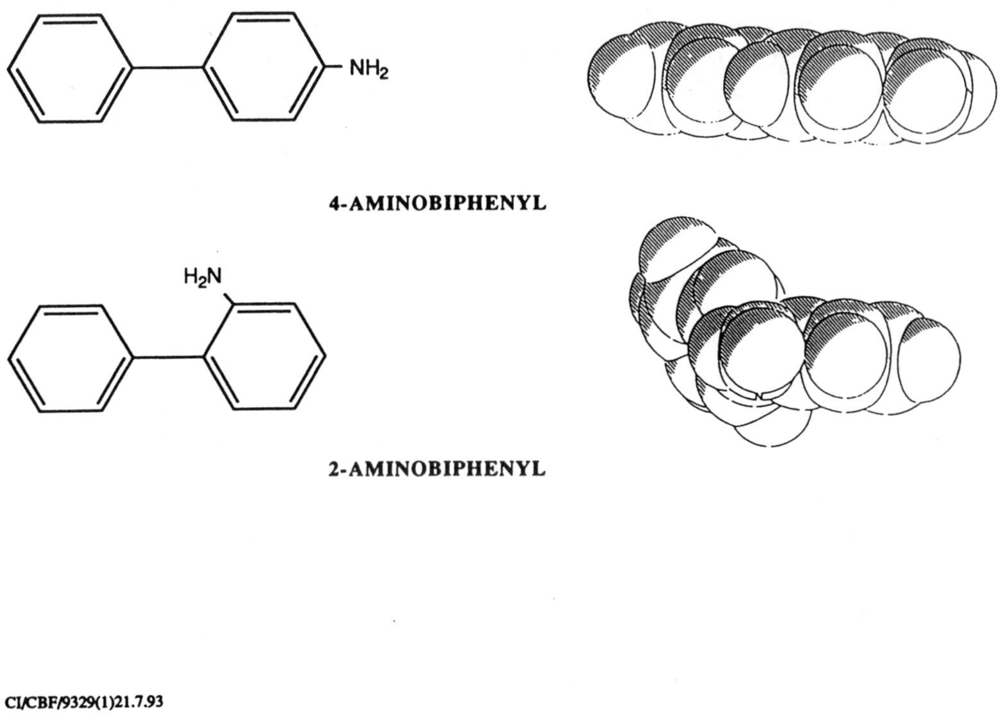


**Figure 13.3** **Space-filled models of 2- and 4-aminobiphenyl**

### 13.5.2 Interaction with the Substrate-binding Sites of Cytochrome P450

The molecular size and shape of a chemical allows it to reach, or be excluded from, the binding site of a cytochrome P450 protein, but it does not reveal how avidly it will interact with the enzyme and how readily the metabolism of the chemical will be facilitated. The enzyme-substrate complex must be activated for oxidative metabolism of the substrate to ensue, so in order to obtain a measure of the interaction between substrate and enzyme, a second parameter, ΔE, has been introduced which estimates the activation energy and is defined as:

$$\Delta E = E(LEMO) - E(HOMO)$$

where: E(HOMO) is the energy of the highest occupied molecular orbital, an indicator of the electron donating capacity of a substrate, and E(LEMO) is the energy of the lowest empty molecular orbital, an indicator of the electron-accepting capacity of a substrate. Generally, CYP1 substrates have low positive or even negative E(LEMO) values, making these good electron acceptors. Their electron-donating capacity, as exemplified by

E(HOMO), like that of substrates of other cytochrome P450 proteins, is also high [76]. The energy of interaction between 2 molecular species is inversely proportional to the difference in energy between the E(HOMO) of the donor molecule and the E(LEMO) of the acceptor molecule [81]. Such interaction may occur when substrates interact with the amino acid residues situated at the cytochrome P450 active site. Thus for a chemical to have a high degree of interaction as an acceptor molecule it must have a small ΔE, *ie*, a high electron-accepting capacity coupled with a low promotional energy, and this tends to be a characteristic of CYP1 substrates (ΔE between 7.1-9.3 eV), compared to those of substrates of other cytochrome P450 families (ΔE between 8.8-11.1 eV or even higher) [76].

When the planarity index of area/depth$^2$, is plotted against ΔE, the CYP1 substrates can readily be discriminated from substrates of other cytochrome P450 families (Figure 13.4). In order to identify CYP2E substrates, a three-dimensional plot is essential using ΔE, area/depth$^2$ and collision diameter as axes. CYP1 and CYP2E substrates form easily recognisable, well-defined clusters (Figure 13.5). Thus, by predicting the possible interaction of a chemical with CYP1 and CYP2E, chemicals may be identified which have the propensity to be metabolically transformed to toxic reactive intermediates. Whether their formation will manifest itself as a carcinogenic, immunotoxic or other toxic response may depend on a number of other factors, including species, sex, dose, diet, etc. Clearly, COMPACT identifies not only carcinogenic potential, but also any form of toxicity that is mediated through a cytochrome P450-generated metabolite.

### 13.5.3 COMPACT Procedure in the Safety Evaluation of Chemicals

The COMPACT procedure involves determining the molecular shape and size of a chemical by defining its structural parameters or dimensions and by calculating its ability to participate in a chemical reaction by acting as an electron acceptor (ΔE) [82,83]. These parameters are determined from molecular orbital calculations and X-ray crystallographic data or, when these are not available, from computer optimization of the total energy using molecular mechanics to identify the most stable configuration [82,84]. A combination of these parameters is used to predict whether a chemical is likely to interact with the CYP1 family or CYP2E subfamily respectively, thereby to result in the formation of a reactive intermediate that can covalently interact with vital cellular components to manifest toxicity in its various forms. For convenience these parameters have been combined to form the COMPACT ratio (CR), defined as area/depth$^2$ divided by the electronic parameter ΔE. High values (*ie*, large area/depth$^2$ and low ΔE) reflect high planarity and electron acceptability, the characteristics of CYP1 substrates. When CR >0.25 there is a high likelihood of the chemical being a CYP1 substrate, whereas with CR <0.1 the chemical is most likely to interact with other cytochrome P450 isoforms. A collision diameter of <6.5 Å renders a chemical a possible CYP2E substrate.

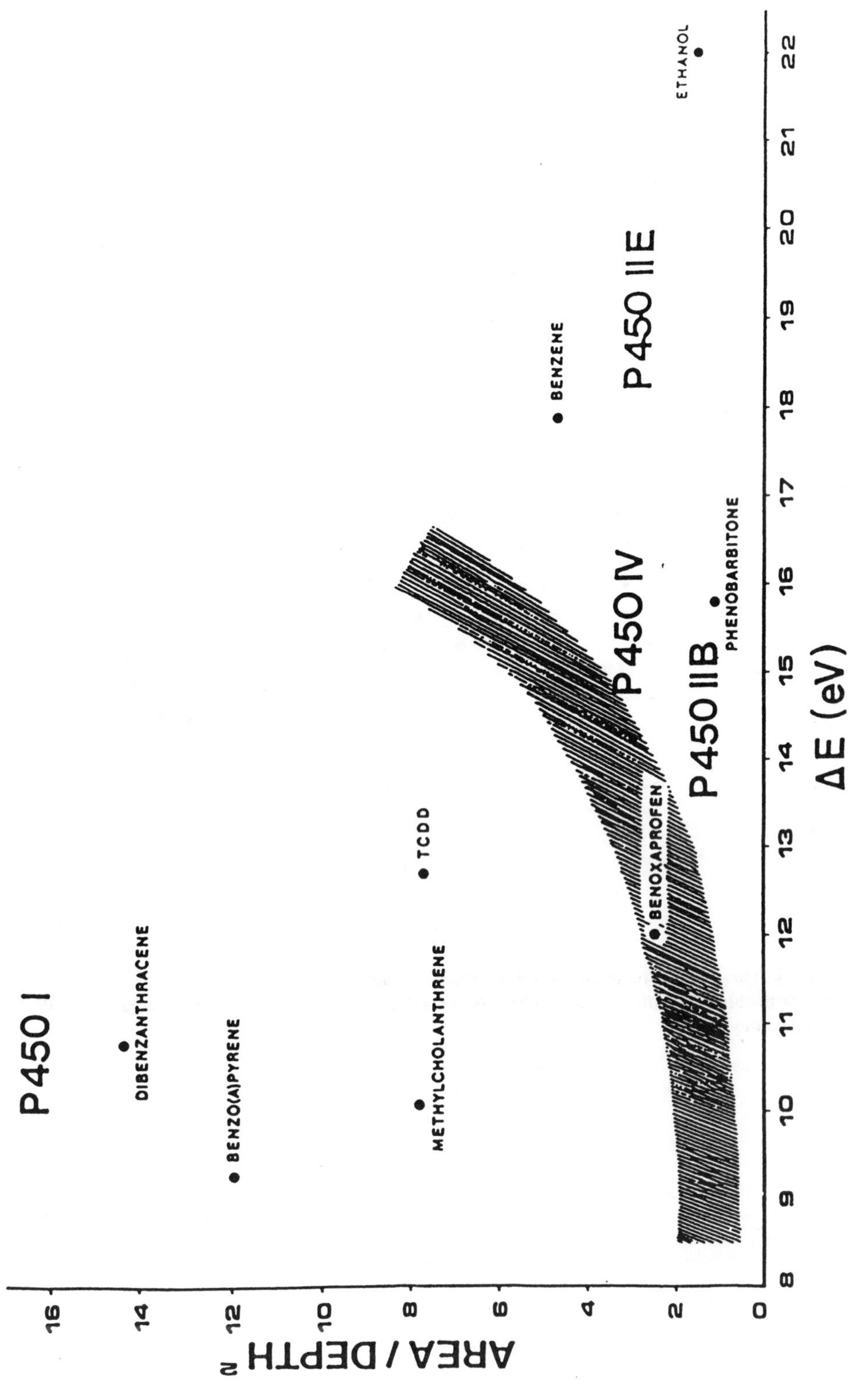


**Figure 13.4** Plot of area/depth$^2$ against $\Delta E$ to distinguish CYP1 substrates

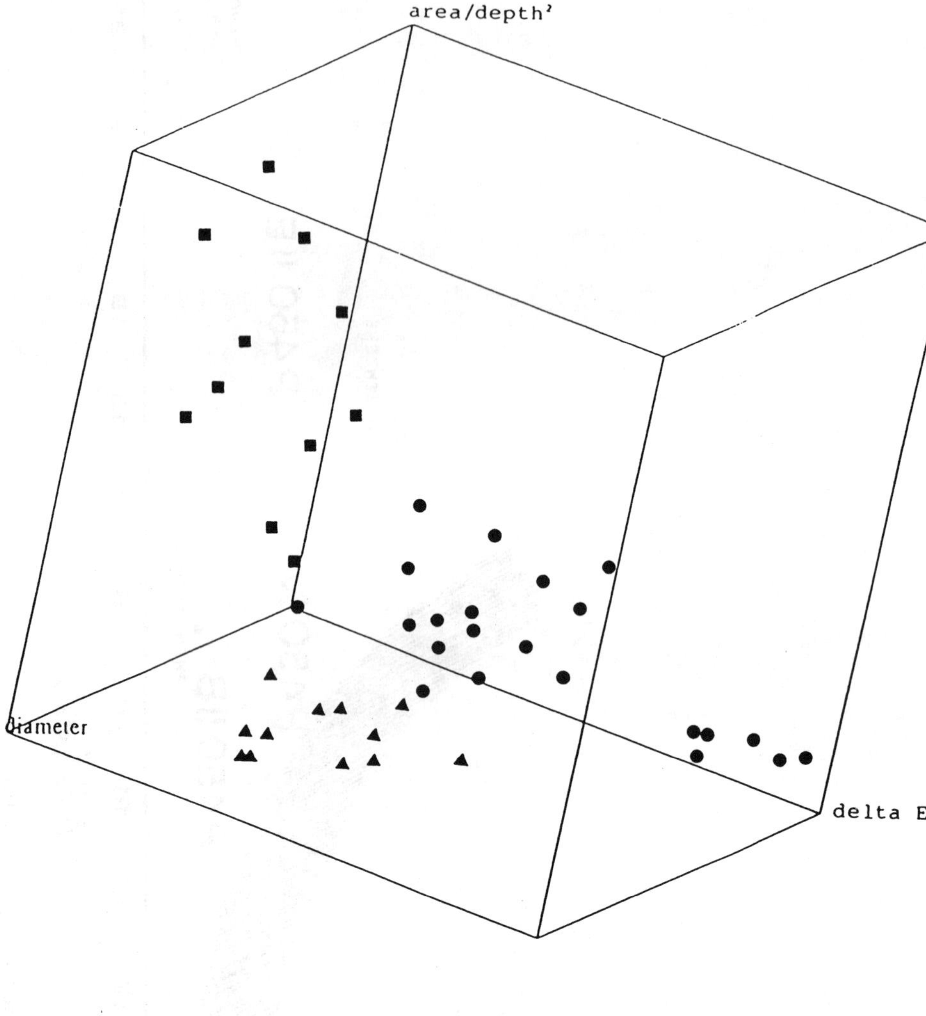


**Figure 13.5** **Three-dimensional plot of cytochrome P450 substrates**
**Substrates with high specificity for CYP1 (■), CYP2E (●), and for other cytochrome P450 families/subfamilies (Δ)**

The performance of the COMPACT assay has been compared with results obtained from long-term animal studies, primarily in rodents. Validation against rodent lifetime bioassay data is hampered by the difficulty of identifying a positive carcinogenic response in animal studies. Such studies are routinely conducted in both sexes of mice and rats, and results are frequently contradictory, not only between species but also between sexes. In our studies concerned with the validation of the COMPACT technique, the most conservative approach was adopted, where a compound was considered to be a carcinogen if any of the sexes of either species showed evidence of carcinogenicity [51]. We have evaluated the first 100 organic chemicals whose carcinogenic potential was assessed in long-term studies in rats and mice as part of the National Toxicology Program (NTP) in the USA. A sensitivity of 92% was attained by the COMPACT procedures as opposed to 60% achieved by the Ames test, undoubtedly the most extensively utilized short-term test for mutagenicity. These findings bear witness to the ability of the COMPACT procedure to detect chemical carcinogens, and it is important to note that the COMPACT procedure recognizes as positive all organic chemicals established as being toxic/carcinogenic to man (Table 13.4). It is also important to emphasize that the ability of the COMPACT method to identify non-carcinogens and other toxicologically inert compounds could not be adequately evaluated, as there was only a very small number of compounds that could be unequivocally described as non-carcinogenic among the 100 NTP compounds studied.

The COMPACT approach is characterized by many advantages over other tests, but also suffers from a number of disadvantages, many of which can be overcome by some limited *ex vivo* animal studies, by a complementary procedure called ENACT (Enzyme Activation in Chemical Toxicity).

### 13.5.4 Advantages of the COMPACT Procedure

The advantages associated with the COMPACT procedure are as follows:

i) A unique feature of the COMPACT technique, being based on molecular orbital calculations, is that it does not require the synthesis of the chemical concerned. Thus it can be performed at the earliest stages of product development, allowing any necessary modifications of the chemical to be effected in order to decrease toxicity. Thus COMPACT is a flexible procedure which can be applied to all classes of organic molecules up to and including 200 atoms;

ii) It is rapid and inexpensive. A week at most is required to evaluate even the most complex structures, including those having an asymmetric centre, thus demanding the evaluation of both enantiomers. For very large chemicals which may cleave into smaller molecules that can themselves undergo oxidative metabolism, it is desirable that these metabolites are also evaluated by COMPACT;

**Table 13.4** **Compact evaluation of known human carcinogens and toxic chemicals**

| Compound | Planarity index (area/depth$^2$) | ΔE (eV) | CYP1 specificity* | Collision diameter (Å) | CYP2E specificity** | Known toxicity |
|---|---|---|---|---|---|---|
| 4-Nitrobiphenyl | 8.4 | 12.7 | Yes | 7.0 | No | Carcinogen |
| 4-Aminobiphenyl | 8.3 | 12.9 | Yes | 6.8 | No | Carcinogen |
| β-Naphthylamine | 7.9 | 12.5 | Yes | 6.4 | Yes | Carcinogen |
| Benzidine | 7.3 | 12.5 | Yes | 7.0 | No | Carcinogen |
| Diethylstilbestrol | 4.8 | 13.0 | Yes | 7.9 | No | Carcinogen |
| Paracetamol | 4.8 | 14.4 | Yes | 6.4 | Yes | Hepatotoxin |
| Dimethylaminoazo-benzene | 3.8 | 10.6 | Yes | 7.4 | No | Carcinogen |
| Tienilic acid | 3.6 | 12.0 | Yes | 7.7 | No | Hepatotoxin |
| Aflatoxin $B_1$ | 3.2 | 11.9 | Yes | 7.7 | No | Carcinogen |
| Vinyl chloride | 2.8 | 16.3 | No | 4.6 | Yes | Hepatocarcinogen |
| Benoxaprofen | 2.5 | 12.0 | Yes | 7.7 | No | Hepatotoxin |
| Chloramphenicol | 2.2 | 13.6 | Yes | 7.6 | No | Acute neonatal toxicity |
| Halothane | 2.0 | 10.8 | Yes | 5.6 | Yes | Hepatotoxin |
| Ethanol | 1.8 | 22.4 | No | 4.5 | Yes | Carcinogen |

*As predicted by the COMPACT procedure by using the area/depth$^2$ vs ΔE plot (Figure 13.4).
**As predicted by COMPACT using a collision diameter value of <6.5Å as positive.

iii) Being a theoretical procedure, COMPACT requires neither animals nor tissues and is consequently more acceptable to the public at large, who may be averse to animal experimentation. Moreover, by identifying toxicity and carcinogenicity at an early stage, animal life is not wasted pursuing biological studies which end up in positive toxicity/carcinogenicity; and,

iv) However, COMPACT is not an empirical procedure, since it is based on current concepts of the function of cytochromes P450 in the bioactivation of chemicals, and particularly on the pivotal role played by CYP1 and CYP2E.

### 13.5.5 Limitations of the COMPACT Procedure

Like every test, COMPACT has a number of limitations, most of which can be readily and effectively overcome by the related procedure ENACT (*vide infra*), based on entirely the same principles as COMPACT. These limitations are:

i) As the COMPACT method requires knowledge of the structure of the chemical, it is not readily adaptable to mixtures, unless of course the chemical structures of the individual components are known;

ii) COMPACT is a semi-quantitative methods which predicts the likely formation of reactive intermediates, but it does not assess the potency of the chemical for CYP1 and CYP2E induction, or the affinity of the chemical for these enzyme isoforms;

iii) COMPACT is not suitable for inorganic compounds. At present no short-term test can evaluate confidently the safety of inorganic compounds;

iv) COMPACT does not take into consideration the pharmacokinetic characteristics of a chemical. It assumes that the chemical possesses the necessary physicochemical properties which make it accessible to the activating enzyme from the site of administration, and this may lead to false positives if not taken into account during the evaluation;

v) Sex, strain and species differences are not detected by the COMPACT procedure used in isolation. Similarly, tissue-specific toxicity and carcinogenicity cannot be recognized as such. However, if a given animal species, strain or sex expresses the enzyme catalyzing the metabolic activation pathway, it will naturally be susceptible to the toxicity/carcinogenicity of this chemical;

vi) At present, COMPACT cannot distinguish between structural isomers, only one of which may be toxic/carcinogenic, unless the isomerism involves a major change in the molecular shape and/or electronic parameters, *eg*, 2- and 4-aminobiphenyls [77]; and,

vii) Large molecular weight compounds may not themselves be CYP1 or CYP2E substrates, but may be metabolized to entities that can serve as substrates of these enzymes. For example, complex azocompounds may be reduced by azo reductases, both of microbial and mammalian origin, to form aromatic amines, such as 4-aminobiphenyl, which are activated by CYP1 enzymes to form genotoxins. An understanding of the pathways of drug metabolism is therefore helpful in evaluating toxicity/carcinogenicity by the COMPACT approach.

## 13.6 The ENACT Procedure

It is logical to assume that toxic chemicals which also induce CYP1 and/or CYP2E enzymes are more likely to be carcinogenic than chemicals which have to rely on the low, constitutive levels of enzyme activity for activation. Cytochrome P450 proteins involved in endogenous metabolism are naturally the major constitutive forms, whereas CYP1 and CYP2E comprise only about 5 and 10% respectively of the total P450, and are therefore minor forms [85,86]. It is reasonable to infer that under such circumstances, where activation depends exclusively on the low basal levels, formation of reactive intermediates will be limited, and the small amounts produced may effectively be detoxicated by tissue nucleophiles such as glutathione and by enzyme systems such as the glutathione S-transferases. If, however, these chemicals can selectively enhance their own activation, *ie*, by induction of the cytochrome P450 isoform that metabolizes them, the generation of reactive intermediates is accelerated and the rate of formation exceeds their rate of detoxication, with a risk that even endogenous nucleophiles essential for detoxication may be depleted, thus increasing the likelihood of DNA damage. It has been proposed that such induction may be important in determining carcinogenic potential [5]. Correlations between CYP1 induction and carcinogenicity have been established for major groups of chemical carcinogens, including polycyclic aromatic hydrocarbons [19], and aromatic amines [20]. Moreover, in successive generations of rats, susceptibility to the carcinogenicity of the CYP1-activated 3′-methyl-4-dimethylaminoazobenzene showed correlation with CYP1 induction [87]. Further studies in carcinogen-resistant and carcinogen-sensitive rat strains, revealed that the resistant strains were less effective in activating 3′-methyl-4-dimethylaminoazobenzene, and this, in turn was associated with low levels of CYP1 induction [88].

Although CYP1 inducers, like 3-methylcholanthrene, also induce detoxication to some extent through other pathways, *eg*, phase II glucuronide conjugation, this is not sufficient to compensate for the much more pronounced induction of CYP1 [89]. Another aspect which is often ignored, is that induction of one cytochrome P450 protein may occur at the expense of others [90,91]. So it is conceivable that CYP1 induction by a chemical may occur at the expense of one or more cytochrome P450 isoforms which could catalyze its deactivation, thus further increasing the activation of the chemical, exacerbating its toxic effect.

An aspect of CYP1 and CYP2E that must be emphasized, is that compounds which induce these isoforms not only enhance the formation of reactive intermediates, but also stimulate cell proliferation. CYP1 inducers achieve this by activating the protein kinase c cascade, through their interaction with the Ah receptor. The high propensity of the CYP2E subfamily to generate ROS ensures that inducers of this subfamily are also potential promoters. It is perhaps not surprising that alcohol ingestion (CYP2E inducer) and tobacco smoking (CYP1 inducer) constitute one of the most carcinogenic combinations in the aetiology of human cancer, as highlighted by many epidemiological studies. Thus CYP1 and CYP2E substrates are complete carcinogens, the former by virtue of their ability to activate the protein kinase c cascade, and the latter by the propensity to produce reactive oxygen species, which similarly stimulate cell proliferation.

### 13.6.1 The ENACT Procedure in the Safety Evaluation of Chemicals

This technique involves exposing animals to the chemical under evaluation through the intended route of administration, at 3 dose levels, covering at least a 100-fold range [92].

The hepatic levels of CYP1A and CYP2E activities are determined by the use of specific, diagnostic chemical probes. It is prudent to confirm such findings through immunological determination of the apoprotein levels since it is conceivable that with some chemicals, characterized by a long half-life and high affinity interaction with the haem moiety of cytochrome P450, residual levels of the chemicals may be present in the incubation systems, attached to the haem, preventing oxygen binding and resulting in gross under-estimation of the inductive effect.

The ENACT procedure complements and extends the COMPACT assessment. Its principal advantages and limitations are as follows:

i) Unlike COMPACT it requires small amounts of the material to be administered to animals. ENACT uses a limited number of animals, a small fraction of that usually employed in the long-term toxicity and carcinogenicity studies. It also lacks the flexibility of the computer method where changes of the molecular structure can be introduced and evaluated almost instantly;

ii) Similar to COMPACT, the ENACT procedure is rapid and inexpensive. Such studies can be completed in less than 2 weeks, at a cost of GB£ 3500 per compound;

iii) It is suitable for mixtures, and in this aspect it can overcome this shortcoming of the COMPACT procedure;

iv) One of the most important advantages of the ENACT assay is that it takes into consideration the pharmacokinetic characteristics of the chemical which are not considered in the COMPACT approach. Moreover, such studies may be extended to investigate different routes of administration, accounting for such phenomena as the first pass effect;

v) ENACT can discern between carcinogenic and non-carcinogenic isomers on the basis of CYP1 induction, as already illustrated for aromatic amines, polycyclic aromatic hydrocarbons and aminoazobenzenes (Table 13.5);

vi) A principal attribute of the ENACT procedure is that it can recognize sex, species, strain and tissue differences, information which is of great value to the toxicologist;

vii) The ENACT procedure is essential to evaluate the safety of chemicals which are borderline in the COMPACT assessment, and thus the 2 procedures are complementary; and,

viii) Perhaps the most important attribute of ENACT is its quantitative nature, allowing dose-dependent relationships to be developed and threshold doses to be established. If, for example, the therapeutic dose of a drug is substantially below the threshold dose for induction, then the chemical may be used safely and merits further investigation.

## 13.7 Conclusions

The rapidly increasing development costs of new drugs and other environmental chemicals, coupled with the increasing cost of promoting a new product, result in very limited finance being available for novel, basic research, running the risk of stifling the discovery of truly novel and original chemicals which entail a high financial risk. The only apparent approach available to deal with this emerging, social problem is to adopt new, less expensive, short-term methods of safety evaluation which would eventually replace the costly, time-consuming rodent lifespan bioassay. That is, safety evaluation should be prospective and not delayed until the later stages of product development, as is now the custom. Computer-assisted methods, utilizing software of high sophistication will inevitably play a major role in these new developments. Such computer-assisted safety evaluation will be complemented by limited, *in vitro*, toxicological studies. The COMPACT and ENACT procedures probably represent the first step in such an approach.

**Table 13.5 Induction of CYP1 activity by structural isomers and structural analogues**

| Isomeric compounds | CYP1A1 induction* (% of control activity) | CYP1A2 induction** (% of control activity) | Carcinogenicity |
|---|---|---|---|
| Benzo(a)pyrene | 7400 | 100 | Carcinogen [19] |
| Benzo(e)pyrene | 600 | 80 | Non-carcinogen |
| 15,16-Dihydro-2-methylcyclopenta[a] phenanthren-17-one 500 | 70 | | Non-carcinogen [19] |
| 15,16-Dihydro-11-methylcyclopenta[a] phenanthren-17-one | 1300 | 50 | Carcinogen |
| 2-Aminobiphenyl | 85 | 65 | Non-carcinogen [20] |
| 4-Aminobiphenyl | 205 | 245 | Carcinogen |
| α-Naphthylamine | 100 | 240 | Non-carcinogen [20] |
| β-Naphthylamine | 910 | 210 | Carcinogen |
| 2-Acetylaminofluorene | 465 | 335 | Carcinogen [21] |
| 4-Acetylaminofluorene | 300 | 145 | Non-carcinogen |
| Diethylaminoazobenzene | 110 | 115 | Non-carcinogen† |
| 3-Methoxy-4-aminoazobenzene | 795 | 1015 | Carcinogen |
| o-Aminoazotoluene | 712 | 395 | Carcinogen |

*As exemplified by the O-deethylation of ethoxyresorufin, and **by either the O-demethylation of methoxyresorufin or the metabolic activation of Glu-P-1 to mutagens in the Ames test. In all cases Western Blot analysis supported the enzymic studies. All activities were expressed in terms of total cytochrome P450 concentration.

†Cheung, Gray and Ioannides, Unpublished.

## 13.8 Acknowledgements

The authors thank the Humane Research Trust, Science and Engineering Research Council, and the Ministry of Agriculture, Fisheries and Food, for financial support.

## 13.9 References


[1] Pessayre, D., Dolder, A., Artigou, J.Y., Wandscheer, J.C., Descatoire, V., Degott, C., and Benhamou, J.P., *Gastroenterology*, 1979, **77**, 264-271.

[2] Ioannides, C. and Parke, D.V., *Drug Metab. Rev.*, 1990, **22**, 1-86.

[3] Barnett, C.R., Flatt, P.R., and Ioannides, C., 'Interrelationships between insulin-dependent diabetes mellitus and enhanced toxicity to environmental chemicals, drugs and carcinogens', in: *Food, Nutrition and Chemical Toxicity*, Parke, D.V., Ioannides, C., and Walker, R., (Eds), London, Smith Gordon Nishimura, 1993, pp. 161-170.

[4] Sohn, O.S., Fiala, E.S., Puz, C., Hamilton, S.R., and Williams, G.M., *Cancer Res.*, 1987, **47**, 3123-3129.

[5] Ioannides, C., *Biochem. Soc. Trans.*, 1990, **18**, 32-34.

[6] Lewis, D.F.V., Ioannides, C., and Parke, D.V., *Biochem. Pharmacol.*, 1986, **25**, 2179-2181.

[7] Shimada, T. and Guengerich, F.P., *Cancer Res.*, 1990, **50**, 2036-2043.

[8] Shimada, T., Yamazaki, H., Shimura, H., Tanaka, R., and Guengerich, F.P., *Carcinogenesis*, 1990, **11**, 103-110.

[9] Butler, M.A., Iwasaki, M., Guengerich, F.P., and Kadlubar, F.F., *Proc. Natl. Acad. Sci. (USA)*, 1989, **86**, 7596-7700.

[10] McManus, M.E., Burgess, W.M., Veronese, M.E., Huggett, A., Quattrochi, L.C., and Tukey, R.H., *Cancer Res.*, 1990, **50**, 3367-3376.

[11] Gonzalez, F.J., *TIPS Reviews*, 1992, **13**, 346-352.

[12] De Matteis, F., Dawson, S.J., Boobis, A.R., and Comoglio, A., *Mol. Pharmacol.*, 1991, **40**, 668-691.

[13] Guengerich, F.P., *Cancer Res.*, 1988, **48**, 2946-2954.

[14] Ioannides, C. and Parke, D.V., *Biochem. Pharmacol.*, 1987, **36**, 4197-4207.

[15] Phillipson, C.E., Godden, P.M.M., Lum, P.Y., Ioannides, C., and Parke, D.V., *Biochem J.*, 1984, **221**, 81-88.

[16] Ryan, D.E. and Levin, W., *Pharmacol. Ther.*, 1990, **45**, 153-239.

[17] Conney, A.H., Pantuck, E.J., Hsia, K.C., Garland, W.A., Anderson, K.E., Alvares, A.P., and Kappas, A., *Clin. Pharmacol. Ther.*, 1976, **20**, 633-642.

[18] Pantuck, E.J., Pantuck, C.B., Garland, W.A., Min, B.H., Wattenberg, L.W., Anderson, K.E., Kappas, A., and Conney, A.H., *Clin. Pharmacol. Ther.*, 1979, **25**, 88-95.

[19] Ayrton, A.D., McFarlane, M., Walker, R., Neville, S., Coombs, M.M., and Ioannides, C., *Toxicology*, 1990, **60**, 173-186.

[20] Ayrton, A.D., McFarlane, M., Walker, R., Neville, S., and Ioannides, C., *Carcinogenesis*, 1990, **11**, 803-809.

[21] Ioannides, C., Cheung, Y.L., Wilson, J.D., Lewis, D.F.V., and Gray, T.J.B., *Chem. Res. Toxicol.*, 1993, **6**, 535-541.

[22] Nebert, D.W., *Crit. Rev. Toxicol.*, 1989, **20**, 153-174.

[23] Paigen, B., Holmes, P.A., Morrow, A., and Mitchell, D., *Cancer Res.*, 1986, **46**, 3321-3324.

[24] Serabjit-Singh, C.J., Bend, J.R., and Philpot, R.M., *Mol. Pharmacol.*, 1985, **28**, 72-79.

[25] Barnett, C.R., Wilson, J., Wolf, C.R., Flatt, P.R., and Ioannides, C., *Biochem. Pharmacol.*, 1992, **43**, 1255-1261.

[26] Barnett, C.R., Flatt, P.R., and Ioannides, C., *Biochem. Pharmacol.*, 1992, **40**, 393-397.

[27] Sesadic, D., Boobis, A.R., and Davies, D.S., *Br. J. Clin. Pharmacol.*, 1988, **26**, 363-372.

[28] Song, B.-J., Gelboin, H.V., Park, S.S., Tsukos, G.C., and Friedman, F.K., *Science*, 1985, **228**, 490-492.

[29] Pasanen, M., Haaparanta, T., Sundin, M., Sivonen, P., Vakahangas, K., Raunio, H., Hines, R., Gustafsson, J.A., and Pelkonen, O., *Toxicology*, 1990, **62**, 175-187.

[30] Vakahangas, K., Raunio, H., Pasanen, M., Sivonen, P., Park, S.S., Gelboin, H.V., and Pelkonen, O., *J. Biochem. Toxicol.*, 1989, **4**, 79-86.

[31] Petruzzelli, S., Camus, A-M., Carozzi, L., Gheladucci, L., Rindi, M., Menconi, G., Angeletti, C.A., Ahotupa, M., Hietanen, E., Aitio, A., Saracci, R., Bartsch, H., and Guntini, C., *Cancer Res.*, 1988, **48**, 4695-4700.

[32] Wong, T.K., Domin, B.A., Bent, P.E., Blanton, T.E., Anderson, M.W., and Philpot, R.M., *Cancer. Res.*, 1988, **46**, 999-1004.

[33] Diaz, D., Fabre, I., Daujat, M., Saint Aubert, B., Michael, H., and Maurel, P., *Gastroenterology*, 1990, **99**, 734-747.

[34] McDonnel, W.M., Scheiman, J.M., and Traber, P.G., *Gastroenterology*, 1992, **103**, 1509-1516.

[35] Rost, K.L., Brosicke, H., Brockmoller, J., Scheffler, M., Helge, H., and Roots, I., *Clin. Pharmacol. Ther.*, 1992, **52**, 170-180.

[36] Anttila, S., Hietanen, E., Vainio, H., Camus, A.-M., Gelboin, H.V., Park, S.S., Heikkila, L., Karjalainen, A., and Bartsch, H., *Int. J. Cancer*, 1991, **47**, 681-683.

[37] Anttila, S., Vainio, H., Hietanen, E., Camus, A.-M., Malaveille, C., Brun, G., Husgafvel-Pursiainen, K., Heikkila, L., Karjalainen, A., and Bartsch, H., *Environ. Hlth. Persp.*, 1992, **98**, 179-182.

[38] Karki, N.T., Pokela, R., Nuutinen, L., and Pelkonen, O., *Int. J. Cancer*, 1989, **39**, 565-570.

[39] Kouri, R.E., Mckinney, C.E., Slomiany, D.J., Snodgrass, D.R., Wray, N.P., and McLemore, T.L., *Cancer Res.*, 1982, **42**, 5030-5037.

[40] Korsgaard, R., Trell, E., Simonsson, B.G., Stiksa, G., Janzon, L., Hood, B., and Oldbring, J., *J. Cancer Res. Clin. Oncol.*, 1982, **108**, 286-289.

[41] McLemore, T.L., Adelberg, S., Liu, M.C., McMahon, N.A., Yu, S.J., Hubbard, W.C., Czerwinski, M., Wood, T.G., Storens, R., Lubet, R.A., Eggleston, J.C., Boyd, M.R., and Hines, R.N., *J. Natl. Cancer Inst.*, 1990, **82**, 1333-1339.

[42] Nebert, D.W., *Mutat. Res.*, 1991, **247**, 267-281.

[43] Kadlubar, F.F., Butler, M.A., Kaderlik, K.R., Chou, H.-C., and Lang, N.P., *Environ. Hlth. Persp.*, 1992, **98**, 69-74.

[44] Nakachi, K., Imai, K., Hayashi, S., Watanabe, J., and Kawajiri, K., *Cancer Res.*, 1991, **51**, 5177-5180.

[45] Tefre, T., Ryberg, D., Hangen, A., Nebert, D.W., Skang, V., Brøgger, A., and Børresen, A.-L., *Pharmacogenetics*, 1991, **1**, 20-25.

[46] Bartsch, H., Castegnaro, M., Rojas, M., Camus, A.-M., Alexandrov, K., and Lang, M., 'Expression of pulmonary P4501A1 and carcinogen adduct formation in high risk subjects for tobacco-related lung cancer', in: *Toxicology from Discovery and Experimentation to the Human Perspective*, Chambers, P.L., Chambers, S.M., Bolt, H., and Preziosi, P., (Eds), Amsterdam, Elsevier, 1992, pp. 477-483.

[47] Pyykko, K., Tuimala, R., Aalto, L., and Perkio, T., *Br. J. Cancer*, 1991, **63**, 596-600.

[48] Butler, M.A., Guengerich, F.P., and Kadlubar, F.F., *Cancer Res.*, 1989, **49**, 25-31.

[49] Wrighton, S.A., Campanile, C., Thomas, P.E., Maines, S.L., Watkins, P.B., Parker, G., Mendez-Picon, G., Hanin, M., Shively, J.E., Levin, W., and Guzelian, P.S., *Mol. Pharmacol.*, 1986, **29**, 405-410.

[50] Minchin, R.F., McManus, M.E., Boobis, A.R., Davis, D.S., and Thorgeirsson, S.S., *Carcinogenesis*, 1985, **6**, 1721-1724.

[51] Lewis, D.F.V., Ioannides, C., and Parke, D.V., *Mutat. Res.*, 1993, **291**, 61-77.

[52] Ekstrom, G., Cronholm, T., and Ingelman-Sundberg, M., *Biochem. J.*, 1986, **233**, 755-761.

[53] Cederbaum, A.I., *Ann. NY Acad. Sci.*, 1987, **492**, 35-49.

[54] Yang, C.S., Tu, Y.Y., Koop, D.R., and Coon, M.J., *Cancer Res.*, 1985, **45**, 1140-1145.

[55] Wrighton, S.A., Thomas, P.E., Ryan, D.E., and Levin, W., *Arch. Biochem. Biophys.*, 1987, **258**, 292-297.

[56] Yoo, J.S.H., Guengerich, F.P., and Yang, C.S., *Cancer Res.*, 1988, **48**, 1499-1504.

[57] Levin, W., Thomas, P.E., Oldfield, N., and Ryan, D.E., *Arch. Biochem. Biophys.*, 1986, **248**, 158-165.

[58] Guengerich, F.P., Kim, D.-H., and Iwasaki, M., *Chem. Res. Toxicol*, 1991, **4**, 168-179.

[59] Raucy, J.L., Kraner, J.C., and Lasker, J.M., *Crit. Rev. Toxicol.*, 1993, **23**, 1-20.

[60] Sohn, O.S., Ishizaki, H., Yang, C.S., and Fiala, E.S., *Carcinogenesis*, 1991, **12**, 127-131.

[61] Koop, D.R., Morgan, E.T., Tarr, G.E., and Coon, M.J., *J. Biol. Chem.*, 1982, **257**, 8472-8480.

[62] Thummel, K.E., Kharasch, E.D., Podoll, T., and Kunze, K., *Drug Metab. Disp.*, 1993, **21**, 350-357.

[63] Raucy, J.L., Lasker, J.M., Lieber, C.S., and Black, M., *Arch. Biochem. Biophys.*, 1989, **271**, 270-283.

[64] Koop, D.R., Crump, B.L., Nordblom, G.D., and Coon, M.J., *Proc. Natl. Acad. Sci. (USA)*, 1985, **82**, 4065-4069.

[65] Barnett, C.R., Petrides, L., Wilson, J., Flatt, P.R., and Ioannides, C., *Xenobiotica*, 1992, **22**, 1441-1450.

[66] Bellward, G.D., Chang, T., Rodrigues, B., McNeill, J.H., Maines, S., Ryan, D.E., Levin, W., and Thomas, P.E., *Mol. Pharmacol.*, 1988, **33**, 140-143.

[67] Hong, J., Pan, J., Gonzalez, F.J. Gelboin, H.V., and Yang, C.S., *Biochem. Biophys. Res. Commun.*, 1987, **142**, 1077-1083.

[68] Song, B.J., Veech, R.L., and Saenger, P.J., *Clin. Endocrinol. Metab.*, 1990, **71**, 1036-1040.

[69] Mufti, S.J., Becker, G., and Sipes, I.G., *Carcinogenesis*, 1989, **10**, 303-309.

[70] Koop, D.R. and Casazza, J.P., *J. Biol. Chem.*, 1985, **260**, 13607-13612.

[71] Lasker, J.M., Raucy, J., Kobota, S., Bloswick, B.P., Black, M., and Lieber, C.S., *Biochem. Biophys. Res. Commun.*, 1987, **148**, 232-238.

[72] Patten, C.J., Ishizaki, H., Aoyama, T., Lee, M., Ning, S.M., Huang, W., Gonzalez, F.J., and Yang, C.S., *Arch. Biochem. Biophys.*, 1992, **299**, 163-171.

[73] Perrot, N., Nalpas, B., Yang, C.S., and Beaune, P.H., *Eur. J. Clin. Invest.*, 1989, **19**, 549-555.

[74] Wrighton, S.A., Thomas, P.E., Molowa, D.T., Haniu, M., Shively, J.F., Maines, S.L., Watkins, P.B., Parker, G., Mendez-Picon, G., Levin, W., and Guzelian, P.S., *Biochemistry (USA)*, 1986, **25**, 6731-6735.

[75] Peter, R., Bocker, R., Beaune, P.H., Iwasaki, M., Guengerich, F.P., and Yang, C.S., *Chem. Res. Toxicol.*, 1990, **3**, 566-573.

[76] Lewis, D.F.V., Ioannides, C., and Parke, D.V., *Chem.-Biol. Interactions*, 1987, **64**, 39-60.

[77] Ioannides, C., Lewis, D.F.V., Trinick, J., Neville, S., Sertkaya, N.N., Kajabf, M., and Gorrod, J.W., *Carcinogenesis*, 1989, **10**, 1403-1407.

[78] Shimada, T. and Sawabe, Y., *Toxicol. Appl. Pharmacol.*, 1983, **70**, 486-493.

[79] Kaminsky, L.S., Kennedy, M.W., Adams, S.M., and Guengerich, F.P., *Biochemistry*, 1981, **20**, 7379-7384.

[80] Parke, D.V., Ioannides, C., and Lewis, D.F.V., *FEST*, 1986, 14-19.

[81] Klopman, G., *J. Am. Chem. Soc.*, 1968, **90**, 223-234.

[82] Parke, D.V., Ioannides, C., and Lewis, D.F.V., *ATLA*, 1990, **18**, 81-102.

[83] Ioannides, C., Lewis, D.F.V., and Parke, D.V., *Eur. J. Cancer Prevention*, 1993, **2**, 275-282.

[84] Lewis, D.F.V., Ioannides, C., and Parke, D.V., *Toxicol. Lett.*, 1989, **45**, 1-13.

[85] Luster, M.I., Lawson, L.D., Linko, P., and Goldstein, J.A., *Mol. Pharmacol.*, 1982, **23**, 252-257.

[86] Thomas, P.E., Bandiera, S., Maines, S.L., Ryan, D.E., and Levin, W., *Biochemistry (USA)*, 1987, **26**, 2280-2289.

[87] Yoshimoto, F., Masuda, S., Higashi, T., Nishii, T., Takamisawa, I., Tateishi, N., and Sakamoto, Y., *Cancer Res.*, 1985, **45**, 6155-6159.

[88] Yano, M., Higashi, T., Kano, S., Tateishi, N., Kido, Y., Takesada, M., Higashi, K., and Sakamoto, Y., *Cancer Res.*, 1989, **49**, 5352-5357.

[89] Orzechowski, A., Schrenk, D., and Bock, K.W., *Carcinogenesis*, 1992, **13**, 2227-2232.

[90] Yeowell, H.N., Linko, P., Hodgson, E., and Goldstein, J.A., *Arch. Biochem. Biophys.*, 1985, **243**, 408-419.

[91] Vlasuk, G.P. and Walz, F.G. Jr., *Arch. Biochem. Biophys.*, 1982, **214**, 248-259.

[92] Parke, D.V., Ioannides, C., and Lewis, D.F.V., *Can. J. Physiol. Pharmacol.*, 1991, **69**, 537-549.

# 14. Environmental Monitoring: Use of Luminescent Bacteria

Don L. Isenberg and Anthony Bulich

## 14.1 Introduction

In order to assess the potential hazard and hence its safety of a chemical substance, a biological or chemical process, or an environmental incident, chemical or biological monitoring is required. Over the years sophisticated analytical methods have been developed and used for both the identification and quantification of inorganic and organic chemicals in air, soil and water samples [1]. In the majority of cases these methods are substance specific, as compared to non-specific techniques which measure biochemical oxygen demand (BOD), chemical oxygen demand (COD), total organic carbon (TOC), volatile organic carbon (VOC), pH, conductivity, etc.

More recently, measurements based upon the use of specific biological methods (bioassays) have become more validated and widely used. Biological measurement systems have significant advantages over chemical specific analytical test methods which cannot measure actual biological effects.

Whilst there is a growing collection of data on the toxicology and ecotoxicology on some chemicals substances, many compounds are in common usage for which there is little relevant toxicological data available [2,3]. While newly notified substances are subject to step-wise toxicological testing procedures, no such program is available currently for pre-existing substances [4].

During the past 10 years, however, there have been a number of biological based methods developed. These include, *eg,* DNA probes [5], induction of P450 cytochrome enzymes, 7-ethoxyresorufin-O-deethylase (EROD), etc. [6,7]. Perhaps the most commonly used technique is that based on the metabolic activity of the luminescent bacterium *Photobacterium phosphoreum* [8,9]. These simple tests are not used in isolation but should form part of a battery of other tests, which could include invertebrates, fish and simple care tests. This chapter will focus upon the use of bioluminescent bacteria as a biological based test system for measuring several types of toxicity, including acute, chronic and genotoxicity.

## 14.2 The Microtox® Acute Toxicity Test

The Microtox acute toxicity test is based upon measuring metabolic inhibition using a standard suspension of luminescent bacteria. Since bioluminescence is a direct measure of metabolic activity in these organisms, measuring the rate of light output is a simple way to measure metabolic inhibition (toxicity). The test system has been in use for over 10 years and is the subject of many reports, reviews and application studies as well as being an accepted standard in several countries [10-16]. The test is based on using a freeze-dried suspension of *Photobacterium phosphoreum* strain NRRL-B-11177, which was earlier referred to as *Vibrio fischeri* strain NRRL-B-11177. This procedure has been revalidated for the rapid characterization of internal and external process waters, effluents, rivers, etc. Excursions and trends in waste streams can be correlated with changes in materials or processes, giving chemists, biologists and process engineers a powerful tool for process monitoring and to assist in meeting effluent compliance requirements. This test method has many applications in wastewater analysis, sediment testing, hazardous waste testing, material screening, quality control, and plant process control.

### 14.2.1 Databases and Correlation with Other Species

A useful table has been published by Kaiser [17] which lists Microtox $EC_{50}$ values for over 1000 chemical substances. Numerous comparative studies have been published where the sensitivity of the test method has been compared with fish and invertebrate species and for consideration of structure/activity relationships [18-20].

### 14.2.2 The Principles of the Microtox Acute Test

Luminescent bacteria possess useful attributes which support their use as biosensors for toxicity testing. These strains divert up to 10% of their metabolic respiratory energy into a flavo-protein and luciferase pathway. This energy transfer depends on the addition of oxygen, reduced flavin mononucleotide (FMNH), and a long chain aldehyde to produce an excited state. This complex then decays to the ground state, releasing water and light and recycling the flavo-protein and luciferase [9].

This dynamic metabolic system functions at 10 to 100 times the rate found in mammalian cells, and can be quantified easily by measuring the rate of light output from a bacterial suspension. Any change in metabolic activity or disruption of cellular structure due to the presence of toxic substances, results in a rapid change in the rate of bioluminescence. Test sensitivity is partially explained by the small cell size which gives a high surface to volume ratio.

Like most bacteria, the Microtox strain has many metabolic pathways which function in respiration, oxidative phosphorylation, osmotic stabilization, and transport of chemicals and nutrients into and out of the cell, and which are located within or near the cytoplasmic membrane. The luciferase pathway [9], which functions as a shunt for electrons directly to oxygen at the level of reduced flavin mono-nucleotide, is also located within the cell membrane complex. This, coupled with lack of membrane-aided compartmentalization of internal functions, gives many target sites at or near the cytoplasmic membrane. These factors all contribute to a rapid response of the organisms to a broad spectrum of toxic substances.

### 14.2.3 Data Handling

When life forms are exposed to toxic chemicals, theory [21] predicts a power curve relationship between concentration and response, where the response is measured as a ratio of activity lost to activity remaining (Gamma or Γ). A log-log transform is predicted to be a linear function and is the basis for using linear regression as a method for characterizing toxic effects.

For Microtox, linear regression compares sets of Γ *versus* concentration data from an assay to determine how closely the data fits the theory, *ie,* to determine if there is a true dose response relationship. Assuming that there is, then an equation can be derived to predict a most probable $EC_{50}$ or $EC_{xx}$. The statistical process attempts to explain sources of variation or variance from the observed data. If there is a true dose/response, then most of the variability can be explained by theory. The statistic which expresses the unexplained portion of the data is the *residual variance.* It is a measure of the variation of the log Γ about the regression line. The larger the residual variance, the less confidence there is in the regression equation. Its source may be human error (*eg,* pipetting) or true deviation from theory. Residual variance is used to compute a 95% *confidence factor* to give the upper and lower concentrations which define the $EC_{50}$, with 95% accuracy.

The *correlation coefficient (R)* is an alternative means to express how near the data describes a straight line. It is a measure of the degree of the relationship between Γ and concentrations. Most Microtox data indicate R values of $\geq 0.97$.

### 14.2.4 Reducing Dependency on Animal Testing

Within the United States of America alone, some 20 million animals (1984 data) were used for a variety of laboratory studies, biomedical and behavioural research, toxicity testing, education, and for various monitoring requirements. Public interest in animal welfare has instigated academic and emotional debates over many of these uses of animals. Stimulated by this concern there has been an effort to identify, refine, and validate non-animal 'alternatives' for research, product safety testing, and monitoring [22].

Over the years a number of alternative test systems have been described in the literature. These include the use of tissue culture, excised animal organs, bacterial systems, computer modeling, protozoan mortality inhibition, chorioallantoic membrane inflammation, and specific biochemical reactions [23]. Most of these alternative test procedures have been proposed or developed with the objective of reducing or replacing animal $LD_{50}$ toxicity tests and the controversial Draize rabbit eye irritancy test [24].

Burton *et al* [25] investigated the sensitivity and specificity of the luminescent bacteria toxicity test (LBT) as compared with the USP mouse safety test, rabbit muscular implantation, mouse systemic injection, and the MEM elution tissue culture test. The samples included industrial plastics/medical devices and low density polyethylene containing different concentrations of toxic organic substances. The results of these comparative tests showed the LBT to be significantly more sensitive than the animal tests and slightly more sensitive than the tissue culture acute toxicity assay for the samples tested.

In another study, several *in vitro* were evaluated as screens for predicting the ocular irritancy potential of consumer products [26]. The 17 substances examined included soaps, laundry agents and cleaners which had been tested previously using the rabbit low volume eye irritation test. The *in vitro* test with the highest correlation with the rabbit eye irritancy test was the Microtox test. When the eye irritancy test maximum average score *versus* the $LC_{50}^{-1}$ concentration was compared, the resulting correlations coefficient was 0.94. A parallel study compared the sensitivity of Microtox with the MEM elution test using the L-929 mouse fibroblast cell line on medical device extracts. In general, the LBT was more sensitive than the animal cells which was consistent with Burton *et al*'s findings [25].

There are a number of reasons why a toxicity test can be more sensitive than others [27]. One significant difference between the LBT and the L-929 cytotoxicity test is the composition of the test median. The luminescent bacteria are suspended in a simple 2% sodium chloride solution, whereas the tissue culture cells require serum to supplemented their growth. Serum proteins and amino acids can complex with many chemicals, particularly metals, and thus render them unavailable to the test cells [27]. It was noted that for the 12 samples which were scored non-toxic with the LBT but positive to tissue culture, the Microtox Γ were <1.0 criteria established for a positive result. Depending upon the products or materials under test, it may be practical and appropriate to use different Γ values as a failure point. These could correspond with the failure concentration established with the tissue culture or animal test for a specific class of material or product category. The highest sensitivity of the LBT should not be viewed as a cause of more materials failing the test, but rather an opportunity to set the failure point at a realistic and safe concentration. These correlations are discussed in depth by Jones [24].

Hence, it may be considered that the luminescent bacteria toxicity test may be used successfully for preliminary screening of toxic concentrations of potentially irritating compounds or products. The LBT is rapid, economical, standardized, and quantitative. It is a useful tool as part of a battery of *in vitro* tests used for the reduction or partial replacement of certain animal tests.

### 14.2.5 Use in the Water Industry

The luminescent bacteria test, in particular the Microtox acute test, is now being used considerably in the water industry for monitoring and control purposes [28-30]. It is recognized in regulatory standards in Canada, France, Germany, The Netherlands, Spain, Sweden, United Kingdom, and the United States [31]. Further draft documents are being produced by AFNOR, DIN, ISO, etc., and a detailed specification is currently being drafted by the United Kingdom's Department of Environment's Standing Committee of Analysts.

One of the outstanding examples of the use of Microtox in jurisdiction was the prosecution of Clean-A-Drain of Ditton, near Maidstone, England. This waste disposal company discharged a tanker of over 10,000 l of waste to the River Taff at Merthyr Tydfil, Wales in October 1988 resulting in the death of 7000 fish. The company was ordered to pay fines, costs, and compensation, totalling some GB £71,000.

This prosecution depended heavily on toxicological evidence, and in particular upon Microtox data. It was the first time Microtox had been used in a successful pollution prosecution. Two of the outstanding advantages of the test when applied by the National Rivers Authority — Welsh Region, were the speed of the test (the estimation was completed in 40 minutes) and the small volume of samples available (about 3 ml). This prosecution would have been difficult to achieve had fish testing been the only alternative.

Microtox is used routinely to help industrial or municipal facilities achieve or remain in compliance regarding effluent toxicity. Plant operators are increasingly conscious of the need to avoid both costly and negative publicity connected with a non-compliance situation. The increasing use of a battery of biological and chemicals specific tests to monitor toxicity levels is becoming more routine. Each facility must develop an effective toxicity control program which fits their particular needs. Such programs usually include the following 4 steps in toxicity control:

i) Identify the toxicity monitoring points;

ii) Establish a baseline of normal toxicity data;

iii) Determine the toxicity control limits; and,

iv) Define a corrective action plan.

The key to implementation is a continuous flow of relevant and speedy toxicity information. Timely information cannot be provided by many toxicity tests, especially those which require some days to obtain results. For effective system control, toxicity information is required in minutes and the use of reliable technology is now available to provide this monitoring information, especially if on-line techniques are used. The Microtox test is now available in an on-line mode [32] which allows for an analysis to be conducted automatically every 30 mins. This test system can operate unattended for 7 d. This ensures that the operator will know what is happening, rather than what has happened, and thus be able to take effective corrective action when toxicity monitoring indicates a biological event outside of acceptable limits.

The ideas of Bulich [33] are reflected by those of Loeber [34] in describing the pinpointing of toxicity sources.

Real-time toxicity testing will enable a toxicity reduction evaluation to be made speedily when unacceptable levels of toxicity are detected by monitoring of industrial waste streams, and thus result in rapid corrective action. Hence decisions can be made before such toxic insults cause interference with processes in a downstream wastewater treatment plant, or cause environmental damage.

### 14.2.6 Needs for Rapid Toxicity Monitoring in War Zones (see chapters by Campbell, Knight, Kulkarni and Nangle)

Drinking water standards are defined in legislation such as EC Directive 80/778/EEC, and the parameters are based on life-time exposures. It is not realistic to expect that such standards could be maintained fully on the battlefield. It is vital to be able to supply adequate quantities of potable water to the fighting soldier. However, with battle fronts which can move rapidly, as is often the case in modern confrontations, 3 options are available:

i) Transport large quantities of water of known quality over long distances;

ii) Supply water from local sources of unknown quality; or,

iii) Purify water from local sources.

Microtox is used in the field to screen water samples rapidly, even in areas where intermittent electricity supplies may preclude the use of more conventional techniques. The use of Microtox is one of screening to monitor signs of toxicity [35]. Chemical analysis would need to be undertaken if long-term use of a water source were required. Alternative bioassay (fathead minnows, trout, *Daphnia magna*, etc.), are unsuitable for field use and requires 48 — 72 h to produce results.

EC Directive 80/778/EEC, NATO STANAG 2136 [36], and the United States prescribe standards both for a number of organic substances and for metals, including arsenic, chromium, copper, lead, magnesium, nickel, and selenium. Under battle conditions, residues from cadmium, mercury, thallium, etc., can be significant. It is noted that after a massive explosion of a munitions dump in Croatia (Ogulin) residues of cadmium and mercury were detected in water and soil over a wide area [37-39] (see also chapter by Srebocan).

Microtox cannot identify individual containments and attention has to be drawn to the varying slopes of dose response curves. It is interesting to note that the slopes for arsenic, nickel, and thallium were all <1.0 in saline solution, whereas the slopes for mercury were >6.0. Unfortunately, these slopes would not be valid for any sample which contained more than one toxicant which could be the usual case in battlefield conditions.

Work has been carried out on solutions containing more than one metal [40-42]. These authors show that can be synergistic, additive or antagonistic activity depending upon the actual metals and concentration ratios.

Microtox can be used effectively for screening of new water supplies, pre- and post-treatment monitoring to evaluate the effectiveness of such treatment and to test waters transported often for long distances under difficult situations to confirm that they remain contamination free. It should be noted that Microtox will detect chemical contamination but will not provide information on microbiological quality unless significant quantities of microbial toxins have been released.

In cases where it is acceptable to screen or monitor water samples by techniques such as the Microtox test, it would be prudent wherever possible to include other test methods. This would require the services of a reliable centralized chemical and microbiological laboratory suitably equipped with instruments such as atomic absorption spectrometers, gas chromatographs, etc. These facilities would be used to check whether a water source is suitable for long-term use.

In a recent survey of the environmental damage caused by the destruction of the chemical industry by the war in Croatia, it is recognized that there is a massive need for monitoring with respect to both environmental pollution and the health of the population [35]. This UNIDO report covers a complex panoramic situation in which many areas (some of which were highly industrialized) are destroyed so badly that finding a solution cannot be based on previous experience and a new approach suitable to the nature of the problem is required.

As many areas additionally suffer from lack of electricity and acute shortages of normal infra-structural facilities, coupled with the fact that there is no idea of the magnitude of the contamination in terms of either concentration or area, the Microtox Acute Test is an ideal tool for initial surveys to enhance the outline hazard assessment and provide useful information for a meaningful risk assessment.

## 14.3 The Mutatox® Genotoxicity Test

As discussed above, luminescent bacteria have been used successfully to measure acute toxicity of chemicals and environmental samples. In addition to acute toxicity testing, chemicals and environmental samples are often tested for potential genotoxicity. There are several validated methods in routine use for assessing genotoxicity of chemicals but they have been practical limitations. These limitations include high cost per test sample and complex protocols which necessitate highly trained personnel to obtain reproducible test data, and to provide reliable interpretation.

A novel extension of the Microtox Acute Test has resulted in the development of a new test system which uses a dark strain of luminescent bacteria to measure genotoxicity of chemicals or environmental samples.

This test, called Mutatox, applies a dark variant (M-169 of *Vibrio fischeri* that exhibits light production when grown in the presence of sub-lethal concentrations of genotoxic substances. This test system consists of lyophilized cultures of M-169 and dried assay medium with and without rat liver activating samples (S-9). To perform the test, aliquots of rehydrated M-169 cells are incubated with several concentrations of the sample diluted in the test medium with and without S-9. Light levels in the test vials are measured using a temperature controlled photometer after 12, 20, and 24 h incubation at 27 °C. Suspected genotoxic agents are defined as those which induce increased light levels of at least twice the average control reading in at least 2 test dilutions [43,44].

Mutatox test strain M-169 is a dim variant of *Vibrio fischeri* [45,46] and the primary genetic lesion responsible for the low light of this strain has not been completely identified. Current data support the assumption that the groBSL activity, a critical component of the lux regulatory system, is altered in this strain. A current model of this regulatory system is discussed in a recent paper by Adar *et al.* [47] and has been outlined by Richardson [48]. Further details can be found in the literature [47-51].

Validation of the Mutatox test system has been underway for over 3 years and several comparative studies have been published [51-54]. Two types of studies have been undertaken. Pure compound studies have been performed to establish a database of sensitivity using an accepted list of compounds with known genotoxic activity. These test data were compared with the commonly used *Salmonella* reverse mutation assay developed by Ames [55] as well as carcinogenicity scores (Table 14.1).

**Table 14.1** **Mutatox test data and corresponding Ames and carcinogenicity data**

| Chemical | Mutatox | Ames | Carcinogen |
|---|---|---|---|
| Acetamide | - | - | |
| Acetone | - | - | |
| Allyl isothiocyanate* | + | + | + |
| Allyl isovalerate* | + | - | + |
| 2-Aminobiphenyl | + | + | + |
| 2-Aminoanthracene | + | + | + |
| 2-Aminofluorine | + | + | + |
| 9-Aminoacridine | + | + | |
| 11-Aminoundecanoic acid* | - | - | + |
| 2-Acetylaminofluorene | + | + | + |
| Acridine orange | + | + | |
| Aflatoxin $B_1$ | + | + | + |
| Ascorbic acid* | - | - | - |
| Benzene* | + | - | + |
| 1,2-Benzanthrazene | + | + | |
| Benzidine | + | + | + |
| Benzoin* | - | - | - |
| Benzo(a) pyrene | + | + | + |
| Benzo(e) pyrene | + | + | - |
| Benzyl acetate* | - | - | + |
| 2-Biphenylamine hydrochloride | + | + | + |
| bis (2-Chloro-1-methylethyl) ether* | - | + | + |
| Bisphenol A* | + | - | E |
| Butyl benzyl phthalate* | - | - | + |
| Caprolactum* | - | - | - |
| Captan | + | + | + |
| Chloroamphenicol ether | - | - | |
| $Chromium^{3+}$ | - | - | - |
| $Chromium^{6+}$ | + | + | + |
| Chlorobenzene* | - | - | - |
| Chlorodibromomethane* | - | - | + |
| 2-Chloroethanol* | + | + | - |
| 3-Chloro-2-methylpropene* | - | - | + |
| Cinnamyl anthranilate* | + | - | + |
| Cyclophosphamide | + | + | + |
| Cyclohexamide | - | - | |
| C.I. Acid Orange 10* | - | - | - |
| Acid Red 14* | + | - | - |
| Acid Yellow 73* | + | - | E |
| C.I. Disperse Yellow 3* | + | + | + |
| C.I. Solvent Yellow 14* | + | + | + |
| Cytembena* | - | + | + |
| D and C Red 9* | + | + | + |
| Diallyl phthalate* | - | - | E |
| 1,2-Dibromoethane (ethylene dibromide)* | + | + | + |
| 1,2-Dichlorobenzene* | - | - | - |
| 1,3-Dichloropropene* | - | + | + |

| Chemical | Mutatox | Ames | Carcinogen |
|---|---|---|---|
| 1,2-Dichloropropane* | + | + | + |
| 2,4-Dichlorophenoxy acetic acid (2,4-D) | - | - | |
| Di(2-ethylhexyl)adipate* | - | - | + |
| 2,6-Dichloro-4-phenylenediamine* | + | + | + |
| Di (2-ethylhexyl)phthalate | - | - | + |
| Diallyl phthalate | - | - | E |
| Diglycidyl resorcinol ether* | + | + | + |
| Dimethyl hydrogen phosphite* | - | + | + |
| Dimethyl morpholinophosphoramidate* | E | - | + |
| Dimethyl terephthalate* | - | - | - |
| 7,12-Dimethylbenz[a]anthracene | + | + | + |
| 1,4-Dioxane | - | - | + |
| Emetine | - | - | + |
| Emodin | - | - | |
| Ethidium bromide | + | + | |
| Ethoxylated dodecyl alcohol* | - | - | - |
| Ethylene Glycol | - | - | - |
| Eugenol* | + | - | + |
| FD&C Yellow No. 6* | - | - | - |
| Geranyl acetate* | - | - | - |
| HC Blue 2* | + | + | - |
| Hamamelis water (Witch hazel)* | - | - | - |
| HC Blue 1* | - | + | + |
| 8-Hydroxyquinoline* | + | + | - |
| Isophorone* | - | - | + |
| Lindane | - | - | - |
| D-Mannitol* | - | - | - |
| Melamine* | - | - | + |
| d,1-Menthol* | - | - | - |
| 4,4'-Methylenedianiline 2HCl* | - | + | + |
| Methotrexate | + | + | |
| Monuron* | + | - | + |
| Mitomycin C | + | + | |
| NTG MNNG | + | + | + |
| Nalidixic acid | + | + | + |
| Sodium azide | + | + | + |
| 4-Nitroguinoline-1-oxide | + | + | + |
| 4,4'-Oxydianiline 2HCl | + | + | + |
| Phenol* | + | - | - |
| Polybrominated biphenyl* | + | - | + |
| Proflavine | + | + | + |
| Propyl gallate* | + | - | + |
| Propylene oxide* | E | + | + |
| Pyrene | + | + | + |
| Quinacrine | + | + | |
| Reserpine* | - | - | + |
| Safrole | + | - | + |
| Selenium sulfide* | - | + | + |
| Sodium (2-ethylhexyl)alcohol sulfate* | + | - | E |

| Chemical | Mutatox | Ames | Carcinogen |
|---|---|---|---|
| Stannous chloride* | + | - | E |
| Sulfisoxazole* | + | - | - |
| 1,1,1,2-Tetrachloroethane* | - | - | + |
| Titanium dioxide* | - | - | - |
| 2,6-Toluenediamine 2HCl* | + | + | - |
| Trichloroethylene* | - | - | + |
| tris (2-Ethylhexyl)phosphate* | - | - | + |
| Urethane | + | + | + |
| Ziram* | + | + | + |

+=positive test result
-=negative test result
E=equivocal result
Blank - no data available
*=designates National Toxicology Program (NTP) Chemical

In addition, several studies have focused on the use of Mutatox to assess the genotoxicity of environmental samples. Each sample set was also tested using the *Salmonella* mutagenicity test. Table 14.2 summarizes comparative data from several of these studies. For both sample types Mutatox compared favorably with the data obtained using the Ames procedure. Additional comparative studies are in process in order to better characterize the sensitivity and specificity of this test procedure.

**Table 14.2** **Mutatox® — Comparison with Ames data**

| Comparison category | Pure chemicals | Environmental samples |
|---|---|---|
| No of samples | 105 | 75 |
| Sensitivity | 88% | 94% |
| Specificity | 74% | 88% |
| Accuracy | 80% | 91% |

In a recently reported study [56], Mutatox was used to measure genotoxic activity in soils contaminated with polycyclic aromatic hydrocarbons (PAHs). Water extracts from clean soil spiked with a mixture of PAHs and soil excavated from a hazardous waste site known to be contaminated with PAHs were tested with Mutatox. One of the major trends revealed by the test data was that removal of the original contaminants (as determined by

GC) was not an accurate measure of complete remediation of the waste site. Genotoxicity initially decreased along with the measured decrease in PAH concentrations. Only after a significant increase in genotoxicity followed by a longer period of biodegradation did the genotoxicity of the soil extracts diminish to background levels. These data, as suggested by the authors, show the importance of genotoxicity monitoring during bioremediation of a hazardous waste site to assure complete degradation of contaminants and biodegradation by-products.

## 14.4 Chronic Toxicity Testing Using Luminescent Bacteria

Environmental testing in the USA, Canada, and Europe has expanded to include chronic test procedures. A chronic toxicity test requires exposing some or all of the growth or reproductive cycle of the test population to dilutions of the test sample. Such tests are usually more sensitive than acute tests but are more complex, require significantly longer exposure times, and are more difficult and expensive to perform. For monitoring purposes, however, such tests can provide a more realistic assessment of actual biological effects from long-term environmental exposure.

The need for a simple, rapid, standardized chronic test procedure has stimulated development efforts using luminescent bacteria.

Research and development efforts over the last 2 years have provided new and useful information about the genetics and physiology of the light producing mechanism in the luminescent bacterium *Vibrio fischeri*. These research and development efforts, along with years of experience gained from the development and application of the Microtox Acute Toxicity Test, has resulted in the development of a new **Microtox® Chronic Toxicity Test System** using luminescent bacteria [57].

This test is initiated using freeze-dried test organisms inoculated into a special test medium which supports cell growth and light induction at 29 °C. After about 20 h incubation, light output from control vials containing no sample are compared with test vials containing dilutions of test sample. Those test dilutions showing a significant light decrease (as compared with the controls) are scored as toxic.

Table 14.3 summarizes comparative data showing the increased sensitivity of the Microtox Chronic Test when compared with the standard Microtox Acute Test. The chronic test shows an average 50 times greater sensitivity over the acute test for the compounds tested. Table 14.4 compares this new chronic test method with the *Ceriodaphnia dubia* chronic test procedure developed by the US EPA. These comparative data show similar sensitivities for these 2 chronic test methods. Additional comparative studies using these 2 test methods are underway using complex environmental samples. These results will be published in the near future and should reconfirm the utility of this relatively simple, rapid, and cost-effective alternative chronic test procedure.

**Table 14.3** $EC_{50}$ (mg $l^{-1}$) values for the Microtox® chronic and acute test methods

| Chemical | Acute | Chronic |
|---|---|---|
| Aflatoxin | 80 | 0.2 |
| Sodium azide | 50 | 0.6 |
| Benzene | 200 | 1.0 |
| Cadmium | 160 | 0.05 |
| Chromium | 25 | 0.07 |
| Copper | 0.1 | 0.01 |
| Cyanide | 50 | 0.2 |
| Diazinon | 10 | 0.05 |
| 2,4-D | 18 | 0.9 |
| 3.5-Dichlorophenol | 9 | 0.1 |
| Dieldrin | 11 | 0.07 |
| Sodium fluoroacetate | 300 | 0.05 |
| Lead | 2 | 0.6 |
| Methoxychlor | 190 | 0.02 |
| Nickel | 8 | 0.08 |
| Phenol | 20 | 1 |
| Zinc | 1 | 0.08 |

**Table 14.4** Comparison ($EC_{50}$) between *Ceriodaphnia dubia* and the Microtox® chronic test

| Compound | *C. dubia* | Luminescent bacteria |
|---|---|---|
| Cadmium | 0.003 | 0.05 |
| Chromium | 3.0 | 0.07 |
| Copper | 0.04 | 0.01 |
| Diazinon | 0.03 | 0.05 |
| 2,4-D | 40 | 0.9 |
| Lead | 0.1 | 0.6 |
| Methoxychlor | 0.01 | 0.02 |
| Phenol | 4.9 | 1.0 |
| Zinc | 0.1 | 0.08 |

## 14.5 Conclusions

It is recognized that in order to secure the vital requirement of chemical safety, the title role of this book, risk assessments, in turn leading to risk management be made, and to that end, monitoring is a necessity.

Hazard assessments can be integrated with monitoring to provide risk assessments and hence, this chapter stresses the requirement of rapid, simple, but at the same time, peer-reviewed techniques for monitoring.

It is well known that one of the best means for keeping out of trouble and to remain in compliance means that it is essential to control or monitor a process in a well-established chemical works, or in the most chaotic situation which result from warfare, or natural or other man-made disasters [58].

Control of toxicity, whether in wastewater treatment plants, or in war-ravaged regions, depends on timely and relevant information. The responsible professional must know *what is happening* not merely *what happened* in order to recommend and to take effective remedial action.

Whilst many chemical-specific tests are fast and effective for detecting known toxicants, some are too slow and/or expensive [1]. They are also unable to answer the more general or the more important question 'is the sample toxic', and 'how toxic is it?', even when recourse can be made to good sources of information (see also chapter by Cowie and Richardson). To answer such questions, living organisms, typically fish, invertebrates, algae, plants, etc., are exposed to the sample and then after a period of time examined for harmful effects caused by that sample.

Many regulatory based or chemical techniques involve a bioassay of some kind. However, because they require several days or even weeks to produce results, they are neither practical nor able to control major processes in which major changes can occur in <1 h. Furthermore, they are impractical to use in the field, either in peaceful or war-ravaged areas.

This chapter outlines the background to 3 very fast bioassays based on luminescent bacteria. These tests are simple, precise, repeatable, portable, and require few services, including electricity. For these tests the freeze-dried test organisms are available at any time for immediate use; the only parameter to measure is light.

Both the Microtox® and Mutatox™ techniques provide results indicating the usefulness of luminescent bacterial assays which are simple, fast and are comparatively inexpensive alternatives to both chemical techniques and to *in vivo* bioassays with higher organisms.

These tests will enhance environmental sustainability and result in available monitoring and enhance the concept that **to do nothing is the worse possible alternative** [59].

## 14.6 Acknowledgements

The authors wish to acknowledge the assistance of the editor in the preparation of this chapter.

## 14.7 References

[1] Richardson, M.L., 'Interpretation of GC-MS Data Derived from Environmental Samples', in: *Ecotoxicology Monitoring*, Richardson, M.L. (Ed.), VCH Publishers, Weinheim, 1993, 49-55.

[2] *Dictionary of Substances and Their Effects (DOSE)*, Richardson, M.L. (Ed.), The Royal Society of Chemistry, London, 1992, **1 (A-B)**, pp. 951, and 1993 **2**(C), pp. 876.

[3] Cowie, A., and Richardson, M.L., 'Pubic Sources of Data' in: *Ecotoxicology Monitoring*, Richardson, M.L. (Ed.), VCH Publishers, Weinheim, 1993, pp. 37-47.

[4] Vosser, J.L., 'The European Community Chemicals Notification Scheme and Environmental Hazard Assessment', in: *Toxic Hazard Assessment of Chemicals*, Richardson, M.L. (Ed.), The Royal Society of Chemistry, London, 1986, pp. 117-132.

[5] Clesceri, L.S., 'The Use of Nucleic Acid Probes and Other Molecular Tools in the Functional Analysis of Microorganisms in Soil and Water', in: *Ecotoxicology Monitoring*, Richardson, M.L. (Ed.), VCH Publishers, Weinheim, 1993, pp. 163-171.

[6] Machala, M., Nezveda, K., Ulrich, R., and Mátlová, L., 'Toxicity Potential Estimation and Biochemical Monitoring of Aromatic Contaminants by the Measurement of Monooxygenase Activities in Chick Embryo Liver', in: *Ecotoxicology Monitoring*, Richardson, M.L. (Ed.), VCH Publishers, Weinheim, 1993, pp. 173-182.

[7] Hansen, P-D, 'Regulatory Significance of Toxicological Monitoring by Summarizing Effect Parameters', in: *Ecotoxicology Monitoring*, Richardson, M.L. (Ed.), VCH Publishers, Weinheim, 1993, pp. 273-286.

[8] Bulich, A.A., 'Use of Luminescent Bacteria for Determining Toxicity in Aquatic Environments', in: *Aquatic Toxicology*, ASTM 667, Markings, L.L. and Kimmerle, R.A., (Eds.), 1979, pp. 98-106.

[9] Isenberg, D.L., 'The Microtox® Toxicity Test. A Developer's Commentary', in: *Ecotoxicology Monitoring*, Richardson, M.L. (Ed.), VCH Publishers, Weinheim, 1993, pp. 3-15.

[10] *Ecotoxicology Monitoring*, Richardson, M.L. (Ed.), VCH Publishers, Weinheim, 1993, pp. 384.

[11] Bulich, A.A., Greene, M.W., and Isenberg, D.L., 'Reliability of the Bacterial Luminescence Assay for Determination of the Toxicity of Pure Compounds and Complex Effluents', in: *Aquatic Toxicology and Hazard Assessment: 4th Conference*, Branson, D.R. and Dickson, K.L. (Eds.), ASTM STP 737, American Society for Testing and Materials, Philadelphia, 1988, pp. 338-347.

[12] Curtis, C.A., Lima, A., Lozano, S.J., and Veith, G.D., 'Evaluation of a Bacterial Bioassay as a Method for Predicting Acute Toxicity of Organic Chemicals to Fish', in: *Aquatic Toxicology and Hazard Assessment: 5th Conference*, Pearson, J.G., Foster, R.B., and Bishop, W.E. (Eds.), ASTM STP 766, American Society for Testing and Materials, Philadelphia 1982, pp. 170-178.

[13] Krebs, F., *Wasser Abwasser*, 1983, **63**, 173-230.

[14] Ribo, J.M. and Kaiser, K.L.E., *Tox. Assess.*, 1987, **2**, 305-323.

[15] Kaiser, K.L.E. and Ribo J.M., *Tox. Assess.*, 1988, **3**, 195-237.

[16] 'Toxicity Test Using Luminescent Bacteria (*Photobacterium phosphoreum)*' Conservation and Protection, Environment Canada, Ottawa, Ontario, Report EPS 1 SRM, 1990, pp. 52.

[17] Kaiser, K.L.E. and Palabrica, V.S., *Water Poll. J. Canada*, 1991, **26**, (3), 361-431.

[18] Kaiser, K.L.E., 'Qualitative and Quantitative Relationships of Microtox® Data with Toxicity Data and Other Aquatic Species', in: *Ecotoxicology Monitoring*, Richardson, M.L. (Ed.), VCH Publishers, Weinheim, 1993, pp. 197-211.

[19] Cronin, M.T.D. and Dearden, J.C., 'The Comparative Toxicology of the Microtox® Test', in: *Ecotoxicology Monitoring*, Richardson, M.L. (Ed.), VCH Publishers, Weinheim, 1993, pp. 213-223.

[20] Kross, B.C. and Cherryholmes, K., 'Toxicity Screening of Sanitary Landfill Leachates: A Comparative Evaluation with Microtox® Analyses, Chemical, and Other Toxicity Screening Methods', in: *Ecotoxicology Monitoring*, Richardson, M.L. (Ed.), VCH Publishers, Weinheim, 1993, pp. 225-249.

[21] Johnson, F.H., Eyring, H., and Stover, B.J., *The Theory of Rate Processes in Biology and Medicine*, New York, John Wiley & Sons, 1974, pp. 523-535, 703 p.

[22] Fentem, J. and Balls, M., 'Replacement of Fish in Ecotoxicology Testing: Use of Bacteria, Other Lower Organisms and Fish Cells *in Vitro*' in: *Ecotoxicology Monitoring*, Richardson, M.L. (Ed.), VCH Publishers, Weinheim, 1993, pp. 71-81.

[23] Fraizer, J.M., Gad, S.C., Goldberg, A.M., and McCulley, J.P., 'A Critical Evaluation of Alternatives to Acute Ocular Irritation Testing, in: *Alternative Methods in Toxicology*, Goldberg, A.M. (Ed.), Mary Ann Liebert Inc, New York, NY 1987, Vol. 4.

[24] Jones, P.A., 'Microtox® and *In Vitro* Testing for Ocular Irritation Potential', in: *Ecotoxicology Monitoring*, Richardson, M.L. (Ed.), VCH Publishers, Weinheim, 1993, pp. 261-268.

[25] Burton, S.A., Petersen, R.V., Dickman, S.N., and Nelson, J.R., *J. Biomed. Mat. Res.*, 1986, **20**, 827-838.

[26] Bruner, L.H. and Parker, R.D., 'Evaluation of the EYTEX System as a Screen for Predicting the Ocular Irritancy — Potential of Consumer Products?, Poster presented at the 2nd International Conference on Practical *in vitro* Toxicology, Nottingham, England, 23-27 July 1989.

[27] Stark, J.M., Shopsis, C., Borenfreund, E., and Babich, H., *Food Chem. Toxic.*, 1986, **24**, 449-455.

[28] Whale, G.F., Jarrill, F.M., and Bashford, V., 'Assessment of the Suitability of the *Photobacterium phosphoreum* (Microtox®) Test to Provide Marine Toxicity Data for Offshore Chemical Control Schemes, in: *Ecotoxicology Monitoring*, Richardson, M.L. (Ed.), VCH Publishers, Weinheim, 1993, pp. 251-260.

[29] Johnson, I., Butler, R., Milne, R., and Redshaw, C.J., 'The Role of Microtox® in the Monitoring and Control of Effluents', in: *Ecotoxicology Monitoring*, Richardson, M.L. (Ed.), VCH Publishers, Weinheim, 1993, pp. 309-317.

[30] Fearnside, D. and Hiley, P.D., 'The Role of Microtox® in the Detection and Control of Toxic Trade Effluents and Spillages', in: *Ecotoxicology Monitoring*, Richardson, M.L. (Ed.), VCH Publishers, Weinheim, 1993, pp. 319-332.

[31] Richardson, M.L. 'Regulatory Status of Microtox®, in: *Ecotoxicology Monitoring*, Richardson, M.L. (Ed.), VCH Publishers, Weinheim, 1993, pp. 271-272.

[32] Levi, Y., Grimaud, A., and Dutang, M., 'Protection of Surface Water Resources by Real Time Automated Toxicity Tests', *5th IAWPRC Workshop on Water and Wastewater Treatment and Transport Systems*, Kyoto, Japan, August, 1990.

[33] Bulich, A., *Environ. Waste Man.*, 1991, **Dec,** 2-5.

[34] Loeber, B., *Waste Business Waste*, December 1991.

[35] Richardson, M.L. and Sugavanam, B., *Effects of War on the Environment*, UNIDO, Vienna, Report 10.R.263, 15 March 1993, Project No. US/CRO/92/164.

[36] STANAG (Standardization Agreement) for Minimization for Public Water (EuroMed Military Medical Working Group), 1990.
[37] Namjesnik, K., Palinkaš, L.A., Miko, S., Durn, G., Polić, D., and Kurgnjaš, L., *Mining and Metallurgy Quarterly*, Ljubljana, 1992, **39**, (1-2), 93-112.
[38] Palinkaš, L.A., Sholupov, S.E., Mashyanov, N.K., Durn, G., and Miko, S., *Rudarsko-Geološko-Nafni Zbornik*, (Zagreb), 1992, **2**, 19-27.
[39] Palinkaš, L.A., Sholupov, S.E., Şinkovec, B., Miko, S., Sesvečan, T., *Rudarsko-Geološko-Nafni Zbornik*, (Zagreb), 1989, **1**, 47-62.
[40] Qureshi, A.A., Coleman, R.N., and Paran, J.H., 'Evaluation and Refinement of the Microtox® Test for Use in Toxicity Screening' in: *Toxicity Screening Using Bacterial Systems*, Toxicity Series DUTKA, B.J., and Liu, D. (Ed.), Marcel Dekkar Inc., New York, 1983, pp. 89-118.
[41] Sellars, K.E. and Ram, N.W., 'Toxicity Assessment of Binary Metal Mixtures Using Bioluminescent Bacteria', University of Massachusetts, 1985.
[42] Michaud, J.P., Bulich, A.A., Gandolfi, A.J., and Brendel, K., 'Use of Bioluminescent Bacteria as a Model for Studying Interactive Toxicity', Microbics Corporation, California, 1990.
[43] Bulich, A.A., 'The Mode of Action of Genotoxic Agents', *SETAC 13th Annual Meeting*, Cincinnati, Ohio, November, 1992.
[44] Johnson, B.T., *Environ. Toxicol. Chem.*, 1992, **11**, 473.
[45] Ulitzur, S., Weiser, I., and Yannai, S., *Mutat. Res.*, 1980, **74**, 113-124.
[46] Ulitzur, S., *Methods in Enzymology*, 1986, **133**, 264-274.
[47] Adar, Y., Simaan, M., and Ulitzur, S., *J. Bacteriol*, 1992, **174**, 7138-7143.
[48] Richardson, M.L., 'Epilogue', in: *Ecotoxicology Monitoring*, Richardson, M.L. (Ed.), VCH Publishers, Weinheim, 1993, pp. 335-343.
[49] Engebrecht, J., Nealson, K., and Silverman, M., *Cell*, 1983, **32**, 773-781.
[50] Ulitzur, S. and Kuhn, J., *J. Biolumin. Chemilumin.* 1988, **2**, 81-93.
[51] Ulitzur, S., *J. Biolumin. Chemilumin*, 1989, **4**, 317-325.
[52] Johnson, B.T., *Environ. Toixocol. Water Qual.*, 1992, **7**, 373-390.
[53] Kwan, K.K., Dutka, B.J., Rao, S.S., and Liu, D., *Environ. Poll.*, 1990, **65**, 323-332.
[54] Guttman-Bass, N., Bairey-Albuquerque, M., Ulitzur, S., Chartrand, A., and Rav-Acha, C., *Environ. Sci. Technol.*, 1987, **21**, (3), 252-260.
[55] Ames, B.N., McCann, J., and Yamasaki, B., *Mutat. Res.*, 1975, **31**, 347-364.
[56] Belkin, S., Stieber, M., Tiehm, A., Frimmel, F.H., Abeliovich, A., Warner, P., and Ulitzur, S., 'Toxicity and Genotoxicity Enhancement During Polynuclear Aromatic Hydrocarbon Biodegradation', Toxicity Assessment Symposium, 1993, Berlin, Germany.
[57] Bulich, A.A. and Ulitzur, S., 'A New Chronic Toxicity Test Using Luminescent Bacteria', First SETAC World Congress, Lisbon, Portugal, March 1993.
[58] Krishna Murti, C.R., 'A Systems Approach to the Control and Prevention of Chemical Disasters', in: *Risk Assessment of Chemicals in the Environment*, Richardson, M.L. (Ed.), The Royal Society of Chemistry, London, 1988, pp. 114-149.
[59] The Royal Society of Chemistry, Toxicology Group Newsletter, Green, J. (Ed.), 1993 (8), Sept. 1993, pp. 19-20.

# 15. Cytogenetic Monitoring

Sharolta Gundy, Eva Susanszky, Jenő Major, and Andrew E. Czeizel

## 15.1 Introduction

### 15.1.1 Overview of the State of Hungarian Environment

For the past few years, a number of Central and East European politicians and scientists have been concerned over the environmental situation of this region, and in health care. With the achievement of parliamentary democracy, the evaluation of environmental health has also changed and increasing powerful efforts are made so that scientists will not hinder attempts to fully characterize the threat to human health.

Environmental pollution does not respect geographical boundaries; therefore, many problems are very common in these countries, while others (occupational ones) present major differences. The uniform opinion of the scientists in the region is that the number and variety of human victims of our environment must be completely different from those of the developed world.

Although there are some biological evidences *eg*, in carcinogenesis, or in the formation of diseases, the environmental effects have far larger and multiple impact on human health than in countries with long ago established and adequate prevention policy. This is the reason why some surveys have more importance in Central and Eastern Europe and appear to be trivial for examination in the Western world.

Hungary is a medium polluted country with some over-polluted areas in the Carpathian basin, and occupies 93,000 $km^2$ with 10 million inhabitants. Hungary has the lowest ranking for life expectancy in Europe and the highest rate for cancer mortality [1].

Is the environment responsible for these facts? An overview regarding the environmental situation in Hungary is summarized [2-4].

#### 15.1.1.1 Water

Ninety-seven percent of Hungarian surface waters flows from abroad. The water quality of the river Danube at the Austrian borderline is first class, but passing the Slovakian and Hungarian sections its quality deteriorates to the second class. Sixty to 75% of all groundwaters is polluted by agricultural runoff and untreated municipal wastewater. Because of local contamination from nitrates, pesticides and arsenic, 570 of the 3064 cities and towns rely on bottled water or piped from other communities.

#### 15.1.1.2 Air

Forty-four percent of the population are affected by unacceptable air quality levels in an area comprising 11% of the country. Two stroke oil and gas vehicle engines up to 40% are inefficient, and high vehicle densities in cities burn high lead content gasoline. The origin of hydrocarbon and lead load of the air is produced in 40-50% by the industrial sector, 30-35% are transport-related and about 20% originates from communal heating. Other hazardous components emitted into the air annually include:

i) 410,000 tonnes of dust, ash and soot;

ii) 280 tonnes of $NO_x$; and,

iii) 1.2 Million tonnes of sulfur equivalents, which originate from the burning lignite or brown coal for industry, home heating, and power plants.

#### 15.1.1.3 Waste

Hungary was a transit country for illegal transportation of hazardous waste to East- and South-East-European countries. Up to very recently only 3% of total amount of 10 million tonnes of industrial waste was recycled. Sixty % of dump sites do not satisfy environmental protection specifications. Present waste management practice is also unacceptable.

#### 15.1.1.4 Soil

Soil pollution is mostly concerned with heavy metals originating from heavy industrial complexes. However, there is a special problem in Hungary which is characterized by 1000s tonnes of gasoline and kerosine in the soil on large territories of abandoned former Soviet military bases; these are often near groundwater sources for local inhabitants.

The list is by no means complete, but it does represent a view of gross environmental problems accumulated from the past. Moreover, the over-polluted regions and the working environment with underdeveloped technology, unhealthy conditions, and bad security techniques makes the problem more complex.

### 15.1.2 The Aim of Cytogenetic Monitoring in Hungary

Environmental or occupational genotoxicants may act on the DNA of somatic cells, which might be inductors of cancer diseases when living, or working in a deteriorated environment, and, therefore, the need to prevent mutagen- and carcinogen-induced diseases is paramount. With the advent of changing environmental policy and general public health there is a vital role to map the real situation, either retrospectively or prospectively. Fortunately, there are some long established and acknowledged risk assessment methods, which have attempted to provide some adequate experiences in public health and now serve as important sources for cancer prevention in Hungary. Cytogenetic monitoring methods were described in the early 1970s, mainly for scientific purposes as part of the new conceptions in risk assessment, but for political reasons they were not involved in risk management [5-7].

This study represents an on-going research programme whose aim is to detect exposures to mutagenic and carcinogenic environmental chemicals, and which will provide an estimate, in the future, of the magnitude of exposures that may increase the risk of cancer incidence or birth defects in the population.

In view of the apparent relationship between chromosomal damage, mutagenesis and carcinogenesis [8-10], analyses of induced chromosomal aberrations have become a useful tool to evaluate potential hazards of environmental or occupational mutagens and carcinogens. The underlying premise, inherent in somatic mutation theory of cancer, is that an elevated frequency of chromosomal aberrations would increase the likelihood of the rearrangements that contribute to neoplastic transformation [11-13].

When evaluating the significance of aberration levels, and when answering the question of mutational origin of cancer, it is necessary to be familiar with the frequency of the spontaneous rate of chromosomal aberrations in the cells of different study populations. The examination of large number of people can provide information about the factors influencing the base-line level of aberrations, and these data have to be taken into consideration when exposures to specific agent or agents are suspected.

Normal healthy people are generally not free from the action of mutagens, such as chemicals, physical agents, viruses, lifestyle habits including smoking and alcohol consumption. There is also scanty information on the variability of spontaneous rate of chromosomal aberrations in lymphocytes, which establishes the upper level of normal variability in adults and children, so that a positive effect of exposure can be recognized more exactly. It is not clear at all how national rates can be different, or how urban or rural lifestyle (or environment) may affect the somatic cell aberration yield.

Present studies describe the findings in many 100s of control Hungarians who were healthy and were selected from environmental viewpoints, depending on outdoor and indoor exposures.

The value of this study lies in that it was undertaken for the characterization of the degree of variability in many *normal* population groups under very rigorous technical and scoring conditions. This is the first study to describe a uniform population of children, who are exposed to the same environment as the adults.

## 15.2 Materials and Methods

### 15.2.1 Study Samples

Subjects are normal healthy volunteers living or working for at least 1 year in their constant macro- and micro-environment. Nine hundred and seventy-seven people were examined, among them there were 140 children. Demographic characteristics of persons are shown in Table 15.1. Donors were distributed into 8 groups, according to the place of their residence, outdoor and indoor exposure types and age. The first Budapest community controls were collected between years 1983-1988, and the others were examined between 1989-1993. The only exclusion criteria for donors were previous radiotherapy, chemotherapy, special environmental or occupational exposures to chemicals or to ionizing radiation, and chronic diseases requiring continuous drug treatment. Viral infection could not occur within 3 months of scheduled sampling. Otherwise they were not preselected (community controls from Budapest and North Hungarian industrial area). Community controls residences were located nearby industrial facilities, within a distance of ≯4 km. All blood samples were taken on site, and transported to the laboratories within 5 h. The cell cultivation, fixation and slide preparation and scoring procedures were undertaken in Budapest at 2 neighbouring laboratories of the National Institute of Hygiene and the National Institute of Occupational Health.

**Table 15.1** **Demographic characteristics of environmentally selected groups in Hungary**

| Group | Number of cases and sex of persons | | | Age (years) | | Smokers | | Drinkers | |
|---|---|---|---|---|---|---|---|---|---|
| | Total | ♂ | ♀ | means ± SD | | No. | % | No. | % |
| Budapest community control (1983-1988) | 211 | 129 | 82 | 36.1 | 10.2 | 72 | 34.1 | no information | |
| Budapest community control (1989-1992) | 250 | 150 | 100 | 34.5 | 10.8 | 73 | 29.2 | 71 | 28.4 |
| Budapest city officers | 73 | 26 | 47 | 38.1 | 5.2 | 34 | 46.6 | none | |
| Budapest worksite officers | 81 | 52 | 29 | 38.3 | 4.9 | 34 | 41.9 | 11 | 13.6 |
| North-Hungary community control | 174 | 110 | 64 | 33.4 | 8.3 | 47 | 27.0 | 54 | 31.0 |
| Village | 47 | 20 | 27 | 47.1 | 19.1 | 28 | 59.6 | 12 | 25.5 |
| Budapest children | 85 | 42 | 43 | 4.0 | 1.8 | — | — | — | — |
| Rural children | 55 | 26 | 29 | 4.7 | 1.9 | — | — | — | — |

Each person was asked to complete a questionnaire designed to provide relevant details of lifestyle. Nutrition habits were different in Budapest and in rural areas. Budapest people's diet contained less fat and smoked meals, while rural groups preferred to consume such foods. Donors were considered as smokers, who smoked regularly for ≥1 y. They were distributed into 3 groups as follows: <10 cigarettes, 10-20 cigarettes, and >20 cigarettes $d^{-1}$. Among regular drinkers only moderate and heavy drinkers were examined. Chronic alcoholics were not found in the cohort, and occasional drinkers (3-5 times $a^{-1}$) were not accepted as a drinking category. Regular moderate drinkers drank <50 ml of 96% alcohol equivalent $d^{-1}$ (beer, wine, etc.), and heavy drinkers' consumption was equivalent to >50 ml alcohol, but <200 ml.

Villagers were particularly interesting because of the high average of the age of inhabitants and elevated radon activity (*ie*, 0.4-0.8 kBq $m^{-3}$) in living houses, compared with the Hungarian average of 0.05 kBq $m^{-3}$.

Non-community controls were collected separately: officers (administratives), from non-industrial office buildings (Budapest city officers), and administratives from chemical industrial worksite office blocks (Budapest worksite officers). Children were separated according to location of residence, either from Budapest or from rural towns and villages in 100 km distances from Budapest. They were descendants of adults under investigation, or healthy controls for other studies from children's hospitals. The adult age ranged from 18 to 74 years and the children were ≤10 years of age.

### 15.2.2 Cytogenetic Protocol

Blood was collected by venepuncture in heparinized Beckton-Dickinson vacutainers and was stored for ≤5 h at 4 °C prior to culture initiation. For each sample, 0.7 ml of whole blood was added to 9 ml RPMI-1640 medium (Gibco) supplemented with L-glutamin and 15% fetal calf serum, and 0.25 ml Phytohemagglutinin M (Difco). Samples were kept in duplicate at 37 °C in disposable sterile 15 ml conical plastic tubes with tightened caps. Two h prior to the 50 h harvesting, at the final concentration, 0.1 μg $ml^{-1}$ colcemid (Gibco) was added to each culture. For sister chromatid exchange (SCE) studies 25 μM 5-bromodeoxy-uridine (BUdR) was used, and these samples were fixed after 56 h of fixation of the culture.

Hypotonization and fixation were carried out according to standard methods. Air-dried slides were stained either by the conventional Giemsa method or by the FPG method, previously described [14]. For chromosomal aberrations 100 cells were scored $person^{-1}$, by 2-4 scores and the identification of aberrations was confirmed by the same cytogeneticist. All aberration types are recorded, but only chromatid-type deletions, chromosome-type acentric fragments and exchange-type dicentrics or centric rings are presented. Aneuploidy and gaps are recorded elsewhere. For SCE analysis 50 cells were examined for each person.

### 15.2.3 Statistics

All statistical analyses were undertaken using Epi Info, Version 5, SPSS.PC programme packages [15].

Data on age, sex, smoking and drinking, etc. were gathered after completion of the study. Statistical comparisons were made by applying 2 tailed $\chi^2$-test and Student's t-test. A multiple regression analysis was performed to explore any association of factors such as age, sex, smoking and drinking habits, and location.

## 15.3 Results

A total of 977 persons were studied for chromosome aberration and SCE analyses. They were selected, from an environmental viewpoint, according to location of residence and workplace. Budapest and North Hungary comprises of districts (or settlements) with very similar $NO_x$, $SO_2$, precipitating dust and soot air pollution data [16]. Hence, the possibilities of indoor and outdoor exposures were taken into account, with some other confounders, *eg*, age (childhood *vs* adulthood), sex, smoking and drinking habits. Demographic characteristics (Table 15.1) gave some surprising findings in different groups. The highest proportion of smokers (60%) was found among village inhabitants (out of 28 smokers only 9 females were found), and it was followed by officers of both non-worksite and worksite groups, 47% and 42%, respectively. In Budapest and North Hungarian community controls more people drank alcohol than the administratives. Unfortunately, such data are not available for the Budapest group prior to 1989.

The age mean of village persons was significantly higher than in any other group because of a special *aged* farmer-miner village in the Matra mountains. The detailed analysis of aberration types and the percentage of aberrant cells are presented in Table 15.2, where the values are indicated without sex distribution.

**Table 15.2** **Types and percentages of chromosomal aberrations and aberrant cells of environmentally selected groups**

| Group | Total No. of cells | Aberrant cells | | Type of aberration: chromatid deletions | | Type of aberration: chromosome fragments | | Type of aberration: dicentrics | |
|---|---|---|---|---|---|---|---|---|---|
| | | No. | % | No. | % | No. | % | No. | % |
| Budapest community control (1980-1988) | 21000 | 171 | 0.81 | 90 | 0.43 | 69 | 0.33 | 12 | 0.05 |
| Budapest community control (1989-1992 | 25000 | 278 | 1.11 | 158 | 0.63 | 103 | 0.41 | 18 | 0.07 |
| Budapest city officers | 7300 | 24 | 0.33 | 16 | 0.22 | 8 | 0.11 | 2 | 0.03 |
| Budapest worksite officers | 8100 | 104 | 1.28 | 72 | 0.88 | 32 | 0.40 | 3 | 0.04 |
| North Hungary community control | 17400 | 260 | 1.49 | 150 | 0.86 | 95 | 0.55 | 16 | 0.09 |
| Village | 4700 | 47 | 1.10 | 13 | 0.27 | 29 | 0.62 | 6 | 0.13 |
| Budapest children | 8500 | 47 | 0.55 | 34 | 0.40 | 13 | 0.15 | 0 | 0.00 |
| Rural children | 5500 | 29 | 0.53 | 17 | 0.31 | 9 | 0.16 | 3 | 0.05 |

According to aberration and SCE analyses the following results are meaningful:

i) Budapest officers, whose office buildings are located away from industrial plants in the City, have the lowest percentage of aberrant cells. Simultaneously, over half of them (46.6%) smoked. It appears that smoking does not influence the spontaneous rate of chromosomal aberrations in these cohorts. Aberrant cell frequency of children from Budapest and rural locations are also equally low;

ii) The highest yield of aberrant cells was found in north Hungarian community controls and it was significantly greater than in the Budapest community controls before and after 1989 (1.49% *vs* 1.11% and 0.81%; $p=0.0005$);

iii) There was no difference between the Budapest and rural children, their aberrant cell frequency is 2-3 times lower than in adults, except Budapest city officers;

iv) When sex differences were analyzed, neither adults nor children exhibited any significant impact of this confounder on chromosomal aberrations. Village females were an exception, because they had 2.5 times higher aberration yield than males (Table 15.3): 1.34 *vs* 0.50% aberrant cell frequency was found ($p=0.003$) in peripheral blood lymphocytes;

v) Among other confounders smoking and alcohol consumption effects were studied by regression analysis. In the total of adults neither smoking nor drinking habits affected the aberrant cell yields;

vi) When the proportion of chromatid and chromosome-type aberrations were compared (Table 15.2), the dominating type of aberrations appeared to be of a chromatid-type, with a 1.5-3.5-fold factor. The only exceptions are village inhabitants, where the rate of chromosome-type aberrations (fragments and exchanges) is much higher than chromatid-type breaks. The frequency of dicentric chromosomes was slightly higher in rural inhabitants than in the Budapest inhabitants, but these differences were not significant;

vii) Distribution of aberrant cells showed significant differences between 2 community controls: Budapest and North Hungarian inhabitants (Table 15.4). More Budapest individuals have cells without aberrations or with a lower percentage, than the North Hungarians ($p=0.0062$). Simultaneously, the distribution of aberrant cells among children does not show differences; and,

viii) Table 15.5 presents an account of the SCE analysis. The ranges of mean SCE values are not too wide. The maximum of low and high levels were found in Budapest city officers, which as a group, showed the lowest rate of chromosomal aberrations. The means of SCEs were not influenced by smoking, alcohol drinking, age, or sex, and the location had also no significant impact on these values. Only children had a slightly lower range of SCEs than adults ($p<0.05$).

**Table 15.3** Aberrant cell frequency in adults and children according to localization and sex distribution

| Group | Total No. | Total % | ♂ No. | ♂ % | ♀ No. | ♀ % | Significance Group | $\chi^2$ | P |
|---|---|---|---|---|---|---|---|---|---|
| | Frequency of aberrant cells (No., %) (Total of cells examined, in brackets) | | | | | | | | |
| 1. Budapest community controls | 278 (25000) | 1.11 | 174 (15000) | 1.16 | 104 (10000) | 1.04 | 1-2 | 11.97 | 0.0005 |
| 2. North Hungary community control | 260 (17400) | 1.49 | 151 (11000) | 1.37 | 109 (6400) | 1.70 | 3-4 | 0.04 | 0.8400 |
| 3. Budapest children | 47 (8500) | 0.55 | 24 (4200) | 0.57 | 23 (4300) | 0.54 | 1-3 | 20.64 | 0.0000 |
| 4. Rural children | 29 (5500) | 0.53 | 16 (2600) | 0.62 | 13 (2900) | 0.45 | 2-4 | 31.36 | 0.0000 |
| 5. Village | 47 (4700) | 1.00 | 10 (2000) | 0.50 | 37 (2700) | 1.37 | ♂-♀ | 7.68 | 0.0055 |

**Table 15.4** Distribution of aberrant cells in community control adults and children

| Aberrant cells % | Percent of inhabitants with aberrations: Budapest adults | North Hungary adults | Budapest children | Rural children |
|---|---|---|---|---|
| 0 | 50.8 | 37.4 | 67.0 | 65.5 |
| 1 | 17.2 | 21.3 | 23.5 | 21.8 |
| 2 | 14.4 | 18.4 | 4.7 | 9.1 |
| 3 | 8.4 | 10.3 | 1.2 | 1.8 |
| 4 | 6.4 | 5.7 | 2.4 | 1.8 |
| 5 | 2.4 | 4.6 | — | — |
| 6 | 0.4 | 1.7 | — | — |
| 7 | — | 0.6 | — | — |
| 8 | — | — | — | 1.2 |

**Table 15.5** **Sister chromatid exchange (SCE) frequency in environmentally selected persons**

| Group | SCE/cell mean | ± | S.D. | Range of SCEs |
|---|---|---|---|---|
| Budapest community control (1983-1988) | 5.6 | | 0.7 | 4.5-7.6 |
| Budapest community control (1989-1992) | 5.6 | | 0.7 | 4.6-7.8 |
| Budapest city officers | 5.9 | | 2.1 | 3.7-9.2 |
| Budapest worksite officers | 5.8 | | 1.1 | 4.0-8.4 |
| North Hungary community control | 6.5 | | 0.4 | 4.9-8.0 |
| Village | | | no information | |
| Budapest children | 4.9 | | 0.5 | 3.7-6.1 |
| Rural children | 5.1 | | 0.6 | 3.4-7.0 |

## 15.4 Discussion

When there is a summation of industrial chemical derived and environmentally related cancer risk, it is obvious that a large preventable risk is associated with man-made chemicals. Currently, there is no other cheaper and routinely used technique for risk assessment than cytogenetic monitoring, which can be interrelated with carcinogenesis. It has a special role in countries, where the occupational cancer risk is much higher, than in countries with a well established technological background for the chemical industry. When the risk from environmental contamination is monitored, the occupational risk would be further minimized, providing a base for a more successful cancer prevention in the workplace.

It is known that cytogenetic monitoring can be used to both predict cancer susceptibility in an individual, and to provide an estimate of the magnitude of exposures that can increase the risk of cancer incidences in the population.

This study represents an on going research programme, which is in progress and runs parallel with the organization of the Hungarian Cancer Morbidity Registry. These studies will be continued in respect to cancer morbidity, and the relationship between cytogenetic damage and other health effects, which are connected with environmental and occupational factors may also be assessed, similar to the Nordic Study Group activities [17,18]. By relating levels of chromosome damage to subsequent cancer morbidity we can compare our findings with the Nordic database, and this will probably be useful in the judgement of the role of more or less contaminated macro- and micro-environment in carcinogenesis.

In this study we tried to separate only environmentally exposed groups, in order to identify those aberration levels, which are induced by indoor and outdoor circumstances and different biological and lifestyle factors associated with genotype and the general health of the individual.

Very often it is not possible to use matched control data. If there are certain accidental exposures, *eg*, at a rural industrial worksite, it is very time consuming to find proper *on site* controls.

One of the largest Hungarian chemical industrial centres is located in the Northern part of the country, and therefore, North-Hungarian community controls were chosen. The likelihood of occupational over-exposure at this location is the greatest, because the occupation can be a considerable constituent in the mutation spectrum and carcinogenesis of these persons. Since the methods used in cytogenetic monitoring were unified 3 years ago, by the Hungarian Environmental Mutagen Society, in accordance with the International Commission for Protection against Environmental Mutagens and Carcinogens (ICPEMC) recommendations [19], the population-based community control data serve as a reference for any laboratory in the country for a given time period.

In few Hungarian laboratories the subjective judgement of chromosome aberration identification did not exceed the 5% interscorer variability in contrast to the international variations [12,17,18]. In order to equalize methods, use was made of the same chemicals. Selected metaphase scoring and comparison of slides are always undertaken. Therefore, common historical control data in cases are used, if no matched controls are possible. This makes our cytogenetic monitoring easier than the procedures in bigger countries.

Currently, in comparison, little attention has been paid to the role of the place of residence or work in causing baseline levels of chromosomal aberrations and SCE variations. In our environmentally selected groups the aberrant cell frequency showed large differences, 0.33% *vs* 1.49%. This means that the most important confounding factor in our cohorts was location, associated with certain indoor and outdoor exposures.

Despite several data on other confounders, such as smoking and alcohol use [17,19,20], these factors had much less, if no influence on chromosomal aberrations.

Another biological variable of concern in the population is the sex of donors. Except for village females, sex did not play a role in the frequency of cytogenetic endpoints in this study; the reason for which is unclear. It might be explained by a more heterogeneous sample, but is probably due to the different age distribution of village females; neither did other confounders such as smoking and drinking habits influence the rate of aberrations in females. Many more males were smokers or drinkers among village inhabitants than females. Nevertheless, several authors have made the observation, that females are more sensitive to clastogens than males [21,22].

Age was also regarded as a biological confounder in the literature [19,23,24]. A simple comparison was made between children (1-10 years) and adults (18-74 years), and a much lower rate of aberrations were found in the children. This age group indicates probably less clastogenic response to environmental mutagens than the adults. In our case study, even the location did not influence the aberration level, as it was equally low in both groups of children. Bender [25] observed no evidence of age-effect on aberrant cell frequency, when the age range of 493 individuals was extended from 1.1-83.7 years. However, it is reported that older persons have a higher aberration rate than younger ones [21], and dicentrics are the single exception for age effects [24].

No further information regarding comparison of children at a very young age, and from the same environment as the adults, were found. It would be interesting to obtain more data on cytogenetic monitoring of children, as we do not know which factors contribute to clastogenicity in the early life of humans. This study group should serve as a base for a further follow-up study when children reach the next age group of 10-15 years.

Regarding different types of aberrations, a small international comparison was made (Table 15.6) on the basis of our summarized and group-related data. The range for chromosome-type acentric fragments was found to be $2 \times 10^{-3}$ to $4.6 \times 10^{-3}$ frequency by different authors, and for the dicentrics $0.1 \times 10^{-3}$, respectively. Our mean values lie within the range of the cited values [26,30], but when the means of acentric fragment frequencies in different groups were separated, they were much higher than those cited.

**Table 15.6** **Comparisons of chromosome-type aberrations found by different authors in control populations**

| Authors [Ref.] | No. of persons examined | Abberation x $10^{-3}$ cell<br>acentric fragments | dicentrics |
|---|---|---|---|
| Lloyd [26]<br>summarized | 2000 | 2.0-4.6<br>(mean:3.7) | 0.1-2.1<br>(mean:0.8) |
| Evans *et al.* [27] | 79 | 2.3 | 1.1 |
| Leonard *et al.* [28] | 23 | 2.4 | 1.1 |
| Galloway *et al.* [29] | 304 | 3.2 | 2.1 |
| Bender *et al.* [30] | 353 | 4.6 | 1.6 |
| Present study | 837 | 1.1-6.1<br>(mean:4.0) | 0.3-1.9<br>(mean:0.6) |

Chromatid-type aberrations are believed to be induced by chemicals. In occupational monitoring it is very important to pay attention to this type of aberration. Some percentile values of chromatid deletions (without gaps) were collected and found by different authors (Table 15.7). A 2-fold difference exists between our data and that of others (0.44 *vs* 0.88%) [22,29,30,31]. However, we found a 4-fold difference, when our environmentally selected groups were taken into account (*qv*, Table 15.2). When consideration is given to the distribution of aberrations (Table 15.4) there were subjects who showed 5-7% of aberrant cells, *ie*, similar to Galloway *et al.* [29]. They found 29% of individuals with aberrant cells, while in our controls 51% and 37% of persons were free from aberrations in cells scored.

Unfortunately, this important question (*ie*, upper limits of aberrant cells) is also open and as for the children's data, it has yet to be clarified. Out of 140 children there was 1 child, with 8% of aberrant cells, which means that more information from other laboratories is needed when an attempt is made to evaluate the possible significance of magnitude of chromosome instability in cancer risk assessment.

The reported SCE values in controls vary widely, from about 4-14 SCE cell$^{-1}$ [19]. In our groups only children had slightly lower frequency of SCEs than adults, otherwise no factors were found to confound the baseline SCEs. We observed 5-6 SCE cell$^{-1}$ in different groups, but it is rather difficult to compare the data with others because the BUdR concentration used is the most meaningful confounder.

**Table 15.7** **Chromatid deletions observed in different laboratories in control populations**

| Authors [Ref.] | Percent of chromatid deletions | No. of cells examined |
|---|---|---|
| Kucerova [31] | 0.88 | 3573 |
| Anderson *et al.* [22] | 0.54 ♂<br>0.82 ♀ | not indicated exactly |
| Galloway *et al.* [29] | 0.64 | 41282 |
| Bender *et al.* [30] | 0.81 | 71950 |
| Present study | 0.43 (mean)<br>0.22-0.88 (range) | 83700 |

## 15.5 Conclusions

Unfortunately, Hungary is the top among 186 countries in cancer mortality, according to WHO statistics [1]. The deterioration in the quality of the environment shows regional differences in the country, similarly as to cancer mortality [32]. Since the enhancement of the Hungarian Cancer Morbidity Registry is under construction, it is only presumed that the cancer morbidity has also territorial distribution, probably depending on the extension of environmental (occupational) contamination. This underlines the necessity of a regional cytogenetic monitoring programme for people living in differently polluted areas.

As far as is known, this is the first study that compares environmentally selected groups of adults and children. On the basis of our results, it can be stated that in Hungary the location of residences may play the most important role in the baseline levels of chromosomal aberrations in the adult population. This finding has not yet been validated for children, under 10 years of age.

Our cytogenetic endpoint of chromosomal damage shows a clear relationship between both urban or rural environments, and with the workplace location, where other outdoor factors might be excluded. Persons of the same profession, *eg*, officers from Budapest city-located office buildings and Budapest industrial worksite buildings show a 4-fold difference in the rate of aberrant cells.

Probably, not only in Hungary, but also in other countries with over-polluted environments, the significance of regional distribution of people is a more powerful confounder in clastogenicity than any other generally investigated lifestyle factors. Existence and duration of the presence of different residences expresses the importance of the additional action of mutagens, which may play a role later in mutagen-induced carcinogenesis.

## 15.6 References

[1] WHO, World Health Statistics Annuals, 1984-1988, Geneva.

[2] Wassersug, S.R., 'Environmental Transformation in Central and Eastern Europe', in: *Proc. of Internat. Symp. on Environmental Contamination in Central and Eastern Europe*, Budapest, 1992, pp. 7-13.

[3] Reiniger, R., 'Overview of Hungary's Environmental Situation', in: *Proc. of Internat. Symp. on Environmental Contamination in Central and Eastern Europe*, Budapest, 1992, pp. 13-15.

[4] Ministry for Environmental and Regional Policy, *Hung. Natl. Report,* UNCED, Brazil, 1992.

[5] Gundy, S. and Varga, L.P., *Mutat. Res.,* 1983, **120**, 187-191.

[6] Gundy, S., *Ann. Inst. Super. Sanita.*, 1989, **25**, 549-556.

[7] Tompa, A., Galambos, E., and Straus, J., *Magyar Onkologia*, 1983, **27**, 246-253.

[8] Knudson, A.G. and Strong, L.C., *J. Nat. Cancer Inst.*, 1972, **48**, 313-324.

[9] Heim, S. and Mitelman, F., *Cancer Cytogenetics*, Alan R. Liss, New York, USA.

[10] Hsu, T.C., *Hereditas*, 1983, **98**, 1-9.

[11] Weinberg, R.A., *Cancer*, 1988, **61**, 1963-1968.

[12] Nordic Study Group, *Cancer Genet. Cytogenet.*, 1990, **45**, 85-92.

[13] Evans, H.J., 'What has been achieved with cytogenetic monitoring?' in: *Monitoring of Occupational Genotoxicants*, Sorsa, M. and Norppa, H., (Eds.), 1985, pp. 3-23, Alan Liss, New York, USA.

[14] Gundy, S., Varga, L.P., and Bender, M.A., *Radiat. Res.*, 1984, **100**, 47-54.

[15] Dean, A.G., Dean, J.A., and Dicher, R.C., *Epi. Info. Version 5, Epidemiology on Microcomputers*, CDC, 1990, Atlanta, USA.

[16] Gundy, S. and Cziczo, T., 'Cytogenetics, as a tool of monitoring in two medium-polluted areas of Hungary', in: *Air-Pollution Epidemiology Report Series, COST-613/2*, Rudnay, P., (Ed.), 1992, pp. 165-169, Budapest.

[17] Nordic Study Group on the Risk of Chromosome Damage: A Nordic database on somatic chromosome damage in humans, *Mutat. Res.*, 1990, **241**, 325-337.

[18] Broegger, A., Norum, R., Hansteen, A.L., Clausen, O.K., Skardal, K., Mitelman, F., Kolnig, A.M., Stroembeck, B., Nordenson, I., Andersson, G., Jakobsson, K., Maki-Paakkanen, J., Norppa, H., Jarventus, H., and Sorsa, M., *Hereditas,* 1984, **100**, 209-218.

[19] Carrano, A.V. and Natarajan, A.T., *Mutat. Res.*, 1988, **204**, 379-406.

[20] Obe, G., Heller, W.D., and Vogt, H.J., 'Mutagenic activity in cigarette smoke', in: *Mutations in man*, Obe, G., (Ed.), Springer, Berlin, 1984, pp. 223-246.

[21] Hedener, K., Hoegstedt, B., Kolnig, A.M., Mark-Vendel, E., Stroembeck, B., and Mitelman, F., *Hum. Genet.*, 1982, **62**, 305-309.

[22] Anderson, D., Jenkinsson, P.C., Dewdney, R.S., Francis, A.J., Godbert, P., and Butterworth, K.R., *Mutat. Res.*, 1988, **204**, 407-420.

[23] Tawn, J., *Mutat. Res.*, 1987, **182**, 303-308.

[24] Tonomura, A., Kishi, K., and Saito, F., 'Type and frequencies of chromosome aberrations in peripheral lymphocytes of general populations', in: *Radiation-induced Chromosome Damage in Man,* Ishihara, T. and Sasaki, M., (Eds.), 1983, Alan Liss, New York, USA, pp. 601-615.

[25] Bender, M.A., Preston, R.J., Leonard, R.C., Pyatt, B.E., and Gooch, P.C., *Mutat. Res.*, 1989, **212**, 149-154.

[26] Lloyd, D.C., 'An overview of radiation dosimetry by conventional methods', in: *Biological Dosimetry*, Eisert, W.G. and Mendelsohn, M.L., (Eds.), 1989, Springer, Berlin, pp. 3-14.

[27] Evans, H.J., Buckton, K.E., Hamilton, G.E., and Carothers, A., *Nature (London)*, 1979, **272**, 531-534.

[28] Leonard, A., Deknudt, G.H., Leonard, E.D., and Decat, G., *Mutat. Res.*, 1984, **138**, 205-212.

[29] Galloway, S.M., Barry, P.K., Nichols, W.W., Wolman, S.R., Soper, K.A., Stolley, P.D., and Archer, P., *Mutat. Res.*, 1986, **170**, 55-74.

[30] Bender, M.A., Preston, J.R., Leonard, R.C., Pyatt, B.E., Gooch, P.C., and Shelby, M.D., *Mutat. Res.*, 1988, **204**, 421-433.

[31] Kucerova, M., *Mutat. Res.*, 1976, **41**, 123-130.

[32] Tompa, A. and Farkas, I., *Hungarian Science*, 1992, **11**, 1310-1324.

# 16. Identification of Carcinogenic Risks — Qualitative Aspects

Julian Wilbourn and Harri Vainio

## 16.1 Introduction

The annual incidence rates (crude and age-standardized) and the numbers of new cases of cancers at 18 major sites in 1985 were estimated for 24 areas of the world [1]; the data for the 15 commonest cancers in men and women are summarized in Table 16.1. Lung cancer is the commonest cancer in men and the incidence rates are increasing in both developed and developing countries; it is now the 3rd commonest cancer among women in North America and the 5th commonest worldwide. Breast cancer is still the commonest cancer in women, followed by cancer of the cervix. Worldwide, cancers of the colon and rectum are the 3rd commonest cancers in both sexes. Cancers of the urinary bladder and pancreas are more common in developed than in developing countries. The incidence of lymphoma appears to be increasing.

Implementation of effective preventive measures against human cancer depends primarily on knowledge about its causes. The International Agency for Research on Cancer (IARC) has been carrying out a program to evaluate carcinogenic risks to humans since 1969, the purpose of which is to provide clear, sound evaluations of degrees of evidence for carcinogenicity. Identification of carcinogenic risks for humans is thus an essential prerequisite for the primary prevention of cancer. Risk identification is the first stage in quantitative risk assessment when the probability of an increased frequency of or death from a disease associated with a given level of exposure is estimated.

Table 16.2 shows the sites at which cancer is most frequent and some of the known risk factors associated with these cancers. For some sites — lung, mouth/pharynx, liver, esophagus, bladder and leukemia — several risk factors have been identified; but for other sites — stomach, breast, colon/rectum, lymphoma, prostate — the epidemiological evidence is far from conclusive. On the basis of present knowledge, the smoking and chewing of tobacco are clearly the major preventable causes of cancer.

**Table 16.1** **The most frequent sites of cancer worldwide, 1985; estimated numbers (thousands) and percent of total**

| Males | | | Females | | | Both sexes | | |
|---|---|---|---|---|---|---|---|---|
| Site | Number | % | Site | Number | % | Site | Number | % |
| Lung | 667 | 17.6 | Breast | 719 | 19.1 | Lung | 896 | 11.8 |
| Stomach | 473 | 12.3 | Cervix uteri | 437 | 11.6 | Stomach | 755 | 9.9 |
| Colon/rectum | 331 | 8.6 | Colon/rectum | 346 | 9.2 | Breast | 720 | 9.4 |
| Prostate | 291 | 7.6 | Stomach | 282 | 7.5 | Colon/rectum | 678 | 8.9 |
| Mouth/pharynx | 270 | 7.0 | Lung | 219 | 5.8 | Cervix uteri | 437 | 5.7 |
| Liver | 214 | 5.6 | Ovary | 162 | 4.3 | Mouth/pharynx | 412 | 5.4 |
| Esophagus | 196 | 5.1 | Mouth/pharynx | 143 | 3.8 | Lymphoma | 316 | 4.2 |
| Bladder | 182 | 4.7 | Corpus uteri | 140 | 3.7 | Liver | 315 | 4.1 |
| Lymphoma | 181 | 4.7 | Lymphoma | 135 | 3.6 | Esophagus | 304 | 4.0 |
| Leukemia | 121 | 3.1 | Esophagus | 108 | 2.9 | Prostate | 291 | 3.8 |
| Larynx | 121 | 3.1 | Liver | 101 | 2.7 | Bladder | 243 | 3.2 |
| Pancreas | 97 | 2.5 | Leukemia | 96 | 2.5 | Leukemia | 216 | 2.8 |

**Table 16.2** **Most frequent sites of cancer worldwide and identified risk factors (excluding exposure circumstances)**

| Target site | Agents |
|---|---|
| Lung | Tobacco smoke, asbestos, arsenic, chromium, cadmium, coal-tars/pitches, beryllium, bischloromethylether, mustard gas, nickel, radon gas, soots |
| Stomach | Nitrosamines, nitroso compounds |
| Breast | ? Estrogens |
| Colon/rectum | ? Diet |
| Cervix uteri | Human papilloma virus |
| Mouth/pharynx | Betel quid with tobacco, alcohol drinking, tobacco chewing, tobacco smoke |
| Lymphoma | Immunosuppressants |
| Liver | Aflatoxins, hepatitis B virus, hepatitis C virus, alcoholic beverages, oral contraceptives, vinyl chloride |
| Esophagus | Alcohol drinking, tobacco smoke |
| Prostate | ? Cadmium |
| Bladder | Aromatic amines, tobacco smoke |
| Leukemia | Benzene, ionizing radiation, chemotherapeutic alkylating agents |
| Pancreas | Tobacco smoke |
| Larynx | Alcoholic beverages, mustard gas, tobacco smoke |
| Corpus uteri | Estrogens |

## 16.2 Tools for Risk Identification

Associations are established by examining the available data from studies of exposed humans, the results of bioassays in experimental animals and studies of exposure, metabolism, toxicity and genetic effects in both humans and animals. The Preamble to the *IARC Monographs* [2] sets out guidelines evaluating carcinogenic risks to humans.

### 16.2.1 Studies of Cancer in Humans

Evidence of the induction of cancer in humans obviously plays an important role in the identification of human carcinogens. Three types of epidemiological studies contribute to an assessment of carcinogenicity in humans: cohort studies, case-control studies and correlation (or ecological) studies. Case reports of cancer in humans may also be reviewed.

Cohort and case-control studies relate individual exposures under study to the occurrence of cancer in individuals and provide an estimate of relative risk (ratio of incidence in those exposed to incidence in those not exposed) as the main measure of association.

In correlation studies, the unit of investigation is usually whole populations (*eg*, particular geographical areas) and cancer frequency is related to a summary measure of the exposure of the population to the agent. Because individual exposure is not documented, a causal relationship is less easy to infer from such studies than from cohort and case-control studies. Case reports generally arise from a suspicion, based on clinical experience, that the concurrence of 2 events — that is, a particular exposure and occurrence of a cancer — has happened rather more frequently than would be expected by chance. The uncertainties surrounding interpretation of case reports and correlation studies make them inadequate, except in rare cases, to form the sole basis for inferring a causal relationship.

In the interpretation of epidemiological studies, it is necessary to take into account the possible roles of bias and confounding. By *bias* is meant the operation of factors in study design or execution that lead erroneously to a stronger or weaker association than in fact exists between disease and an agent. By *confounding* is meant a situation in which the relationship with disease is made to appear stronger or weaker than it truly is as a result of an association between the apparent causal factor and another factor that is associated with either an increase or decrease in the incidence of the disease.

In the assessment of the epidemiological studies, a strong association (*ie*, a large relative risk) is more likely to indicate causality than a weak association, although it is recognized that relative risks of small magnitude do not imply lack of causality and may be important if the disease is common. Associations that are replicated in several studies of the same design or using different epidemiological approaches or under different circumstances of exposure are more likely to represent a causal relationship than isolated observations from single studies. An increase in risk for cancer with the amount of exposure is considered to be a strong indication of causality, although absence of a graded response is not necessarily evidence against a causal relationship. Demonstration of a decline in risk after cessation of or reduction in exposure in individuals or in whole populations also supports a causal interpretation of the findings.

When several epidemiological studies show little or no indication of an association between an exposure and cancer, the judgment may be made that, in the aggregate, they show evidence suggesting lack of carcinogenicity. The possibility that bias, confounding or misclassification of exposure or outcome could explain the observed results must be considered and excluded with reasonable certainty. Evidence suggesting lack of carcinogenicity obtained from several epidemiological studies can apply only to the type(s) of cancer studied and to dose levels and intervals between first exposure and observation of disease. For some human cancers, the period between first exposure and the development of clinical disease is seldom <20 years; latent periods substantially shorter than 30 years cannot provide evidence suggesting lack of carcinogenicity.

The evidence relevant to carcinogenicity from studies in humans can be classified into one of the following categories:

#### 16.2.1.1 Sufficient Evidence of Carcinogenicity

A causal relationship has been established between exposure to the agent, mixture or exposure circumstance and human cancer. That is, a positive relationship has been observed between the exposure and cancer in studies in which chance, bias and confounding could be ruled out with reasonable confidence.

#### 16.2.1.2 Limited Evidence of Carcinogenicity

A positive association has been observed between exposure to the agent, mixture or exposure circumstance and cancer for which a causal interpretation is considered to be credible, but chance, bias or confounding could not be ruled out with reasonable confidence.

#### 16.2.1.3 Inadequate Evidence of Carcinogenicity

The available studies are of insufficient quality, consistency or statistical power to permit a conclusion regarding the presence or absence of a causal association, or no data on cancer in humans are available.

#### 16.2.1.4 Evidence Suggesting Lack of Carcinogenicity

There are several adequate studies covering the full range of levels of exposure that human beings are known to encounter, which are mutually consistent in not showing a positive association between exposure to the agent and the studied cancer at any observed level of exposure. A conclusion of *evidence suggesting lack of carcinogenicity* is inevitably limited to the cancer sites, conditions and levels of exposure and length of observation covered by the available studies. In addition, the possibility of a very small risk at the levels of exposure studied can never be excluded.

The applicability of an evaluation of the carcinogenicity of a mixture, process, occupation or industry on the basis of evidence from epidemiological studies depends on time and place. The specific exposure, process or activity considered most likely to be responsible for any excess risk should be sought and the evaluation focused as narrowly as possible. The long latent period of human cancer complicates the interpretation of epidemiological studies. A further complication is the fact that humans are exposed simultaneously to a variety of chemicals, which can interact either to increase or decrease the risk for neoplasia.

### 16.2.2 Studies on Carcinogenicity in Experimental Animals

Studies in which experimental animals (rodents) are exposed chronically to potential carcinogens and examined for evidence of cancer were introduced about 50 years ago with the aim of introducing a scientific approach to the study of chemical carcinogenesis and to avoid some of the disadvantages of using only epidemiological data in humans.
In the *IARC Monographs*, all available, published studies of carcinogenicity in animals are summarized, and the degree of evidence of carcinogenicity is then classified into one of the following categories:

#### 16.2.2.1 Sufficient Evidence of Carcinogenicity

A causal relationship has been established between the agent or mixture and an increased incidence of malignant neoplasms or of an appropriate combination of benign and malignant neoplasms in 2 or more species of animals, or in 2 or more independent studies in one species carried out at different times or in different laboratories or under different protocols. Exceptionally, a single study in one species might be considered to provide sufficient evidence of carcinogenicity when malignant neoplasms occur to an unusual degree with regard to incidence, site, type of tumor or age at onset.

#### 16.2.2.2 Limited Evidence of Carcinogenicity

The data suggest a carcinogenic effect but are limited for making a definitive evaluation because:

i) The evidence of carcinogenicity is restricted to a single experiment;

ii) There are unresolved questions regarding the adequacy of the design, conduct or interpretation of the study; or,

iii) The agent or mixture increases the incidence only of benign neoplasms or lesions of uncertain neoplastic potential, or of certain neoplasms which may occur spontaneously in high incidences in certain strains.

#### 16.2.2.3 Inadequate Evidence of Carcinogenicity

The studies cannot be interpreted as showing either the presence or absence of a carcinogenic effect because of major qualitative or quantitative limitations, or no data on cancer in experimental animals are available.

#### 16.2.2.4 Evidence Suggesting Lack of Carcinogenicity

Adequate studies involving at least 2 species are available which show that, within the limits of the tests used, the agent or mixture is not carcinogenic. A conclusion of evidence suggesting lack of carcinogenicity is inevitably limited to the species, tumor sites and levels of exposure studied.

### 16.2.3 Other Data Relevant to an Evaluation of Carcinogenicity

Data on biological effects in humans that are of particular relevance are summarized. These may include toxicological, kinetic and metabolic considerations and evidence of DNA binding, persistence of DNA lesions or genetic damage in exposed humans. Toxicological information, such as that on cytotoxicity and regeneration, receptor binding and hormonal and immunological effects, and data on kinetics and metabolism in experimental animals are summarized when considered relevant to the possible mechanism of the carcinogenic action of the agent. The results of tests for genetic and related effects are summarized for whole mammals, cultured mammalian cells and non-mammalian systems. Structure-activity relationships are mentioned when relevant.

For the agent, mixture or exposure circumstance being evaluated, the available data on end-points or other phenomena relevant to mechanisms of carcinogenesis from studies in humans, experimental animals and tissue and cell test systems are summarized within one or more of the following descriptive dimensions:

i) Evidence of genotoxicity (*ie*, structural changes at the level of the gene): *eg*, structure-activity considerations, adduct formation, mutagenicity (effect on specific genes), chromosomal mutation/aneuploidy;

ii) Evidence of effects on the expression of relevant genes (*ie*, functional changes at the intracellular level): *eg*, alterations to the structure or quantity of the product of a proto-oncogene or tumor suppressor gene, alterations to metabolic activation/inactivation/DNA repair;

iii) Evidence of relevant effects on cell behavior (*ie*, morphological or behavioral changes at the cellular or tissue level): *eg*, induction of mitogenesis, compensatory cell proliferation, preneoplasia and hyperplasia, survival of premalignant or malignant cells (immortalization, immunosuppression), effects on metastatic potential; or,

iv) Evidence from dose and time relationships of carcinogenic effects and interactions between agents: *eg*, early/late stage, as inferred from epidemiological studies; initiation/promotion/progression/malignant conversion, as defined in animal carcinogenicity experiments; toxicokinetics.

These dimensions are not mutually exclusive, and an agent may fall within more than one. Thus, for example, the action of an agent on the expression of relevant genes could be summarized under both the 1st and 2nd dimension, even if it were known with reasonable certainty that those effects resulted from genotoxicity.

### 16.2.4 Overall Evaluations

Finally, the body of evidence is considered as a whole, in order to reach an overall evaluation of the carcinogenicity to humans of an agent, mixture or circumstance of exposure.

An evaluation may be made for a group of chemical compounds that have been evaluated by the Working Group. In addition, when supporting data indicate that other, related compounds for which there is no direct evidence of capacity to induce cancer in humans or in animals may also be carcinogenic, a statement describing the rationale for this conclusion is added to the evaluation narrative; an additional evaluation may be made for this broader group of compounds if the strength of the evidence warrants it.

The agent, mixture or exposure circumstance is described according to the wording of one of the following categories, and the designated group is given. The categorization of an agent, mixture or exposure circumstance is a matter of scientific judgment, reflecting the strength of the evidence derived from studies in humans and in experimental animals and from other relevant data.

#### 16.2.4.1 Group 1 — The Agent (mixture) is Carcinogenic to Humans

*The exposure circumstance entails exposures that are carcinogenic to humans.*

This category is used when there is sufficient evidence of carcinogenicity in humans. Exceptionally, an agent (mixture) may be placed in this category when evidence in humans is less than sufficient but there is sufficient evidence of carcinogenicity in experimental animals and strong evidence in exposed humans that the agent (mixture) acts through a relevant mechanism of carcinogenicity.

#### 16.2.4.2 Group 2

This category includes agents, mixtures and exposure circumstances for which, at one extreme, the degree of evidence of carcinogenicity in humans is almost sufficient, as well as those for which, at the other extreme, there are no human data but for which there is evidence of carcinogenicity in experimental animals. Agents, mixtures and exposure circumstances are assigned to either group 2A (probably carcinogenic to humans) or group 2B (possibly carcinogenic to humans) on the basis of epidemiological and experimental evidence of carcinogenicity and other relevant data.

#### 16.2.4.3 Group 2A - The Agent (mixture) is Probably Carcinogenic to Humans

*The exposure circumstance entails exposures that are probably carcinogenic to humans.*

This category is used when there is limited evidence of carcinogenicity in humans and sufficient evidence of carcinogenicity in experimental animals. In some cases, an agent (mixture) may be classified in this category when there is inadequate evidence of carcinogenicity in humans and sufficient evidence of carcinogenicity in experimental animals and strong evidence that the carcinogenesis is mediated by a mechanism that also operates in humans. Exceptionally, an agent, mixture or exposure circumstance may be classified in this category solely on the basis of limited evidence of carcinogenicity in humans.

#### 16.2.4.4 Group 2B - The Agent (mixture) is Possibly Carcinogenic to Humans

*The exposure circumstance entails exposures that are possibly carcinogenic to humans.*

This category is used for agents, mixtures and exposure circumstances for which there is limited evidence of carcinogenicity in humans and less than sufficient evidence of carcinogenicity in experimental animals. It may also be used when there is inadequate evidence of carcinogenicity in humans but there is sufficient evidence of carcinogenicity in experimental animals. In some instances, an agent, mixture or exposure circumstance for which there is inadequate evidence of carcinogenicity in humans but limited evidence of carcinogenicity in experimental animals together with supporting evidence from other relevant data may be placed in this group.

#### 16.2.4.5 Group 3 — The Agent (mixture or exposure circumstance) is not Classifiable as to its Carcinogenicity to Humans

This category is used most commonly for agents, mixtures and exposure circumstances for which the evidence of carcinogenicity is inadequate in humans and inadequate or limited in experimental animals.

Exceptionally, agents (mixtures) for which the evidence of carcinogenicity is inadequate in humans but sufficient in experimental animals may be placed in this category when there is strong evidence that the mechanism of carcinogenicity in experimental animals does not operate in humans.

#### 16.2.4.6 Group 4 - The Agent (mixture) is Probably not Carcinogenic to Humans

This category is used for agents or mixtures for which there is *evidence suggesting lack of carcinogenicity* in humans and in experimental animals. In some instances, agents or mixtures for which there is inadequate evidence of carcinogenicity in humans but evidence suggesting lack of carcinogenicity experimental animals, consistently and strongly supported by a broad range of other relevant data, may be classified in this group.

## 16.3 Carcinogens Identified So Far

In the first 59 volumes of *IARC Monographs* [3], carcinogenicity to humans has been evaluated for over 750 agents (chemicals, groups of chemicals, complex mixtures, occupational exposures, cultural habits or physical and biological factors). Only 62 agents have been classified as carcinogenic to humans (Tables 16.3-16.6). Of these, 13 are exposure circumstances, for which studies in experimental animals are not available. For the human hepatitis viruses B and C, studies in experimental animals do not reflect the pathology of the disease in humans, although hepadnaviruses related to hepatitis B virus occur in woodchucks and ground squirrels and are carcinogenic to the liver of those species. Of the remaining 47 human carcinogens, only 4 (alcoholic beverages [ethanol], sequential oral contraceptives, smokeless tobacco products and talc containing asbestiform fibres) have not been proven to be carcinogenic to experimental animals. A 5th (treosulphan) has not been tested in animals. For all of the other agents, there is either sufficient or limited evidence of carcinogenicity in animals; for the mixture MOPP, there is sufficient evidence in animals for the carcinogenicity of one of its components, procarbazine. The absence of confirmatory data in experimental animals for 4 of the agents may simply be due to the fact that proper animal models or protocols were not available. Although ethanol *per se* does not appear to be carcinogenic to experimental animals, alcoholic beverages contain many other potential carcinogens, and ethanol may modify the carcinogenicity of other endogenous and exogenous carcinogens. For instance, it was reported recently that ethanol greatly enhances the induction of tumors of the exocrine pancreas in Syrian golden hamsters by a tobacco-specific nitrosamine [4].

**Table 16.3** **Chemicals and groups of chemicals causally associated with human cancer**

| Agent | Target organs |
|---|---|
| Aflatoxins | Liver (lung) |
| 4-Aminobiphenyl | Bladder |
| Arsenic and arsenic compounds[a] | Skin, lung (liver, gastrointestinal tract, kidney) |
| Asbestos | Lung, pleura, peritoneum, (gastrointestinal tract, larynx) |
| Azathioprine | Lymphoma, skin, mesenchymal tumors, hepatobiliary system |
| Benzene | Leukemia |
| Benzidine | Bladder |
| Beryllium and beryllium compounds | Lung |
| N,N-Bis(2-chloroethyl)-2-naphthylamine (Chlornaphazine) | Bladder |
| Bis(chloromethyl)ether and chloromethyl methyl ether (technical grade) | Lung |
| 1,4-Butanediol dimethanesulfonate (Myleran) | Leukemia |
| Cadmium and cadmium compounds | Lung (prostate) |
| Chlorambucil | Leukemia |
| 1-(2-Chloroethyl)-3-(4-methylcyclohexyl)-1-nitrosourea (Methyl-CCNU) | Leukemia |
| Chromium [VI] compounds | Lung (nasal cavity) |
| Ciclosporin | Lymphoma |
| Cyclophosphamide | Bladder, leukemia |
| Diethylstilbestrol | Cervix/vagina, breast, testis (endometrium) |
| Erionite | Pleura, peritoneum |
| Estrogen replacement therapy | Endometrium (breast) |
| Estrogens, nonsteroidal[a] | Cervix/vagina, breast, testis (endometrium) |
| Estrogens, steroidal[a] | Endometrium (breast) |
| Melphalan | Leukemia |
| 8-Methoxypsoralen (Methoxsalen) plus UV radiation | Skin |
| MOPP and other combined chemotherapy including alkylating agents | Leukemia |
| Mustard gas (Sulfur mustard) | Lung, larynx, pharynx |
| 2-Naphthylamine | Bladder (liver) |
| Nickel compounds | Nasal sinus, lung (larynx) |
| Oral contraceptives, combined[b] | Liver |
| Oral contraceptives, sequential | Endometrium |
| Radon and its decay products | Lung |
| Talc containing asbestiform fibers | Lung (pleura) |
| Thiotepa | Leukemia |
| Treosulfan | Leukemia |
| Vinyl chloride | Liver, lung, brain, blood vessels (lymphatic and hematopoietic system) |

Suspected target organs are given in parentheses.

[a]This evaluation applies to the group of chemicals as a whole and not necessarily to all individual chemicals within the group.

[b]There is also conclusive evidence that these agents protect against cancer of the ovary and endometrium.

**Table 16.4** **Complex mixtures causally associated with human cancer**

| Agent | Target organs |
|---|---|
| Alcoholic beverages | Oral cavity, pharynx, larynx, esophagus, liver (breast) |
| Analgesic mixtures containing phenacetin | Renal pelvis/ureter, bladder |
| Betel quid with tobacco | Oral cavity (pharynx, larynx, esophagus) |
| Coal-tar pitches | Skin, lung, bladder (gastrointestinal tract, leukemia) |
| Coal-tars | Skin, lung (bladder) |
| Mineral oils, untreated and mildly treated | Skin (respiratory tract, bladder, gastrointestinal tract) |
| Salted fish (Chinese style) | Nasal cavity |
| Shale-oils | Skin (colon) |
| Soots | Skin, lung |
| Tobacco products, smokeless (chewing tobacco, oral snuff) | Oral cavity (pharynx, esophagus) |
| Tobacco smoke | Lung, bladder, oral cavity, larynx, pharynx, esophagus, pancreas, renal pelvis (stomach, liver, cervix) |

Suspected target organs are given in parentheses.

**Table 16.5** **Exposure circumstances causally associated with human cancer**

| Agent | Target organs |
|---|---|
| Aluminum production | Lung, bladder (lymphoma, esophagus, stomach) |
| Auramine, manufacture of | Bladder |
| Boot and shoe manufacture and repair | Leukemia, nasal sinus (bladder, digestive tract) |
| Coal gasification | Skin, lung, bladder |
| Coke production | Skin, lung, kidney |
| Furniture and cabinet making | Nasal sinus |
| Hematite mining (underground), with exposure to radon | Lung |
| Iron and steel founding | Lung (digestive tract, genito-urinary tract, leukemia) |
| Isopropanol manufacture (strong-acid process) | Nasal sinus (larynx) |
| Magenta, manufacture of | Bladder |
| Painter (occupational exposure as) | Lung (esophagus, stomach, bladder) |
| Rubber industry | Bladder, leukemia (lymphoma, lung, renal system, digestive tract, skin, liver, larynx, brain, stomach) |
| Strong inorganic acid mists containing sulfuric acid (occupational exposure to) | Lung, larynx (nasal cavity) |

Suspected target organs are given in parentheses.

**Table 16.6** **Physical and biological factors causally associated with human cancer**

| Agent | Target organs |
|---|---|
| Hepatitis B virus | Liver |
| Hepatitis C virus | Liver |
| Solar radiation | Skin, nonmelanocytic and melanoma |

A number of agents were first identified as carcinogens in experimental studies and were only later confirmed as human carcinogens in epidemiological studies. Most of these compounds are drugs or chemicals used in occupational settings, which were identified as carcinogens after the 1970s (see Figure 16.1). There is also a growing number of agents for which there is sufficient evidence for carcinogenicity in animals and for which there is either limited evidence of carcinogenicity in humans (sometimes accompanied by other relevant data), which are, therefore, considered to be *probably carcinogenic to humans*. There is a longer list of agents that have been found to cause cancer in long-term animal bioassays but for which no adequate data are available in humans. These agents are normally classified as *possibly carcinogenic to humans*, but, for the purposes of cancer prevention, it is practical and biologically plausible to regard all such agents as if they presented a carcinogenic risk to humans.

## 16.4 Use of Data on Mechanisms of Action

Of the 771 overall evaluations of carcinogenicity to humans made in the 59 volumes of *IARC Monographs*, 44 were influenced directly by consideration of other relevant data. For 8 groups of agents, other relevant data were used as the basis for extending the evaluation of one member of the group to the group as a whole. In the case of the other 36 evaluations, supporting evidence was used to make stronger or weaker overall evaluations of carcinogenicity to humans than would have been the case if the evaluation had been based solely on data on carcinogenicity. Such supporting data have been used to influence overall evaluations in three ways:

i) From Group 3 to 2B: *eg*, an agent for which there were no data or inadequate evidence for carcinogenicity in humans but limited evidence in animals supported by other relevant data;

ii) From 2B to 2A: *eg*, an agent for which there were no data or inadequate evidence of carcinogenicity in humans but sufficient evidence in animals supported by other relevant data; and,

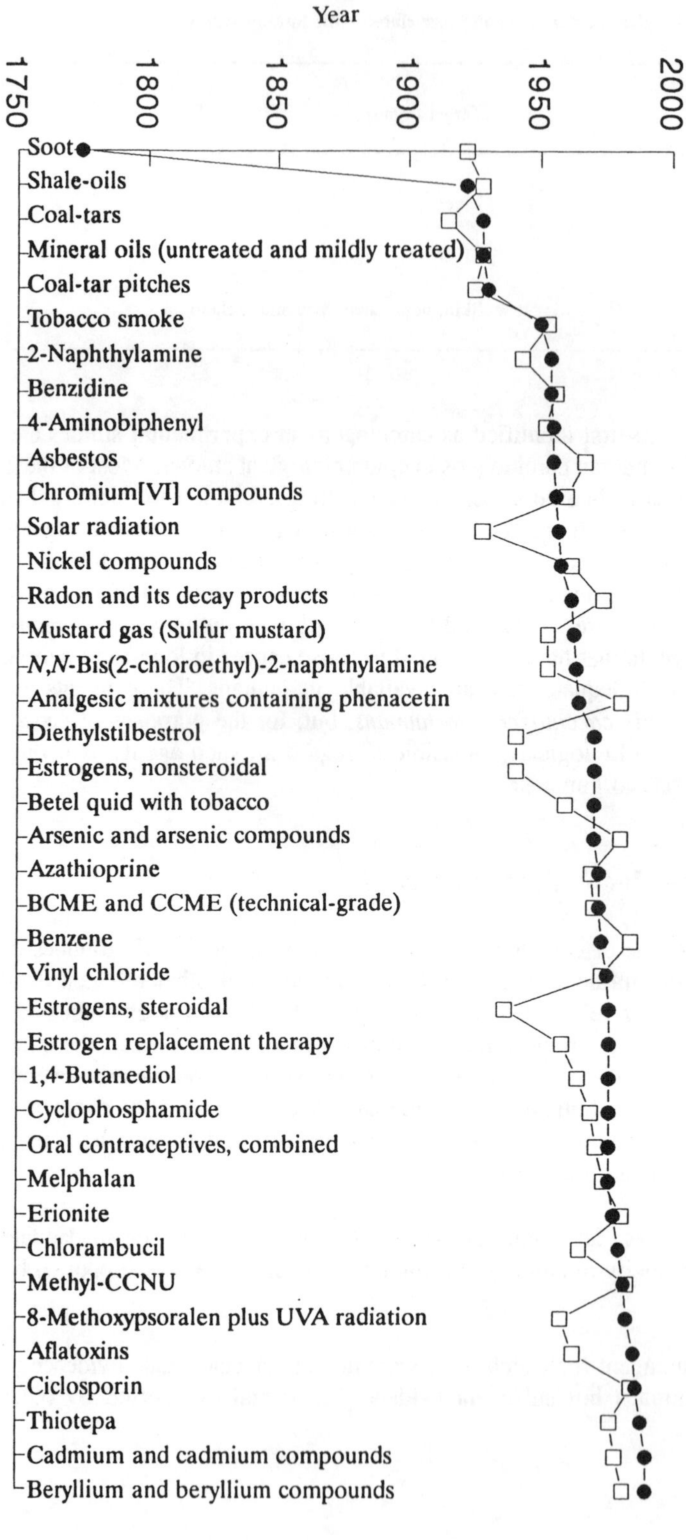


**Figure 16.1** Carcinogens in humans (circles) and experimental animals (squares) and year in which association was made

iii) From Group 3 to 4: the one example is caprolactam, for which there is evidence suggesting lack of carcinogenicity in experimental animals, which, in the absence of similar evidence in humans, can allow an agent to be placed in Group 4 only on the basis of supporting evidence from other relevant data; in this case, consistently negative results were found in a wide range of assays for genetic and related effects *in vitro*.

The revised preamble, which first appeared in volume 54 of the *IARC Monographs*, allows for the possibility that an agent for which epidemiological evidence of cancer is less than sufficient can be placed in Group 1 when *there is sufficient evidence of carcinogenicity in experimental animals and strong evidence in exposed humans that the agent acts through a relevant mechanism of carcinogenicity*. During 1992, that possibility was considered on 2 occasions. In the case of ultraviolet (UV) radiation, while the epidemiological evidence for induction of cancer came mainly from studies of solar radiation, a large amount of data was available on the mutagenicity of UVA, UVB and UVC radiation in experimental models and an increasing amount on mutagenicity in exposed humans. Special tandem base substitutions (T:T to C:C) in a tumor suppressor gene, *p53*, have been found in human skin carcinomas and in melanomas that have developed at sites exposed to the sun. After considerable discussion, the Working Group adopted a conservative attitude and classified UV radiation (UVA, UVB and UVC) into Group 2A, probably carcinogenic to humans. Solar radiation was considered to be carcinogenic to humans (Group 1) (IARC 1992, Vol. 55) [3].

The second case in which the possibility of placing an agent in Group 1 in the absence of sufficient epidemiological evidence was considered was 4,4'-methylene-bis(2-chloroaniline) (MOCA). MOCA is carcinogenic in dogs and rodents and is comprehensively genotoxic. It binds to DNA through reaction with *N*-hydroxy-MOCA, and the same adducts that are formed in target tissues for carcinogenicity in animals have been found in urothelial cells from a small number of exposed humans. The evidence from epidemiological studies was inadequate. After lengthy discussions, the Working Group again made an overall evaluation of Group 2A, *probably carcinogenic to humans* (IARC 1993, Vol. 57) [3].

The preamble also allows for the possibility that an agent for which there is sufficient carcinogenicity in animals can be placed in Group 3 (instead of Group 2B, in which it would normally be categorized), when *there is strong evidence that the mechanism of carcinogenicity in animals does not operate in humans*. This possibility has also not yet been used by any working group.

## 16.5 Conclusions

Identification of human carcinogenic risks is an important step in the primary prevention of cancer. IARC, through its Monographs program, aims to provide independent, scientifically sound evaluations of degrees of evidence for carcinogenicity, thus furnishing qualitative assessments of risks to humans.

To date, 62 agents have been identified as *carcinogenic to humans*, 51 as *probably carcinogenic to humans* and 206 as *possibly carcinogenic to humans*. Since the aim of the program is to identify carcinogenic risks, few agents have been classified as *probably not carcinogenic to humans*. Our environment contains man-made industrial chemicals, pesticides and drugs, and it is important to identify the risks associated with such exposures. We are also exposed, however, to life-style factors, including cultural habits, and to numerous chemical mixtures associated with diet. Some such exposures, such as tobacco use in its various forms and the eating of Chinese-style salted fish, have already been proven to be carcinogenic. It will be the challenge of the future to determine which of the less easily definable factors in our environment are responsible for some of the cancer burden of the world.

## 16.6 References

[1] Parkin, D.M., Pisani, P., and Ferlay, J., *Int. J. Cancer,* 1993, **54**, 594-606.

[2] IARC Monographs on the Evaluation of Carcinogenic Risks to Humans, Occupational Exposures to Mists and Vapours from Strong Inorganic Acids; and other Industrial Chemicals, 1992, **54**, pp.13-32, Lyon.

[3] IARC Monographs on the Evaluation of Carcinogenic Risks to Humans, Lyon.
IARC, Some Inorganic Substances, Chlorinated Hydrocarbons, Aromatic Amines, *N*-Nitroso Compounds, and Natural Products, 1972, **1**, pp. 181.
IARC, Some Inorganic and Organometallic Compounds, 1973, **2**, pp. 181.
IARC, Certain Polycyclic Aromatic Hydrocarbons and Heterocyclic Compounds, 1973, **3**, pp. 271.
IARC, Some Aromatic Amines, Hydrazine and Related Substances, *N*-Nitroso Compounds and Miscellaneous Alkylating Agents, 1974, **4**, pp. 286.
IARC, Some Organochlorine Pesticides, 1974, **5**, pp. 241.
IARC, Sex Hormones, 1974, **6**, pp. 243.
IARC, Some Anti-thyroid and Related Substances, Nitrofurans and Industrial Chemicals, 1974, **7**, pp. 326.
IARC, Some Aromatic Azo Compounds, 1975, **8**, pp. 357.
IARC, Some Aziridines, *N*-, *S*- and *O*-Mustards and Selenium, 1075, **9**, pp. 268.
IARC , Some Naturally Occurring Substances, 1976, **10**, pp. 353.
IARC, Cadmium, Nickel, Some Epoxides, Miscellaneous Industrial Chemicals and General Considerations on Volatile Anaesthetics, 1976, **11**, pp. 306.
IARC, Some Carbamates, Thiocarbamates and Carbazides, 1976, **12**, pp. 282.
IARC, Some Miscellaneous Pharmaceutical Substances, 1977, **13**, pp. 255.
IARC, Asbestos, 1977, **14**, pp. 106.
IARC, Some Fumigants, the Herbicides 2,4-D and 2,4,5-T,Chlorinated Dibenzodioxins and Miscellaneous Industrial Chemicals, 1977, **15**, pp. 354.
IARC, Some Aromatic Amines and Related Nitro Compounds - Hair Dyes, Colouring Agents and Miscellaneous Industrial Chemicals, 1978, **16**, pp. 400.
IARC, Some *N*-Nitroso Compounds,1978, **17**, pp. 365.
IARC, Polychlorinated Biphenyls and Polybrominated Biphenyls, 1978, **18**, pp. 140.
IARC, Some Monomers, Plastics and Synthetic Elastomers, and Acrolein, 1979, **19**, pp. 513.
IARC, Some Halogenated Hydrocarbons, 1979. **20**, pp. 609.

IARC, Sex Hormones (II), 1979, **21**, pp. 583.
IARC, Some Non-nutritive Sweetening Agents, 1980, **22**, pp. 208.
IARC, Some Metals and Metallic Compounds, 1980, **23**, pp. 438.
IARC, Some Pharmaceutical Drugs, 1980, **24**, pp. 337.
IARC, Wood, Leather and Some Associated Industries, 1981, **25**, pp. 412.
IARC, Some Antineoplastic and Immunosuppressive Agents, 1981, **26**, pp. 411.
IARC, Some Aromatic Amines, Anthraquinones and Nitroso Compounds, and Inorganic Fluorides Used in Drinking-water and Dental Preparations, 1982, **27**, pp. 341.
IARC, The Rubber Industry, 1982, **28**, pp. 486.
IARC, Some Industrial Chemicals and Dyestuffs, 1982, **29**, pp. 416.
IARC, Miscellaneous Pesticides, 1983, **30**, pp. 424.
IARC, Some Food Additives, Feed Additives and Naturally Occurring Substances, 1983, **31**, pp. 314.
IARC, Polynuclear Aromatic Compounds, Part 1: Chemical Environmental and Experimental Data, 1983, **32**, pp. 477.
IARC, Polynuclear Aromatic Compounds, Part 2: Carbon Blacks, Mineral Oils and Some Nitroarenes, 1984, **33**, pp. 245.
IARC, Polynuclear Aromatic Compounds, Part 3: Industrial Exposures in Aluminium Production, Coal Gasification, Coke Production, and Iron and Steel Founding, 1984, **34**, pp. 219.
IARC, Polynuclear Aromatic Compounds, Part 4: Bitumens, Coal-tars and Derived Products, Shale-oils and Soots, 1985, **35**, pp. 271.
IARC, Allyl Compounds, Aldehydes, Epoxides and Peroxides, 1985, **36**, pp. 369.
IARC, Tobacco Habits Other than Smoking; Betel-quid and Areca-nut Chewing; and Some Related Nitrosamines, 1985, **37**, pp. 291.
IARC, Tobacco Smoking, 1986, **38**, pp. 421.
IARC, Some Chemicals Used in Plastics and Elastomers, 1986, **39**, pp. 403.
IARC, Some Naturally Occurring and Synthetic Food Components, Furocoumarins and Ultraviolet Radiation, 1986, **40**, pp. 444.
IARC, Some Halogenated Hydrocarbons and Pesticide Exposures, 1986, **41**, pp. 434.
IARC, Silica and Some Silicates, 1987, **42**, pp. 286.
IARC, Overall Evaluations of Carcinogenicity: An Updating of *IARC Monographs* Volumes 1-42, 1987, **Supp. 7**, pp. 440.
IARC, Man-made Mineral Fibres and Radon, 1988, **43**, pp. 300.
IARC, Alcohol Drinking, 1988, **44**, pp. 416.
IARC, Occupational Exposures in Petroleum Refining; Crude Oil and Major Petroleum Fuels, 1989, **45**, pp. 322.
IARC, Diesel and Gasoline Engine Exhausts and Some Nitroarenes, 1989, **46**, pp. 458.
IARC, Some Organic Solvents, Resin Monomers and Related Compounds, Pigments and Occupational Exposures in Paint Manufacture and Painting, 1989, **47**, pp. 536.
IARC, Some Flame Retardants and Textile Chemicals, and Exposures in the Textile Manufacturing Industry, 1989, **48**, pp. 341.
IARC, Chromium, Nickel and Welding, 1990, **49**, pp. 677.
IARC, Pharmaceutical Drugs, 1990, **50**, pp. 415.

IARC, Coffee, Tea, Mate, Methylxanthines and Methylglyoxal, 1991, **51**, pp. 513.
IARC, Chlorinated Drinking-water; Chlorination By-products; Some Other Halogenated Compounds; Cobalt and Cobalt Compounds, 1991, **52**, pp. 544.
IARC, Occupational Exposures in Insecticide Application, and Some Pesticides, 1991, **53**, pp. 612.
IARC, Occupational Exposures to Mists and Vapours from Strong Inorganic Acids; and Other Industrial Chemicals, 1992, **54**, pp. 366.
IARC, Solar and Ultraviolet Radiation, 1992, **55**, pp. 316.
IARC, Some Naturally Occurring Substances: Food Items and Constituents, Heteroclyclic Aromatic Amines and Mycotoxins, 1993, **56**, pp. 600.
IARC, Occupational Exposures of Hairdressers and Barbers and Personal Use of Hair Colouring Materials; Some Hair Dyes, Cosmetic Colourings, Industrial Dyestuffs and Aromatic Amines, 1993, **57**, pp. 427.
IARC, Beryllium, Cadmium, Mercury and Exposures in the Glass Manufacturing Industry, 1993, **58**, (in press).
IARC, Hepatitis Viruses, 1993, **59**, (in press).

[4] Schüller, H.M., Jorquera, R., Reichert, A., and Castonguay, A., *Cancer Res.*, 1993, **53**, 2498-2501.

# 17. New Approaches for the Evaluation of Carcinogenic Risks of Chemicals

Boris L. Rubenchik

## 17.1 Introduction

Cancer is sometimes associated with a single carcinogenic agent as complex environmental factors play a significant role. Major problems in estimating cancer risk include the ubiquity of exposure and measurement difficulties. Very little is known about carcinogens as agents affecting the communities of various living organisms in nature — *biocenoses.* In this chapter the strategy of estimating cancer risk from both individual carcinogens and long term environmental exposures will be discussed. Approaches to improve human cancer risk assessment of chemicals must be based on integral monitoring systems tp pursue the final control of carcinogenic ability relating to the environment and its impact on humans and natural ecosystems.

## 17.2 Environmental Determinants and Cancer Endogenous Factors

There is no universal component as the sole cause of cancer; it is more likely that certain exogenous or endogenous factors may influence cells involved in the one or many steps towards malignancy.

A number of individual chemicals, group of chemicals, mixtures, cultural habits, together with physical and biological factors, have been associated with induction of cancers at various body sites [1]. These substances are listed in Table 17.1.
This list is based on the deliberations of the International Agency for Research on Cancer (IARC) working groups [2], which evaluated all available data from studies on cancer in humans and in experimental animals, from studies of the chemistry, metabolism and kinetics of the exposure, and from the results of short term tests for genetic and related effects (see also chapter by Wilbourn and Vainio).

Epidemiological studies are consistent in demonstrating a causal relationship between exposure to different kinds of radiation and cancers; also viruses and other biological agents may be associated with human cancer. A number of studies have indicated that diet, tobacco, and certain drugs, may play a role in different tumor formations. Some of the cancers are associated with endogenous hormones, reproductive factors, and sexual behaviour [3]. It is impossible to exclude the role of psychological and socio-economic factors in the frequency of cancer.

**Table 17.1** **Human carcinogens [2]**

| | |
|---|---|
| **Industrial processes or occupational exposures** | |
| Aluminium production | Furniture and cabinet making |
| Auramine, manufacture | Haematite mining (with exposure to radon) |
| Boot and shoe manufacture/repair | Iron and steel founding |
| Coal gasification | Isopropyl alcohol manufacture (strong acid process) |
| Coke production | Magenta, manufacture |
| | Rubber industry |
| **Soots, tars and oils** | |
| Coal-tar pitches | Shale oils |
| Coal-tars | Soots |
| Mineral oils, untreated and mildly treated | |
| **Hormones** | |
| Diethylstilbestrol | Estrogens, steroidal |
| Estrogen replacement therapy | Oral contraceptives, combined |
| Estrogens, non-steroidal | Oral contraceptives, sequential |
| **Metals** | |
| Arsenic compounds | Nickel and nickel compounds |
| Chromium compounds (hexavalent) | |
| **Fibres** | |
| Asbestos | Talc containing asbestiform fibres |
| Erionite | |
| **Tobacco-related products** | |
| Tobacco smoke | Betel quid with tobacco |
| Tobacco products, smokeless | |
| **Organic compounds, combinations or groups** | |
| Aflatoxins | 8-Methoxypsoralen+UV |
| 4-Aminobiphenyl | Methyl-(1-(2-chloroethyl)-3-cyclohexyl-1-nitrosourea) |
| Analgesics containing phenacetin | MOPP-(Combined therapy with nitrogen mustard, vincristine, procarbazine, and prednisone) (and other combined therapies) |
| Azathioprine | Mustard gas |
| Benzene | Myleran |
| Benzidine | 2-Naphthylamine |
| Bis(chloromethyl)ether and chloromethyl ether | Treosulphan |
| Chlorambucil | Vinyl chloride |
| Chlornaphazine | |
| Cyclophosphamide | |
| Melphalan | |

Cancer is rarely associated with a single environmental agent, which can be either an initiator or a promoter of carcinogenesis, but plays significantly different modifying roles concerned with both environmental factors and the organism. For this reason, it is very important to investigate both the cancer risk of some chemicals, viruses or tobacco, with the *carcinogenic dangers associated with the environment*. The causes of most human cancers remain obscure, and it is likely that the causes will prove to be complex and multifactorial. The total number of cancers associated with exposure to particular synthetic chemicals (*eg*, aromatic amines and bladder cancer, vinyl chloride and angiosarcoma of the liver, arsenic and skin cancer, etc), or particular virus infections (Burkitt's lymphoma, Epstein Barr virus, hepatitis B infection, etc.) is significant; but there is no explanation of the sum total of all cancers and their high incidence observed in developed societies.

There is no adequate evidence of environmental components as dominant causes of cancer, but it is likely that tobacco and diet play a very important role [4]. However, there is little activity in investigating complex environmental conditions and toxicological studies involving natural ecosystems as part of a process of risk management and control.

## 17.3 Risk Assessment of Exposure from Complex Mixtures

Establishing a risk assessment for exposure to complex mixtures plays an important role in elucidation of the causes of carcinogenesis [5]. Most of carcinogenic and other chemical exposures in the real world involve mixtures rather than single agents; but, the scientific database for these mixtures is generated almost entirely from studies of the individual components (Figure 17.1).

There is no unanimously agreed definition for the term 'risk assessment'. In relation to human cancer, risk assessment entails the use of qualitative and quantitative data directed at the identification of carcinogenic hazards and the estimation of carcinogenic risk. Within a public health context, risk assessment is directed at estimating incremental risk of cancer in groups or populations in relation to variations in exposure to a number of carcinogenic agents. Ultimately, the full range of chemicals on the basis of short-term toxicological experiments in bacteria, cell cultures, and animals will need to be considered; and the data from these experiments used to identify chemical carcinogens in the environment.

Increased information concerning the quantitative relationship between dose-response data from animal bioassays, short-term tests and cancer epidemiology will assist in the extrapolation of non-human data to human cancer risk estimation. People are rarely exposed to single chemicals, pollution of air, soil and water involves a multitude of chemicals as complex mixtures, the biological effects of which are only partially known. Different occupations, lifestyles involve complex mixtures of mutagens and carcinogens. Hence the strategy for risk assessment of complex mixtures is an important step for investigation of carcinogenic risk to the environment.

**CHEMICAL CHARACTERIZATION MIXTURES**
(analysis, active principles-macromolecular adducts, etc.)

***IN VIVO* TESTS IN ANIMALS**

DNA-damage
Bone marrow assays
Carcinogenicity experiments, etc.

***IN VITRO* TESTS**

Bacterial assay for gene mutation
Clastogenicity in mammalian cells
Gene mutation in mammalian cells, etc.

**HUMAN EXPOSURE AND RELEVANT BIOLOGICAL EFFECTS**

*Non-specific indicators* (ie, chromosome aberration, micronuclei, sister chromatid exchanges, point mutation, oncogene activation, etc.)

*Specific indicators: DNA adducts*
(spectrum, chemical class specific, eg, polycyclic aromatic hydrocarbons, benzo[a]pyrene adducts, etc.)

*Metabolitic exposure indicators*
(urinary mutagenicity, 1-hydroxyperene, other metabolites).

**Figure 17.1** Risk assessment of complex mixtures

## 17.4 Risk Assessment of Chemical Carcinogens Involving Communities of Living Organisms in Nature

Oncologists define a carcinogen as an agent capable of inducing tumors in animals and humans. All definitions of the term carcinogen are incomplete, *ie*, they are based on observational data rather than on knowledge of mechanisms. There is agreement with Purchase [6] that the word 'carcinogen' should be qualified by several adjectives, describing the species, primary mechanism of action (genotoxic or non-genotoxic), route of administration, the dose, etc. However, tumors and malignancy are not induced in all living organisms. Almost nothing is known about carcinogens as agents which affect communities of various living organisms in nature, the so-called *biocenoses* [7].

Some carcinogens are much more ancient than humans, and their presence in nature is not related to human activities. Carcinogens may be abiotic or biotic, but not necessarily anthropogenic. Many carcinogenic substances are formed in the process of volcanic activity (*eg*, benzopyrenes and other PAHs). Some carcinogens have been found in meteoritic substances (*eg*, indole), or in samples of lunar rocks. Beryllium, chromium, and nickel belong to ancient carcinogens. Many plants produce carcinogens such as aflatoxins, cykasine, pyrrolizidine alkaloids, etc. [8].

It is well known that the evolutionary process is subject to significant alterations under the influence of chemical and physical factors, which may result in the appearance of new forms of organisms. Thus, as a response to the exposure to some toxins, toxin-resistant forms of insects have appeared. Similarly, widespread use of antibiotics resulted in new forms of bacteria which are antibiotic resistant.

The possibility that the natural carcinogens originating both from abiotic or biotic materials were 'peaceful aborigines' of ecosystems or even the driving forces of their development. However, the newcomers of the technological era have become the 'barbarians' which affect the *biocenoses*. What is the basis for this suggestion? [7].

Most carcinogenic agents are neither able to induce both neoplasms in certain organisms, nor to possess a wide range of biological effects (mutagenicity, teratogenicity, toxicogenicity, immunosuppression, growth stimulating action, etc.).

As can been seen from Figure 17.2, tumors and tumor-like disorders appear in the upper part of the 'iceberg' of different biological effects of chemical carcinogens.

It is known, for instance, that some PAHs accelerate the growth and reproduction of plant organisms — algae, turnip-rooted cabbages, and others. Gräf and Diehl [9] believed that benzo(a)pyrene at low concentrations possess the properties of a growth hormone for plants. Slepian [10] showed that the modes of action of carcinogenic N-nitroso compounds on plants are multiform. Other studies [11] showed that benzopyrenes enters the soil and subsequently determines the number and composition of soil microorganisms (*ie*, spore-forming bacteria, actinomycetes, and soil fungi). Experimental studies have shown that this carcinogen affects the formation of soil *microbiocenosis* and the biological activity of the soil. Damages inflected on the natural ecosystems by carcinogenic agents are less well known. Nevertheless, the possibility that carcinogens and other transforming compounds play an important part in the transformation of *cenoses* and the earth's ecosystems cannot be excluded.

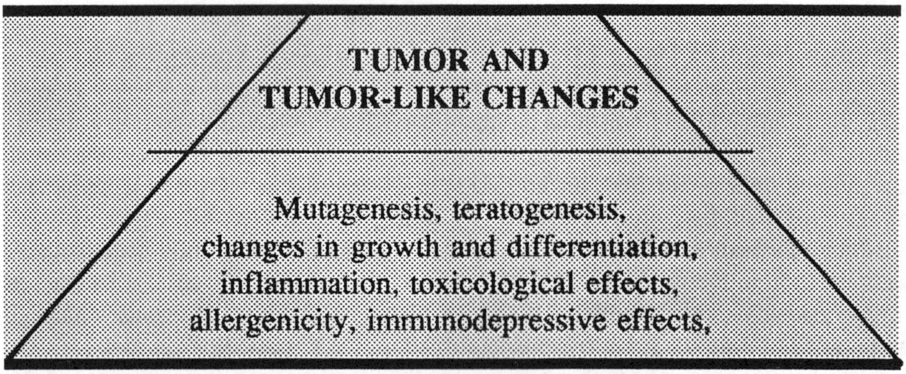


**Figure 17.2** How carcinogens influence natural ecosystems

## 17.5 Estimation of the Risk from Synthetic and Natural Pesticides

Approximately 1500 chemicals have been registered for use in >1000 pesticide formulations (herbicides, insecticides, fungicides, etc.).

Arsenic and arsenic compounds were evaluated by IARC working groups of experts [12] as human carcinogens, and many pesticides as carcinogenic to animals, and probably carcinogenic to humans (dimethyl carbamoyl chloride, ethylene dibromide, captafol, aramite, DDT, mirex, toxafen, and many others).

For these and other carcinogenic pesticides the effects on humans, animals, and natural ecosystems, were investigated. Epidemiological studies of cancer risk following exposure, metabolism, toxic and mutagenic/genetic effects of pesticides in humans and experimental animals were considered. Their circulation in natural *biocenoses* enter the soil hence into plants, and from water basins into the various communities of organisms and aquatic animals. A wide spectrum of biological effects on *biocenoses* were also investigated. Unfortunately, there are no comparisons between the effects of carcinogenic pesticides and their non-carcinogenic analogs which is important in understanding the peculiarity of the specific influence of carcinogens on ecosystems.

Bruce N. Ames [13,14] concluded recently that toxicological examination of synthetic pesticides and other chemicals, without similar examination of naturally occurring pesticides, has resulted in an imbalance in both the data and the perception relating to chemical carcinogens.

There is a considerable number of natural chemicals in the diet, such as plant pesticides and the products resulting from cooking, that have not been a focus for carcinogenicity testing. A comparison of the possible hazards for 80 daily exposures to rodent carcinogens from a variety of sources, were presented, using the Human Exposure/Rodent Potency index (HERP), which relates human exposure to the carcinogenic potency in rodents. When viewed against the large background of naturally occurring carcinogens in typical portions of common foods, the residues of synthetic pesticides or environmental pollutants rank low. A similar result is obtained in a separate comparison of 32 average daily exposures to natural pesticides and synthetic pesticide residues in diets. It was concluded that these findings do not indicate that natural dietary carcinogens are important in human cancer, but cast doubt on the relative importance for human cancer of low dose exposures to synthetic chemicals.

A detailed examination of HERP-index did not provide the possibility to conclude that the risk of exposure to industrial carcinogens and pesticides outside the workplace are trivial compared with those of naturally occurring carcinogens found mostly in the diet [15]. While qualitatively useful the HERP index does not take into account important interactions among naturally occurring and synthetic constituents in foods, nor does it permit examination of the possible role of evolved resistance. But the papers of Ames and co-authors pay attention to the problem of carcinogenicity of natural chemicals which have not yet been investigated.

## 17.6 Ecological Monitoring of Carcinogens

Until recently, the chemicals usually chosen were carcinogens which could be monitored by physico-chemical methods: PAH, polychlorinated biphenyls, N-nitroso compounds, asbestos, carcinogenic metals, *eg*, nickel, chromium, beryllium, etc. [16]. The monitoring of benzo[a]pyrenes and other PAHs in urban atmospheres is one example [17]. Such monitoring can be characterized as sanitary-hygienic, because the measurements of carcinogenic levels in the environment were compared to the oncological morbidity of the population in the regions monitored. However, this monitoring did not take into consideration the response of natural ecosystems.

Therefore, an *integral monitoring system* must be designed in order to estimate the influence of carcinogens and/or carcinogen-containing environments on living organisms, including humans. *Integral monitoring* has to include sanitary-hygienic, medico-biological, and bioecological methods. Hence, integral monitoring will permit the control of the levels of carcinogens, including complex mixtures or environmental contaminants, in addition to their *impacts* on individuals, population groups, and environmental ecosystems.

Integral monitoring serves as a basis for an epidemiological approach to assess the human cancer risks in the environment. The sanitary-hygienic monitoring technique are used to investigate cancer risks in groups of people, such as human populations who are exposed by example to low doses of environmental carcinogens, and thus form the basis for medico-biological clinical case studies.

### 17.6.1 Metabolic Studies (molecular/epidemiology)

Until recently, environmental epidemiology was an observational, rather than an experimental science. Higginson [18] stated that the problem is the development of biochemical (molecular) epidemiology. It is important to apply to epidemiological surveys techniques such as biochemical methods, molecular biology and genetics for the monitoring and control of the cancer risk of environmental agents.

Consideration of some biomarkers used for the investigation of humans make it possible to apply sanitary-hygienic, in addition to medico-biological, monitoring. Some of these are shown in Figure 17.1. Methods available for assessing human exposure to carcinogenic and mutagenic agents [19] include:

- Chemical metabolites found in the body;
- Thioethers in urine;
- Mutagenic activity in excreta;
- Blood protein adducts;
- DNA-adducts in somatic cells;
- Protein variants in blood;
- Point mutations in blood cells;
- Chromosomal aberrations in somatic cells;
- Sister chromatid exchanges in somatic cells;
- Micro-nucleated cells;
- DNA repair of sperm morphology; and,
- Detection of tumor markers.

Molecular epidemiology can provide new perspectives for the investigation of all interactions between the environment and the host. These include the study of:

i) Host factors that influence susceptibility to carcinogens; and,

ii) Detection of carcinogens in human tissues, fluids and cells, including measurement of early biological events that are causally linked to exposure.

Molecular epidemiology can unite non-genetic, genetic host factors, and environmental factors associated with cancer development. Such systems of markers is very important for integral monitoring, *eg,* new approaches in ecogenetics made it possible to demonstrate the association of various ecological and familiar factors, including the study of lung cancer and smoking, genetic polymorphisms and environmental factors, polymorphic expression of acetylation activity as risk factors in human susceptibility to bladder cancer from aryl amine carcinogens, etc. [20]. There is now a perspective of parallel cancer risk investigations to the environmental, in addition, to modifiable host factors including dietary habits and lifestyle.

Molecular techniques can be applied to both integral monitoring, and to epidemiological studies for investigating genetic and environmental factors of carcinogenesis. For example, carcinogenic DNA adducts or oncogene proteins can be used as dosimeters, making it possible to detect carcinogens in human fluids, animal and plant organisms in polluted areas. It initiates the perspective for the investigation of cancer risk in humans exposed to natural environmental ecosystems.

### 17.6.2 Bioecological Monitoring

A new part of integral monitoring is bioecology, which requires the study of the alteration in living organisms and their communities (*biocenoses*) under the influence of carcinogens. There are many examples of neoplastic or cancer-like disorders in fish, shellfish, and other aquatic animals found in various geographic areas of the world that are polluted by chemical contaminants [21]. The incidence of papillomas and other tumors sometimes increases to 50-57%, and in some populations, can be as high as 80-90% [22].

Environmental pollutants have not been proved to be the causal agents for these disorders, but it is not possible to refute the existence of neoplasm-inducing pollutants. Thus, a rise in a neoplasm's *hydrobionts* (water organisms) may be associated either directly with the influence of carcinogens, or indirectly, with species evolution resulting from 'polluted' ecosystems.

Malignant transformation by chemical agents are believed to be the earliest steps which involve covalent binding of the substances to cellular DNA. Fish taken as samples from PAH-contaminated areas of the Buffalo and Detroit rivers have been shown to have elevated liver cancer rates and have demonstrably higher levels of aromatic carcinogens — DNA adducts [23].

Enhanced liver metabolism of mutagens and carcinogens observed in fish living in polluted water is a further example. In the sea bream (*Diplodus annularis*), when exposed to polluted sea water, a significant and marked enhancement of the metabolic activation of the pyrolysis product Trp-2, and of benzo[a]pyrene-*trans*-7,8-diols, cytochrome P-450, arylhydrocarbon hydroxylase, glucose-6-phosphate dehydrogenase and 6-phosphogluconate dehydrogenase activities were observed [24]. These results provide evidence that both biochemical parameters and the overall capacity of fish liver to activate or detoxify certain mutagens can be assumed to be sensitive indicators of exposure to mixed organic pollutants including carcinogens in the marine environment.

Accumulation of some carcinogens can also be assumed to be indicators of environmental pollution. Hence, exceeding a benzo[a]pyrene level leads to its accumulation in fish and shellfish [21,25] (*eg, Umio pectorum*), are capable of accumulating carcinogens selectively. They are resistant to the contamination of water basins and can indicate the presence of harmful substances.

Environmental pollution exposure indicators can be found among different plants.

## 17.7 Strategy for Investigating Cancer Risk from the Environment

There are difficult policy decisions and unresolved scientific issues in the testing of carcinogenic risk of chemicals to humans. There has been considerable discussion on how to define an *acceptable risk* for populations exposed typically to low doses of environmental carcinogens. The relevance of animal results to man, and methods of extrapolation, appears to be more appropriate to handle *living with uncertainty*.

It is proposed that the strategy for evaluation of carcinogenic risks in the environment should be based on investigations both for individual agents, and carcinogen-containing complex mixtures, together with their impact on living organisms, including humans (Figure 17.3). Biochemical, genetic, and molecular markers, as well as the use of natural living 'indicators' should be united into an integral monitoring system; this will permit the eventual control of the levels of carcinogens and their complex mixtures in addition to their impact on individuals, population groups, and environmental ecosystems.

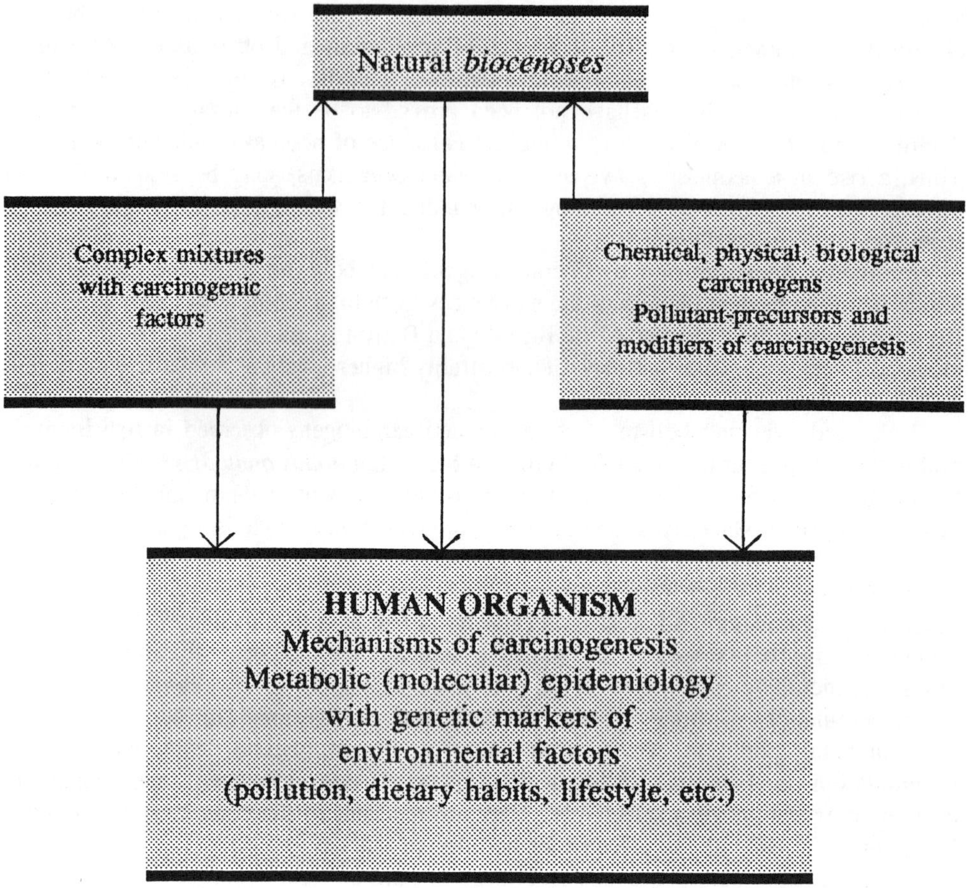


**Figure 17.3** A strategy for the investigation of carcinogenic risk for human to environmental factors

Molecular epidemiology opens perspectives for the investigation of cancer risk on humans on the basis of amalgamating environmental factors with modifiable host factors (lifestyle, dietary habits, etc.).

Cancer prevention may be achieved by moderating environmental carcinogenic factors. According to our conception of *oncoecology* [7] cancer prophylactics must be based on both human protection and on the defense of natural ecosystems and exposure of living organisms to carcinogenic agents. Although human gene alteration as a strategy for modulating genetic cancer predisposition is not yet available, ecological aspects of cancer prevention must be effective for the future.

## 17.8 Conclusions

The major problems in estimating cancer risk are the ubiquity of the exposure and difficulties in their monitoring. The strategy for improved human cancer risk assessment of chemicals must be based on integral monitoring systems for evaluation of the carcinogenic ability to individual carcinogens and to long-term environmental exposure, together with the impact on human and natural ecosystems. Only by such means can chemical safety be considered seriously.

## 17.9 References


[1] Tomatis, L., Aittio, A., Wilbourn, J., and Shuker, L., *Jpn. J. Cancer Res.*, 1989, **80**, 795-807.

[2] Rall, D.P., 'Carcinogens in our Environment', in: *Complex Mixtures and Cancer Risk,* Vainio, H., Sorsa, M., and McMichael, A.J., (Eds.), IARC Sci. Publ., 1990 (No. 104), pp. 233-239, Lyon, International Agency for Research for Cancer (IARC).

[3] *Reproductive Toxicology*, Richardson, M.L., (Ed.), VCH Publishers, Weinheim, 1993, pp. 286.

[4] Doll, R., and Peto, C. *J. Natl. Cancer Inst.*, 1981, **66**, 1191-1308.

[5] Introduction, in: *Complex Mixtures and Cancer Risk*, Vainio, H., Sorsa, M., and McMichael, A.J., (Eds.), IARC Sci. Publ., 1990 (No. 104), pp. 1-8, Lyon, International Agency for Research for Cancer (IARC).

[6] Purchase, I.F., *Int. J. Exp. Pathol.*, 1991, **72**, 725-744.

[7] Rubenchik, B.L., *J. Environ. Pathol. Toxicol. Oncol.*, 1990, **10**, (6), 269-272.

[8] Hirono Iwao, *CRC Crit. Rev. Toxicol.*, 1981, **8**, (3), 235-277.

[9] Gräf, W. and Diehl, H., *Arch. Hyg. Bakteriol*, 1986, **150**, 49-59.

[10] Slepian, E.I., *Znanie*, Moscow, 1977, 1-64.

[11] Tonkopy, N.I., Pertsovskaya, A.F., and Kaskarova, G.P., *Experimentalnaya Oncologia*, 1987, **9**, 24-27.

[12] *General Remarks*. IARC Monographs of the Evaluation of Carcinogenic Risk to Humans, IARC Occupation Exposures in Insecticides Applications, and some Pesticides, 1991, **53**, 33-92, Lyon, International Agency for Research for Cancer (IARC).

[13] Ames, B.N. and Gold, L.S., *Science*, 1989, **244**, 755-757.

[14] Ames, B.N. and Gold, L.S., 'Environmental Pollution and Cancer: Some Misconception', in: *Phantom Risk*, Huber, P.W. and Foster, K.R. (Eds.), 1992, MIT-Press, pp. 1-19.

[15] Davis, D.L., *Environ. Res.*, 1989, **50**, 322-340.

[16] Rubenchik, B.L. and Bykorez, A.I., *Experimentalnaya Oncologia*, 1987, **9**, 3-7.

[17] Yanysheva, N.Ya. and Kireeva, I.S., 'Monitoring of Chemical Carcinogenic Agents in the Human Environment', in: *Ecology and Cancer*, Bykorez, A.I. (Ed.), Naukova Dumka, Kiev, 1985, pp. 168-197.

[18] Higginson, J., *Cancer Res.*, 1988, **48**, 1381-1389.

[19] Lohman, P.H., Lauwerys, R., and Sorsa, M., 'Methods of Monitoring Human Exposure to Carcinogenic and Mutagenic Agents', in: *Monitoring Human ?Exposure*

*to Carcinogenic and Mutagenic Agents*, IARC Sci. Publ., 1990 (No. 59), pp. 423-427, Lyon, International Agency for Research for Cancer (IARC).

[20] Chu, M.M. and Chin, A., *J. Biotechnology*, 1990, **16**, 17-36.

[21] Mix, M.C., *Marine Environ. Res.*, 1986, **20**, 1-141.

[22] Khudoley, V.V., and Bogovsky, S.P., *Adv. Modern. Biol.*, 1982, **3**, 466-472. (Rus.).

[23] Dunn, B.P., Black, J.J., and Maccubbin, A., *Cancer Res.*, 1987, **47**, 6543-6548.

[24] Bagnasco, M., Camoirana, A., De Flora, S., Melodia, F., and Arillo, A., *Muta. Res.*, 1991, **262**, 129-137.

[25] Bykorez, A.I. and Rubenchik, B.L., 'Oncological Ecology and its Problems', in: *Ecology and Cancer*, Bykorez, A.I., (Ed.), Naukova Dumka, Kiev, 1985, pp. 5-22.

# 18. Risk Assessment of Chemicals: Contrast and Comparison, An International Perspective

Prabhu Kulkarni and Brendan J. Nangle

## 18.1 Introduction

The adverse effect of chemicals on human health and on the environment, whether proven or unsubstantiated, will in the future dominate production, availability and the international trade of many chemicals. Proliferation of organizations undertaking toxicological evaluation and risk assessments of these on behalf of industry, environmental organizations and national and international regulatory authorities, often produces conflicting interpretations and confusing results. In an increasingly interdependent world, there is need for a more global approach to chemical safety and risk assessment. This requires a higher degree of uniformity and harmonization between various national and international assessment groups.

To succeed at the international level cooperation between the regulatory authorities of developed and developing country is of primary importance. Given the regulatory diversities that exist within the EC countries and between the EC, Japan and the USA, total global harmonization of risk assessment policies is an unrealistic goal. Nevertheless in spite of the considerable disparities in national regulations, cooperation and uniformity in evaluation of risk assessment is likely to increase in the future. Resource rich developing countries are likely to play an important part in the global harmonization of risk assessment.

The Environmental (Protection) Act 1986 of India increased the government's authority to establish and enforce environmental standards. The law is likely to follow western model of chemical safety and risk assessment. The Indian Law Institute recommends that 'The import and/or use of any chemical substance that is banned in the country of its origin or the country where the substance was first manufactured for its hazardous impact on the environment ... should also be banned in India' [1].

This is acceptance of risk management decisions of other countries and of the risk assessment on which such decisions are based. If accepted universally by developing countries, this concept will have a significant effect on the world chemical industry and hasten the harmonization of regulations.

## 18.2 Why Assess the Risk?

'Occupational Safety and Health as a special phenomenon is the Cinderella area of the world of work. Neither society, the State, management, the workers, nor their representatives have perceived it to be a priority area. It is only in relatively recent times that it has become the norm to expect to be able earn a living for a life time at work and retain one's health and be free from relatively serious injury' [2].

Researchers who worked in chemical laboratories 25 years ago will remember well that benzene was one of the common solvents used extensively, without any special precautions, for column chromatography and for general cleaning. Diethyl ether extraction of organic substances was carried out in laboratories equipped with gas hot water geysers, with ever lit pilot flame, and metals like lead, mercury, cadmium and arsenic were detected by carrying out 'flame test' using Bunsen burners on the work bench.

The chemical industry has been fortunate in its development and was held in high esteem by the public till the late 1960s. Its fortunes have changed dramatically due to factors:

i) The public awareness of the damage to the environment and its unfortunate association with chemical pollutants; and,

ii) a series of major accidents in the last 20 years, which included incidents like the Sandoz spills in Switzerland, the Seveso disaster in Italy, Petrol Storage Fire in Mexico, and the Bhopal gas leak in India.

These factors resulted in a dramatic change in the public perception of the chemical industry. In an uninformed public mind, it became the principal culprit for all environmental ills. During the 1980s almost every country in the world passed their own environmental protection laws, transforming the whole concept of work and occupational safety. The pendulum has swung totally in the opposite direction to its position in the late 1960s. Today, we cannot manufacture, market, transport or dispose of chemicals without proper authorization and/or documentation in industrialised countries.

Against this background, it is essential that the chemical industry determines in a realistic manner the actual risk posed by its products. Assessment of chemical risk gives the data on which to base the safety of chemical industry workers, the public at large and the environment.

## 18.3 Hazards and Risks

In the USA alone there are over 6000 laws enforced by the various State and Federal Government Departments to control the manufacture, sale, transport, labelling, storage and disposal of chemicals. If we count the various laws of the 12 member states and the regulations of the EC, we would probably not be far behind the USA in this area. Additionally, many other parts of the developing world are showing signs of similar regulatory activity. The aims and objectives of all regulatory authorities are very similar. They wish to avoid dangers by identifying the 'hazards' and minimising the 'risk'.

- Hazard in the chemical industry can be defined as an inherent property of a chemical or process which makes it capable of causing adverse effects in a living system — man or animal or the environment — if exposed to it.

- Risk in the chemical industry can be regulated as the likelihood of that hazard actually causing harm to man or the environment. It usually also embraces the magnitude of the consequences of occurrence. This can be expressed as a mathematical equation as follows:

$$\text{Risk} = \text{probability} \times \text{consequences}$$

## 18.4 Chemical Hazards

Chemical hazards can be broadly categorised into physico-chemical, toxicological and environmental.

### 18.4.1

**Physico-chemical hazards** are those dictated directly by the chemistry or physical properties of the chemical. These include *explosivity* (the potential to evolve highly reactive gases, with the evolution of heat, which can cause an explosion), *oxidizing ability* (the potential to react exothermally in contact with other substances, particularly flammable substances) and *flammability* (the capability to ignite and burn). These hazards are categorised in terms of defined criteria by various regulatory bodies (for example, the EC). *Radioactivity* is a very unique hazard associated with molecules possessing a special electronic structure.

### 18.4.2

**Toxicological hazards** are those which may result in the chemical causing a deleterious effect when it comes into contact with a living organism; in practice, this usually refers to the chemical's ability to cause death, injury or other adverse health effect to man, when ingested, inhaled or absorbed through the skin. Toxicological hazards include the ability to produce toxic effects which can be acute or chronic, local or systemic, and reversible or irreversible. They are usually also understood to encompass *corrosivity* (the destruction of living tissue) and *irritancy* (manifested by the generation of inflammation) both on skin and in the respiratory system. Other specific toxic effects include *sensitisation* (skin and respiratory) which involves an alteration of the immunological system such that characteristic (usually enhanced) adverse effects will result from subsequent exposures to the chemical. Probably the more insidious of the toxic hazards are *carcinogenicity* (cancer inducing), *mutagenicity* (effects on genes) (see also chapter by Franekic, *et al.*), and *toxic for reproduction* (effects on foetus) [3]. The existence of these hazards for a given chemical can often be difficult to determine with certainty and, while they understandably create great concern among workers, there are, relatively speaking, not very many chemicals for which causal relationships to these hazards have been established with certainty.

**18.4.3**

**Environmental hazards** relate to the ability of a chemical to cause damage to one or more compartments of the environment (air, soil, water). In the broader sense, such chemicals are often taken to include those which can cause adverse effects on man via the environment (*eg*, lead and benzene from vehicle emissions), those which cause damage to non-human biota (*eg*, PCBs) and those which, while not directly toxic to humans or other biota, are capable of causing environmental damage (*eg*, CFCs).

In addition to the hazards associated directly with the properties of chemicals, it should not be forgotten that even relatively 'safe' chemicals can sometimes present hazards with extremes of temperature. Water, normally a relatively benign chemical, can be extremely hazardous in contact with human tissue when at 100ºC. Carbon dioxide can cause severe skin injury when cooled to its liquid state. And even a relatively 'harmless' ester or hydrocarbon can cause severe injury if a worker slips on a spillage of the liquid on the plant floor! However, it is the intrinsic hazards of the chemical itself which will be of concern in this chapter.

Identification of hazard, whether physico-chemical, toxicological or environmental, requires knowledge of the physical and chemical properties of the chemical. While this information should be the same, irrespective of the researcher; the **quantification** of the hazard may give rise to different results depending on the test procedures and criteria used by the researcher. While there are, in many instances, standard procedures laid down for carrying out hazard assessment tests, these may not always be followed. Even these standard tests may vary depending on region or regulatory body. Flammability tests performed by the various 'open cup' procedures may be expected to give flash point values a few degrees higher than a 'closed cup' method; while the latter is now gaining ground as the universally acceptable method, many of the flash points quoted in the chemical literature were obtained using other methods. Similarly, at what LD50 value should a chemical be regarded as 'toxic'?; as will be seen later, various regulatory bodies have assigned different limit values in establishing such criteria. Hence significant variations in the quantification of chemical hazard have resulted over the years; and the chemical literature bears testimony to this.

## 18.5 Acceptable Risk

**Risk assessment** may be defined as the process of decision making applied to problems where there are a variety of possible outcomes and it is uncertain which event will happen. In other words, evaluation of risk involves predicting possibilities of something going wrong and the consequences of the error. Risk assessment must start by consideration of the following steps [4]:

i) Identification of hazards;

ii) Evaluation of likelihood of occurrence of identified hazardous events;

iii) Evaluation of extent and probability of consequences of hazards;

iv) Evaluation of risk-combination of likelihood and consequences; and,

v) Consideration of degree of risk.

In order to evaluate risk and make meaningful decisions on the implementation of safety procedures, it must take into account that there is no such thing as absolute safety. Every action we take has some risk associated with it [5].

Depending on our socio-cultural background we may or may not accept certain risks. In the modern industrial culture, we accept certain risks associated with industries. Acceptable risk and accepted risks are different in every society and these differences are particularly significant when we talk about the acceptable risks in the developing countries. A slight risk is acceptable to us, if the cost of remedying it is unreasonably high. In the European countries we accept the possibility of one death per million in an industrial operation. This number may be considerably lower in the developing countries.

Even in the industrialised countries perception of risks by individuals are significantly different. A cyclist riding on the highway will not be afraid to ride between the fast moving cars but will consider himself in danger if he thinks that there is a shiny coating of silicone on his apple. Perception of risks is based on one's familiarity with the entity involved and on and the social and cultural background of individuals and nations.

## 18.6 Risk Assessment Programmes

Against a background of growing public mistrust of the chemical industry, the necessity of collating existing information and carrying out authentic risk assessment programmes has been recognised by various governments and the chemical industry itself. Over the past few years, a number of programmes have been launched aimed at initiating the generation and organization of the necessary data. These include the International Programme on Chemical Safety (IPCS), the International Register of Potentially Toxic Chemicals (IRPTC) and the International Agency for Research on Cancer (IARC). In addition, various legislative acts regulating the marketing, use and transport of chemicals have appeared. These defined the classification and labelling of chemicals on the basis of their inherent properties (*ie,* their hazards). Primary examples are the EC Dangerous Substances Directive together with the national legislations derived from it, the US Toxic Substances Control Act (TSCA), the UN Transport Recommendations and various EFTA and OECD country legislation's. The very recent 'EC Existing Chemicals Regulation' requires the submission of defined hazard data on a certain number of high volume chemicals currently on the European market.

There are also major voluntary chemical testing programmes already set up by the European Chemical Industry Council (CEFIC) and by OECD. The aims of all of these programmes are similar, that is to build comprehensive data bases on all key chemicals on the market so that better judgements may be made on the possible risks to the user. Due to the enormity of this task, priority setting schemes have had to be established. Not surprisingly, risk assessment methodology has also been the subject of intense debate.

The International Programme for Chemical Safety (IPCS) is a cooperative programme of the United Nations Environment Programme (UNEP), The World Health Organization

(WHO) and the International Labour Office (ILO). It is reviewing specific chemicals or groups of chemicals for toxicity, risk and safety. So far have they completed 75 Environmental Health Criteria Documents, 55 monograms, 10 on toxicological methodology.

According to Mercier of the IPCS 'The proliferation of groups undertaking toxicological evaluation and safety assessment of chemicals today is a fact that is looked upon by national regulatory authorities, as well as industry, since the point of these evaluations often diverge from one another' [6].

The US EPA evaluated all the various national and international health guidelines for dioxin (TCDD) in an effort to select the most appropriate one. The data, expressed as doses considered virtually safe or those that may pose a theoretical cancer risk of 1 in 1,000,000, varied from EPA and Californian values (1987) of $<0.01$ pg $kg^{-1}$ $d^{-1}$ to FDA and Canadian values (1985) of 10.0 pg $kg^{-1}$ $d^{-1}$ (*ie*, a factor of $>1{,}000$). As the evaluation clearly showed, equally creditable scientific bodies can occasionally have very different views about what constitutes a safe level of human exposure to a chemical [7].

As indicated earlier, there is potential for different interpretations in assessing and quantifying the *hazard* of a chemical. Using such variable data, there are further opportunities for variations in the assessment of the resultant *risk* in the use of that chemical. It is not surprising, therefore, that the risk assessment of chemicals by individuals and institutions throughout the world results in conclusions which must be thoroughly confusing and possibly even suspicious to the layman, who is often the end-user of a chemical. In addition, the principal use of hazard classification systems has been as a tool for hazard communication, via package labels and Material Safety Data Sheets (MSDS), to the worker and consumer.

The labelling and MSDS format are also subject to different schemes, again resulting in the potential to confuse the recipient. Some of these areas of differences are reviewed in the following sections.

### 18.6.1 The European Community

In 1967, the European Community (EC) published its first Directive on the Classification, Packaging and Labelling (CPL) of dangerous substances (Directive 67/548/EEC) [8]. This landmark Directive, now incorporating a number of Annexes, Amendments and Adaptations to Technical Progress (ATPs), defines 8 major hazard classes for chemicals: explosive (E), oxidizing (O), flammable (F) (3 sub-classes), toxic (T), harmful (Xn), corrosive (C), irritant (Xi) and dangerous for the environment (N). It gives detailed criteria by which chemicals may be judged in relation to these classes. The Directive also defines the hazard symbols and labelling text associated with these various hazards and gives detailed rules on the format of the label. It also defines the actual hazard classification for about 1400 hazardous substances (Annex I). More recently, an equivalent Directive (88/379/EEC) [9] covers in a very detailed fashion the CPL of preparations (defined as mixtures of chemicals).

These EC CPL Directives provide a solid groundwork for harmonized national laws on the Classification, Packaging and Labelling of dangerous chemicals and consequently most EC countries now have corresponding laws and regulations which are generally very similar as regard to the CPL of chemicals. However, slight differences in interpretations of the details of the EC Directives by national authorities have been known to occur and these can be reflected in the national regulations. In addition, some Member States have laws which go significantly beyond the requirements of the Directives. Directive Amendments and ATPs are published at intervals and different countries will frequently enact laws to bring these into effect at different times, despite the Directive requirements of compliance by a specified date. Hence, it is possible that different CPL requirements are operable simultaneously (albeit briefly) in different EC Member States.

In 1982 the EC established the European Inventory of Existing Commercial Chemical Substances (EINECS). Only the chemicals listed in this register can be marketed without testing in the community. Those not listed ('New chemicals') must be notified prior to commercialisation and this notification involves generation of hazard data, normally quite extensive. (See also chapter by Campbell.)

During the last ten years, about 600 new chemicals have been notified for the inclusion in EINECS. Out of over 100,000 chemicals listed in the EINECS, these are the only chemicals so far fully assessed under EC criteria for their Environmental Hazards. Table 18.1 gives a general picture of the prospects for the future when a large number of existing chemicals will be assessed for their impact on the Environment.

**Table 18.1** **New Substances Notified**

| | | | |
|---|---|---|---|
| Total number of substances Notified to date | | | 600 |
| Substances classified by experts under EC Directive 67/548/EEC | | | 400 |
| of which classified as **'not dangerous'** | | (70%) | 280 |
| and **'dangerous'** | | (30%) | 120 |
| Of the 120 dangerous substances classification is as follows: | | | |
| E/F/O | 10 | (8%) | |
| T⊕/T | 10 | (8%) | |
| C | 15 | (12.5%) | |
| Xn | 30 | (25%) | |
| Xi | 50 | (42%) | |
| N* | 50 | (42%) | |

*Dangerous for the aquatic environment only

If the experience of new substance classification is extrapolated to all dangerous substances listed in Annex 1 of the Directive 67/548 (total 1400) it will result in 500 substances being classified as dangerous to aquatic Environment.

If EC experts reclassify 30% of the 100,000 substances registered in EINECS as dangerous, similar to the above new registrations, we will have a list of 30,000 dangerous substances of which 12,600 will be dangerous to the aquatic environment [10]. This will have a major impact on marketing of these substances and the preparations containing them.

Presently the EC new chemical testing requirements are relatively straightforward and are implemented by all member States. In spite of this there can be several different interpretations and the regulatory authorities give divergent rulings. The following example of a water soluble dyestuffs for garments illustrates this case.

A registration Agency was interested in notifying a water soluble textile dyestuff for use in dying clothing which would be in contact with the skin of humans.

The Agency decided to follow the text and the test method described in the 6th amendment, Annex VII,4.2.2, which states that '...route of administration should be the most appropriate having regard to intended use.'

They chose an aqueous solution of the substance for the dermal route for the subacute 28 d test.

Notification was made in the UK and was accepted by the authorities, The same dossier was rejected by the German Authorities on the grounds that the route selected was incorrect. They wanted oral administration. Finally the courts settled this on the basis of legal argument and not scientific reasoning. According to German chemical laws, the dossier could only be rejected if it is 'Obviously incomplete or erroneous' [11].

### 18.6.2 Outside the EC

Similarly, many significant differences exist between the EEC and Nordic countries in relation to chemical risk assessment, though they all have aspirations to harmonize their regulations. These countries have more substances classified as carcinogens than the EC, based on results from animal tests. The EC gives more importance to human experience.

Product Registration is mandatory in Sweden, Norway, Finland and Denmark though Denmark is a member of the EEC.

In Sweden there is a principle of 'reverse burden of proof' *ie,* every substance is suspected of dangerous effects until it is proved that the suspicion is not correct.

Norway proposes that, if a preparation contains more than 1% substance dangerous to the environment then the complete preparation is to be classified and labelled as dangerous to the environment.

Even the unified group of these countries have their differences of opinion. The same toxicological data is interpreted differently for labelling as illustrated in Table 18.2.

Hydroxyethyl methacrylate is labelled as an Irritant (Xi) in Sweden, Denmark and Finland while it is classified as Harmful (Xn) in Norway.

Hydroxypropyl methacrylate (HPMA) is labelled as irritant (Xi) in EC, including Denmark, while it is classified as a skin sensitiser in Sweden. Concentration limits for sensitising substances in formulations is 1%, and for irritant substances it is 10% before appropriate hazard labelling is required. Toxicological information used for these interpretations is derived from the same source. It may be hoped that such Scandinavian issues should start to resolve themselves when these EFTA countries combine with EC to form EEA.

**Table 18.2** Labelling classification

| **2-Butanone (ethyl methyl ketone)** | | |
|---|---|---|
| EC( Denmark) | Xi | Irritant |
| Finland | — | Non-hazardous |
| Sweden | — | {Las vaming texten} Moderately Harmful |
| Norway | Xn | Harmful |

All countries consider Butanone as Highly Flammable (F).

## 18.7 Chemical Inventory — New National Status Symbol?

Prior to the introduction of EINECS by the EEC, the USA had their own register, the TSCA inventory. Registers now exists in Australia, Canada and in Japan. Similar to the EC, these countries insist that only the chemicals registered in their national list are allowed to be marketed in the country. This is an artificial short term barrier to trade. Most countries accept internationally recognised toxicological tests, and notification in most countries is simple enough. The new entrants to the national registers are South Korea and the Philippines. It is not unreasonable to expect that, within the next few years, we may have to face perhaps 10 or 20 more national registers from developing countries.

Apart from the notification of new chemicals a large number of countries insist on registration of preparations or products. Presently this is not a requirement in the EC. However Norway, Sweden, Finland, Austria, Switzerland, Malta, and now South Korea, insist on product registration which require complete disclosure of formulations, including trace amounts of additives such as colorant and stabilisers. Denmark, though a member of the EC, still requires product registration.

If some of the developing countries decide to join the product registration system very complex problems could present themselves for international trade (see also chapter by Knight).

## 18.8 The Chemical Industry and Developing Countries

During the last few decades the chemical industry in the developing countries is expanding at an unprecedented rate. China, Mexico, Brazil, India, Indonesia, and a few middle Eastern countries have developed a sizeable chemical industry. These countries, though at a very different level of development, share a number of common problems.

Ulrich Beck, the most influential European social analyst of the late twentieth century, in his book *Risk Society* writes that 'Hazardous industries have been transferred to the low wage countries of the Third World. There is a systematic attraction between extreme poverty and extreme risk... on the international scale it is emphatically true that material misery and blindness to hazards coincide' [12].

Developing countries have very poor records on environmental health and safety, and outwardly it is felt that they do not have concern for the environment. They all have sophisticated industrial operations in the midst of appalling poverty. A very well trained and highly educated middle class amongst the illiterate masses. Highly trained professional managers are usually of a different social background and are isolated from the illiterate workforce and untrained supervisors.

Most developing countries are relatively thickly populated, and the population density tends to increase near industrial plants. Except in communist China, most developing countries have poor public transport. The casual and the temporary workers build their shanty towns around the chemical plants (see also chapter by Shen Li).

Major industries, due to the availability of infrastructural facilities, are located close to urban centres. Concentration of potentially hazardous industries in some cities is alarmingly high (Bombay, Sao Paulo, Shanghai, Mexico city).

The safety and health problems due to the use of chemicals in the developing countries are serious due to the following reasons:

i) Low literacy level among workers;

ii) High cost of personal protective equipment (PPE) compared with the wages of the workers — 'danger money' is sometimes as much as 3 times the daily wages, and is far more attractive to the worker than PPE;

iii) Climatic conditions of the work place make it difficult to wear — there is also a shortage of PPE;

iv) Lack of Governmental enforcing machinery and possible local level corruption — supervisors share in the 'danger money' and avoidance in purchasing PPE; and,

v) Poor or non-existent health care facilities.

This situation can be improved if all those involved in the production, import and sale of chemicals in developing countries play a responsible role in ensuring 'safety in use'. Multinational corporations should not set up hazardous operations or export products that are considered dangerous for use in their own countries. Imposition of regulations by developing countries, similar to that suggested by the Indian Law Society could be of importance [1].

## 18.9 The Killing Fields

It is estimated that there are 3.8 million cases of occupational diseases due to exposure to chemicals in the world each year. Of these, acute pesticide poisoning accounts for about 3 million cases. About 220,000 of these are fatal. Over 90 % of exposure incidents and about 99% of deaths take place in the third world countries [13]. German Development expert reports on the careless use of pesticides, in Sri Lanka — there they spread DDT with bare hands, people are powdered white', 'On the Antilles island of Trinidad a total of 120 deaths from pesticides were reported, a farmer: 'If you don't feel sick after spraying, you haven't sprayed enough' [14].

These accident figures are extremely high if we consider the 1991 manufacturing statistics for the production of chemicals and pesticides given in Table 18.3.

**Table 18.3 Chemical and pesticides production data**

| Area | Chemicals US \$ Billion | Pesticides US \$ Million |
|---|---|---|
| USA | 304.7 | 5712 |
| Western Europe | 336 | 6811 |
| Japan | 163.3 | 1977 |
| Eastern Europe | 190 | 879 |
| Rest of the World | 214 | |
| Australasia-Pacific Rim | — | 3296 |
| Latin America | — | 2417 |
| Africa | — | 879 |
| Total | 1230.0 | 21970 |

## 18.10 Shifting Balance

The overwhelming dominance of the USA and Europe in the chemical industry is likely to change significantly in the near future. Natural cost advantages are growing features of the South East Asian Chemical industry. By the year 2000, for example, the urea demand of China will be greater than 24.2 million tonnes and that of India will be greater than 16.5 million tonnes. The Asia-Pacific region is expected to produce over 44 million tonnes of urea, mainly by China, India and Indonesia [17].

Similarly the Middle Eastern region will alter the balance of manufacturing petrochemicals, primarily due to cheaper feed stock. It is expected that Middle-Eastern Producers will replace about 8 to 10 million tonnes $a^{-1}$ of the commodity plastics capacity in Europe.

Examination of the factors which might have bearing on the risk assessment of chemicals in some of these countries.

### 18.10.1 China

Among the major chemical producers in the third world countries, China has a long standing environmental policy. Their environmental protection law dates back to 1979 and was modified and updated in 1983 and 1989. They have their own threshold limit values for exposure to chemicals at the work place 'Maximum Allowable Concentration', TWA

(24 h) and STEL. Recently (1989) these values have been amended to include MAC for Soil and Water. The Chinese prefer to carry out their own toxicology testing and have assigned $LD_{50}$ and $LC_{50}$ values to most common chemicals. Further classification of chemicals as 'toxic' or 'harmful' is similar to internationally accepted values.

#### 18.10.1.1 Evidence During Chronic Intoxication

In principle, this is assessed by incidence rate for chronic intoxication for highly exposed workers. If the incidence rate for chronic intoxication is not available, the incidence rate of intoxication symptoms or signs can be used.

#### 18.10.1.2 Outcome of Chronic Intoxication

After the cessation of exposure, the outcome is divided into 4 levels, progressive, non-curable, curable and spontaneous recovery [18].

The Chinese National Environmental Protection Agency was established in 1970 and now cooperates with the UNEP, WHO, ILO and FAO.

### 18.10.2 India

Unlike China, India is still recovering from the traumatic events of the Bhopal disaster in 1984 in which over 2,500 people were killed and over 200,000 injured. Because of this perhaps, the Indian chemical industry is under constant observation and likely to be one of the most regulated. As in other developing countries, the regulatory enforcement is very poor and the law breakers are difficult to control.

Presently India does not have a National Chemical Register and there is no requirement to register products. However it tends to follows some of the EC regulations.

The Environmental (Protection) Act 1986 of India increased the central government's authority to establish and enforce environmental standards. The law follows the Western model of chemical safety and risk assessment. The American Chemical Society CAS registry numbers and threshold limit values have been directly adopted, though there is an open ended commitment to the introduction of national standards in the future. Unusually heavy emphasis is placed on the release of every chemical into the atmosphere by accident — perhaps the Bhopal syndrome.

The Indian Law Institute recommends that 'stringent conditions [1].

This is a defacto acceptance of certain risk management methods and decisions of other countries. The recommendation is likely to have a profound effect on multinational companies operating in India, and, if adopted by other developing Countries, then the effect will be felt internationally. As an initial step in this direction, the EC has introduced a regulation [19] on the export of banned or severely restricted chemicals which requires the *Prior Informed Consent* of the receiving country.

### 18.10.3 Other Asia-Pacific Countries

With the possible exception of Switzerland, Japan appears to be the first country in the world to issue a general law on chemical substances under which new substances are required to be examined and notified. This was entitled 'Law concerning the Examination and Regulation of Manufacture etc. of Chemical Substances' and enacted in 1973. As in the more recent counterparts of that Japanese notification law, the examination of chemical substances involved testing in a prescribed manner and the utilisation of criteria to categorise the chemical as hazardous or not. However, unlike the other major world chemical assessment schemes, Japanese regulations view chemical hazards in terms of their possible effect on man via the environment. Thus, the first priority in their testing scheme is a biodegradation test, the results of which determine what subsequent testing is required. As a consequence of this testing and notification requirement, the Japanese 'Handbook of Existing and New Chemical Substances' [20] lists some 22,000 chemicals the hazards of which have been assessed to one degree or another.

Very recently, 2 more countries in the Asia-Pacific area have set in motion the mechanisms to establish chemical inventories. These are South Korea and the Philippines. In 1992, as part of their 'Toxic Chemicals Control Law', South Korea initiated the requirement to nominate candidate chemicals for their 'Existing Chemicals List'; the list closes for nominations on 31st December 1993. Similarly, embodied in the Philippine 'Toxic Substances and Hazardous and Nuclear Waste Control Act' (R.A.6969, 1990), the Philippine 'Inventory of Chemicals and Chemical Substances' was established. Again, the nomination period closes at the end of 1993 (see chapter by Knight).

While chemicals nominated for these 2 inventories (*ie,* 'existing chemicals') do not have to undergo any testing at this time, new chemicals notified after 1993 will be subject to defined hazard testing regimes. It may reasonably be assumed that, at some future date, the South Korean and Philippine authorities may establish testing programmes for their existing chemicals, following the example of the EC. In all such testing programmes, whether relating to existing or new substances, the requirements of the different authorities may not be expected to be identical. Indeed, it is unfortunate that such countries are not encouraged to accept existing inventories and testing requirements (*eg,* those of the EC) in order to minimise further diversity of hazard and risk assessment criteria.

### 18.10.4 Mexico

Mexico has the largest Chemical industry in Central and Southern America and is one of the most advanced countries of the region. It is estimated that it generates about 30 million tonnes of hazardous waste. Mexico has only one permitted hazardous waste landfill site and no incinerators. Mr. Bennett Jaffee, director of Environmental Services for Consultants' Group, Latin America estimates that 90 % of the total hazardous waste is dumped into rivers, trash heaps, available open spaces or discharged into sewers. Only about 10% hazardous waste is disposed of in safe landfills or storage areas [21].

During the last few years the Mexican Government has introduced severe strict regulations and hope they will be policed effectively. EC and US environmental companies feel that this is one of the growth areas for investment.

### 18.10.5 Central European Countries (CEC) and Commonwealth of Independent States (CIS)

The appalling environmental degradation and total lack of regulatory controls in effluent treatment and waste disposal in the former Soviet Union and the Eastern Europe could be a topic for an independent chapter. In March 1991, a member of the Soviet Academy of Science Mr. Boris Porfirive, informed the National War College's annual conference that the estimated cost of Soviet Pollution and natural resource degradation could be about 15-17% of GNP. At the same conference, the distinguished Soviet Biologist A.V. Yablokov said that 'over half the Soviet population now lives in environmental crises area, every 3rd man in those regions has a cancer and the life expectancy is 4 to 8 years shorter than in the developed countries' [3]. Over 50 million Soviet citizens breath air, 10 times more contaminated than the Soviet legal maximum limits for the industrial air pollutants. Poland is regarded to be the most polluted country in the Europe. Bulgaria, Romania, Hungary, Slovakia and the Czech Republic are moderately polluted in comparison with former USSR and Poland [22].

Serious environmental problems and significant risks exist in the outdated and poorly funded chemical plants of the CEC and the CIS. Political and social conditions in these states are in turmoil, and both the implementation of the regulations and the monitoring of chemical industry will suffer significantly. Hungary, Slovakia, Poland and the Czech Republic are accepting and implementing the EC guidelines.

## 18.11 Transport Agencies

The various hazard classification and chemical risk assessment systems reviewed above are designed in general with the end user of the chemical in mind. However, one of the oldest and best known chemical classification systems in the world is the United Nations (UN) Recommendations on the Transport of Dangerous Goods, first published in 1956 [23].

While such recommendations have, in themselves, no force in law, they form the basis for the codes and regulations of the various international modal transport organizations covering the conveyance of dangerous chemicals by air, sea, rail, road and inland waterway. The UN chemical hazard classification scheme is distinctly different from that of the EC. For transportation purposes, a chemical is regarded as hazardous if it meets the criteria of one or more of 8 hazard classes, all related to the possible immediate adverse consequences to both man and the environment resulting from an accident or fire during conveyance of a chemical.

These UN Recommendations have been embraced in principle by various transport agencies. The regulations governing the international transport of dangerous goods by air are found in the Technical Instructions issued by the Montreal-based International Civil Aviation Organization (ICAO) [24]; these are mandatory for all International Air Transport Association (IATA) member airlines (most of the world's airlines). The International Maritime Dangerous Goods Code (IMDG) [25], which covers sea transport, is prepared by the London-based International Maritime Organization (IMO). The European Agreement concerning the International Carriage of Dangerous Goods by Road (ADR)

[26] is a product of the Geneva-based UN Economic Commission for Europe (ECE) and has been adopted by 24 European countries (not just EC). Whilst the transport of goods by rail has been regulated since 1890, the International Regulations for the Carriage of Dangerous Goods by Rail (RID) [27] is a more recent product of collaboration between the Central Office for International Rail Transport and ECE. RID applies to about 20 European countries plus some North African and Middle Eastern states. There are also the European Provision Concerning the International Carriage of Dangerous Goods by Inland Waterway (ADN Recommendations) covering inland navigation in Europe (ECE responsibility) and the closely related code specifically for the River Rhine (ADNR).

While all of these transport agency codes and regulations are based on the UN recommendations, there are differences in many of their criteria for determining what constitutes a hazardous chemical. The ADR and RID Regulations are maintained closely in line with each other due to ECE involvement in both; however, they are probably the most out of line with the UN recommendations. Also, there are several significant differences between ICAO, IMDG and ADR/RID. Many of these are understandable since they relate to the particular characteristics and requirements of the individual modes. Nevertheless, there are instances where such divergence can be difficult to justify. One example is flammability: liquid chemicals having flash points <100 °C are classified as 'flammable' (Hazard Class 3) by ARD/RID while the equivalent cut-off point for air and sea are 60.5 °C and 61 °C respectively. Thus, it is possible for a chemical to be classified as 'flammable' on its journey by road to the airport and then become 'non-flammable' when placed on board the aircraft!

Harmonization of the transport agency codes is a major objective of the relatively newly constituted UN Sub-Committee of Experts on the Transport of Dangerous Goods. A major effort involves the alignment of ADR/RID with the basic UN recommendations. Such considerations are becoming of greater importance with the rapid increase in multi-modal transport (*eg*, 'Ro-Ro' traffic). However, a more profound and ambitious aim is the harmonization of UN and EC requirements .

## 18.12 Current Harmonization Programmes

As we have seen, a key component in any chemical risk assessment is the prior assessment of the hazard of the chemical. A meaningful and uniform hazard assessment can be based only on a set of universally acceptable criteria. The harmonization of chemical hazard classification systems has been the subject of discussion between various bodies for some years, the focus of attention being the substantial differences between the UN recommendations relating to classification for transport and the EC Directives relating to classification for supply . The need and benefits of such a harmonized scheme relating to the use of chemicals at work were recognised by the International Labour Office (ILO) in 1989; the integration of existing chemical classification schemes is an essential part of improving workplace safety [28]. The movement in that direction is currently gathering momentum internationally. The issue was taken up by the OECD in 1991. Harmonization of chemical classification and labelling has been accepted by the International Council of Chemical Associations (ICCA) as a key element of a global strategy for the environmentally sound management of chemical products. An action programme has been drawn up by the UN Conference on Environment and Development (UNCED) and other organizations now involved include OECD, IMO, the UN Committee of Experts on the Transport of Dangerous Goods (UN CETDG) and IPCS.

The benefits of harmonization are fairly obvious — improved hazard communication throughout the industry, less burden on multi-national companies in regulatory compliance efforts, less hazard testing (*eg*, toxicity tests on animals) and improved credibility for the chemical industry as a whole. The European Chemical Industry Council (CEFIC), while not considering that the coexistence of differing major classification systems has, under present circumstances, given rise to unacceptable risks, supports any such activity which removes existing ambiguities in hazard communication.

## 18.13 Conclusion

This chapter has outlined some examples of the considerable difficulties which confront the chemical industry, regulatory agencies and the general public in relation to a truly meaningful and internationally acceptable risk assessment policy for chemicals. The task of addressing the problem in enormous, requiring considerable resources. Whatever country is considered, whether industrialised or developing, it is the small local chemical manufactures and dealers who are difficult to regulate and monitor.

Mervyn Richardson, editor, of several publications on risk management refers to his personal experience. When double glazing his residence in the United Kingdom, he found that 'no company representative was aware of, or could obtain details of, the chemicals used in adhesives, sealants, or stains. During the installation the fitters, were almost totally devoid of any knowledge associated with the risks and safety involved in handling solvents including 1,1,1-trichloroethane (the container even quoted an out of date TLV, but they were unaware of its meaning). Cleaning with solvents and staining of wood was carried out late in the day with no instruction to the house owner of the hazards of sleeping in a room with high levels of organic solvents — this could obviously cause severe consequences for the very young, the old, or infirm, suffering from respiratory conditions. Their attitude to the environment was poor, pouring solvents down the surface water drains, spilling solvent on lawns...' [29].

Perhaps the most difficult task facing chemical regulators is that of presenting straightforward, plausible data which will enable the general public to put chemical hazards in proper perspective.

There is a certain abstractness to chemicals which tends to frighten the layman and allows him to misinterpret the risks potentially associated with chemicals. The consequences of any such misinterpretations can vary in extreme cases from dangerous complacency on the one hand to unnecessary fear on the other. Educating the public in these matters, while extremely difficult, is vital to the future of the chemical industry as a whole. As Andrew Butler, President of Dow Europe said: 'We have too easily become lost in our science and divorced from the outside world; while the public was losing confidence in us, we were also losing touch with them' [30]. If any such education programme is to be successful, it has to be based on an internationally unified approach to chemical hazards built on internationally accepted standards, criteria and interpretations.

## 18.14 References

[1] Jasanoff, S., 'Reasoning about Risk', in: *Risk Assessment of Chemicals in the Environment*, Richardson, M.L. (Ed.), The Royal Society of Chemistry, London, 1988, p.92-113.

[2] O'Mochain, S., Accidental Statistics, Lecture notes. Dip.HSWW University College, Dublin, 1993.

[3] *Reproductive Toxicology*, Richardson, M.L. (Ed.), VCH Publishers, Weinheim, 1993, pp. 286.

[4] Clerinx, J. and Jourdan, L., Quantitative assessment of risks from installation in the chemical industry. World Conference on Chemical Accidents, Rome,1987, pp. 103

[5] Lovell, D.P., 'Risk assessment — general principles', in: *Toxic Hazard Assessment of Chemicals*, Richardson, M.L. (Ed.), The Royal Society of Chemistry, London, 1988, pp. 92-113.

[6] Mercier, M., 'Risk assessment of chemicals: A global approach,' in: *Risk Assessment of Chemicals in the Environment*, Richardson, M.L. (Ed.), The Royal Society of Chemistry, 1988, p. 73-91

[7] Paustenbach, D., Jernigan, J.D., Finnley, B.L., Riple, S.R., and Keeenan, R.E., *Air Waste Man. Assoc. J.*, 1990, **40**, (12), 1620-1630.

[8] EC Council Directive of 27 June 1967 on the approximation of laws, regulations and administrative provisions relating to the classification, packaging and labelling of dangerous substances (67/548/EEC), *Off. J. Eur. Comm.*, No. 196/1 of 16-8-67.

[9] EC Council Directive of 7 June 1988 on the approximation of the laws, regulations and administrative provisions of the Member States relating to the classification, packaging and labelling of dangerous preparations (88/379/EEC), *Off. J. Eur. Comm.*, No. L 187/14 of 16-7-88.

[10] Hinton, A., EC Classification for Environmental Dangers, Charles Simeons Conference, London, 1992, Mill Leet, Clay-Next-the-Sea, Norfolk NR25 7RR, England.

[11] Rudin, E., Competent Authority Attitudes & Producers Dilemmas-Charles Simeons Conference, London, 1992, Mill Leet, Clay-Next-the-Sea, Norfolk NR25 7RR, England.

[12] Beck, U., *Risk Society*, SAGE Publications, London, 1992, p. 41.

[13] Rantanen, J., 'Global overview' in: *The role of Workers in Preventing Occupational Hazards*, Rice, A., (Ed.), International Federation of Chemical, Energy and General Work, Belgium, 1986, pp. 5-19.

[14] Der Spiegel, 1984, (50), 119.

[15] US Chemicals Industry Statistics Handbook 1992, 158.

[16] Layman, P.L., *Chem & Eng. News*, 2nd Nov. 1992, 16-17.

[17] Krishna Murti, C.R., 'Human health impact of pesticides in environment' in: *Chemistry, Agriculture and the Environment*, Richardson, M.L., (Ed.) The Royal Society of Chemistry, Cambridge, 1991, p. 491-510.

[18] Li, S., 'Regulation and health standards in management of risk in Chinese chemical manufacturing Industry', in: *Risk Management of Chemicals*, Richardson, M.L., (Ed.), The Royal Society of Chemistry, Cambridge, 1992, p. 167-190

[19] EC Council Regulation No. 2455/92 of 23 July 1992 concerning the export and import of certain dangerous chemicals, *Off. J. Eur. Comm.*, L 251/13, 29-8-92.

[20] Handbook of Existing & New Chemical Substances (Fifth Edition), Chemical Products Safety Division, Basic Industries Bureau, Ministry of International Trade & Industry, published by The Chemical Daily Co., Ltd., Tokyo, 1992.

[21] Rotman, D., 'Pollution woes could mean big business', Mexican Chemicals, An Industry Review, *Chemical Week*, 16th June,1993, p. 18.

[22] Merritt, G., 'Eastern Europe and the USSR — The challenge of freedom', Office for Official Publication of the European Community, chapter 10.

[23] United Nations Economic and Social Council, Transport of Dangerous Goods, Recommendations prepared by the United Nations Committee of Experts on the Transport of Dangerous Goods, International Regulations Publishing and Distributing Organization, Chicago, USA (published periodically).

[24] International Civil Aviation Organization, Technical Instructions for the Safe Transport of Dangerous Goods by Air, INTEREG, Chicago, USA, and the associated International Air Transport Association Dangerous Goods Regulations (published periodically).

[25] International Maritime Organization, International Maritime Dangerous Goods Code, IMO, London (published periodically).

[26] European Agreement concerning the International Carriage of Dangerous Goods by Road (ADR), HMSO, London (published periodically).

[27] Regulations concerning the International Carriage of Dangerous Goods by Rail (RID), HMSO, London (published periodically).

[28] International Labour Office (ILO) Convention No. 170 and ILO Recommendation No. 177, both adopted in 1990, United Nations, Geneva.

[29] *Risk Management of Chemicals*, M.L.Richardson, (Ed.), The Royal Society of Chemistry, 1992, pp. 355

[30] *Chem. Brit.*, 1993, **29**, (1), 5.

# 19. Assessment of Pesticide Action on Human Health and the Environment in the Ukraine

Yuri Kundiev

## 19.1 Introduction

The wide use of pesticides in the former Soviet Union, including Ukraine, has been the subject of controversy since the 1950s.

Earlier studies [1-3] showed that mankind is paying for crop preservation by contaminated environment and agricultural products, danger of human, domestic animals, wild life poisoning, and the impairment of ecological systems. The ability of organochlorine insecticides to accumulate in living organisms was elucidated when the very high toxicity of the first generation of organophosphorus pesticides was established. During this period, the principles of toxic and hygienic assessment of pesticides were developed; these principles remain of importance [4].

In 1964, in Kiev within the system of the Ministry of Public Health, the All-Union Scientific Research Institute of Toxicology of Pesticides, Polymers and Plastics (now the Ukrainian Institute of Ecohygiene and Toxicology of Chemicals) was organized which soon became a large center involved with the coordination of this problem in the former Soviet Union.

In 1968, the classification of pesticides depending on their degree of hazard was proposed for the purposes of hygienic selection, and was modified in 1987. In addition to the WHO classification it covers the chemical assessment for both concordance with the $LD_{50}$ and criteria such as cumulation, persistence, carcinogenicity, embryotoxicity, and ability to cause allergy (see Table 19.1).

## 19.2 Health Requirements

In 1981, health requirements for pesticides were developed [7]. They are as follows:

i) To apply, as a rule, chemicals that are only slightly toxic for man and animals for agricultural purposes;

ii) To neither register nor to apply very persistent substances which are not decomposed in the environment within ≥1 year, to limit significantly rates of application, to regulate strictly periods of application for persistent pesticides, if there is no opportunity to replace them by less persistent ones which are decomposed during a one crop cycle;

**Table 19.1** **Hygienic classification of pesticides based on the main criteria of hazards**

| | |
|---|---|
| **1. Intragastric administration** | |
| Extremely toxic substances | <50 mg kg$^{-1}$ |
| Highly toxic substances | 50-200 mg kg$^{-1}$ |
| Moderately toxic substances | 200-1000 mg kg$^{-1}$ |
| Slightly toxic substances | >1000 mg kg$^{-1}$ |
| **2. Skin-absorption toxicity** | |
| Strongly marked | <500 mg kg$^{-1}$ cutaneous oral coefficient <3 |
| Marked | 500-2000 mg kg$^{-1}$ cutaneous-oral coefficient 3-10 |
| Slightly marked | >2000 mg kg$^{-1}$ cutaneous oral coefficient >10 |
| **3. Hazard of chemicals by their degree of volatility (chronic exposure)** | |
| Strongly marked | Saturation concentration ≥300 above lethal dose |
| Marked | Saturation concentration is 300-30 times above lethal dose |
| Slightly marked | Saturation concentration is 30-3 times above lethal dose |
| Low toxic | Saturation concentration is ≤3 times above lethal dose |
| **4. Accumulation** | |
| Super-marked | Cumulation coefficient ($C_{cum}$) is <1 |
| Marked | Cumulation coefficient ($C_{cum}$) is within 1-3 |
| Moderately marked | Cumulation coefficient ($C_{cum}$) is within 3-5 |
| Slightly marked | Cumulation coefficient ($C_{cum}$) is >5 |
| **5. Persistence (in soil)** | |
| Very persistent | *t*½ 1 year |
| Persistent | *t*½ 6-12 months |
| Moderately persistent | *t*½ 1-6 months |
| Low persistent | *t*½ <1 month |
| **6. Blastomogenicity** | |
| Evidently carcinogenic | Known incidence of cancer in humans; strong carcinogens in animal experiments |
| Carcinogenic | Carcinogenicity proved in animal experiments but not proved in humans |
| Slightly carcinogenic | Slight carcinogenicity in animal experiments |
| Suspected blastomogenes | No evidence of carcinogenicity |
| **7. Teratogenicity** | |
| Evidence of teratogenicity | Abnormalities found in humans and reproduction defects in animals |
| Suspected teratogenicity | Experimental animal data available |
| **8. Embryotoxicity** | |
| Selective | Detectable in doses non-toxic to maternal animal |
| Moderate | Apparent with other toxic effects |
| **9. Allergic properties** | |
| Strong allergens | Produce allergic reactions in the majority of affected persons even under low dose exposures which occur in real life situations |
| Weak allergens | Produce allergic reactions in selected individuals |

(See also chapter by Wilbourn and Vainio).

iii) To not apply pesticides with high cumulative properties; and,

iv) To not apply pesticides involving carcinogenic, mutagenic, embryotoxic and allergic effects.

## 19.3 Pesticide Usage

However, the problems of the environmental and human health protection in connection with the wide usage of pesticides in agriculture remains to be one of the priority problems in the Ukraine, this is despite a decrease in the use of pesticides since 1986 for economic reasons.

In 1986, 194,000 tonnes of chemicals were used. In 1992 71,000 tonnes, and in 1993 — only 65,000 tonnes. About 80% of pesticides applied in the Ukraine are purchased from other countries (Germany, France, Japan, etc.). The data on the extent of cultivated areas and on the amount of pesticides applied in the Ukraine are summarized in Table 19.2. It can be seen that in recent years the extent of agricultural areas treated with pesticides and the pesticide loads $ha^{-1}$ decreased significantly. At the same time the variety of pesticidal preparations increased, although as a rule only ~10% of them are used widely.

Probably in the future a gradual decrease in pesticide usage in agriculture in the Ukraine will occur. This is because the adoption of the concept of integrated plant protection. The chemical methods are allowed only in such situations when non-chemical methods cannot assist in decreasing the density of populations of harmful organisms to safer levels. Therefore, it is very important to take into account both ecological and economic situations.

**Table 19.2** **Amounts of pesticides usage in the Ukraine**

| Year | Area ha x $10^3$ according (a.i.) | Amounts, kg $ha^{-1}$ according (a.i.) | Number of chemicals |
|---|---|---|---|
| 1965 | 33456.2 | 0.42 | 41 |
| 1970 | 33203.3 | 1.02 | 32 |
| 1975 | 33200.4 | 2.82 | 46 |
| 1980 | 33179.7 | 3.02 | 64 |
| 1985 | 32967.1 | 2.93 | 103 |
| 1990 | 31922.3 | 2.05 | 170 |
| 1991 | 30724.0 | 1.87 | 150 |
| 1992 | 30710.0 | 0.86 | <200 |

## 19.4 Contamination

It is well known that use of chemicals in agriculture requires constant control regarding their residues in food products and the environment. Therefore, it is vital to improve preventive measures and reduce the risks to human health. In the Ukraine such supervision is carried out by the authorities of the State sanitary supervision and sanitary-epidemiological stations. They are located in every region, city, and district. A computer system was developed for monitoring pesticide residues in food products, water and working zone atmospheres.

Some data on the contamination of food products by pesticides in the Ukraine in the period 1963-1991 are summarized in Table 19.3. It is seen that during the 10 most recent years the number of samples with pesticide residues increased; whereas the % of samples exceeding permissible levels remains relatively low.

There are cases of acute human poisoning by pesticides in the Ukraine. In the last 20-25 years this occurred more often in workers not involved directly in the application of pesticides, but amongst those workers who cultivate agricultural crops on fields treated previously with pesticides. This problem was the subject of a special investigation [8].

It was established that under certain conditions of pesticide application after certain time periods (sometimes exceeding the re-entry period) products of pesticide degradation can enter the working zone atmosphere. The toxicity of these products was often higher than the original preparations. The probability of development of toxic mist under specific meteorological conditions was studied [9].

The number of cases and patients with acute poisoning in the Ukraine over the last 22 years are summarized in Table 19.4. There is a tendency for the number of registered patients to decrease.

The long-term usage of persistent organochlorine pesticides, such as DDT, HCH, herbicides of the s-triazine group resulted in soil contamination. More than 20% of the soils studied in the Ukraine contained DDT and its derivatives; 4% of soils were polluted with HCH. The considerable quantities of DDT were found in breast milk, blood and fat tissues of humans. This is supported by the data obtained during the period of 1981-1985 [10] (see also chapters by Franekic, Gundy, and Vasilescu).

The comparison with the results of biomonitoring carried out in different countries shows that in the Ukraine the average level of p,p-DDT content in breast milk fat is 0.21±0.06 (0.03-1.02) mg $kg^{-1}$ (fat). This is lower than in breast milk in India (see chapter by Nag and Jaffrey), China, Mexico, and is approximately equal to the data registered in West Germany, Israel, former Yugoslavia, Japan, but higher than in women in the USA, Sweden and Belgium. The concentrations of p,p-DDE is 0.66±0.12 (0.03-4.00) mg $kg^{-1}$. These values are significantly lower than in most countries and approximate to the levels registered in Belgium and Sweden.

The mean values and ranges of β and γ-isomers of HCH 0.2±0.07 (0.001-1.16), 0.01±0.003 (0.01-0.06), respectively, in breast milk fat in the Ukraine do not exceed values registered in Belgium, West Germany, Sweden, Israel, or the former Yugoslavia, but are significantly lower than that in India, China and Japan.

**Table 19.3** **Contamination of food products by pesticides in the Ukraine within the period 1963-1991**

| Year | Total number of the samples studied | Samples with pesticide residue | % of the total contamination | % of contamination exceeding MPL |
|---|---|---|---|---|
| 1963 | 1749 | 372 | 21.2 | 11.2 |
| 1965 | 5782 | 968 | 16.6 | 9.6 |
| 1966 | 18359 | 3395 | 18.4 | 9.6 |
| 1967 | 29676 | 4203 | 13.4 | 7.9 |
| 1968 | 55287 | 7587 | 13.7 | 8.7 |
| 1969 | 88622 | 9941 | 11.2 | 7.5 |
| 1970 | 108114 | 9812 | 8.5 | 8.4 |
| 1971 | 121511 | 8770 | 7.2 | 4.6 |
| 1972 | 150591 | 8803 | 5.8 | 3.6 |
| 1975 | 156710 | 7309 | 4.0 | 2.3 |
| 1980 | 104150 | 2097 | 2.0 | 0.7 |
| 1984 | 89376 | 2503 | 2.7 | 1.2 |
| 1985 | 95760 | 2969 | 3.1 | 1.2 |
| 1986 | 105264 | 3095 | 2.9 | 1.2 |
| 1987 | 106206 | 3505 | 3.3 | 1.4 |
| 1988 | 97600 | 6149 | 6.3 | 2.3 |
| 1989 | 112523 | 8089 | 7.1 | 2.6 |
| 1990 | 114360 | 7205 | 6.3 | 1.8 |
| 1991 | 128804 | 7084 | 5.5 | 1.4 |

**Table 19.4** **Number of patients with acute poisoning resulting from pesticides in the Ukraine**

| Year | Number of patients |
|---|---|
| 1970 | 338 |
| 1975 | 334 |
| 1980 | 177 |
| 1985 | 109 |
| 1990 | 175 |
| 1992 | 45 |
| In total over 20 years | 2182 |

## 19.5 Regulations

In the Ukraine, the State Commission on Chemical Means for Plant Protection (Goskhimkomissiya) was organized under the Cabinet of Ministers. The representatives of various authorities (Ministry of Health, Ministry of Agriculture, Ministry of

Environmental Protection), in addition to outstanding scientists, are members of this Commission. The Commission is responsible for the state registration of pesticides. All new pesticides of Ukrainian or foreign productions are under thorough study at special scientific institutions. Only after comprehensive toxicological and ecological assessments can the question of their state registration or whether they can be included into the list of substances which are permitted for usage be considered. Naturally, only pesticides which meet the requirements adopted in the Ukraine are registered and included into the list. The list is updated and supplemented annually. The Ministry of Health of the Ukraine is entitled to ban any registered chemical when during any process or use negative effects are revealed.

On the basis of the adopted criteria for hazard for humans and the environment, a number of substances which are used widely in many countries have been banned for usage in the former Soviet Union and in the Ukraine due to their high toxicity and hazards; these include the organophosphorus pesticides (thimet, azinophos-methyl, gusathion, diallyphos, dicrotophos, izophenophos, ultracide, nemacur), organochlorine pesticides of diene moiety (aldrin, dieldrin, endrin, isodrin), carbamates (temic, dioxycarb), dithiocarbamates (ziram, maneb), and dipyridyl pesticides (paraquat — which is well-known for its selective pulmonotrophic effects).

A number of pesticides after short-term applications in agriculture are banned for usage. Among these are parathion, demeton, methyldemeton, ecatin, thiocron, dinoseb, which are extremely teratogenic; nitrochlor (nitrafen, sodium pentachlorphenolate), which produce mutagenic, carcinogenic, and teratogenic effects; and, chlordane and heptachlor, which are extremely cumulative and persistent in the environment. In 1970, DDT was banned for use in cattle-breeding and for treatment of food crops and fodder. In general, according to toxicological and hygienic criteria over 100 pesticides used in other countries were not registered or are excluded from the list of pesticides allowed for use in the Ukraine.

It is considered that the hazard of pesticides for humans should be determined, largely by their ability to biocumulate. It is now possible to obtain data on the prognosis of toxic effects during long-term intake of chemicals and to prescribe safe exposure levels.

For the quantitative assessment of the cumulative affects the cumulation coefficient is used, this is the ratio of the total $LD_{50}$ (n) obtained in daily administration of a selected part of the $LD_{50}$ (*eg*, $^1/_{10}$) in acute experiments to determine the $LD_{50}$ value.

$$C_{cum} = \frac{LD_{50}(n)}{LD_{50}}$$

When the comparative assessment of cumulation of various substances is required, values of their $C_{cum}$ obtained from 0.05 $LD_{50}$ and 0.1 $LD_{50}$ administrations are compared. Depending on $C_{cum}$ value, 4 degrees of cumulation can be specified. This criterion was used for the hygienic classification of pesticides.

$C_{cum}$ can be determined not only by lethal dose but additionally to any graduated index. In the latter case doses causing 50% of changes in the selected index are used: $ED_{50}$ (n) and $ED_{50}$, respectively.

The purpose of chronic experiments in laboratory animals is to study the cumulative properties of a substance, to establish the threshold of harmful effects, and the non-effective doses and concentrations. The duration of the experiment is 6-12 months for pesticides administered orally and 4-6 months by inhalation (when studying delayed effects the experiments may need longer periods). A set of indices must be detailed adequately in order to reveal the character of the pathological characteristics and changes which can be on the border of normal pathology, and also to determine non-effective doses. When establishing the threshold of harmful effects, particular significance is given to the systems of biochemical and immunological adaptation because they are the first to respond to the effect of chemical substances. The analysis of the changes of these systems provides information allowing differentiation of reactions of adaptation and injury, although significant difficulties may occur in every specific case.

These tests are recommended for use in chronic experiments and are described in detail [11-13].

## 19.6 Conclusions

It is known that one of the most complicated tasks in investigations on toxicology of pesticides is the extrapolation of the data from laboratory animals to man. It is particularly complicated in cases of delayed effects associated with the exposure to pesticides (cardiotoxic, neurotoxic, carcinogenic, mutagenic, embryotoxic, and teratogenic effects). This is explained, primarily, by insufficient knowledge of the mechanisms of chemical carcinogenesis, teratogenesis and mutagenesis. This, in turn, makes it difficult to establish regularities between the ability of pesticides to provoke certain pathological changes and their chemical structure. In order to fill this knowledge gap, further accumulation of experimental data in this field needs to be obtained from animal experiments, and compare these data with the results from health examinations including wide-scale epidemiological investigations.

In the former Soviet Union, and in the Ukraine, a large program was developed aimed at finding relationships between the population's health and the intensity of pesticide usage. The results show that morbidity from cardio-vascular and nervous system diseases (based on statistical data) is significantly higher in areas with intensive application of pesticides than in the control group where the pesticide 'load' is 3-4 times lower. The occurrence of cardio-vascular and nervous system diseases, in addition to diseases of the gastro-intestinal tract and respiratory system, was found to be high in areas where the usage of pesticides was 9 times higher [14].

The most important tasks to be undertaken immediately are:

i) To review the total list of applied pesticides based on new data concerning delayed effects; and,

ii) Withdrawal of chemicals that in natural conditions can become dangerous for humans, animals, and the environment.

There is a requirement to improve standards and regulations for the safe use of pesticides, to introduce modern technologies and techniques for their application, and to raise the efficiency of the state sanitary supervision.

## 19.7 References


[1] Medved, L.I., 'Results and further purposes of scientific investigation on the hygienic and toxicological assessment of insecto-fungicides', in: *Labour Hygiene, Toxicology and Treatment of Poisonings*, Moscow, Medgiz, 1959, pp. 3-4.

[2] Serebryanaya, S.G., *Assessment of organochlorine agrochemicals from the viewpoint of hygiene and nutrition*, Moscow, Medgiz, 1959, pp. 131-141.

[3] Kagan, Y.S., *Toxicology of Organophosphorus Insecticides and their Safe Use*, Moscow, Medgiz, 1963, pp. 327.

[4] Medved, K.I., Kagan, Y.S., Spynu, E.I., and Bury, V.S. *Zhurnal Vsesoyuznogo Khimicheskogo Obshchestva im D.I. Mendeleyeva, 1978, **23**, 123-130.*

[5] *Methodological Instructions for the Hygienic Assessment of New Pesticides*, Kiev, Vniigintox, 1969, pp. 14-15.

[6] *Methodological Instructions for the Hygienic Assessment of New Pesticides*, Kiev, Vniigintox, 1988, pp. 13-14.

[7] Medved, L.I., 'Toxicology of pesticides', in: *Occupational Health in Agricultural Production*, Moscow, Meditsina, 1981, pp. 156-241.

[8] Kundiev, Y.I., Nikitin, D.P., Erman, M.I., and Khokholkova, G.A., *Gigiyena i sanitariya*, 1975, (No. 10), 6-10.

[9] Goncharuk, E.I., Filatova, I.N., and Lipatova, T.E., *Gigiyena i sanitariya*, 1987, (No. 11), 15-18.

[10] Demchenko, V.F., Klisenko, M.A., and Aleksandrova, L.G., 'Principles and experience of regional and occupational pesticide biomonitoring', in: *Ukrainian-Finnish Symposium on Occupational Health in Agriculture*, 19-21 August 1992 (in press).

[11] *Toxicometry of Environmental Chemical Pollutants*, A.A. Kasparov, A.A. and Sanotsky, I.V., (Eds.), Centre for International Projects, GKNT, Moscow, 1986, pp. 350.

[12] Kagan, Y.S., *Principles of Pesticide Toxicology*, Centre for International Projects, GKNT, Moscow, 1985, pp. 176.

[13] Health aspects of pesticide use. Collection of training materials, Centre for International Projects, Moscow, 1992, Vol. 1, 259.

[14] Polchenko, V.I., Mukhtarova, N.D., Baida, L.K., Zinchenko, D.V., Pugachev, A.T., and Sarnitskaya, N.P., *Effect of pesticides on indices of health and test-indicators for their detection*, Vrachebnoye delo, 1990, (No. 10), 121-124.

# 20. Some Organochlorine Pollutants in the Water Environment and Their Influence on Drinking Water Quality

Vlasta Drevenkar, Sanja Fingler, and Zlatko Fröbe

## 20.1 Introduction

The evaluation of environmental presence of toxic compounds provides a basis to manage natural water resources in an effective and sustainable manner. Diverse groups of organic chlorinated compounds, *eg*, organochlorine (OC) pesticides, chlorophenols (CPs) and polychlorinated biphenyls (PCBs) are discharged and their presence and distribution in water environments need to be controlled by means of an environmental risk assessment.

The use of OC pesticides in Croatia has been restricted for some 20 years, but due to their high resistance to chemical and biological degradation they are still found in the water environment. The presence of CPs in surface and ground waters is usually a consequence of municipal and industrial waste discharges. Contamination of drinking water supplies originates principally from polluted water resources but CPs can also be formed by routine disinfection of drinking water by chlorination. PCBs are very persistent chemicals with diverse industrial applications. Whilst their use is prohibited, they have been substituted only partially to date and are still contained in many electricity facilities in Croatia. The presence of these compounds has been estimated in several surface/ground waters.

High resolution gas chromatographic (HRGC) techniques: capillary gas, chromatography with electron capture and mass spectrometric (MS) detection, enable reliable identification and trace levels quantification of OC pollutants. Such pollutants need to be concentrated in water samples by efficient extraction procedures and transformed into more volatile derivatives (in the case of CPs). Due to relatively high cost of such sophisticated techniques, the determination of concentrations, origins and distribution of OC pollutants in the water environment in Croatia has not been maintained on a regular basis to date. Monitoring programmes are carried out randomly, in the case of accidents or upon request. Therefore data compiled on the presence of CPs, OC pesticides and PCBs in water environment are available only to a limited extent. The diversity of the geographic, hydrological and climatic factors plays an important role in determining local specificities in water quality. This chapter summarizes results of several studies of drinking water quality which are focused in 3 regions of Croatia, chosen to represent different drinking water resources and water managing systems. The city of Zagreb, the capital and major industrial center, is receiving its drinking water from ground water wells dispersed around the city area and along the catchments of the Sava river. The town of Sisak, the center of an industrialized region in continental Croatia, is using the Kupa river water after appropriate treatment for drinking water supplies. The third region is the Istrian peninsula in Northern Adriatic, in particular the town of Labin, supplied with drinking water from the karst water sources. The results obtained by the control of the quality of both raw and drinking water in these 3 regions are compared in order to provide an insight in risks imposed by environmental presence of hazardous OC compounds.

**Table 20.1** **Concentrations of PCBs in water and sediment of rivers in Slovenia (SLO) and Croatia (CRO) downstream of the primary contaminated karst area in Slovenia**

| River (Year) | Concentration (N) Water ng $l^{-1}$ | | Sediment $\mu g\ kg^{-1}$ dry weight | | Ref. |
|---|---|---|---|---|---|
| Krupa river (SLO) (1983) | 270-350 | (3) | 41000-70000 | (3) | [1] |
| Krupa river (SLO) (1983/84) | 200-600 | (12) | 1500-55000 | (10) | [2] |
| Lahinja river (SLO) (1983/84) | 2 | (14) | 4500-9000 | (3) | [2] |
| Kupa river (SLO) (1983/84) | 1 | (20) | <1-320 | (12) | [2] |
| Kupa river (CRO) (1985) | 1-52 | (32) | 7-39 | (6) | [5,6] |
| Kupa river (CRO) (1985/86) | 1-6 | (6) | | not measured | [7] |
| Kupa river (CRO) (1988/89) | <1-8 | (24) | | not measured | [8] |

N=Number of samples

## 20.2 Polychlorinated Biphenyls in the Kupa River

Ten years ago a very serious PCB contamination in a relatively narrow karst area in Slovenia near the town of Semič was found [1,2]. Extremely high concentrations of PCBs were found in the source water and in the main stream water of the Krupa river as well as in the river sediment (Table 20.1). The water source (mean capacity of 1 $m^3\ s^{-1}$) was checked as drinking water supply for a large populated region. The contamination was ascribed to improper disposal of waste by an electrocapacitor manufacturing plant which has been discharging since 1962. The plant was using various technical mixtures of PCBs as Clophen A-30 and A-50 and Pyralene 1500 and 3010, and disposed of the waste at 2 locations within a radius of 5 km from the water source. From the waste tip the PCBs migrated into the karst ground water streams and finally contaminated the source of the Krupa river. In 1984, as a direct consequence of the river water pollution, high levels of PCBs in samples of blood (mean of 10 samples 155 ng $g^{-1}$, range 35-480 ng $g^{-1}$) and skin fat (concentrations in 2 samples 270 and 320 µg $g^{-1}$) in a group of residents living in the Krupa river gorge were determined [3]. Dermal absorption by direct uptake from the air, direct uptake through the skin by bathing in the river or indirect transport through underwear washed in the river water were suggested as predominant routes of PCBs intake. Twenty-five months after ceasing the use of river water for bathing and washing, the level of PCBs in residents blood samples decreased 10-fold and in skin fat 20-fold confirming the proposed exposure pathway.

From the heavily polluted Krupa river, the PCBs migrated into the small Lahinja river in Slovenia. PCBs determined in samples of the Lahinja river sediment (downstream) were found to have results 2 orders of magnitude greater than those collected 100 m upstream (35 µg $kg^{-1}$) from the Krupa river (Table 20.1) [4]. The Lahinja river is a tributary of the Kupa river which flows partly along the border line between Slovenia and Croatia. In Croatia the Kupa river and its ground water system serve as drinking water resources for the public water supplies in the rural and urban areas along a longitudinal river segment of about 200 km downstream from the primary contaminated karst area. In samples of the Kupa river water, suspended particles and sediment collected upstream of the Lahinja river mouth PCBs were either not detected or present in concentrations near the detection limit [4,5]. These findings indicated that the contaminated Lahinja river is the main source of PCBs found in the Kupa river downstream of its inflow [2,4-8]. The PCBs profile determined by HRGC-MS analyses in Pyralene and in extracts of the Kupa river sediment and fish collected in Croatia in 1985 [6] was almost identical to the previously reported profile of PCBs extracted from a sediment sample collected in the Krupa river in Slovenia [1].

The results of PCB analyses in the Kupa river water and sediments collected during a 6-year period at locations which were 0.1 to 200 km downstream from the Lahinja river mouth are summarized in Table 20.1. Compared to the Krupa river, the concentrations found in the Kupa river were by 1 — 2 orders of magnitude lower in water and by 3 — 4 orders of magnitude lower in sediment. In most water samples the PCB concentrations were <10 ng $l^{-1}$ regardless on the distance of sampling site from the Lahinja river inflow. Moreover, the highest concentrations (up to 52 ng $l^{-1}$) were measured 200 km downstream from the contamination source, *ie,* in water samples collected in July 1985 near the town of Sisak [5]. This result suggested the possibility of appearance of highly contaminated river water peaks due to the specific hydrological conditions at the time of sampling. However, by analysis of the Kupa river samples collected monthly from March 1988 to April 1989 35 km upstream and in the Sisak area, no seasonal variations in PCB concentrations were observed [8]. The concentrations were not dependent upon the flow rate of the Kupa river, and the maximum in the PCBs load profile (1.8 mg $s^{-1}$) in the river water was measured at highest flow rate.

Sorption of PCBs to the river bottom sediments as well as to suspended particles with subsequent sedimentation are among the most important factors determining the fate and behaviour of PCBs in natural water systems. Contaminated sediment could be a standing 'secondary' source of slow contamination of the water environment and could be activated especially during the intensive rising of the river water. The amounts of PCBs detected in the Kupa river sediments (Table 20.1) decreased gradually with the increasing distance from the primary contaminated area, and a similar trend was observed in the suspended particles [5]. The concentrations of PCBs in particles isolated from the Kupa river water collected 10, 100 and 200 km downstream from the Lahinja river inflow were 190, 135 and 50 µg $kg^{-1}$ dry weight, respectively. The PCBs distribution coefficient of an order of magnitude of $\leq 10^4$ between particles and water was determined confirming the suspended particles as an important route in the transport of PCBs over a considerable distance from the primary contaminated area. Their varying amounts in the run-off waters from this area could contribute greatly to the periodical decrease/increase of the PCBs level in the Kupa river water.

According to the World Health Organization Criteria for concentrations of PCBs in fresh waters, the Kupa river may be classified among the low to moderately contaminated waters [9]. A wide range of PCB concentrations in fish samples from the monitored segment of the Kupa river in Croatia confirmed a long-term river contamination with PCBs. The PCB concentrations determined in different fish from the Krupa, Lahinja and Kupa rivers are compared (Table 20.2). The highest concentration was determined in a 4-years old trout caught in the Krupa river [2]. The fish from the Kupa river could be considered to be moderately to highly contaminated and their use for human food should be controlled permanently.

**Table 20.2** **Concentrations of PCBs in different fish caught in the rivers downstream from the primary contaminated karst area in Slovenia**

| River (Year) | Number of samples | Concentration range µg $g^{-1}$ | Ref. |
|---|---|---|---|
| Krupa river (SLO) (1983) | 1 | 116 | [2] |
| Lahinja river (SLO) (1983/1984) | 3 | 0.03-1.80 | [2] |
| Kupa river (SLO) (1983/1984) | 2 | 0.05-3.30 | [2] |
| Kupa river (CRO) (1985) | 7 | 0.06-0.81 | [7] |
| Kupa river (CRO) (1985/1986) | 30 | 0.10-42.3 | [5] |

## 20.3 Organochlorine Pesticides and Polychlorinated Biphenyls in Drinking Water

The maximum allowable concentrations of hazardous substances in fresh waters in Croatia, which are potential sources for drinking water supplies, are defined by the relevant Croatian regulatory act [10]. The values given for single OC pesticides are in the range from 1 to 30 ng $l^{-1}$. The maximum allowable concentration established for PCBs is 1 ng $l^{-1}$. If higher concentrations of pollutants are found more efficient purification procedures, *eg*, treatment of raw water with activated carbon, should be used in addition to the conventional water treatment (coagulation, filtration, chlorination). However, despite additional purification the appearance of persistent OC compounds in drinking water is not an exception, especially in areas where surface or karst source waters not purified by natural filtration through the subsurface sediments are used for drinking water supplies. The purification procedures may not be always sufficiently efficacious and applied properly as indicated by results of OC compounds monitoring in samples of drinking water in the town of Sisak (Table 20.3) [8]. The water used for the public network in Sisak area is actually the water from the Kupa river. At the time of sampling from March 1988 to April 1989 the raw river water was purified by different procedures involving ozonization and treatment with activated carbon. Both the raw and drinking water were analyzed for selected OC pesticides listed in Table 20.3 and special attention was paid to the occurrence of PCBs due to the contamination of the Kupa river [5-8]. Out of the 7 analyzed OC pesticides, only β-HCH was not detected in any sample of raw and drinking water, and γ-HCH, which is still used in Croatia for public health care, was present in all samples. The maximum γ-HCH concentration in the Kupa river was higher than the maximum allowable concentration limit of 10 ng $l^{-1}$ prescribed for fresh waters of the I and II categories in Croatia [10], but they were still significantly below the ecotoxicologically acceptable level for γ-HCH in fresh waters which was taken to be 100 ng $l^{-1}$ [11]. The maximum γ-HCH concentration in the Sisak drinking water was even higher than that determined in the Kupa river water but it was much lower than both the maximum admissible concentration of 0.1 μg $l^{-1}$ established by the European Communities for single pesticides in water intended for human consumption [12] and the maximum contaminant level of 0.2 μg $l^{-1}$ proposed for γ-HCH in drinking water by the US Environmental Protection Agency [13]. The PCB concentrations in most drinking water samples were <1 ng $l^{-1}$ but their incidence was comparable to that observed in samples of the Kupa river water.

Traces of PCBs and OC pesticides appeared more frequently in the Sisak drinking water (Table 20.3) than in samples of drinking water from the 2 other urban areas in Croatia: Zagreb and Labin (Table 20.4) [8]. Out of the 7 analyzed OC pesticides, traces of only HCB in Zagreb drinking water and of γ-HCH in both Zagreb and Labin drinking water were detected regularly. The ground water in Zagreb area, which is partly recharged through the Sava river water, and the karst spring water in the area of Labin are used as the municipal drinking water supplies. The purity of ground water in the Zagreb city area is likely to be deteriorated by both improper industrial and domestic waste disposal and occasional chemical spills, and also by the infiltration of the polluted water of the Sava river and of a number of small streams in the city area which are often loaded with industrial and municipal waste waters. An investigation of OC pesticides and PCBs in the

Sava river and selected streams and lakes in the Zagreb city area, undertaken in 1992, showed that all samples contained PCBs at levels of 3-25 ng $l^{-1}$, comparable to those measured in the Kupa river. The highest PCB concentrations were determined in the Sava river water, while the levels of OC pesticides (<1-2 ng $l^{-1}$) were in all water samples near or at the detection limit. The principal and, in most cases, efficient purification stage of ground waters in the Zagreb city area is natural filtration through the subsurface sediment layers. Due to their favourable composition soil and sediments serve as natural sorbents for the removal of major water contaminants.

**Table 20.3** **Concentrations of OC pesticides and PCBs (A) in the Kupa river in the area of the town of Sisak (13 samples) and (B) in the Sisak drinking water (16 samples) in the period from March 1988 to April 1989 [8]**

| Compound | Number of positive samples | | Concentration range ng $l^{-1}$ | |
|---|---|---|---|---|
| | A | B | A | B |
| HCB | 9 | 13 | <1-3 | <1-4 |
| α-HCH | 5 | 11 | <1-1 | <1-1 |
| β-HCH | 0 | 0 | | |
| γ-HCH | 13 | 16 | 1-17 | 1-59 |
| 4,4'-DDE | 3 | 9 | <1-2 | <1-2 |
| 4,4'-DDD | 2 | 3 | 1-2 | <1-1 |
| 4,4'-DDT | 3 | 6 | 2-3 | <1-3 |
| PCBs | 13 | 12 | <1-8 | <1-5 |

**Table 20.4** **Concentrations of HCB, γ-HCH and PCBs in 10 samples of drinking water from (A) Zagreb (sampling 1988), and (B) Labin (sampling 1989) [8]**

| Compound | Number of positive samples | | Concentration range ng $l^{-1}$ | |
|---|---|---|---|---|
| | A | B | A | B |
| HCB | 10 | 0 | 1-3 | |
| α-HCH | 0 | 1 | | 2 |
| γ-HCH | 10 | 10 | <1-1 | 1-6 |
| PCBs | 3 | 5 | <1-5 | 1-3 |

In Labin, an Istrian town located in the karst area, the purity of the spring water was found to depend largely on migration of micropollutants through a network of karst surface and ground water streams. In this area the elimination of pollutants from water by natural filtration is almost negligible and even highly lipophilic compounds may be transported to the water sources from both the adjacent and from very distant industrially and/or agriculturally contaminated regions. According to a report on the purity of raw source waters, used on the Istrian peninsula for drinking water supplies [15], the concentrations of inorganic and organic pollutants were often higher than those recommended as maximum allowable concentrations in water intended for human consumption. The main sources of contamination which affect the purity of Istrian ground water streams are the wastewaters of industrial and municipal origin (about 40 x $10^6$ $m^3$ $a^{-1}$ is percolating directly into subterranean passages), disposal of muddy and solid waste (about 150 000 tonne $a^{-1}$), and precipitation washing out pollutants from the atmosphere and contaminated soil. The quality of raw waters, sampled at 21 different locations, was controlled during a 10-year period (1981-1990) [15]. The results obtained by analysis of OC pesticides and PCBs in the spring and well waters used for drinking water supplies in towns of Labin, Pula and Buzet are shown in Table 20.5. The highest concentrations of total OC pesticides were found in 4 Labin karst water sources. During the 10-year period on average 20-30% of analyzed samples (depending on the spring) contained >80 ng $l^{-1}$ of total OC pesticides, which was the maximum concentration in drinking water allowed by the relevant Croatian regulation [16]. Compared to the 1981-1985 period, when 60 to 90% of analyzed water samples were not satisfying this criterion, particularly in the later drought years, a decrease in pesticide concentrations was noticed. During the 10-year period the concentrations exceeding those allowed were also measured in 10% of samples from 1-2 springs supplying waterworks in Buzet, and in 7-22% of samples from 7/15 wells/springs in Pula. In all controlled well and spring waters a wide range of PCB concentrations was found and the highest concentrations were determined in a well water supplying waterworks in Pula.

**Table 20.5** **Concentrations of total OC pesticides and PCBs measured from 1980 to 1990 in raw spring/well waters supplying waterworks of Labin, Buzet and Pula on the Istrian peninsula [15]**

| Waterworks (number of springs/wells | Concentration range ng $l^{-1}$ | |
|---|---|---|
| | Total OC pesticides | PCBs |
| Labin (4) | 7-574 | 2-48 |
| Pula (15) | 1-180 | 4-176 |
| Buzet (2) | 11-260 | 4-50 |

## 20.4 Chlorophenols in Surface Waters

The presence of CPs was confirmed in several surface waters in the continental part of Croatia: in the Sava river along a river stretch extending up to 26 km upstream and 36 km downstream of the central Zagreb city area [17], in a number of small streams and lakes within the Zagreb city area [14], and in the Kupa river both upstream and in the area of the town of Sisak [8].

The Sava river is the major reservoir of fresh water in the Zagreb city area (average flow of 200 $m^3$ $s^{-1}$). Before entering the Zagreb area it flows through a length of about 200 km of rural and urban regions in Slovenia and in the northwest of Croatia. Directly or through its tributaries the Sava river receives untreated municipal waste waters and effluents from numerous industrial facilities including a pulp and paper mill and a nuclear power plant. An investigation of organic micropollutants in the Sava river indicated the presence of CPs in the river water samples collected before and after the discharge point of the municipal wastewater effluent of the Zagreb city and in the water sample from the main waste water canal immediately before it joins the river [18]. The results of CPs determination in the Sava river near and in the Zagreb city area, performed on several occasions from 1984 to 1992, are summarized in Table 20.6. Pentachlorophenol (PCP) and 2,4,6-trichlorophenol (2,4,6-TCP) occurred in almost all river water samples and 2,3,4,6-tetrachlorophenol (2,3,4,6-TeCP) was present in 60% of the samples. During a 12-month monitoring period in 1984/1985 mono- and di-CPs and 2,4,5-trichlorophenol (2,4,5-TCP) were not detected [16], but in samples collected a few years later (1989-1992) traces of 2,4-dichlorophenol (2,4-DCP) and 2,4,5-TCP were also detected. No great variations in the concentration of single compounds in respect to the time of sampling and the river flow rate were observed. The highest concentrations were measured for PCP and the highest loading of the river water with PCP (up to 47 mg $s^{-1}$) occurred at highest flow rates of the Sava river. The average concentrations and loadings determined in the period 1984/1985 for 2,4,6-TCP and 2,3,4,6-TeCP were almost the same upstream and downstream, but PCP decreased slightly downstream of the Zagreb city area [17]. The impact of the Zagreb industrial and municipal waste discharge on the levels of CPs in the Sava river was not observed.

As in the Sava river, the highest CP concentrations in the Kupa river were measured for PCP. PCP was present in all river water samples collected monthly from March 1988 to April 1989 (Table 20.6) [8]. PCP concentrations in the Kupa river water was in general not dependent on the river flow rate. Unlike the Sava river, the Kupa river contained occasionally traces of 4-CP and the incidence of 2,4-DCP and 2,4,5-TCP was significantly higher. The concentrations of CPs in both the Sava and the Kupa river were far below the maximum limits of 0.1 μg $l^{-1}$ for 2-CP, 0.3 μg $l^{-1}$ for 2,4-DCP and 1 μg $l^{-1}$ for 2,4,5-TCP, 2,3,4,6-TeCP and PCP established for fresh waters of the I and II category by the relevant Croatian regulatory act [10]. Low concentrations (1-6 ng $l^{-1}$) of single CPs were also measured in 8 lakes in the Zagreb city area, some of which are used for bathing and recreation [14]. However, in small streams adjacent to industrial facilities in the Zagreb city area higher concentrations of CPs were found as a consequence of direct discharges of industrial waste waters (Table 20.6).

Due to possible infiltration of different pollutants into ground water, the contaminated stream waters in the industrial zones are a constant threat for the purity of ground waters, which serve as municipal drinking water supplies.

**Table 20.6 Concentrations of CPs in the water of the Sava river (sampling period 1984-1992) and small streams (sampling period 1988-1992) near and in the Zagreb city area and in the water of the Kupa river in the area of town of Sisak (sampling period 1988-1989)**

| Compound | Concentration range ng $l^{-1}$ | | |
|---|---|---|---|
| | Sava river N=52 | Kupa river [8] N=21 | Streams in Zagreb city area N=6 |
| 4-CP | not detected | <2-50 (5) | 37-119 (3) |
| 2,4-DCP | 2-20 (4) | <2-18 (11) | 4-32 (5) |
| 2,4,5-TCP | 4-18 (3) | <2-23 (11) | 4-31 (4) |
| 2,4,6-TCP | 4-62 (44) | 3-15 (10) | 3-17 (4) |
| 2,3,4,6-TeCP | <4-69 (32) | <4-42 (9) | <4-8 (4) |
| PCP | <4-163 (40) | <4-95 (21) | 9-27 (4) |

N=Number of samples; the number of positive samples is given in brackets

## 20.5 Chlorophenols in Ground and Drinking Water

Several comprehensive studies designed to investigate ground water quality in the Zagreb city area and behaviour of pollutants in the alluvial aquifer of the Sava river were conducted between 1986 and 1989 [19]. More than 300 single organic compounds were identified in the pollutant sources (the Sava river, municipal and industrial dumping sites, waste waters) and in ground waters. The simultaneous analysis of CPs in the water of the Sava river and in ground water from wells 0.2-0.4 km from the river bed proved the occurrence of the same compounds in all water samples [17]. The levels in well water were almost identical to those in the river indicating that the compounds were not affected by any elimination processes during subsurface water movement. A measurable sorption of CPs in the area between the investigated wells and the Sava river was noticed only in the soil at depth of 0.2-0.4 m [17]. Consequently, if the Sava river water infiltrates into ground water into deeper ground layers, elimination of CPs from the water by their sediment sorption is negligible. The concentrations of CPs in different ground waters in the Zagreb city area, which are not used as drinking water, and in the water from privately owned wells used without any purification as drinking water are compared in Table 20.7. The highest concentrations of more highly chlorinated phenols were measured in the private well waters which were located >2 km from the Sava river but in a populated area, often near industrial plants [17]. Although the concentrations determined were below the maximum limit concentrations of 1 $\mu g\ l^{-1}$ [10] they were still of concern because their origin could not be unambiguously defined. In Table 20.8 the concentrations of CPs determined in municipal drinking water samples from Zagreb and Sisak are compared [8,17]. CPs were not detected in any of the controlled wells supplying water to the Zagreb city waterworks, but in 6/10 chlorinated municipal drinking water samples single compounds were present. The appearance of CPs in Zagreb drinking water does not arise solely as a consequence of regular water treatment by chlorination but reflects the occasional contamination of ground water network in the city area. The incidence of CPs in drinking waters from Zagreb and Sisak was comparable, but the maximum concentrations measured in Sisak were lower. They were also lower than the simultaneously measured concentrations in the Kupa river (Table 20.6) confirming the efficiency of the procedures applied at that time for the river water purification.

**Table 20.7** **Concentrations of CPs in ground waters not used as drinking water (sampling period 1986-1989) and in drinking water from private wells (sampling 1986) in the Zagreb city area**

| Compound | Concentration range ng $l^{-1}$ | |
|---|---|---|
| | Ground water N=17 | Private wells [16] N=9 |
| 4-CP | 8-10 (2) | 4-10 (3) |
| 2,4-DCP | 2-61 (6) | 30 (1) |
| 2,4,5-TCP | 2-9 (4) | 7-39 (3) |
| 2,4,6-TCP | 2-24 (5) | 9-26 (2) |
| 2,3,4,6-TeCP | 4-46 (7) | 9-270 (4) |
| PCP | 4-151 (13) | 17-411 (4) |

**Table 20.8** **Concentrations of CPs in drinking water from Zagreb (sampling 1986) [16] and Sisak (sampling period 1988-1989) [8]**

| Compound | Concentration range ng $l^{-1}$ | |
|---|---|---|
| | Zagreb N=10 | Sisak N=13 |
| 4-CP | 6 (1) | (0) |
| 2,4-DCP | 17 (1) | <2-2 (2) |
| 2,4,5-TCP | 5-22 (5) | <2-3 (3) |
| 2,4,6-TCP | 5-9 (4) | 2 (2) |
| 2,3,4,6-TeCP | 10 (1) | <4-4 (2) |
| PCP | 26-123 (5) | <4-39 (12) |

N=Number of samples; the number of positive samples is given in brackets

A particular problem is the regular appearance and the levels of phenolic compounds in the karst ground water wells and springs on Istrian peninsula. According to the phenol concentration in water the springs/wells in Istria can be divided in 2 groups [15]. Waters with a phenol incidence of 50-67% and concentrations up to 5.5 µg $l^{-1}$ belong to the first group and the second group comprises the waters in which lower incidence (30-50%), but higher maximum concentrations of phenol (up to 9 µg $l^{-1}$ ) were observed. All karst water springs supplying waterworks in the town of Labin belong to the second group. In the same springs CPs were detected in the raw water probably as a consequence of use of tri- to penta-CPs as biocides in wood preserving facilities and some other industries. Due to the presence of phenolic compounds the concentrations of particularly lower chlorinated phenols were often increased after the treatment of well water by chlorination. The maximum concentrations determined in the chlorinated spring waters in the period 1989-1990 together with the results of CP measurements in Labin drinking water are shown in Table 20.9. In drinking water samples only 2 CPs were detected but the maximum concentration of PCP was 4 times higher than that in Zagreb and one order of magnitude higher than in Sisak. It was approaching the value of 0.5 µg $l^{-1}$, established by the European Communities as the maximum admissible concentration of phenols in water intended for human consumption [12]. Having in mind the occasionally very high concentrations of CPs in spring waters supplying the Labin waterworks this finding was not a surprise.

**Table 20.9 Concentrations of CPs in drinking water from Labin (sampling 1989) [8] and maximum concentrations in chlorinated spring waters supplying waterworks of Labin (sampling period 1989-1990) [15]**

| Compound | Concentration range ng $l^{-1}$ | |
|---|---|---|
| | Range in drinking water N=10 | Maximum in spring water |
| 2-,3- and 4-CP | not detected | 4040 |
| 2,4- and 2,6-DCP | not detected | 1770 |
| 2,4,5- and 2,4,6-TCP | not detected | 1280 |
| 2,3,4,6-TeCP | <4-5 (7) | 1660 |
| PCP | 9-474 (10) | 740 |

N=Number of samples; the number of positive samples is given in brackets

## 20.6 Conclusions

The results compiled in this chapter are presented in order to indicate relationship between the contamination of surface and ground waters and quality of water intended for public use.

The presence of PCBs in the Kupa river is a well established fact. Since there are only a few or no alternatives for drinking water resources along that river, the installation and proper use of water purification facilities are urged in order to provide this highly populated area with drinking water of appropriate quality.

Regarding the persistent OC compounds the quality of ground water in the Zagreb city area may be considered to be acceptable within limits to provide for drinking water supply. In spite of the fact that this area is both densely inhabited and heavily industrialized, and surrounded with agricultural fields with high rate of application of crop protection chemicals, the quality of municipal drinking water is maintained on a reasonably satisfactory level, apparently due to the natural filtration processes which eliminate major proportions of contaminants from polluted surface and ground waters. However, if a serious pollution accident were to be encountered, it can be anticipated that both the natural elimination processes and artificial purification, based in most cases on water chlorination only, are not likely to have a capacity to maintain proper quality of water for public use.

The Istrian peninsula is the area of the highest probability of deterioration of water quality. The regular occurrence of OC pesticides observed in well and spring waters is ascribed to agricultural activities. The presence of PCBs in water is attributed mainly to the uncontrolled discharge of transformer oils. Having in mind the harmful effects of these and other organic and inorganic contaminants on human health, considerable attention should be given to the more effective protection and strict control of karst ground water purity. A zone of protection from the contamination is defined for every well and spring in Istria. The Istrian peninsula is rich in specific geological forms, such as holes, caves and abysses, which are typical for a karst terrain, and it is rather difficult to apply the common protection regulations and measures to preserve the environmental quality. Therefore, it is necessary to treat the whole area as a primary zone of protection. In that zone the contamination of the karst ground waters should be prevented by rigorous control of industrial and municipal waste disposal, rational use of chemicals for agricultural protection, and by building the non-permeable sewage systems in the areas most likely to be contaminated. The industrial and other specific facilities when hazardous waste substances are eventually released into environment should be equipped with purification devices. Additionally, the same protection measures should be applied in all other karst regions in Croatia.

The national monitoring programme to control and evaluate the environmental presence of OC and other organic and inorganic contaminants is necessary to provide a complete insight into the quality of water resources. Such an approach becomes important especially from the viewpoint of destructions which have taken place during recent war conditions in Croatia. Potential to contaminate drinking water resources, threatening to result in long term adverse effects on human health, has increased dramatically in last 3 years as a consequence of the war situation. Not only the destruction of numerous chemical factories, electric power facilities, sewage treatment works etc. has incurred severe hazards upon the soil and water environment by creating new points of emission of pollutants, but many of water purification systems has been damaged as well, reducing drinking water resources available for public use.

The data presented in this chapter provides a base for undertaking risk assessments of water pollutants. This knowledge will provide the necessary criteria to ensure effective management of chemical safety.

## 20.7 References

[1] Brumen, S., Medved, M., Vončina, E., and Jan, J., *Chemosphere* 1984, **13**, 1243-1246.

[2] Brumen, S., Medved, M., Vončina, E., Lobnik, S., Jan, J., and Malneršič, S., *Hrana i ishrana* 1984, **25**, 179-183 (in Serbian).

[3] Jan, J. and Tratnik, M., *Bull. Environ. Contam. Toxicol.* 1988, **41**, 809-814.

[4] Herlander, D., *Zdrav. Vestn.* 1986, **55**, 137-139 (in Slovenian).

[5] Šmit, Z., Drevenkar, V., and Kodrić-Šmit, M., *Chemosphere* 1987, **16**, 2351-2358.

[6] Šmit, Z., Drevenkar, V., and Kodrić-Šmit, M., 'Polychlorinated Biphenyls in the Kupa River, Croatia, Yugoslavia', in: *Organic Micropollutants in the Aquatic Environment, Proceedings of the Fifth European Symposium*, Rome 1987, Commission of the European Communities, Angeletti, G. and Bjørseth, A., (Eds.), Dordrecht, Kluwer Academic Publishers 1988, pp. 198-203.

[7] Picer, N., Picer, M., and Perkov, S., 'Polychlorinated Biphenyls and Chlorinated Insecticides in Water and Fish of the Kupa River', in: *Proceedings of the Conference on Water Protection 'Zaštita voda '86'*, Kragujevac 1986, pp. 291-296 (in Croatian).

[8] Fingler, S., Drevenkar, V., Tkalčević, B., and Šmit, Z., *Bull. Environ. Contam. Toxicol.* 1992, **49**, 805-812.

[9] World Health Organization, 'Polychlorinated Biphenyls and Terphenyls', *Environ. Health Crit.* 1976, **2**, pp. 1-85.

[10] Croatian Regulatory Act on Maximum Allowable Concentrations of Hazardous Substances in Fresh Waters and Coastal Sea-Waters, *Narodne novine* 1984, **2**, 7-11 (in Croatian).

[11] United Nations Environment Programme, III. News about chemicals. Hexachlorocyclohexanes (HCHs). *International Register of Potentially Toxic Chemicals Bulletin* 1989, **9**, 23-24.

[12] Council of the European Communities, Council Directive of 15 July 1980 Relating the Quality of Water Intended for Human Consumption (80/778/EEC), *Off. J. Eur. Commun.*, 1980, **L229**, 11-29.

[13] US Environmental Protection Agency, *National Pesticide Survey. Lindane.*, Office of Water, Office of Pesticides and Toxic Substances, Washington 1990, USA, 1990.

[14] IMI-ZGO-1, Monitoring of persistent organochlorine pollutants in samples collected in the Zagreb city area, Report for the period March 1992-March 1993, Institute for Medical Research and Occupational Health, Zagreb, 1993, pp. 1-28, (in Croatian).

[15] Buttignoni, V., *Water Quality of Springs and Wells in Istria. Period 1981-1988 and 1989-1990*, Zavod za zaštitu zdravlja Pula, Pula, Croatia, 1990 (in Croatian).

[16] Croatian Regulatory Act on Purity of Drinking Water, *Službeni list* 1987, **33**, 865-874 (in Croatian).

[17] Fingler, S. and Drevenkar, V., *Toxicol. Environ. Chem.* 1988, **17**, 319-328.

[18] Ahel, M. and Giger, W., *Kem. Ind.* 1985, **34**, 295-309 (in Croatian).

[19] Ahel, M., *Bull. Environ. Contam. Toxicol.* 1991, **47**, 586-593.

## Note Added in Proof

Drevenkar, *et al.* were able to estimate concentrations of organochlorine pesticides etc. in some samples at Oštarije (see Tables 20.10 and 20.11 below). This work compliments that of Palinkaš, *et al.*, Chapter 21.

**Table 20.10** **Concentration of PCBs, organochlorine pesticides and chlorophenols in samples surface and ground water collected in and near the town of Oštarije (2/3 July 1993)**

| Compound | Concentration, ng $l^{-1}$ Sample A | Sample B | Sample C |
|---|---|---|---|
| PCBs as Aroclor 1242+1262 | 10 | 10 | 11 |
| Organochlorine pesticides | | | |
| HCB | 1 | ND | ND |
| α-HCH | 2 | ND | ND |
| β-HCH | 5 | 4 | 1 |
| γ-HCH | 7 | 2 | 1 |
| Chlorophenols | | | |
| 2,3,4,5-TeCP | 4 | 1 | 3 |
| PCB | 9 | 9 | 6 |

ND=Not detected
Sample A: Surface water from the centre of the military depot explosion in Oštarije
Sample B: Ground water from a private well in Oštarije
Sample C: Source water near the town of Tounj

**Table 20.11** **Concentration of PCBs, organochlorine pesticides in the soil/sediment samples collected in the town of Oštarije (2/3 July 1993)**

| Compound | Concentration, μg $kg^{-1}$ Sample D | Sample E | Sample F |
|---|---|---|---|
| PCBs as Aroclor 1242+1262 | 1.05 | 2.27 | 3.60 |
| Organochlorine pesticides | | | |
| HCB | ND | 0.04 | 0.13 |
| α-HCH | 0.24 | 0.06 | 0.28 |
| β-HCH | ND | 0.75 | 0.56 |
| Aldrin | 0.14 | 0.14 | ND |
| 4,4'-DDE | 0.15 | 0.94 | 0.70 |
| 4,4'-DDT | 0.07 | 1.20 | 0.25 |

ND=Not detected
Sample D: Soil from the centre of the military depot explosion in Oštarije
Sample E: Soil from a garden in Oštarije 500 m from the barrack entrance
Sample F: The Mrežnica river sediment near Oštarije

Editor, November 1993

# 21. Regional Contamination of Soil and Biota with Heavy Metals Following an Explosion of an Ammunition Stockpile near Oštarije, Croatia

Ladislav A. Palinkaš, Emil Srebočan, Slobodan P. Miko, Jelena Pompe-Gotal, Ksenija Namjesnik, and Simon Pirc

## 21.1 Introduction

During the early morning of the 13 October 1991, an ammunition stockpile (assessed at 6000 tonnes) was blown up and set ablaze by the Yugoslav army during their retreat from the village of Oštarije (Figure 21.1). As much of the region is covered by forests and arable lands, it caused severe impact on the natural environment (Figures 21.2-21.3), degradation of soil quality, and destruction of flora and fauna. Other adverse effects, *eg*, health hazards due to contamination of ground waters, agricultural products and livestock remain to be investigated. The effects to wildlife are unknown, and need to be evaluated, however, wild animals have been observed tottering about deaf and blind. The target of the investigation has been the intensity and extension of the man-made dispersion of heavy metals in soil due to atmospheric fallout, particularly the most toxic elements mercury and cadmium with possible accumulation by mushrooms and earthworms.

## 21.2 Material and Methods

### 21.2.1 Soil

Soil sampling along a grid, irregularly spaced on the surface of 50 $km^2$ in the vicinity of the devastated ammunition stockpiles (Figure 21.4) was undertaken within 6 months of the explosion. A total of 37 soil samples were collected from a surface layer thickness 5 cm. Total mercury, following air drying and sieving to 0.36 cm screen, was determined by pyrolysis (700 °C) with a gold wire mercury vapor analyzer, AGP-1. Mean analytical sensitivity of 5 $\mu g\ kg^{-1}$ was achieved. In addition, cadmium, nickel, lead, chromium, and manganese where extracted from the sieved soil samples by aqua regia digestion on a water bath for 6 h. The resulting sample solution (diluted 1:25) was analyzed for the elements by the flame Atomic Absorption Spectrophotometry (AAS) (Pye Unicam atomic absorption spectrophotometer, model SP9).

In early September 1993, an attempt was made to follow up the changes to the pollution patterns and possible influence on wildlife in the region. This failed due to heavy shelling from the nearby front line. However, an additional 4 samples of soil from the site of the biota sampling were analyzed for mercury, cadmium, and lead.

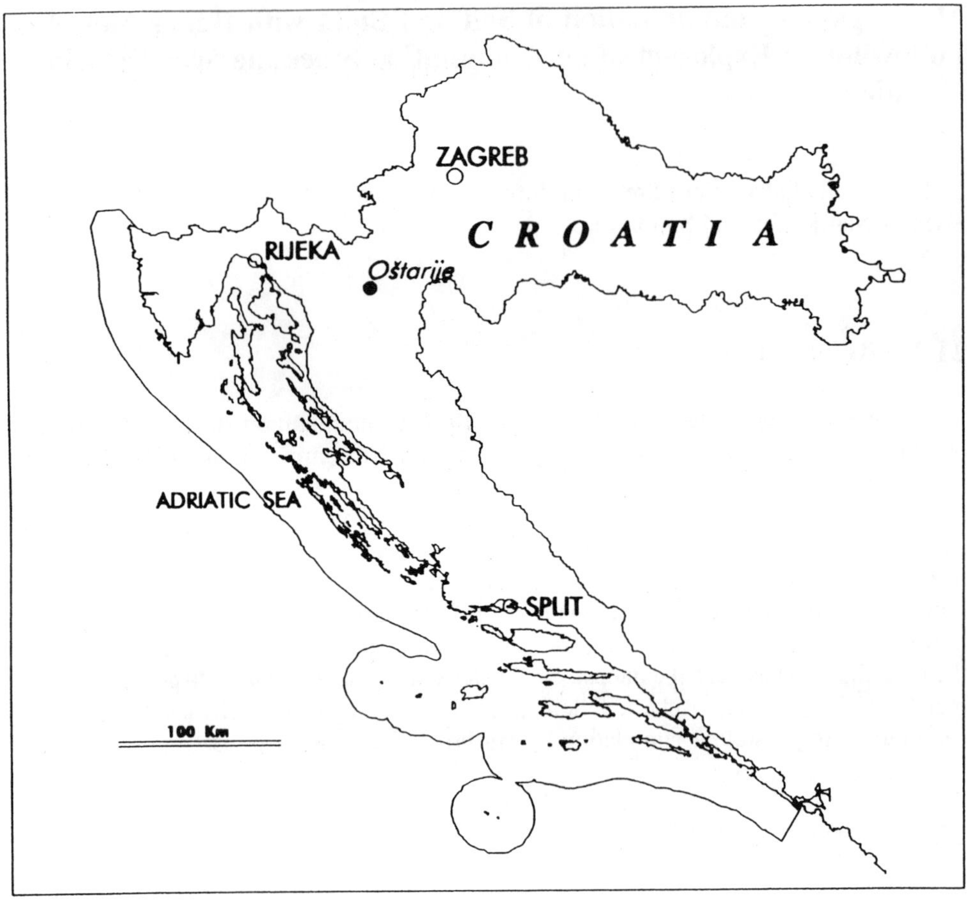


**Figure 21.1** **Geographical position of the ammunition stockpile explosion near the village of Oštarije**

### 21.2.2 Biota

In addition to shelling, an extremely dry summer, of greater severity than had been recorded for decades, made earthworm sampling difficult. The amount of collected earthworms, *Lumbricidae* family, was sufficient for only 5 samples. One pooled sample was collected at the center of the explosion and 4 others 50 m from the entrance gate of the former ammunition depot, where 8 mushrooms were collected. One mushroom was picked 150 m from the gate. Two mushrooms, examined as a control, were collected about 20 km from the explosion site, and 4 other mushrooms were gathered at another region in Croatia, where possible pollutants are at least 15 km distant. These samples also served as controls. All the mushrooms were of *Macrolepiota procera* species.

**Figure 21.2** Aerial view of the explosion site. The town of Ogulin is in the background

**Figure 21.3** Unexploded shells and other debris

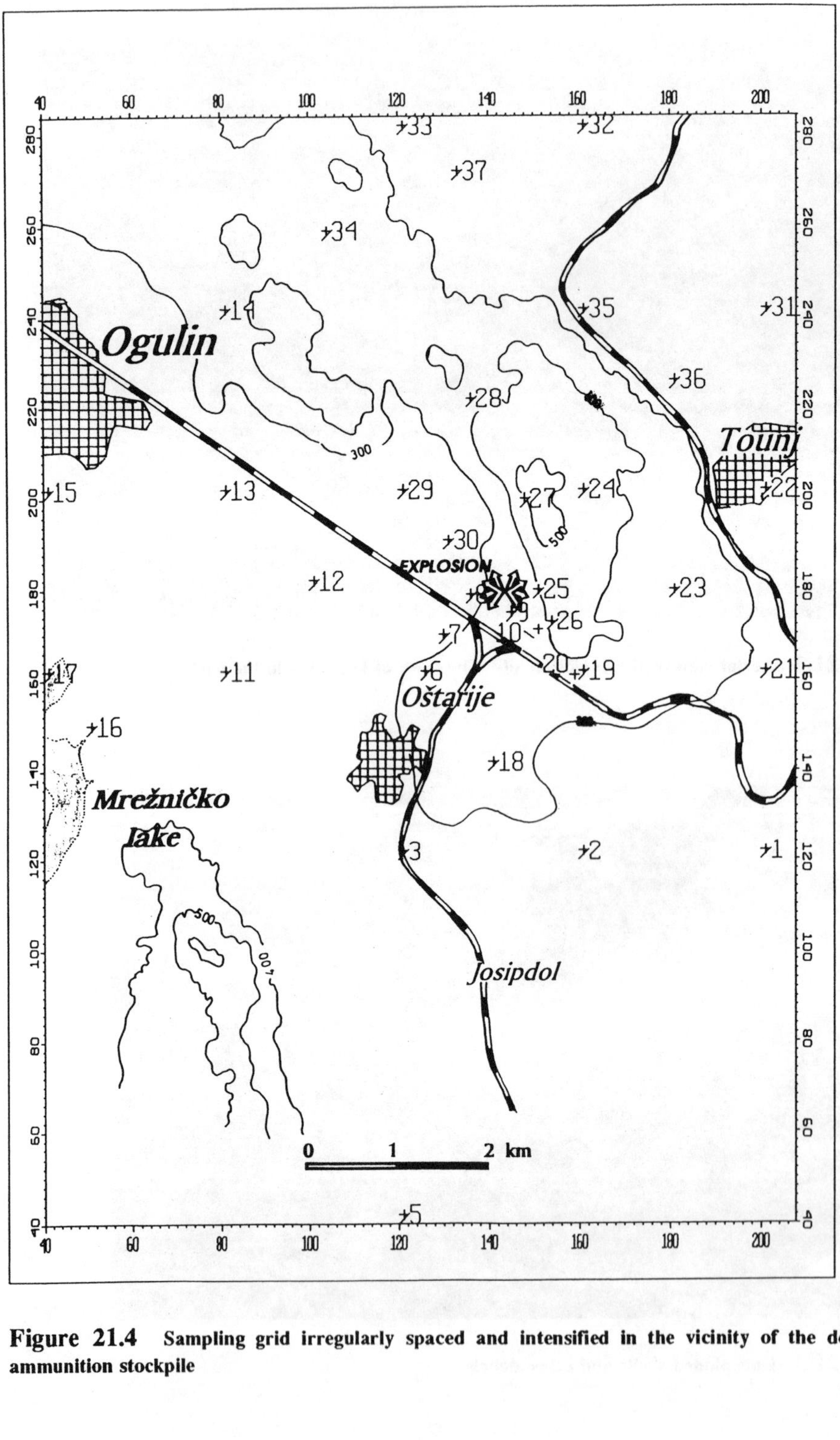


**Figure 21.4** **Sampling grid irregularly spaced and intensified in the vicinity of the devastated ammunition stockpile**

To avoid the problem of unsuccessful earthworm collection, data previously obtained for a dissertation on heavy metal contamination of flora and fauna in a predicted unpolluted ecosystem 50 km north of the investigated region [1] were used. These data were also used for comparison. The earthworms were left in water during one night to evacuate some of the gut content. The next day they were dissected and completely cleaned from soil. The mushrooms were chopped and dried at 50 °C. The mercury content was determined using CVAAS (Coleman MAS-50). The cadmium content was determined using flame AAS (Pye-Unicam SP 192). The National Institute of Standards and Technology SRM No. 1577b (bovine liver) was analyzed and confirmed inside ± 2% of the certified cadmium value. The mercury content was not certified and was detected at the trace level. Concentration of metals in the earthworms are expressed on wet weight, and in the mushrooms on dry weight basis.

## 21.3 Results and Discussion

### 21.3.1 Soil

Data analysis, using elementary statistics and Kriging techniques [2,3] in the construction of the geochemical maps enables an understanding of the heavy metal distribution and the origin of the regional pollution.

The soil sample group (37) shows fairly homogeneous log-normal distributions for all elemental variables, judged by the frequency diagrams and the probability plots (Figures 21.5 and 21.6, and Table 21.1) [4].

Deviation from the straight line in the case of mercury is a characteristic truncation at the low values due to the limited sensitivity of the analysis. The distribution of manganese is more complex, at least bimodal, consisting of the 2 symmetrical parts, divided by the geometric mean at the inflection point (Figures 21.5 and 21.6). It is influenced by the local lithogeochemistry. Lead shows an even more complex distribution, as observed by inspection of the Kriging contour maps (Figures 21.7-21.10). In addition to the explosion at the ammunition stockpile, as a point pollution source, another more dispersed anthropogenic contamination related to urbanization and traffic must also be taken into consideration.

From the given data and the sampling scheme (Figure 21.4), it is obvious that the size of the anomalous sample group is favored with respect to the natural background. It incurs difficulties in determination of the threshold values and in the contrast of the anomalies (maximum/threshold) [5]. In order to obtain a rough pollution assessment, we compared the background values obtained in the rural area of the surroundings of Zagreb (mercury in $\mu g\ kg^{-1}$) and other elements in $mg\ kg^{-1}$ [6]; Hg (50), Cd (0.39), Cr (36), Mn (896), Ni (26), Pb (20), and in Zagreb city as a whole [7]; Hg (88), Cd (0.41), Cr (30), Mn (559), Ni (35), Pb (27), with the maximum value in the center of the explosion: Hg (280), Cd (2.2), Cr (54), Mn (3200), Ni (35). The highest value, determined in the disturbed soil-like material in the vicinity of the blown up barracks; Hg (5600) and Cd (12.5) [8], however, was excluded from the statistics (Figure 21.11).

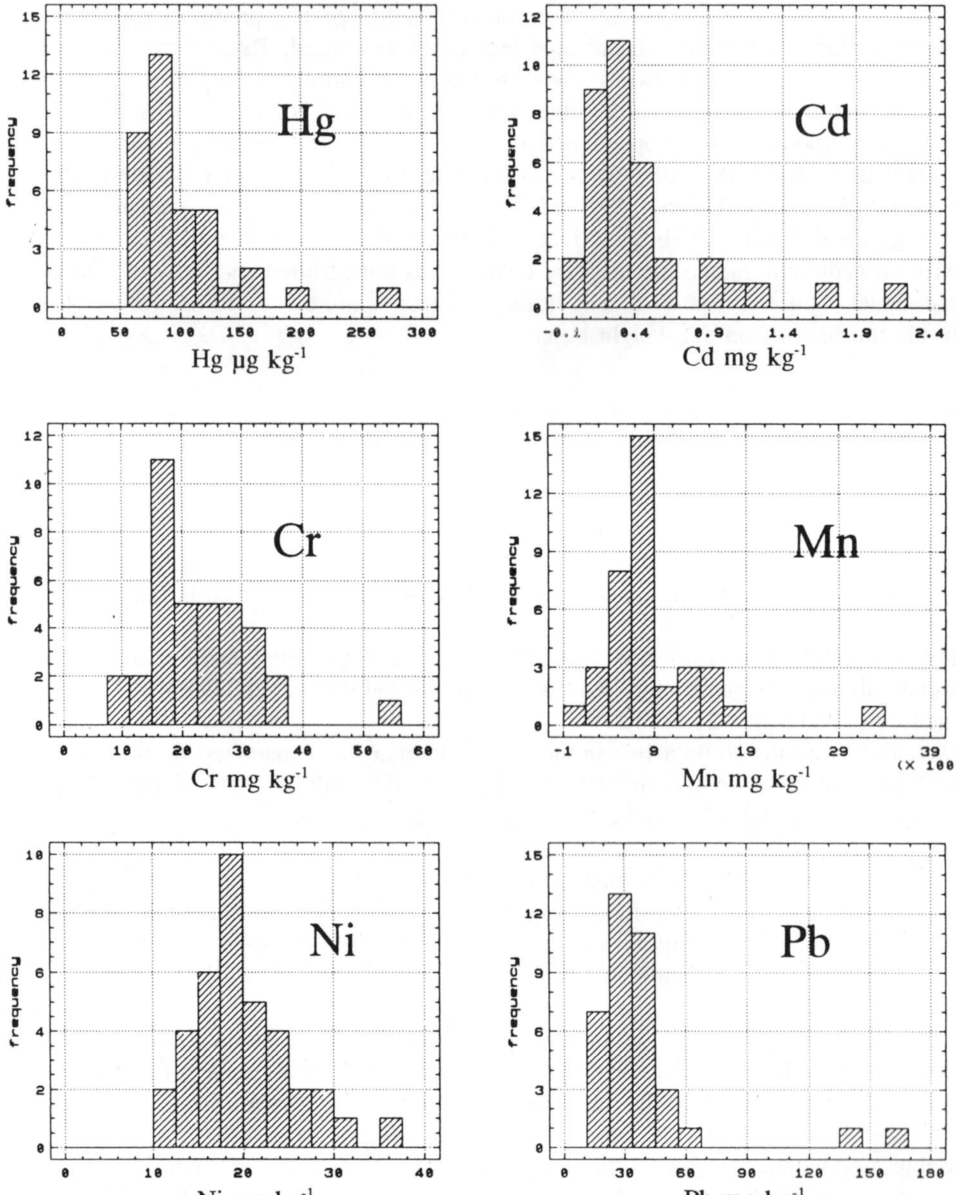


**Figure 21.5** Frequency distribution diagrams

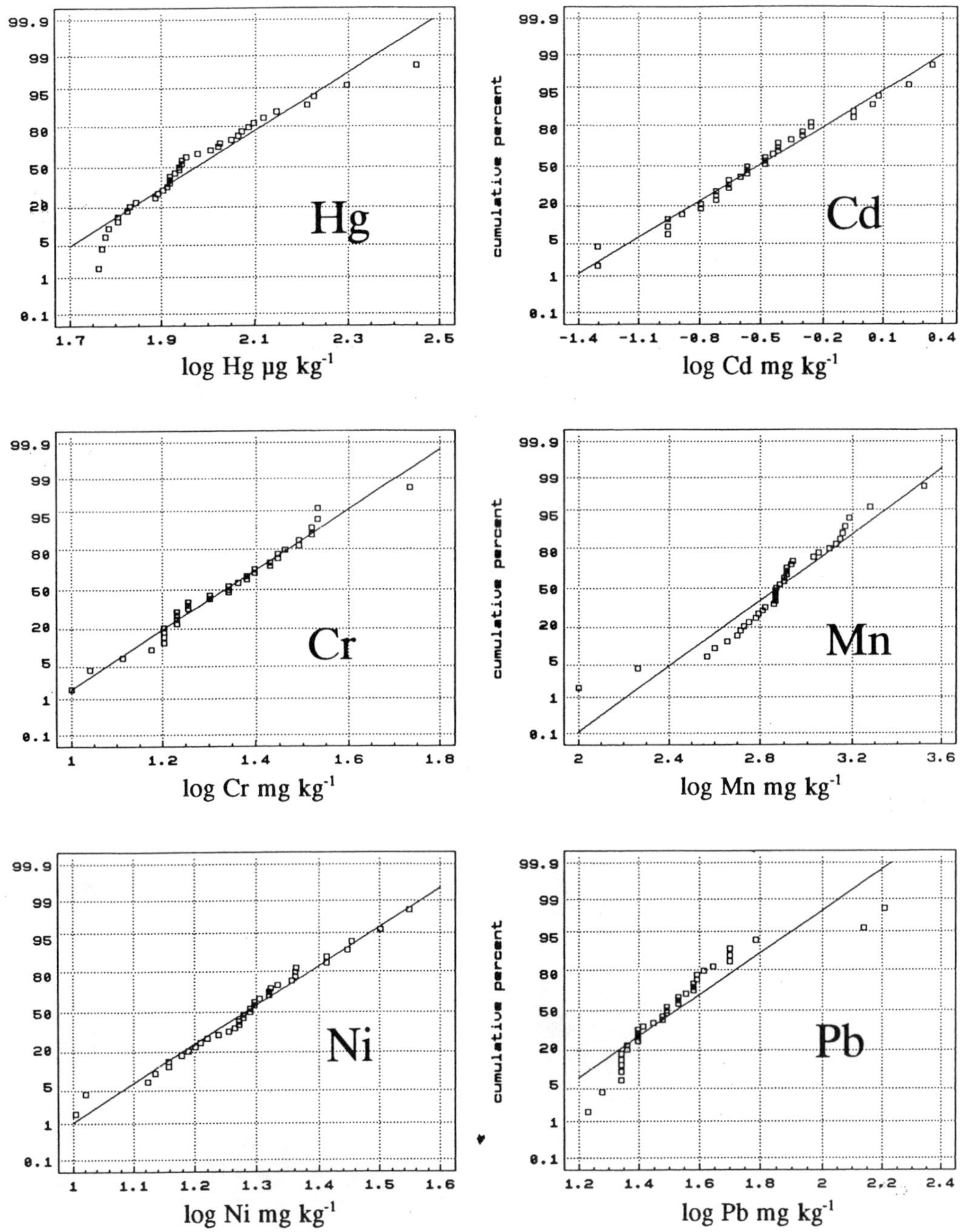


**Figure 21.6** **Probability plots**

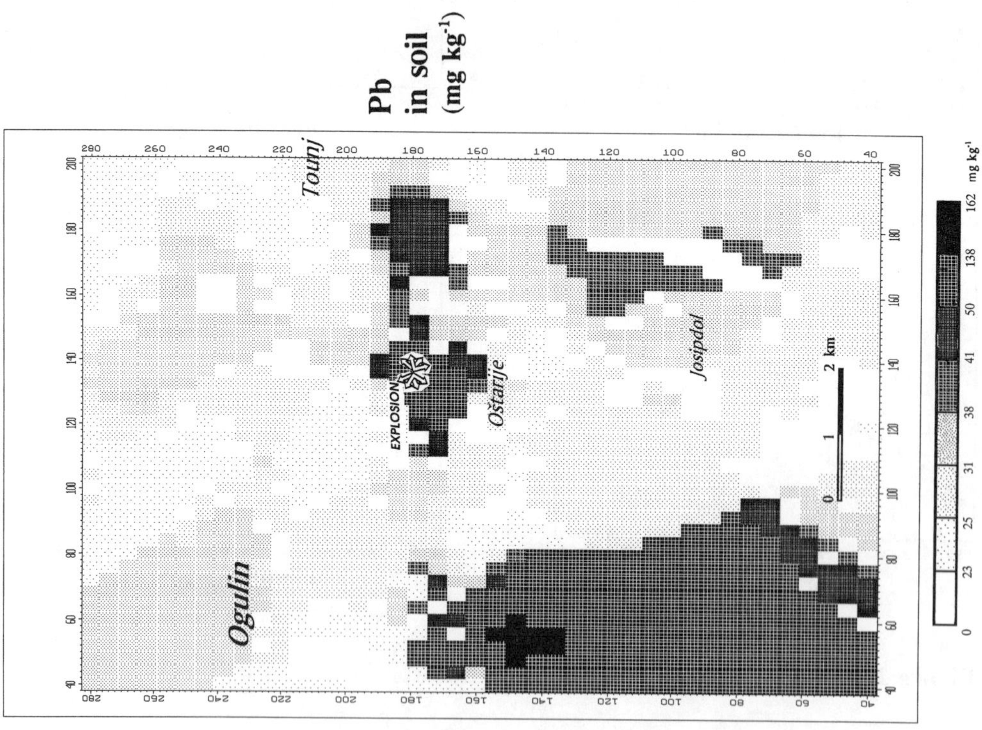


**Figure 21.7** Kriging contour maps for lead

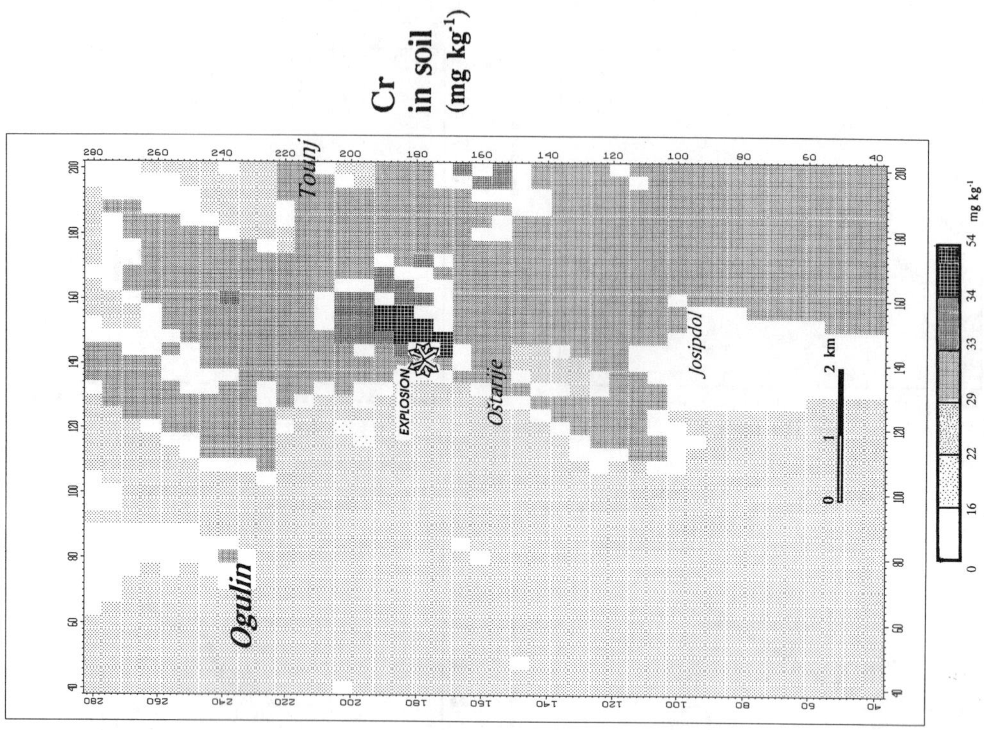


**Figure 21.8** Kriging map contour for chromium

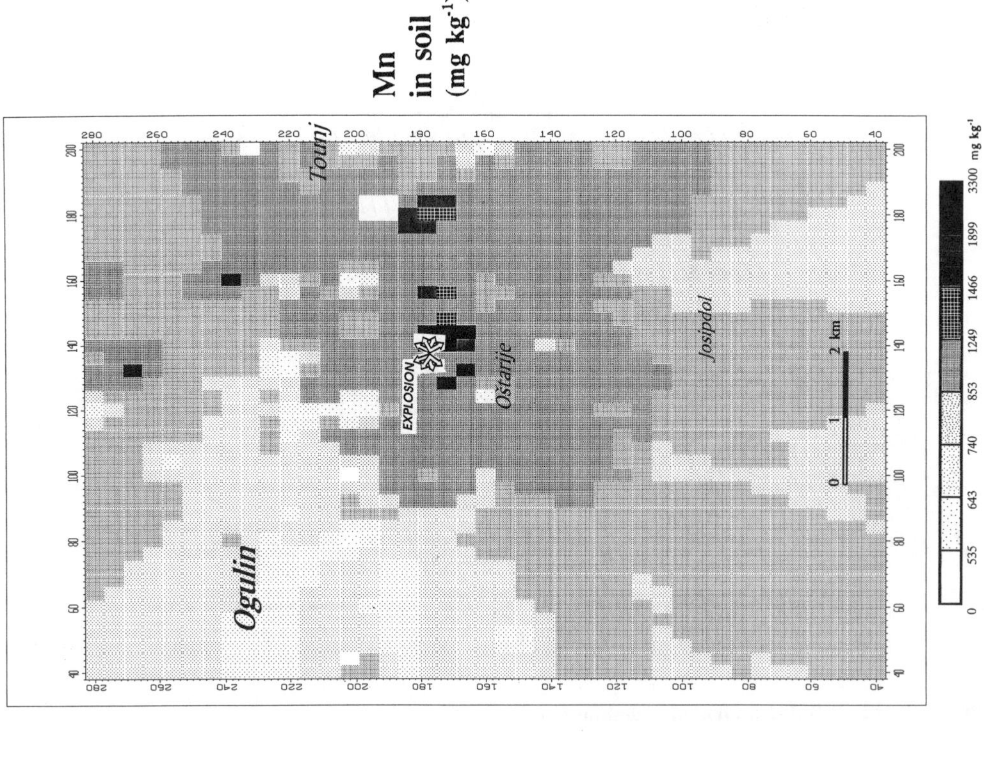


**Figure 21.9** Kriging contour maps for manganese

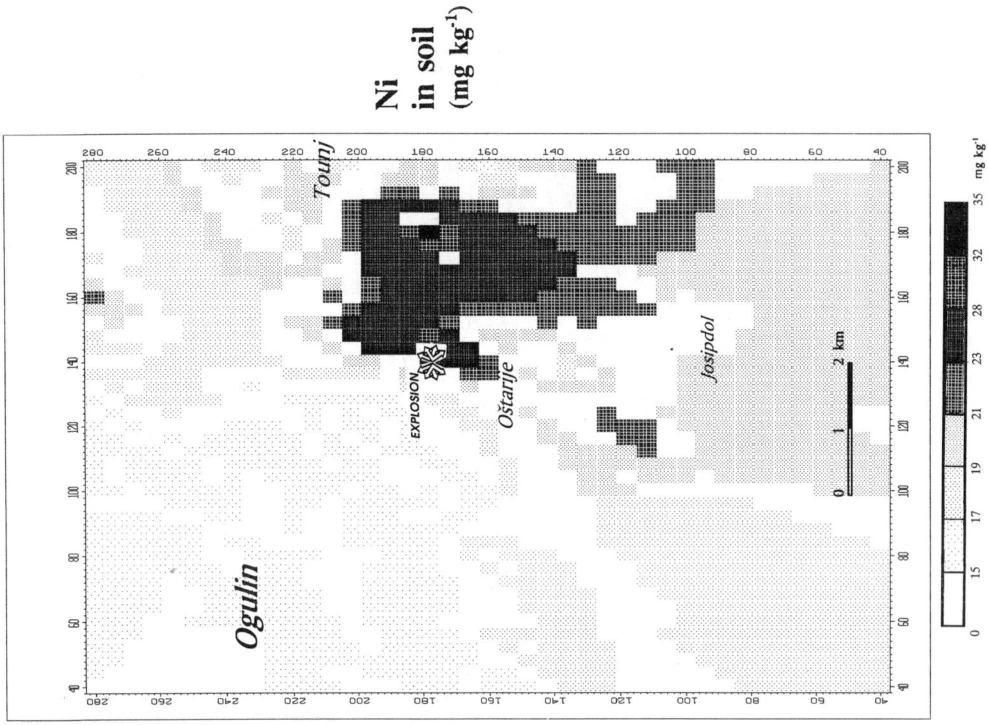


**Figure 21.10** Kriging map contour for nickel

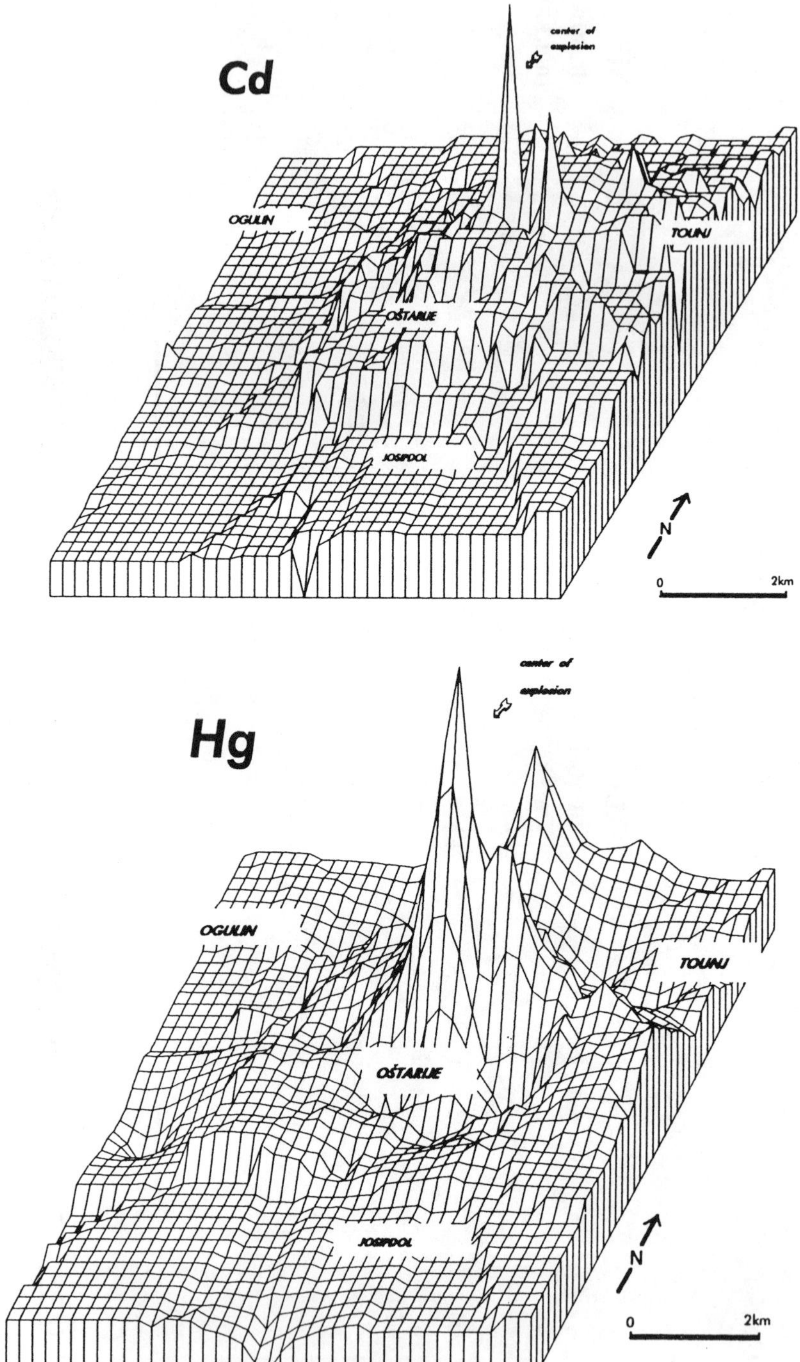


**Figure 21.11** 3-D distribution of cadmium and mercury

The global average concentration of mercury in soil is estimated to be between 50 and 100 µg $kg^{-1}$ [9]. Figures depend on numerous parameters; locally and near to the heaviest polluters, mercury levels can be ≥10 mg $kg^{-1}$ [10].

Literature data on heavy metal soil pollution caused by an accidental or intentional misuse of the ammunition explosions are scarce and are not currently available. Taskanen *et al.* [11] studied heavy metal pollution (arsenic, nickel, lead, antimony, and zinc) in a shooting range environment which might be analogous in some details. A significant quantity of the ammunition is used as lead pellets and jacketed lead bullets. They reported extremely high lead concentrations (Pb; 10300-40300 mg $kg^{-1}$) in the uppermost soil layer due to accumulation of the shotgun lead pellets. A few 10 cms deep in the soil profile, however, it fell to the range 41-465 mg $kg^{-1}$.

The contamination in our case differs greatly in many respects; it includes small or large sized pieces and particles of the ammunition jackets, particulate airborne matter, and even vapor, due to high conflagration temperature. Mercury as fulminates and lead as azide from detonators, as well as trace elements in the explosive itself were vaporized.

**Table 21.1** **Statistics, heavy metals in soil (mercury µg $kg^{-1}$, the others in mg $kg^{-1}$)**

| Variable | Hg (µg $kg^{-1}$) | Cd mg $kg^{-1}$ | Cr mg $kg^{-1}$ | Mn mg $kg^{-1}$ | Ni mg $kg^{-1}$ | Pb mg $kg^{-1}$ |
|---|---|---|---|---|---|---|
| Sample size | 37 | 36 | 37 | 37 | 37 | 37 |
| Average | 101 | 0.45 | 23 | 888 | 20 | 39 |
| Geometric mean | 94 | 0.31 | 22 | 751 | 19 | 33 |
| Standard deviation | 44 | 0.46 | 9 | 562 | 5 | 29 |
| Minimum | 58 | 0.05 | 10 | 1000 | 10 | 17 |
| Maximum | 280 | 2.22 | 54 | 3300 | 35 | 162 |
| Range | 222 | 2.17 | 44 | 3200 | 25 | 145 |

The transport of the pollutants at the point of the explosion was mechanical preferentially, and airborne, depending largely on the concomitant wind direction and the local topographic conditions. It is suggested by the shape of the aerial distribution of the explosion halo, directed clearly northward for mercury (Figure 21.11). Stochastic relation between the distance from the center of explosion and the heavy metal content is conspicuously non-linear for mercury, cadmium, and chromium (Figures 21.8, 21.11, and 21.12), approaching linear for manganese and nickel (Figures 21.9 and 21.10), while lead has 2 different pollution sources (Figures 21.7, and 21.12). The influence of the explosion was observed as far as 6 km from the explosion center (Figure 21.12).

Correlation matrices indicated the dependence of the heavy metal contamination *vs.* distance from the explosion by significant negative correlation coefficients for the majority of elements. The positive correlation coefficients with the high significance level indicate the common pollution source (Table 21.2).

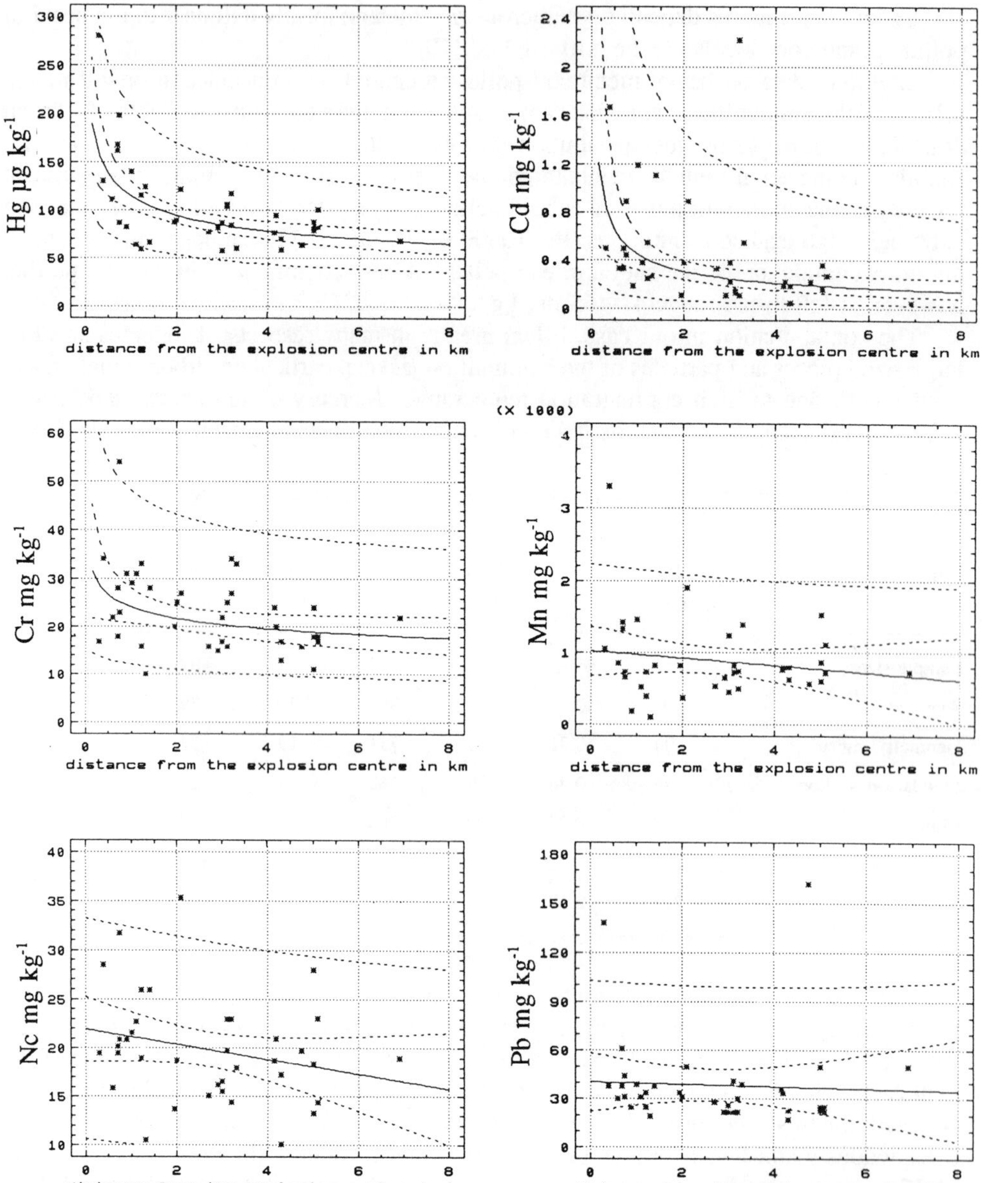


**Figure 21.12** Heavy metal content vs. distance from the explosion

**Table 21.2** Correlation matrices (correlation coefficient, significance level)

| | Distance | Hg | Cd | Mn | Pb | Cr | Ni |
|---|---|---|---|---|---|---|---|
| Hg | -0.517<br>0.001 | 1.000<br>0.000 | | | | | |
| Cd | -0.349<br>0.037 | 0.307<br>0.069 | 1.000<br>0.000 | | | | |
| Mn | -0.162<br>0.339 | 0.264<br>0.115 | 0.459<br>0.005 | 1.000<br>0.000 | | | |
| Pb | -0.043<br>0.801 | 0.412<br>0.011 | 0.007<br>0.970 | 0.123<br>0.468 | 1.000<br>0.000 | | |
| Cr | -0.384<br>0.019 | 0.268<br>0.108 | 0.552<br>0.001 | 1.173<br>0.305 | -0.072<br>0.671 | 1.000<br>0.000 | |
| Ni | -0.247<br>0.141 | 0.267<br>0.110 | 0.348<br>0.038 | 0.508<br>0.001 | 0.200<br>0.235 | 0.526<br>0.001 | 1.000<br>0.000 |

The soil samples taken on the 20 September 1993, 2 years later, inside the former ammunition depot yard contain high concentrations of mercury which increases with depth, in contrast to lead, while cadmium was unexpectedly low (Table 21.3).

**Table 21.3** Heavy metals in soil, control samples taken 2 years later

| | Hg<br>$\mu g\ kg^{-1}$ | Cd<br>$mg\ kg^{-1}$ | Pb<br>$mg\ kg^{-1}$ | Depth<br>cm |
|---|---|---|---|---|
| Sample 1 | 158 | 0.22 | 55 | 0-6 |
| Sample 2 | 150 | <0.1 | 50 | 0-6 |
| | 432 | <0.1 | 45 | 6-12 |
| | 432 | <0.1 | 33 | 12-18 |

The small number of samples taken under heavy shelling, a few km from the front line are only a preliminary test and necessitates continuation of the study. Chemical partitioning of the heavy metals through soil constituents and variable retention ability of the soils regarding different metal ions will change the geochemical pattern on the surface and in the depth of the soil horizon with time [12-14]. Any method of decontamination, if necessary, has to be undertaken after a more detailed study. Statistical criteria (analysis of variance) in planning sampling grid, and the knowledge of heavy metal distribution in the soil layer and in the region are a prerequisite prior to any decision regarding remedial work.

### 21.3.2 Biota

Feeding behaviour, ubiquity, and the ability to accumulate various materials make earthworms useful species for soil pollution monitoring. Two of these substances are mercury and cadmium, which are highly toxic and non-essential for life. Both metals are proved to accumulate in earthworms in concentrations much higher than in the soil they inhabit [15-19].

Mushrooms have proved to be a good indicator for soil pollution monitoring, because certain species grown in unpolluted areas accumulate mercury and cadmium in concentrations which exceed the norm given for foodstuffs [20,21].

At least 3 factors affect mercury content in mushrooms:

i) Ecological characteristics of the species; *ie*, lawn decomposers, wood decomposers, or mycorrhizal mushrooms;

ii) Species; and,

iii) Growing site [22].

Considering ecological aspects, the content of mercury in the mushrooms sampled at the explosion site are consistent with concentrations found in the same species in the unpolluted areas of Croatia (Table 21.4), and in the neighbouring Slovenia, where average values of 3.52 and 6.00 mg kg$^{-1}$ were reported by Byrne *et al.* [23].

**Table 21.4** **Mercury and cadmium in mushrooms (average ± SD, range, d/w)**

| Sampling site | No of samples | Hg µg kg$^{-1}$ | Cd mg kg$^{-1}$ |
|---|---|---|---|
| 50 m from the entrance gate | 8 | 3056±1201<br>(2228-5915) | 7.444±3.132<br>4.079-14.297) |
| 150 m from the entrance gate | 1 | 2710 | 1.432 |
| Control — the same region | 2 | 1765 and 2475 | 0.982 and 1.075 |
| Control — other regions in Croatia | 4 | 3428±0757<br>(2658-4451) | 0.604±0.045<br>(0.545-0.639) |

In the polluted area, Byrne and coworkers [23] found unexpectedly 2000 mg $kg^{-1}$ mercury (average) in the same species of *Macrolepiota procera*, a mushroom known as a lawn decomposer that accumulates mercury efficiently [22].

Comparing cadmium content in the mushrooms from the explosion area with the controls (Table 21.4), it can be observed that there is a noticeable accumulation due to the soil contamination. The investigation in Slovenia recorded an average cadmium content in mushrooms in an unpolluted area as 5.72 and 7.24 mg $kg^{-1}$ d/w respectively, and in the contaminated area 11.0 mg $kg^{-1}$ [23].

According to norms, concentration of mercury and cadmium, should not exceed 3 mg $kg^{-1}$ in dry mushrooms. Considering hygienic aspects, the mushroom specimens at the explosion area should not be used as a foodstuff because of high content of both metals, but especially cadmium (according to FAO/WHO recommendations, a maximum weekly intake of mercury for an adult is 300 µg, and 0.5 mg for cadmium, respectively).

Concentration of mercury in the earthworms collected at the explosion center and 50 m distant are consistent with the controls (Table 21.5) and results reported by Heinz *et al.*, 60 and 80 mercury µg $kg^{-1}$ w/w, which can be considered as a background level [24].

Concentration of cadmium in earthworms, gathered 50 m from the entrance gate, varied in the same range as the controls (Table 21.5), and the background values determined by Gish and Christensen in the USA, *ie*, 3 mg $kg^{-1}$ d/w which appropriates to 0.75 mg $kg^{-1}$, w/w [18]. Cadmium content in the single pooled sample from the center of the explosion doubled.

**Table 21.5** **Mercury and cadmium in earthworms (average ± SD, range, Hg µg $kg^{-1}$, Cd mg $kg^{-1}$, w/w)**

| Sampling site | No of samples | Hg µg $kg^{-1}$ | Cd mg $kg^{-1}$ |
|---|---|---|---|
| Center of explosion | 1 (pool) | 43 | 1.356 |
| 50 m from the entrance gate | 4 (pool) | 35±7 (2.8-41) | 0.799±0.093 (0.671-0.871) |
| Control — other regions in Croatia | 16 (pool) | 62±21 (11-95) | 0.724±0.309 (0.243-1.198) |

The preliminary results of the biota investigation suggest that cadmium pollution, originally superficial, persists due to the retention ability of the surface soil layer, since the mushrooms, in contrast to the earthworms, continue to accumulate cadmium. This is conceivable due to the high organic content of the soil and high pH (carbonate substratum). Alternatively, mercury is readily volatilized and its distribution is expected to have changed earlier.

## 21.4 Conclusions

The surroundings of the village of Oštarije is covered by forests and arable lands and is a tourist, hunting and recreation resort, and a health-food production area. It suffered an intentional explosion of an ammunition stockpile during the retreat of the Yugoslav army. The disastrous explosion of 6000 tonnes of the ammunition incurred a severe impact on the rural environment of a 50 $km^2$ surface. The investigation revealed:

i) Soil contamination by heavy metals in a wide area surrounding the explosion site. Average values of the heavy metal content, Hg (101 μg $kg^{-1}$), Cd (0.45 mg $kg^{-1}$), Cr (23 mg $kg^{-1}$), Mn (888 mg $kg^{-1}$), Ni (20 mg $kg^{-1}$), Pb (39 mg $kg^{-1}$) are consistent with averages found in the acutely contaminated area of Zagreb city, Hg (88 μg $kg^{-1}$), Cd (0.39 mg $kg^{-1}$), Cr (30 mg $kg^{-1}$), Mn (559 mg $kg^{-1}$), Ni (35 mg $kg^{-1}$), and Pb (27 mg $kg^{-1}$);

ii) The highest values were found in the center of the explosion, Hg (280 μg $kg^{-1}$), Cd (2.22 mg $kg^{-1}$), Cr (54 mg $kg^{-1}$), Mn (3300 mg $kg^{-1}$), Ni (35 mg $kg^{-1}$), Pb (145 mg $kg^{-1}$). Extremely high values obtained in the disturbed soil-like material in the ammunition depot yard, Hg (5600 μg $kg^{-1}$), and Cd (12.5 mg $kg^{-1}$) were excluded from the statistics;

iii) Shape of the heavy metal dispersion halo is fan-like, directed northward, and can be traced as far as 6 km from the center of the explosion. Its formation is non-ambiguously related to atmospheric fallout of the wind blown particles and airborne particulate matter;

iv) Test soil samples (4), taken almost 2 years after the explosion, collected close to the explosion center, contain a high level of mercury (150-432 μg $kg^{-1}$) and lower results for cadmium (0.1-0.22 mg $kg^{-1}$). A limited number of samples, collected during heavy shelling at the front line, however, cannot be used to describe and predict heavy metal behavior in soil;

v) Test biota samples of the mushrooms (15) and the earthworms (21) provided equivocal information. While the cadmium content correlates well with the distance from the source of pollution, the mercury content does not permit the same conclusion. A possible explanation might be in the heavy metal distribution along the vertical profile of the soil horizon, *ie*, cadmium may be retained at the surface whilst the mercury volatilized. Currently, many unknowns make any further discussion impossible; and,

vi) Although the regional contamination does not appear to be catastrophic, apart from the highest values, Hg (5600 μg $kg^{-1}$), Cd (12.5 mg $kg^{-1}$), recorded at the ammunition depot yard, the average heavy element contents are definitely similar to those found at Zagreb city.

These findings should alert public awareness, since the unpolluted Oštarije region, regarded as a potential health-food producer and water resource area, has become affected adversely and now has to be ranked as lower quality land.

Final assessment of the explosion consequences and choice of decontamination remedies, if necessary, can be undertaken only after additional examination of the soil geochemistry and contaminated biota. Currently, this investigation, with its limited size and intention, can only be considered as a mere registration of the phenomenon.

This preliminary assessment indicates the risks assessed during severe explosion, and indicates the need for further monitoring for both metals and other contaminants prior to undertaking a thorough investigation in all relevant aspects of chemical safety.

## 21.5 Acknowledgements

We express our appreciation to Mervyn Richardson for his stimulation in preparing this chapter and his understanding of the difficulties which we have encountered during the performance of our investigation under current war conditions. Also, thanks are attributed to the members of the Croatian army who assisted and guarded us during field sampling.

## 21.6 References

[1] Olujić, Z., *Cadmium, Lead and Mercury Content of Flora, Fauna and Soil in Kupčina Ecosystem*, Dissertation, Veterinary Faculty, University of Zagreb, 1992, pp. 76-78.

[2] *Statistics and Data Analysis in Geology*, Davis, J.C., (Ed.), John Wiley & Sons, New York, 1986, pp. 646.

[3] *STATGRAFICS*, 1988, Version 3.0, STSC Inc., USA.

[4] Sinclair, A.J., *The Assoc. of Expl. Geochemists*, Richmond, Canada, 1976, Vol. 4, pp. 1-78.

[5] *Geochemistry in mineral exploration*, Rose, A.W., Hawkes, H.E., and Webb, J.S., (Eds.), Academic Press, London, 1979, pp. 657.

[6] Namjesnik, K., Palinkaš, L.A., Miko, S., Durnk G., Polić, D., and Kvrgnjaš, L., *Min. Metallurgy, (quarterly), Ljubljana*, 1992, **39**, 94-112.

[7] Namjesnik, K., *Distribution of heavy metals in soil of Zagreb city and its surroundings*, Master thesis, Zagreb University, (in preparation).

[8] Palinkaš, L.A., Namjesnik, K., Miko, S., and Pirc, S., *8th Meeting of the Assoc. of Europ. Geol. Societies*, Abstracts of papers, Budapest, 1993, pp. 70.

[9] Kaiser, G., and Tölg, G., 'Mercury', in: *Handbook of Environmental Chemistry*, Paul, A., Hutzinger, O., (Eds.), Springer Verlag, Berlin, 1980, Vol. 3, pp. 1-57.

[10] Poelstra, P., Frissel, M.G., van der Klugt, N., and Tap, W., *Neth. J. Agric. Sci.*, **21**, 77-88, cited in: *The biogeochemistry of mercury in the environment*, Nriagu, J.O., (Ed.), Elsevier, Amsterdam, 1979, Vol. 3, pp. 1-671.

[11] Taskanen, K., Kukkonen, I., and Kaija, J., *Current Research 1989-90*, 1991, Geol. Survey of Finland, Spec. Paper 12, Espoo, Finland, pp. 181-193.

[12] King, L.D., *J. Environ. Qual.*, 1988, **7**, (2), 239-250.

[13] Hickey, M.G., and Kittick, J.A., *J. Environ. Qual.*, 1984, **13**, (3), 372-376.
[14] Amoozegar-Fard, A., Fuller, W.H., and Warrick, A.W., *J. Environ. Qual.*, 1984, **13**, (2), 290-397.
[15] Gish, C.D., and Christensen, R.E., *Environ. Sci. Technol.*, 1973, 1060-1062.
[16] Helnike, P.A., Robarge, W.P., Korotev, R.L., and Schomberg, P.J., *J. Environ. Qual.*, 1979, **8**, 322-327.
[17] Beyer, W.N., Chancy, R.L., and Mulhern, B.M., *J. Environ. Qual.*, 1982, **11**, 381-385.
[18] Beyer, W.N., Cromartic, E., and Moment, G.B., *Bull. Environm. Contam. Toxicol.*, 1985, **35**, 157-162.
[19] Srebočan, E., Gregurić, J., and Bata, I., *Period. Biol.*, 1989, **91**, 101-102.
[20] Seeger, R., *Z. Lebensm. Unters. Forsch.*, 1976, **160**, 330-312.
[21] Seeger, R., *Z. Lebensm. Unters. Forsch*, 1978, **166**, 23-34.
[22] Laaksovirta, K., Lodenius, M., *Ann. Bot. Fennici.*, 1979, **16**, 208-212.
[23] Byrne, A.R., Ravnik, V., and Kosta, L., *Sci. Total Environ.*, 1976, **6**, 65-78.
[24] Heinz, G.H., Haseltine, S.D., Hall, R.J., and Krynitsky, A.J., *Bull. Environm. Contam. Toxicol.*, 1980, **25**, 738-743.

# 22. Assessment and Management of Environmental Exposure to Colorants

Herbert Motschi

## 22.1 Introduction

Dyes consist of a wide range of organic and organometallic compounds which are designed for application to a variety of substrate materials, *eg*, textile, leather, paper, plastic. The broad classes of organic colorants with their corresponding application areas have been summarized by Clarke and Anliker [1].

In previous publications, Ecological and Toxicological Association of Dyes and Organic Pigments Manufacturers (ETAD) has addressed the importance of workplace risk reduction by evaluating carefully human health hazard and occupational exposure [2-4]. This chapter addresses the environmental exposure assessment as a complementary information to data on ecotoxicological hazard profiles of colorants.

ETAD has also launched a waste minimization program at production facilities [5] and has provided advice for reduction of environmental releases from customer dyehouses [6]. Waste reduction parallels the worker exposure approach as an effective means of reducing possible risk levels.

As it is virtually impossible to monitor environmental release of ~3000 colorants, ETAD has developed a simple environmental exposure scenario to calculate initial environmental concentrations of dyes [7].

Such simple models need validation and for this reason ETAD is conducting in a field study to investigate some representative dyes (at manufacturing sites and dyehouses) under a project termed *Pathways of Colorants to the Environment*. The environmental risk posed by a colorant is a function of both its inherent ecotoxicity and the concentrations attained in the environmental compartments. Unlike other substances (*eg*, household detergents) which are emitted continuously, dyes releases result mainly from batch processes and result in spatial and temporal peak emissions. Obviously, short-time concentrations should be compared with acute data on ecotoxicity, whereas long-term residual concentrations need to be compared with chronic effect levels. Because, data on chronic effects are not often available, empirical information serves as a basis for the effects assessment, *ie*, the extrapolation to a *Predicted No Effect Concentration* (PNEC). This PNEC value is to be compared with the so-called *Predicted Environmental Concentration* (PEC) in order to estimate safe levels of residual dye in the environment. Since it is the dissolved state in which a dyes may become biologically available, it is the aquatic environmental compartment which is primarily addressed here. Nonetheless, some consideration of the impact of dyes on sewage and soil is also included.

## 22.2 Colorants in the Environment

Human exposure to dyes occurs primarily at manufacturing plants and in dyehouses. Indirect human exposure through the aquatic and terrestrial food chain is theoretically possible, but is considered as negligible in the case of colorants (apart from deliberate use of food colorants). As depicted in Figure 22.1, dyes enter the environment mainly through the wastewater streams from production facilities and dyehouses.

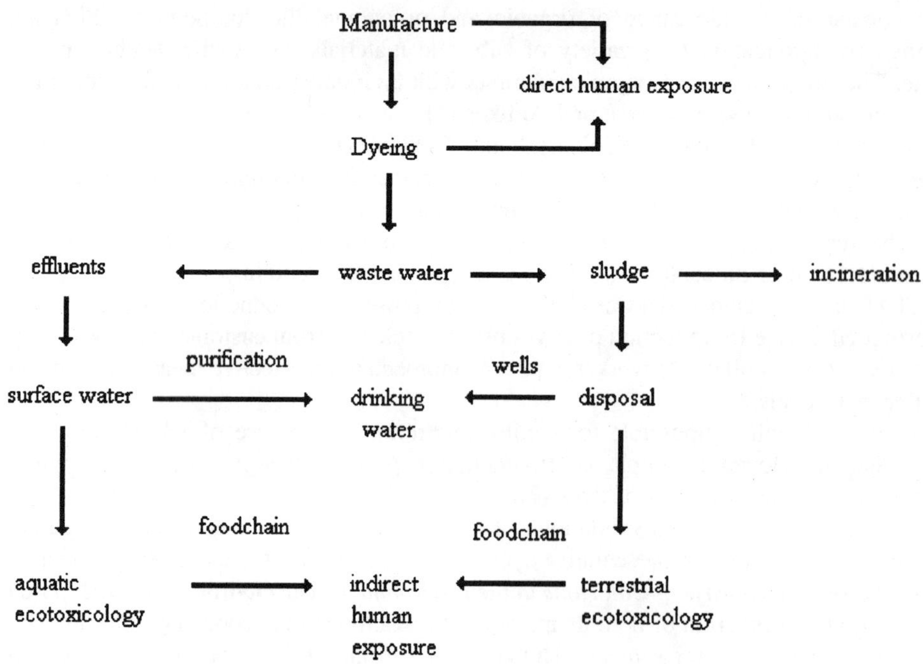


**Figure 22.1** **Pathways of colorants into the environment**

A prerequisite for a colorant to enter the environment is its solubility. Water-insoluble dyes and pigments, either processed in non-aqueous systems or dispersions in water, could not reach surface waters due to rapid settling/sedimentation processes. Fine dispersible dyes (disperse dyes) may form meta-stable colloids that partially could be convected by the wastewater streams for short distances but their tendency to adsorb in suspended particles and sediments will effectively remove them into the solid phase. Colorants that enter the wastewater streams (estimations are 10% of the world-production) normally pass through a wastewater treatment plant where they are eliminated to a large degree by adsorption on the sludge. The extent to which residual amounts reach the surface waters depends on the efficiency of treatment processes. The fate of dyes adsorbed to sludge is generally incineration or disposal in a controlled landfill.

### 22.2.1 Environmental Exposure Assessment

Under the so-called 7th amendment (EC directive 92/32/EEC) a notifier of a new substance may submit a preliminary risk assessment (see chapters by Campbell, Knight, Kulkarni and Nangle). The principles of the risk assessment of new substances are laid down in the Commission Directive 93/67/EEC and contain the elements: Hazard identification, dose-response assessment, exposure assessment for the environmental compartments, and risk characterization.

The objective of the exposure assessment is to predict the concentration of a substance in the environment, and a technical guidance document details the procedure for this. Exposure scenarios for use categories are described in Annexes to the guidance document, and are subject to periodical review and update. In collaboration with the German Umweltbundesamt (UBA), ETAD provided *Guidelines for the Assessment of Environmental Exposure to Dyes* [7]. Within the framework of the EC directives the exposure assessment relates to dyes in the processing industries. Losses during manufacture are not addressed by this directive. It is estimated that about 2% is an average loss in a production campaign [8].

The major pathway of a dye entering the environmental compartments is through the wastewater streams as illustrated by the flow diagram (Figure 22.2) for a typical textile dyeing plant.

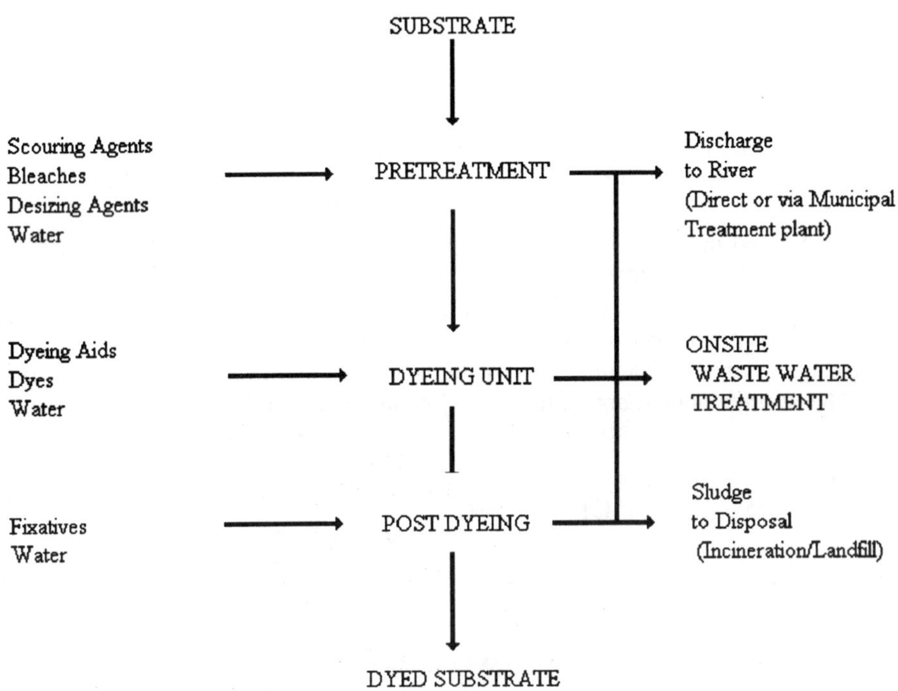


**Figure 22.2** **Flow diagram for a typical textile dyeing plant**

#### 22.2.1.1 Calculation of Estimated Environmental Concentrations

The initial Environmental Concentration (IEC) during a day may be estimated using the equation

$$IEC = W \times \frac{100-F}{100} \times \frac{100-P}{100} \times \frac{1}{Q} \ (ppm) \qquad (1)$$

where W = weight of PMN dye processed (g $d^{-1}$)
F = degree of fixation (%)
P = degree of elimination (%)
$Q_{tot}$ = total flow of receiving water ($m^3$ $d^{-1}$)
(*ie*, flow of wastewater plus flow of river)

In the absence of $Q_{tot}$ (*ie*, total flow of receiving water is unknown) the EC guidance document proposes to introduce a dilution factor for the flow of wastewater:

$$IEC = W \, x \, \frac{(100-F)}{100} \, x \, \frac{(100-P)}{100} \, x \, \frac{1}{Qw} \, x \, \frac{1}{D} \ (ppm \ d^{-1}) \qquad (2)$$

where Qw = flow of wastewater (normally 2000 $m^3$ $d^{-1}$)
D = dilution factor (normally 50)

It has to be noted that dyes are typically applied during a limited time at a number different dyehouses (point sources).

As detailed marketing data are not generally available for new substances, it is not normally possible to predict usage (W) at individual customers. Instead it is assumed that the full capacity of a dyeing machine is run with the dye during a certain number of days each year. The average annual concentration [*C*] would therefore be:

$$[\overline{C}] = IEC \, x \, \frac{n}{365}$$

where n = number of days during which process is running.

The above equations are applicable strictly to batch (exhausted) dyeing processes only. Generally, continuous dyeing results in lower emissions than batch dyeing because of the higher rate of dye fixation. Because continuous dyeing is not an exhaust process there is in principle no direct method to determine the dye residue during the washing and fixation sequence which can be related to the quantity of fabric dyed and to the depth of shade. For descriptive purposes equation (1) can be considered as an upper confidence limit for both processes.

#### 22.2.1.2 Textile Dyeing

Three types of dyeing techniques can be distinguished:

i) Batch dyeing;

ii) Continuous dyeing; and,

iii) Printing.

Batch dyeing involves applying a dye in solution or suspension at a specified liquor ratio which determines the depth of the colour obtained. At the end of the dyeing operation the spent dye-bath liquor is drained off. The post-dyeing stage consists of washing out with water to remove any unfixed dye from the textile substrate. The complete dyeing and washing cycle is typically between 3 and 6 h [9].

Continuous dyeing is operated at constant composition of dyeing liquor, *ie,* textile fabric is pulled through each stage of the dyeing process at a rate of about 40 m $min^{-1}$.

Printing involves transferring patterns to the surface of fabrics and carpets by screen printing systems, either on a flat bed or on rollers. Dye fixation is carried out by steaming or baking followed by washing to remove surplus dye and thickness.

US EPA statistics indicate that the average duration of operation per site is 22 d for batch dyeing, 38 d for continuous processes and 32 d for printing.

A study carried out by the Dutch RIVM [10] arrived at the following estimates for degrees of dye fixation (Table 22.1).

'Extra' losses due to washing out of textile, cleaning operations, paste preparation for printing are estimated as follows [10]:

i) Continuous dyeing — loss 5.5% (range: 2.25-11);

ii) Printing — loss 12% (range: 3.4-42); and,

iii) Batch dyeing — loss 1% (range: 0.5-2).

These losses should be disposed of by proper waste-management procedures and not drained-off into receiving waters without prior treatment.

**Table 22.1** Estimated values for fixation (F)

| Type of dye | | Process | Type of fiber | F Degree of fixation estimate | (range) |
|---|---|---|---|---|---|
| Disperse | | c | CE,PES | 96 | (88-99) |
| " | | p | | 97 | (91-99) |
| Direct | | b | C | 88 | (64-96) |
| Reactive | - wool | b | | 95 | (90-97) |
| | - cotton | b | | 70 | (55-80) |
| | - general | b | | 85 | (55-95) |
| Vat | | c | C,P | 80 | (70-95) |
| " | | p | | 75 | (70-80) |
| Sulfur | | c | C | 70 | (60-90) |
| " | | b | | 70 | (65-95) |
| Acid | - one $SO_3$-group | b | P,PAM,PAc | 90 | (85-93) |
| | - >1 $SO_3$-groups | b | | 95 | (85-98) |
| Basic | | b | PAc,PES,PAM,P,C | 99 | (96-100) |
| Azoic (naphthol) | | c | | 84 | (76-89) |
| " | | p | | 87 | (80-91) |
| Metal complex | | b | P | 94 | (82-98) |
| Pigment | | c | | ≅100 | |
| " | | p | | ≅100 | (98-100) |
| Unknown | - hardly soluble | c | | 97 | (85-99½) |
| | - acid groups | p | | 96 | (84-99) |

c=continuous dyeing, p = printing, b = batch dyeing
P=protein, C-cotton, CE-cellulose ester, PES=polyester, PAM=polyamide, PAc=polyacryl

#### 22.2.1.2.1 Dye Removal at Wastewater Treatment Plants

Wastewater emitted from a dyehouse eventually passes through an on-site treatment process or through a sewage treatment plant. Elimination of dyes may occur through adsorption on sediments and suspended particles (colloids) with subsequent removal from the wastewater by settling or filtration. Few data are available on the removal of dyes by activated sludge. Because dyes are designed to be stable in consumer goods they are normally not readily biodegradable under aerobic conditions. However, elimination of dyes through adsorption on activated sludge can be quite significant, depending on the nature of the molecule (molecular mass, functional groups, electric charge and other factors). It is therefore not surprising that there is a significant range within one class of dye (see Table 22.2).

**Table 22.2** Adsorption P (in %) of the most important dye classes on activated sludge

| Type of dye | Typical range P (%) |
|---|---|
| Acid dyes | 30-80 |
| Reactive dyes | 20-50 |
| Direct dyes | 65-95 |
| Disperse dyes | 60-90 |
| Basic dyes | 20-100 |

Because of the substantial scatter of the degree of elimination it is advisable in critical cases to determine P-values experimentally in simulated systems or from field measurements. In an ETAD-project [11] P-values have been determined by Zahn-Wellens measurements but such values have to be considered as worst-case situations because test conditions require relatively high soluble dye concentrations in relation to the amount of suspended sludge [11]. Furthermore, P-values are pH-dependent and can be determined from adsorption isotherms. In the case of wool and polyamide dyeing, P-values can be estimated from the data on fixation (F), due to the similarity of the surface functional groups of sludge particles to those of the textile substrate.

Another key-parameter in equations (1) and (2) is W, the coloring capacity of a dye-house which also varies widely.

A recent survey amongst ETAD-member companies has displayed estimates for typical quantities of processed goods per day and processed amount of dyes [7], which is shown in Table 22.3.

**Table 22.3** Estimated textile dyeing capacities and corresponding weight of dyes used

| Fiber | Dye | Process | Size | Weight of goods dyed ($kg\ d^{-1}$) | Weight of dyes used ($kg\ d^{-1}$) 0.25% | 1.0% | 2.5-3.5% |
|---|---|---|---|---|---|---|---|
| Polyester | d | e | average | 1000 | 2.5 | 10 | 25-35 |
| Cellulose ester | | | large | 20000 | 50.0 | 200 | 500-700 |
| | | c | large only | 30000 | 75.0 | 300 | 750-1050 |
| | | p | average | 1500 | 7.5 | 30 | 75-105 |
| Wool | a | e | average | 1500 | 3.8 | 15 | 37-52 |
| Cotton | f | e | average | 3000 | 7.5 | 30 | 75-105 |
| | | c | large | 4000 | 10.0 | 40 | 100-140 |
| Polyamide | a | e | average | 1500 | 3.8 | 15 | 37-52 |
| | | | large | 6000 | 15.0 | 60 | 150-210 |
| | | c | average | 6000 | 15.0 | 60 | 150-210 |
| Acrylic | b | c | average | 10000 | 25.0 | — | — |

Processes: c=continuous dyeing, p=printing, e=batch dyeing
Dye: d=disperse, a=acid, b=basic, r=reactive
color shade: 0.25%=pale shade, 1%=average shade 2.5-3.5%=deep shade

#### 22.2.1.2.2 Example: Environmental Emission of an Acid Dye Used for Wool Batch Dyeing

For a large capacity dyehouse it is assumed that 10 tonnes of wool are dyed $d^{-1}$. For a medium to deep shade coloration 1.5% of active dye is applied.

Hence, realistic parameters for equation (1) could be:

W = 150 kg $d^{-1}$
F = 90
P = 55
Q = 0.5 $m^3$ $g^{-1}$ (=40,000 $m^3$ $d^{-1}$) small river flow

resulting in an Initial Environmental Concentration (IEC) of **0.2 ppm $d^{-1}$**.

If the flow of the receiving water is not known, it can be assumed that 150 $m^3$ of process water is discharged $tonne^{-1}$ of fiber resulting in daily flow of wastewater $Q_w$=1500 $m^3$ $d^{-1}$. Applying equation (2) results in an IEC of **0.1 ppm $d^{-1}$**.

Such values appear to be typical peak concentrations that may be encountered during short periods in receiving waters situated in the close vicinity of a dyehouse. A limited number of field studies thus far have monitored the level of some dyes in the catchment basin of rivers that receive large amounts of effluents from dyehouses [12-14]. In the absence of sewage treatment plants, steady-state concentrations in the lower ppb-range are normally observed.

#### 22.2.1.3 Leather Dyeing

An EPA survey has shown that leather tanneries typically operate 10 to 12 $d^{-1}$ [15] and are specialized in dyeing either grain or suede sides. The most common dyeing method applied is so-called drum-dyeing in which the dye preparation is mechanically pumped into rotation wheels. Environmental releases occur during the opening of the wheel batch and dumping the wet and rinsed dyed sides. Major dye-classes applied in the leather industry are acid dyes (which account for about 90% of the leather market), metal complex dyes and, to a lesser extent, cationic dyes.

The calculation of environmental releases is straightforward by applying equations (1) or (2). Parameters on fixation (F) and elimination (P) can, in principle, be applied as for textile dyeing.

ETAD advocates a strict waste minimization and management program which should prevent emissions from cleaning or disposal of emptied containers (which account up to 10% of unexhausted dyebath) to wastewater streams. Estimates of typical dyeing capacities in the leather industry are depicted from Table 22.4.

**Table 22.4** Estimated leather dyeing capacities and corresponding Ws

| Type | Duration of release (d $a^{-1}$) | Weight of leather dyed (kg $d^{-1}$) | Weight of dye used (w) (kg $d^{-1}$) |
|---|---|---|---|
| Grain | 100 | 150 | 0.75-7.5 |
| Suede | 30 | 400 | 2.75-22.5 |

#### 22. 2.1.3.1 Example: Environmental emission of a metal-complex dye for leather dyeing

The EPA study mentioned above estimates that a new dye may typically be used in up to 9 batches per day. For a large plant dyeing 1 tonne of leather (dry weight) at a shade of 4% (active dye material), the initial environmental concentration can be calculated with the following parameters:

$W = 40$ kg $d^{-1}$
$F = 98$
$P = 50$
$Q = 0.5$ $m^3$ $s^{-1}$ (or 40,000 $m^3$ $d^{-1}$)

Applying equation (1) results in an **IEC of 0.01 ppm**. Such a concentration is well below any concern level for ecotoxicity and would not be visible in a well-mixed effluent.

#### 22.2.1.4 Paper Dyeing

Colored paper can be obtained either by mass coloration or by coating coloration with (insoluble) pigments [16]. Other methods such as dip-dyeing or site-press dyeing are rarely used and will not be further discussed.

Mass coloration is applied in 2 modes:

i) Batch operation by addition of the dye to a stock suspension; or,

ii) Continuous operation by pumping liquid colorant from a storage tank into the flow system.

Direct dyes (anionic and cationic) constitute about 60% of the market, basic dyes ~30%, and the remaining 10% are made up by Acid dyes and Pigments [16].

Dye concentrations applied range from about 0.005% (w/w) for very pale shades up to 4% for dark shades and blacks. The dyeing process is affected by the sizing system (acid or neutral), fiber structure, filler materials, additives (fixing agents), temperature, water hardness, etc. The tendency of a dye to be adsorbed by cellulose fibers is dependent on electrostatic forces, hydrogen bonding, Van der Waals' forces and hydrophobic interactions. Dyes for paper should possess both high substantivity (degree of adsorption) and affinity (degree of fixation) in order to limit the addition of fixatives and additives.

Colored papers, especially for food packaging purposes, must pass a bleeding test. Poor bleed fastness is often coupled with highly colored backwaters which can be overcome by increasing the degree of fixation. Estimations of the degree of fixation for various types of paper dyes have been collated in Table 22.5.

**Table 22.5** **Estimated values for fixation of paper dyes**

| Type of dye | Substantivity | Substrate | Fixation |
|---|---|---|---|
| Anionic direct (+stilbene type FWAS) | high | bleached and unbleached | 80% (70-90) with fixing agents or alum up to 98% |
| Cationic direct | very high | all types | 95% (90-100) |
| Basic | low<br>medium | bleached pulp<br>mechanical pulp | 60% (50-70)<br>70% (60-80) with anionic fixation up to 95% |
| Acid | low | sized packaging paper | 50% (40-60) with cationic fixation 80-90% |

The elimination in wastewater treatment plants can be characterized by the range of P values as given in 22.2.1.2 (textile dyes), although paper dyes should be placed on the upper end of the range due to the larger molecular sizes.

#### 22.2.1.4.1 Water Circulation and Wastewater

Paper manufacturing plants reuse the backwater to different degrees: The traditional so-called *open* circulation corresponds to a wastewater production of 50 to 100 $kg^{-1}$ paper. A *partially closed* system exists in cases where one part of the processed water is reused. In *completely closed circulations* no wastewater is charged to the environment.

Therefore equation (1) has to be modified to account for the degree of closure (or recycling of water) C:

$$IEC = W \times \frac{100-F}{100} \times \frac{100-P}{100} \times \frac{1}{Q} x \frac{100-C}{100} \qquad (4)$$

where W,F,P,Q, are defined in 22.2.1.1 and C=degree of closure.

Estimated values of paper dyeing capacities and corresponding amounts of paper-dyes applied are tabulated in table 22.6.

**Table 22.6** **Estimated values of paper dyeing capacities and corresponding Ws**

| Type of paper machine | Size | Amount of paper dyed (tonne $d^{-1}$) | pale shade 0.01-0.1% | medium shade 0.1-1% | deep shade 1-4% |
|---|---|---|---|---|---|
| Weight of dye used (kg $d^{-1}$ | | | | | |
| Tissue | small | 40 | 4-50 | 40-400 | 400-1600 |
| | large | 200 | 20-200 | 200-2000 | 2000-8000 |
| Writing and printing paper | small | 100 | 10-100 | 100-1000 | — |
| | large | 1000 | 100-1000 | 1000-10000 | — |

#### 22.2.1.4.2 Example: Environmental Emission of a Cationic Direct Dye Applied to the Pulp in Tissue and Packaging Coloration

It is assumed that a medium-sized company has a dyeing capacity of 100 tonnes of tissue paper $d^{-1}$. A medium to deep shade coloration requires about 1% of active dye as weight % of dry paper. A water consumption of 60 l $kg^{-1}$ $paper^{-1}$ is rather low and the degree of closure of 30% are assumed. The following parameters can be applied in equation (3):

W = 1 tonne $d^{-1}$
F = 95%
P = 70%
Q = 40,000 $m^3$ $d^{-1}$
C = 30%

Hence, the **IEC is 0.26 ppm** $d^{-1}$.

### 22.2.2 Management of Environmental Exposure

ETAD studies have been initiated to provide a perspective of the fate of dyes in the environment. This information, combined with data on toxicological and ecotoxicological properties, will provide a basis for evaluating whether or not colorants may pose a risk to health or environment at any stage.

The user industry has to consider 4 potential routes of how colorants might enter the environment (see Figure 22.2):

i) Through routine process effluents or emissions;

ii) Through disposal of surplus materials and process residues;

iii) Through the disposal of used packages; and,

iv) Through accidental release.

#### 22.2.2.2 Effects of Colorants in the Environment

Even low concentrations of colorants in receiving waters can cause visible coloration and raise public concern. Although the low concentrations involved do not normally pose any significant environmental risk, such coloration is unacceptable for aesthetic reasons. The *environmental risk* is a function of both the hazard characteristics and the environmental exposure (concentration and duration). Hence the risk can be reduced by reducing the emissions into the various environmental pathways. Guidance for colorants is provided in section 22.2.2.5 of this chapter. Effects on organisms in the environment can be either short-term, *eg*, acute toxicity to fish or daphnia or reproductive effects, or long-term (chronic), *eg*, effects on growth. There are currently no data known that would indicate accumulation of dyes in terrestrial and aquatic foodchains. Available data indicate that the partition coefficient is a poor indicator of bioaccumulation potential for fat soluble dyes (*eg*, Disperse dyes).

#### 22.2.2.3 The Fate of Colorants in the Environment

For satisfactory technical performance, dyes need to be highly stable and durable. Carpets need to be light-fast and most consumers expect clothing to be wash-fast. It is not to be expected that dyes will be readily degradable and any degradation of colorants in the environment is likely to be a slow process. Nevertheless, studies by ETAD and other investigators have shown that azo-dyes break down, particularly under anaerobic conditions (reductive cleavage), to metabolites which may be further degradable under aerobic conditions.

#### 22.2.2.4 Organic Pigments

The mode of use and very low water solubility of organic pigments are such that any discharges to the environment are likely to be small. They are of low concern as they are not bioavailable due to extremely low solubility in both water and fats.

#### 22.2.2.5 Pollution Prevention Action Plan

An environmental impact analysis will almost certainly reveal areas where improvement can be made. In many instances it may show up points at which urgent improvement must be made in order to conform with local regulatory requirements.

The development of an action plan should give consideration to the following factors:

i) The available equipment and the technical requirements of the process;

ii) The regulatory requirements; and,

iii) Financial impact.

The improvement of a dyeing process with respect to its environmental compatibility is best performed through an iterative decision scheme as outlined in Figure 22.3.

A prerequisite to improve a dyeing process is an adequate definition of the parameters involved. Once the qualitative concept to measure emissions to the environment is established, assessments or measurements of releases should follow. The whole project should be promoted by an early involvement of the workforce by implementing a pollution prevention commitment and training program. With this basis the need for effluent control will be understood and precise instructions given.

Clearly, spillages should be prevented as much as possible; but nevertheless facilities should be at hand to control such events. As a general rule, spillages of dyes should not be washed to drain but taken up with a suitable sorbent material which can then be disposed of to controlled landfill or to an incinerator.

By their Code of Ethics ETAD member companies are required to provide a Material Safety Data Sheet (MSDS) that contains parameters relevant to the ecotoxicity ($LC_{50}$, $EC_{50}$, elimination, COD, BOD; for some categories of dyes the partition coefficient n-octanol/water is available).

If the hazard of a mixture preparation of dyes can be traced back to specific ingredients this information should be passed to the customer.

If an environmental compatibility assessment (according to Figure 22.3) leads to the conclusion that the set quality criteria cannot be met, because of the product characteristics, the supplier should be contacted for further information. There may be instances where it is easy to check the assessments made on the effluent produced by measuring effective concentrations.

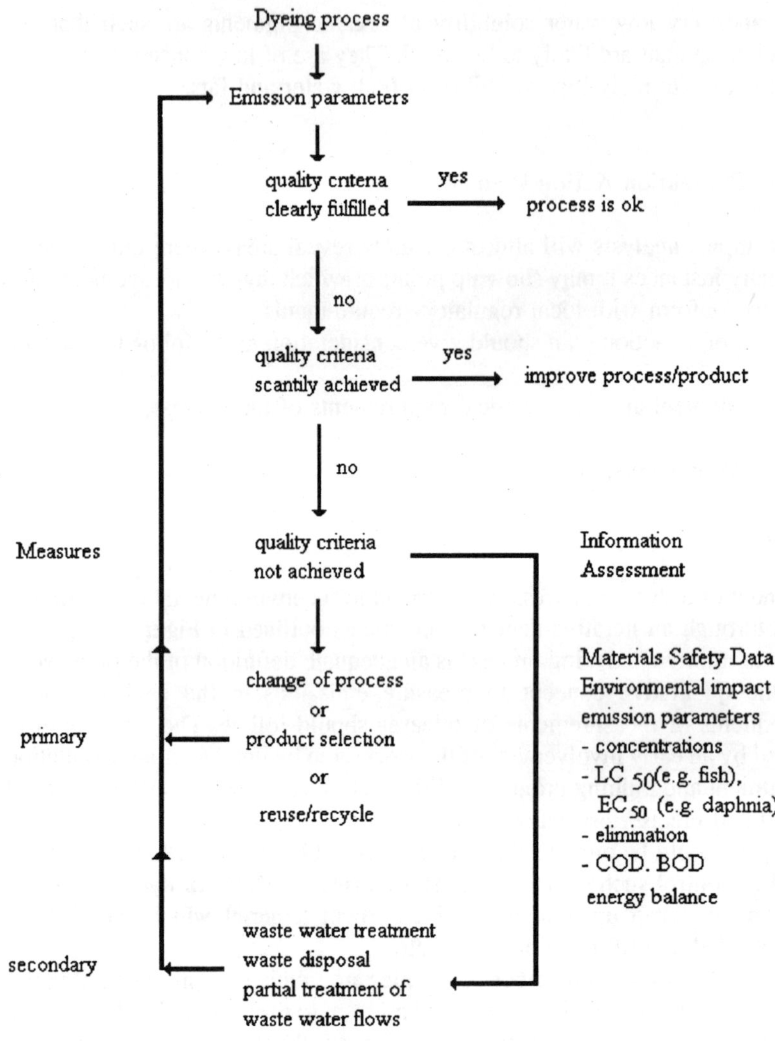


**Figure 22.3** **Iterative decision scheme**

If the load to the effluent is critical, process modifications should be considered.

**Preventive options** (=primary measures) are normally to be preferred compared to **curative methods** (=secondary measures in Figure 22.3) because they tend to be more flexible and often offer a cost benefit.

The analysis of the process may lead to a more efficient dyeing operation, recycling of surplus dyebath liquor and in some instances to product replacements. There may be circumstances that treatment of effluent streams cannot be avoided. If effluents are to be pre-treated on site, careful selection of the optimum treatment process will become crucial but should still have the flexibility to deal with more stringent effluent quality levels. Although there may be situations where the discharge of existing effluents is permitted by the authorities the costs involved in the wastewater treatment may render this option unfavorable. Wastewaters from batch dyeing operations may need to be balanced to avoid peak emissions. A reduction of disposal costs may be achievable by separating strongly colored effluents from other wastestreams.

Amongst all the points outlined above, the key point is probably the nature of the effluent being generated. This must be accurately characterized. The possibilities open for dealing with an effluent whose main problem ingredient has a high COD may be quite different from those for an effluent whose main problem is that it is highly colored. Once the nature of the effluent and its problem constituents are well understood, detailed consideration should be given to alternative process and on-site treatment options.

Even when all economically feasible improvements have been made to site, equipment and processes, an effluent will remain and the decision to discharge, to send away for disposal, or treat on site will be necessary. This decision may be constrained in that discharge may not be legally acceptable; if it is acceptable then the costs concerned become the deciding factor. The technology of on-site pre-treatment is developing rapidly at the present time and a number of methods are commercially available. Some of these methods (oxidation or reduction by various means) are aimed at breaking down the chemical structure of the dye to environmentally acceptable substances which can be discharged in effluents.

Others are aimed at separation of the dyes by physico-chemical means (precipitation, flocculation, adsorption) to give an unobjectionable bulk effluent and a relatively small quantity of separated dye sludge which is suitable for further treatment or direct disposal as chemical waste.

In practice, a combination or sequence of treatment methods may be needed to arrive at an acceptable quality of effluent and a viable waste disposal situation. The choice of method will depend critically on the nature and volume of effluents which must be dealt with, the regulatory demands on final effluent quality, and the constraints upon disposal of the sludges and spent materials which are an inevitable product of treatment processes.

For effluents with high initial levels of heavy metals, the final disposal of treatment sludges may be problematical, and it is probably best to seek a process resulting in a small quantity of highly contaminated sludge to reduce the amount for final disposal as hazardous waste.

#### 22.2.2.6 Inventory Management

Careful inventory management can help to minimize waste production from unused products. Obsolete stocks may cause process or application inefficiency resulting in loss of quality or need for disposal. Losses can also result from packaging damage, deterioration and from product damage caused by temperature variations or atmospheric conditions. There is certainly a commercial stimulus to develop better sales and production forecasting and cooperation with dye-suppliers to improve their ability to deliver in a timely manner.

## 22.3 Aspects of Environmental Hazard and Risk Assessment

### 22.3.1 General Description

The so-called risk assessment directive 93/67/EEC describes a stepwise procedure for both human health and environmental risk assessment according to the scheme (Figure 22.4).

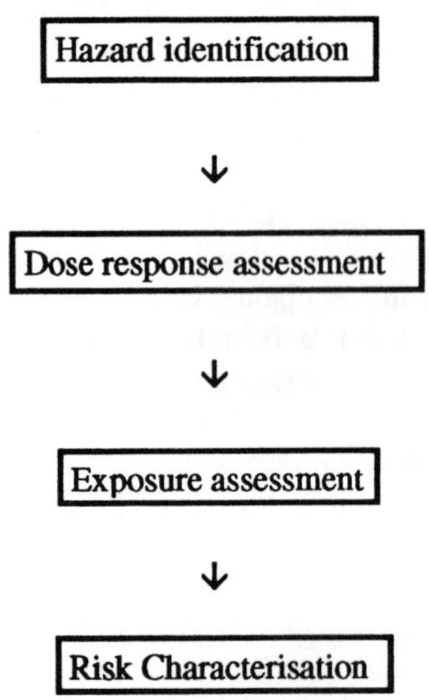


**Figure 22.4** **Stepwise procedure**

Whereas human health risk assessment is expressed in terms of a probability of a person or a cohort of exposed person at risk, environmental risk assessment is confined to the comparison of ecotoxicity data with exposure level.

The principle that leads to the comparison between ecotoxicity and environmental exposure has been proposed by ECETOC [17] and is illustrated in Figure 22.5.

The rationale behind this scheme is to extrapolate environmental release concentrations into steady-state 'Predicted Environmental Concentrations' (PEC) by modelling fate and distribution of a substance using specific exposure scenarios.

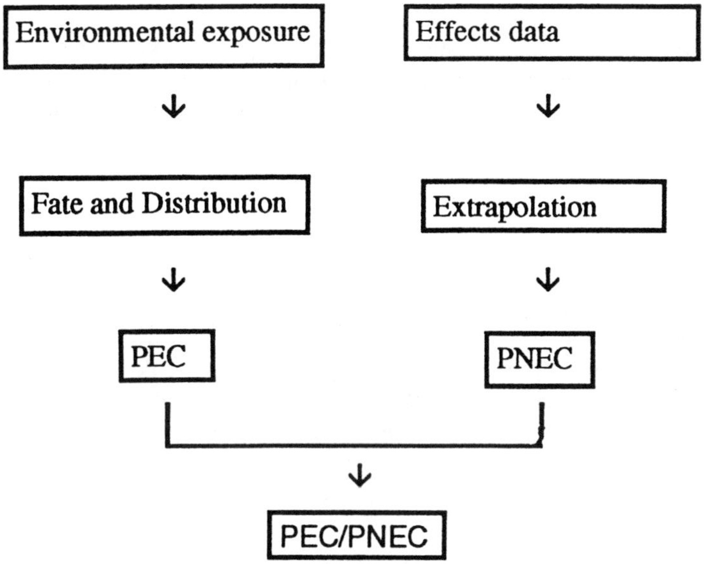


**Figure 22.5** Comparison between ecotoxicity and environmental exposure

The 'Predicted No Effect Concentration' may be derived from laboratory, field or theoretical data. Studies conducted on single species such as acute toxicity to fish ($LC_{50}$) over a relatively short time scale (normally 40 or 96 h) and with death as the only recorded endpoint is, by itself, only of limited value in deciding whether or not a predicted environmental level of a dye is, or, is not, acceptable. Extrapolation from acute effects to chronic and ecosystems effects involves numerous uncertainties. In order to protect the ecosystem, conservative assessment factors have been introduced based on the statistical analysis of a set of data [17] for chronic exposure. The US-EPA [18] has proposed to apply a factor of 1000 for a single acute $L(E)C_{50}$ value or 100 to the lowest value if all 3 tests are available (fish, daphniae, algae). These models have in common that they **assume steady state** concentrations in the aquatic environment.

The situation in the dye-processing industry is remarkably different, *ie*, small volume batch operations lead to an **intermittent** (short duration) **peak release at point sources.** As stated in the EC risk assessment directive the **duration and frequency** of releases have to be taken into account.

### 22.3.2 Environmental Risk Posed by Dyes

#### 22.3.2.1 Possible Impact on Receiving Waters

The impact of dyes in natural waters needs to be considered from 3 standpoints, namely, visual pollution due to color, possible effects on aquatic organisms and possible effects on the suitability of the water for drinking (animals or humans), or other possible uses.

##### 22.3.2.1.1 Visual Pollution

There is no doubt that for dyehouses whose effluent discharge is via relatively small treatment works to small clear rivers, visual pollution of the receiving river may be of major concern. The perception of color in a river depends on many factors. These include: the degree of mixing of the effluent plume or discharge; the shade of color concerned (reds are particularly noticeable); and, the depth over a light coloured bottom. With these variables it is difficult to give clear guidance on what level of a dye will give rise to visual pollution, but ETAD suggests that levels <0.1 mg $l^{-1}$ are unlikely to give rise to problems, whereas levels >1 mg $l^{-1}$ may well do so.

For example, a dye which is used at 10 kg $d^{-1}$ with a level of fixation of 60% and which is not eliminated during the sewage treatment process, the average level in a small stream (4 x $10^4$ m $d^{-1}$) is 0.1 mg $l^{-1}$. If the mixing of the effluent plume into the stream is (as is likely) incomplete for some distance below the discharge and/or the peak discharge concentration is significantly above the daily average, a dye with these characteristics may from time to time form a visible plume in this size of stream.

##### 22.3.2.1.2 Effects on Aquatic Organisms

ETAD has selected 47 dyes (11 Acid, 11 Disperse, 8 Reactive, 7 Direct, 6 Basic, 3 Mordant, and 1 Sulfur) representing commercially important dye classes to determine their ecotoxic hazard properties [11]. The dyes were examined in the state that would be the most likely form to enter the environment, *ie*, technical grade and reactive dyes in the hydrolyzed form. The following studies were carried out:

i) A 96 h acute fish toxicity using the Zebra fish (*Brachydanio rerio*);

ii) A 48 h acute study on *Daphnia magna*; and,

iii) A 72 h growth inhibition on the alga *Scenedesmus subspicatus*.

Furthermore, the inhibition rate of activated sludge samples were determined and a Zahn-Wellens test carried out to assess the potential for removal of the dyes entering the biological stage of a wastewater treatment plant. Dyes were tested up to a concentration of 100 mg $l^{-1}$ (the EC cut-off limit for classification and labelling). The ecotoxicological profile can be summarized as follows:

i) Most dyes have fish $LC_{50}$ >100 mg $l^{-1}$ (34/47). Previous findings of higher toxicity for basic dyes were confirmed (1-10 mg $l^{-1}$);

ii) *Daphnia magna* results grossly parallel the findings for fish toxicity; and,

iii) A significantly larger number of dyes would fall into stricter classification categories based on algae toxicity.

In view of this set of data on algae, ETAD has recently started a project to discriminate between a light inhibition effect under the test conditions and a real toxic effect to identify the reason for the algal growth inhibition [19]. A number of studies have already shown that the observed growth inhibition was caused by the indirect effect, *ie*, the light absorption in the colored test solutions (which would exempt from classification in the EC according to the 12th adaptation of directive 67/548/EEC).

There is a considerable body of evidence that synthetic colorants in general, and water-soluble dyes in particular, are unlikely to be bioaccumulative. On this basis it may be predicted that long-term chronic effects to aquatic organisms are very unlikely to result from continuous exposure at concentrations below 1% of the $LC_{50}$, but a more conservative level of 0.1% of the $LC_{50}$ of the most sensitive species is perhaps more widely accepted.

Where acute data for other species are available, 1% of the lowest acute toxicity may be used for this more conservative level.

For intermittent exposures, such as for a dye used on a few occasions $a^{-1}$, these suggested factors of 1% or 0.1% of the $LC_{50}$ are almost certainly overly conservative. It is suggested that 10% and 1% of the $LC_{50}$ would be adequate to protect fish and other aquatic life of the river.

Calculations, and some limited environmental monitoring, have indicated that dye levels in river systems receiving appreciable quantities of dyehouse effluent may be in the $\mu g\ l^{-1}$ (ppb) level. On this basis dyes with both low fixation levels and low elimination potential may require further experimental data on aquatic toxicity if they are used in substantial quantities of their $LC_{50}$ value is <10 mg $l^{-1}$. Relatively few dyes fall into this category but in such cases additional information on exposure and/or effects may be needed.

### 22.3.2.1.3 Effect on Water Supplies

Only a very few dyes are classified as 'very toxic' in the EEC classification for mammalian toxicity, the upper limit for this class being 25 mg $kg^{-1}$ b.w. Although, as a matter of principle, every effort should be made to exclude synthetic chemicals from drinking water supplies, calculations show that even in a 'reasonable worst case' scenario the levels of dyes present in natural water are most unlikely to present a health risk to animals or humans drinking that water.

### 22.3.2.2 Assessment of Possible Impact on Sewage Treatment

Where a dyehouse discharges to a municipal sewage treatment works, consideration should be given to whether the effluent (and for the purposes of this document specifically the dye content of the effluent) may adversely affect the sewage treatment processes. Three specific aspects may be considered.

#### 22.3.2.2.1 Possible Effect on Aerobic Sewage Treatment

Certain types of dyes could affect the ability of aerobic sewage treatment microorganisms to biodegrade normal sewage components. The concentrations at which such adverse effects may be seen can be indicated by a variety of studies including the ETAD Ecological Method 103 [20].

The potential concentration of dye in a municipal sewage treatment works $C_{tp}$ may be calculated from the concentration of the dye in the effluent discharge from the dyehouse according to equations (1) or (2). Thus,

$$C_{tp} = C_{av} \; x \; \frac{Ve}{Ve+Vm} \qquad (4)$$

where $V_e$ = effluent discharge from processing plant ($m^3 \; d^{-1}$)
$V_m$ = effluent from municipal sources ($m^3 \; d^{-1}$)
$C_{tp}$ = concentration in municipal treatment plant ($mg \; l^{-1}$)

Where the actual mean flow, Vm, is not obtainable it may be estimated on the basis of the population served and an approximate sewage flow (in Europe) of 0.2 $m^3 \; d^{-1}$ $person^{-1}$.

The calculation of $C_{tp}$ gives a daily average, but since the primary settlement process at a sewage treatment works normally provides considerable flow balancing ahead of the aerobic biological stage this is almost certainly acceptable. As a more conservative alternative twice the daily average concentration of the dye may be used.

#### 22.3.2.2.2 Possible Effect on Sewage Sludge Treatment

Sewage sludge may be treated by anaerobic digestion which can be susceptible to inhibition by certain types of organic substance. The potential concentration of a dye in sewage sludge, $C_{sl}$ (%), may be calculated using equation (5).

$$C_{sl} = Q_{30} \times \frac{E}{0.08P} \qquad (5)$$

where $Q_{30}$ = total quantity of dye in sewage treatment works input over a 30 d period (kg).
E = proportion of dye likely to be eliminated (adsorbed) during treatment (%)
P = population served by effluent treatment plant.

This approach recognizes that the sludge digestion process gives very considerable averaging of the levels of any contaminant in the sludge. The proportion likely to be eliminated during treatment may be taken from the Material Safety Data Sheet (if no data provided assume 100% as worst case estimate). The total daily sludge production is calculated on the basis of a typical 0.08 kg person$^{-1}$.

Information on the level at which a specific dye may cause inhibition of sludge digestion may well not be available, but even for the relatively few dyes which do show inhibitory effects these are not in general significant below 0.1% (w/w) dry sludge (or 1000 mg kg$^{-1}$ dry solids). It is anticipated that for most dyes the calculated level will be below 0.1%.

#### 22.3.2.2.3 Possible Effect on Sewage Sludge Disposal

Where sewage sludge is used as an agricultural fertilizer, the possible effects of sludge contaminants on that use should be considered.

A typical application rate for sewage sludge to soil is 1 tonne dry solids ha (United Kingdom figures ex OECD [21]), and the weight of soil to a 1 cm depth in 1 ha is 100 tonnes at a soil density of 1 g cm$^{-3}$. On this basis the dye concentration in the soil, $C_{so}$ mg kg$^{-1}$, can be estimated by equation (6).

$$C_{so} = 10 \times C_{sl} \ (mg\ kg^{-1}) \qquad (6)$$

where $C_{sl}$ = concentration in sewage sludge (%)

ECETOC has concluded that levels of organic substances in soil below 1 mg kg$^{-1}$ are unlikely to adversely affect plant growth [22] and work by ETAD on 4 different dyes has shown no-effect levels against a range of plants at or above 100 mg kg$^{-1}$. Therefore it seems unlikely that a calculation of the theoretical concentration of a dye in sewage sludge will lead to any concern about use as an agricultural fertilizer.

For example, consider the case of a dye which is used at the rate of 100 kg over a 30 d period with a 90% fixation in a batch dyeing process, the effluent being discharged without prior treatment to a municipal sewage treatment works serving 10,000 people. If it is assumed that all the dye is adsorbed on the sludge and this is applied at 1 tonne sludge (dry solids $ha^{-1}$ then the concentration of dye in the sludge would be 420 mg $kg^{-1}$ and in the soil 0.42 mg $kg^{-1}$.

## 22.4 Conclusions

Human health and environmental hazard identification and communication undoubtedly are important prerequisites for risk assessment. Good quality information on exposure is needed to address the objective risk and possible options for risk reduction. Risk management should indeed start with a careful selection of colorants that exhibit the required performance with regard to substrate affinity, fastness and other boundary conditions. Although testing substances is an integral part of the '7th amendment' in the EC, there are limitations on the generation of additional data on hazard. ETAD's strategy to reduce risk by exposure minimization should offer a cost-effective and preventive strategy for risk reduction. The assessment of the risk associated with a specific substance and the possible options of risk reduction are illustrated in Figure 22.6.

The constant improvement of exhaustion and fastness properties of dyes is paralleled by a progressive improvement of wastewater treatment technologies which reduces the overall environmental impact both by primary and secondary measures.

There is an increasing body of circumstantial evidence that the small portion of colorants entering the environment is ultimately degradable either by biological or photochemical pathways. Recent studies reveal that especially anaerobic compartments (in natural sediments and soil) act through reductive cleavage as transforming sinks to dyes in the environment.

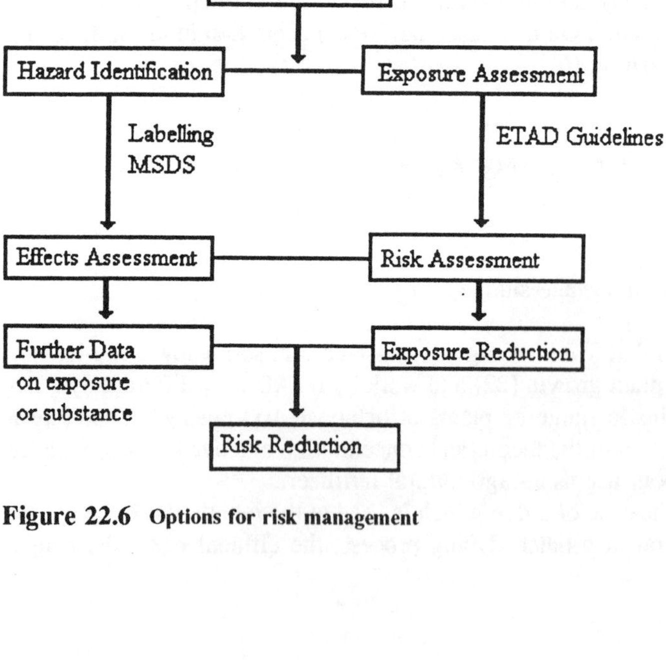


**Figure 22.6** Options for risk management

## 22.5 Acknowledgement

The author gratefully acknowledges the input and support from many experts from member companies who collaborate within ETAD. Particular thanks are due to Derek Brown, Eric Clarke, Peter Grindley, Josef Inauen, and Udo Pagga.

## 22.6 References

[1] Clarke, E.A. and Anliker, R., 'The Handbook of Environmental Chemistry', in: *Organic Dyes and Pigments*, O. Hutzinger, O., (Ed.), Springer Verlag, 1980, Vol. 3A, pp. 181-210.

[2] Anliker, R. and Steinle, D., *J. Soc. Dyers and Colourists*, 1988, **104**, 377-384.

[3] Clarke, E.A. and Anliker, R., *J. Soc. Dyers and Colourists*, 1984, **14**, 84-89.

[4] 'Guidelines for Safe Handling of Dyes', US Operating Committee (USOC) of ETAD, 1989, pp. 15.

[5] 'Pollution Prevention Guidance Manual for the Dye Manufacturing Industry', A cooperative project between US EPA and US Operating Committee of ETAD, 1991, pp. 146.

[6] ETAD Information Notice No. 4: *Colorants and the Environment; Guidance for the User*, June 1992, pp. 20.

[7] ETAD publication *Guidelines for the Assessment of Environmental Exposure to Dyestuffs*, November 1992, pp. 12.

[8] Hobbs, S.J., *Industry Category Document: UK dye production and use in the textile industry*, Department of the Environment, June 1988, pp. 62.

[9] Heath, G.A. in: *The Dyeing and Printing of Textile Fibers relative to Worker Exposures and Environmental Releases*, EPA Report, 1984, pp. 122.

[10] Ros, J.P.M., in RIVM (NL) Report No. 85 150 3001: *System for assessing new substances*; section: expected emissions from textile dyes, 1985, pp. 46.

[11] ETAD Project E-3020: *Ecological Assessment of Important Dyestuffs*, 1992.

[12] Tincher, W.C., *Survey of Coosa River Basin for Organic Contaminants from Carpet Processing*, Final Report, Contract No. E-27-630, Prot. Div., Dept of Natural Resources, State of Georgia, USA, 1978, pp. 85.

[13] Weber, E.J., Sturrock, P.E., and Camp, S.R. in: US-EPA Environmental Research Brief, *Reactive Dyes in the Aquatic Environment: A Case Study of Reactive Blue 19*, August 1990, pp. 7.

[14] Maguire, R.J. and Tkacz, R.J. *Water Poll. Res. J. Canada*, 1991, **26**, 145-161.

[15] Vorbach, J., *Leather Dyeing: Occupational Exposure and Environmental Release*, EPA Report, 1987, pp. 38.

[16] 'Dyes and fluorescent whitening agents for paper', in: *Paper Chemistry*, Roberts, J.C. (Ed.), Blackie & Son Ltd., 1991, Chapter 9, pp. 132-161.

[17] ECETOC Technical Report Nr.51, *Environmental Hazard Assessment of Substances*, January 1993, pp. 92.

[18] Bascietto, J., Hinckley, D., Plafkin, J., and Slimak, M., *Environ. Sci. Technol.*, 1990, **24**, 10-15.

[19] ETAD Project E-3023, *Algal Growth Inhibition.*
[20] ETAD, *Ecological Method*, No. 103, 1979, pp. 7.
[21] OECD, Activated Sludge, Respiration Inhibition Test, OECD Guideline for testing of chemicals, No. 203, 1984, pp. 10.
[22] ECETOC Technical Report No. 40: *Hazard Assessment of Chemical Contaminants in Soil*, Brussels, August 1990, pp. 50.

# 23. Fate of Pesticides in the Environment and the Quality of Drinking Water in Relation to Human Health

Mihaela Vasilescu

## 23.1 Introduction

Mankind wishes to live longer, better, and to dominate nature; in order to satisfy his inborn curiosity, he discovered fire, agriculture, the wheel, steam power, chemical organic synthesis, artificial intelligence, etc. to enhance his lifestyle.

In the perpetual confrontation between bad and good, the seen and unseen, pesticides have their own fate. They were created to help man, but currently pesticides are global contaminants, which can be found in air, rainfall, snow, soil, ground and surface water, fog and even in ice from Arctic regions.

Globally all living creatures — birds, fish, wildlife, domestic animals, human beings, even the newborn — are contaminated with pesticides. The circle is closing, man is the starting point and it is paradoxical that he integrates by bioconcentration pollution from every environmental media via foodchains.

## 23.2 Historic

Pesticides are among the few classes of toxic substances which are added deliberately into the environment.

The use of some compounds against pests was known from earlier times; these were based on sulfur and arsenic. Natural extracts from plants such as nicotine from tobacco, or pyrethrum from chrysanthemums were used initially in the 16th and 19th centuries respectively.

The use of a synthetic chemicals in pest control began in the middle 1940s when Paul Mueller, a Swiss chemist, discovered insecticidal properties of dichlorodiphenyl-trichloroethane(DDT), which was commercialized in 1942.

German scientists, undertaking experiments nerve gas during World War II, synthesized the organophosphorus insecticide, parathion, which was marketed in 1943. The phenoxyacetic acid herbicides 2,4-D and 2,4,5-T, were also marketed during the 1940s.

Organochlorine and organophosphorus insecticides became the major agent in pest control in the 1960s. They were extensively used in developed countries' agriculture and in malaria, and other vector controls in developing countries [1].

The first serious warning against the use of synthetic pesticides was in the book 'Silent Spring' written by the biologist Rachel Carson and published in 1962. Carson blamed DDT and the related organochlorine insecticides, for their persistence in the environment, bioacummulation in human adipose tissue, and animal fat, and also for toxic effects on birds and fish, pointing out the potential danger to the environment and for human health. Discussion on this subject has generated justifiable doubts and severe attacks from ecologists. These facts were transposed into practice by strengthening research in order to obtain less toxic active substances, and economically competitive for those with superior biological action.

## 23.3 Definition, Classification

The term pesticide is generic and applies to all chemicals used in pest control. According to the type of pest to which they are targeted, pesticides are classified as: insecticides, herbicides, fungicides, acaricides, rodenticides, ovicides, molluscides, nematocides, and growth regulators.

According to chemical type pesticide classification includes: organophosphates, N-methyl carbamates, chlorinated hydrocarbons, bisdithiocarbamates, phenoxyaliphatic acids, phenol derivatives, etc.

Resulting from years of controlling pests using organic chemical substances, most having synthetic insecticides, 3 generations of pesticides have appeared:

i) Domination by organochlorinated compounds;

ii) Organophosphorus insecticides and carbamate groups; and,

iii) Pyrethroids, hormonal insecticides, attractants, repellents, chemosterilants and 'living' insecticides such as bacteria, fungi, protozoa and parasite nematodes.

## 23.4 Use

Pesticides commenced from their manufacture in organic synthesis chemical plants. In 1939, the USA Agricultural Department recorded 32 pesticides, whereas in 1987 the US EPA catalogued 1200 active compounds with insecticide action, formulated in 37,000 commercial products.

In 1987, the US EPA estimated that 1.8 x $10^9$ pesticides were in use for agriculture (62% herbicides, 22% insecticides, and 9% fungicides) [1].

Most organochlorine pesticides are now banned (DDT, aldrin, endrin, dieldrin, chlordane, heptachlor, lindane, toxophene and hexachlorobenzene), or severely restricted in developed countries, but they are still used in developing countries.

Because of the restriction and banning of most chlorinated pesticides in agriculture, there has been an increase in the use of acutely toxic, but biodegradable organophosphorous and N-methyl carbamate insecticides. The future trend in pesticide use maintains the organophosphorus compounds as having the most important role for developing countries but it is stressed that the most toxic substances will need to be eliminated. The use of carbamates and pyrethroids will also increase concomitant by diminishing the use of organochlorine insecticides. In the next few years, the demand for triazine and carbamate herbicides will be probably increase 3-fold, and 2-fold for the urea-based compounds [2]. Although the major application of pesticides is in agriculture, there are also non-agricultural uses such as: industrial, wood preservatives, household disinfectants, public health, etc.

## 23.5 Environmental Transport, Distribution, and Transformation

As a result of pesticides' widespread usage, they are now present at all environmental levels with different distributions related to their physical and chemical properties. Examples include:

### 23.5.1 DDT

DDT is one of the most incriminated compounds belonging to organochlorine insecticides' class which is sprayed as a dust or solution on crops, forests, households and the human population. There is always a percentage of insecticide that does not reach the target and is redistributed.

In addition to the active substance that enters soil and which evaporates, it is possible to identify DDT's evaporation, above treated fields for up to 6 months after application. The major part of these vapors settle in the vicinity, the amount being a linear function of the inverse logarithm of the distance from the source. These studies show that the DDT is generally concentrated in a soil layer up to 2.5 cm depth; other proportions are disseminated by the winds on a planetary scale.

Previous studies indicated DDT concentrations in the atmosphere in non-cultivated areas, ranging from below the detection limit to $2.36 \times 10^{-6}$ mg m$^{-3}$, compared to concentrations measured in agricultural areas that were from $1 \times 10^{-6}$ mg m$^{-3}$ to $22 \times 10^{-6}$ mg m$^{-3}$ [3]. Such concentrations could be higher in the regions with increased atmospheric nebulosity.

Although difficult to measure, DDT concentrations in rainfall have the same order of magnitude in agricultural and non-agricultural areas, thus indicating an homogeneous distribution. The insecticide's concentrations in surface or ground waters is modified through the influence of soil and rainfall. DDT has a strong propensity to adsorb on different surfaces. As a result, a significant amount of the insecticide entering the water is strongly absorbed on soil particles. Thus DDT is eliminated progressively from clear waters by accumulation in sediments. These amounts could be transported downstream, reaching estuaries and deltas [4].

There remains gaps in our knowledge concerning the destination, transport and degradation of DDT and its related compounds in the environment, in spite of the fact that the DDT was the first synthetic insecticide.

It was proved experimentally that 99% of DDT is degraded after 12 wks of incubation under anaerobic, and biologically active conditions [5]. Gäb [6,7], have proved that vapors of DDT and DDE transport to the photochemical active ionosphere by the atmospheric turbulence, yield carbon dioxide and hydrochloric acid. This disintegration is so complete that it was called photo-demineralization.

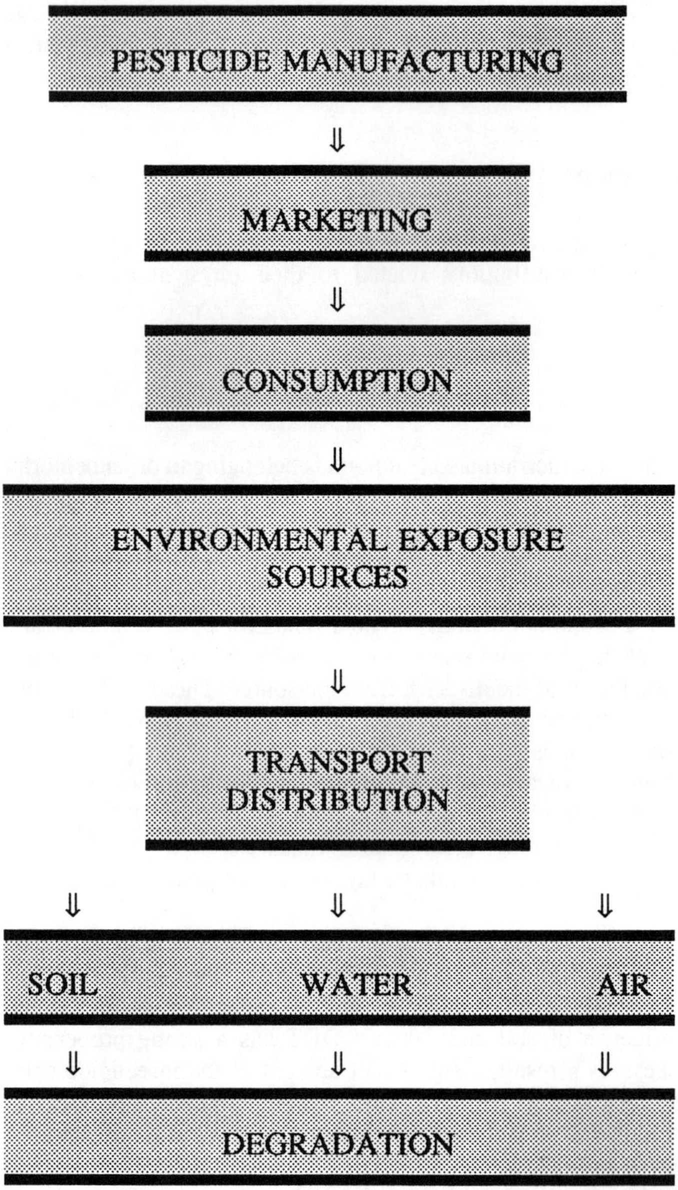


**Figure 23.1** **Flow chart for organochlorine pesticide's distribution**

The fast disintegration of DDT under UV radiation is even more important. In 1969 the photolysis of DDT and its principal metabolite DDE, was studied, by irradiation ($\gamma$=260 nm) in methanol. Besides other products of degradation such as DDD, DDMU, dichlorobenzophenone, dichloro-3,6-fluorenone, the presence of PCBs was highlighted. The hypothesis that the DDT could be a source of PCBs in the environment was proved only for the bi-, tri-, and tetra-chlorinated biphenyls [8].

DDT transforms into many degradation products in the environment. More than 20 compounds have been identified, but there are many others with unknown chemical structures [9].

The toxicological implications of all these related compounds have not been elucidated entirely, except for DDE and DDD (TDE) metabolites. The toxicological effects are important, not only for the specific case of DDT, as these are related to the estimation of human exposure.

### 23.5.2 Carbamate Pesticides

Most of the carbamate pesticides are used in agriculture as insecticides, fungicides, herbicides, nematocides, and growth regulators. Also, they are used as biocides in industry and greenhouses, and latterly for vector control. This class of synthetic pesticides includes over 50 compounds with the generic formula:

$$R_1NH - \overset{\overset{\displaystyle O}{\|}}{C} - OR_2 \qquad\qquad R_1;R_2 = \text{alkyl or aryl groups}$$

In general, the N-substituted derivatives of carbamic acid are unstable compounds, especially under alkaline conditions, their decomposition results in the formation of an alcohol or phenol, ammonia, amines and carbon dioxide. These salts and esters of N-substituted carbamic acid are more stable, this enhanced stability is the basis for their use as biologically active pesticides.

Carbamate insecticides are applied principally to plants, and can reach the soil, while carbamate nematocides and herbicides are applied directly to the soil, which is their route of entry to surface and ground waters.

A proportion of the active compound is biodegraded in soil. This process is related to compound solubility and volatility, soil characteristics, humidity, capacity of absorption, pH, temperature, photo degradation, and photo decomposition. In addition to physical and chemical degradation, there is microorganism activity. The first stage in the metabolic degradation of carbamates in soil is the hydrolysis, followed by further metabolism in the soil-plant system.

In general, the vapor pressure of carbamates is low, but some may sublimate slowly at room temperature, and this would appear to explain their loss from soil surfaces. As the distribution in air is considered to be minor, the aquatic media is an important transport route for the very soluble carbamates. In this case, the hazard is limited by their rapid decomposition under aqueous conditions. Carbamates are hydrolyzed spontaneously yielding, as final products, an amine, carbon dioxide, and an alcohol or phenol:

$$R_1HN\text{-}COOR_2 + H_2O \rightarrow R_1HN_2 + CO_2 + R_2OH$$

The hydrolysis of the carbamates is catalyzed, both *in vitro* and *in vivo*, by A-esterases or arylesterases.

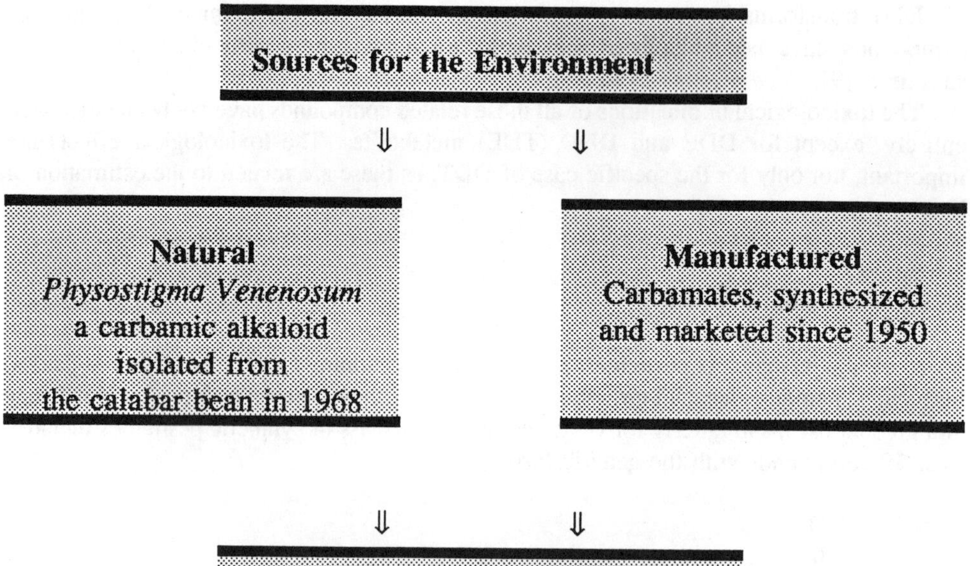


**Figure 23.2** Flow chart of the carbamate's transport

Carbamate insecticides in water are subject to photo decomposition under the effects of ultraviolet radiation, the rate of which is related with pH, tending to increase with increasing pH. The first effect of UV irradiation is the cleavage of the ester bond, resulting in the phenol or the heterocyclic enol of the carbamate ester [9]. The studies concerning the half-life for photo decomposition process suggest that the light source characteristics influence the extent of the process.

It appears reasonable to suggest that photo decomposition may account for some loss of carbamate insecticides in clean surface waters exposed to sunlight for a long period. This photolysis is considered to be a minor factor in the decomposition of these compounds in highly-turbid waters, where the penetration of light is reduced greatly.

The carbamates are decomposed in soil and water, and are metabolized by the microorganisms, plants and animals, the metabolites being less toxic for the environment, than the parent compounds.

Many studies suggest that the bioaccumulation of carbamates in different species and food chains take place on a limited scale, but exceptions could be considered.

### 23.5.3 Predictive Models

A considerable effort is dedicated currently to the elucidation of the mechanisms and rates of transportation and environmental behaviour for toxic substances in general, and pesticides in particular. For this purpose various predictive models to estimate the pollutant's concentration at each environmental level are being developed. The scale of complexity ranges from very simple models, based on the extrapolation of particular examples, followed by those taking into consideration toxic distribution between different media to reach equilibrium, to very complex models including all environmental levels, including biota [10].

### 23.5.4 Fugacity

A fugacity model could be an example for elucidating (with high accuracy) chemical behavior profiles, determination of dominant fate processes, and establishing which environmental data are required [11].

Fugacity can be regarded as the 'escaping tendency' of a chemical substance from a phase, usually expressed in units of pressure. Five environmental compartments are considered as phases: atmosphere, soil, water, sediment, and aquatic biota.

For example, PCB, mirex, and DDT, can be detected earlier and environmental damage held to an acceptable level if the characteristics of the substances can be inserted into a model which can predict:

i) Transport;

ii) Rates of transformations;

iii) Regions of accumulation; or,

iv) Concentrations.

It is understood that the concept of fugacity can be potentially very useful in identifying the static and dynamic behavior of toxic substances in the environment. Phenomena such as bioaccumulation becomes readily understandable and predictable. Also, it is valuable in assisting in the elucidation of the dominant process responsible for a substance's degradation or removal from the environment, and in identifying the significant transfer process.

The concept of fugacity is capable of implementation at various levels of complexity and could form the basis for a procedure to assess the likely environmental behavior of a chemical substance, and also for indicating adverse environmental effects.

There remains many other environmental problems for which there are no suitable models or alternative models are under development. For new chemicals, many of their physical, chemical, and biological properties, which are necessary to estimate the rate of transformation, persistence and distribution, are unknown.

Models can be applied successfully at the transport of pollutants from agricultural areas to surface or ground waters. These approaches for estimating the pollutants' residues in food and irrigation waters as a result of pesticides and fertilizers agricultural use, or their storage, are under elaboration and/or perfection.

The uncertainties and limitations of these models should be identified and eliminated by comparison with monitoring data.

## 23.6 Drinking Water Contamination Levels and Human Exposure

Pesticides that modify water quality include chlorinated hydrocarbons and their related compounds, persistent herbicides, and insecticides directly applied to the soil, which could easily leach into the ground water, and pesticides used for vector's control at water surfaces.

Among these compounds, the organochlorinated insecticides are found in water with a high frequency, due to their persistence. Traces of organochlorinated insecticides from water could accumulate progressively at different levels of foodchains. For example, DDT can accumulate in fish at concentration levels 10,000 times higher than those found in the living aquatic medium.

For several insecticides in theis class, and potentially present in water, established acceptable limits can be derived from Admissible Daily Intake (ADIs). FAO and WHO experts have established that a pesticide's intake via drinking water cannot exceed 1% of ADI. For substances considered to be carcinogenic, the acceptable limits are even smaller than those calculated by a multifactorial model that estimates a risk of 1 case to 100,000 persons [12].

The accidental concentrations of toxic substances, exceeding ADI could be tolerated, but careful surveillance is required. As the range of concentrations for such substances are large, and involve regional circumstances, the chemical monitoring of drinking water is a further requirement.

## 23.7 The Estimation of Environmental Pollution Impact on Human Health

### 23.7.1 Risk Assessment

The risk for human health could be defined as the probability that one or more exposures of chemical substances may lead to injuries, diseases, or death for that exposed person (see also chapter by Kulkarni and Nangle).

Health risk assessment involves the analysis of previous exposures and related adverse effects that either occurred or might appear in the future, together with the prediction of the most likely consequences of subsequent exposures.

Risk may be expressed in quantitative terms, or can be described qualitatively, as 'high', 'low', or 'trivial' [13].

Risks associated with the exposure of chemical substances cannot be evaluated and quantified easily. Although many data for different chemicals are available (*ie*, annual risk of death from deliberate or accidental exposures by overdoses of drugs, pesticides and industrial chemicals) these data are usually limited to acute poisoning.

A risk assessment for chemical exposure that does not cause immediately or observable effects is more complex. Additionally, the term risk, in such analysis, use simple concepts such as toxic, non-toxic, safe, dangerous, exposure, dose, etc.

Scientists are unable to establish conditions under which the exposure to a chemical substance is of zero risk, but only describe the conditions where the risks are so low to be considered to have no practical consequence to a specific population.

In technical terms, the safety of a chemical substance is defined as when the exposure leads to absence of effects.

People are exposed to chemical compounds in the air, water or food in the environment. But there is a further exposure route, *viz*, direct dermal contact with the substance or with a contaminated soil. The amount of substance present in the environment can be called the concentration of exposure. The amount of substance that may reach the target in the human body is the dose which may be different to the exposure concentration.

Every environmental compartment must be analyzed separately. But a human could be exposed by one substance through many routes simultaneously (*ie*, inhalation, ingestion, and dermal contact). In this case, the total individual dose is the sum of the doses received by each route.

Health risk assessment has 4 major components: hazard identification; dose-response assessment; exposure assessment; and, risk characterization.

#### 23.7.1.1 Hazard Identification

Environmental contamination by any chemical substance, including pesticides, involves gathering and evaluation of 2 types of data, concerning:

i) Injuries to health and/or diseases; and,

ii) Exposure conditions.

It may also include the characterization of a substance's behavior within the body, target organs and the interactions at the cellular level [14].

Hazard identification is the first step in a risk assessment process that establishes if the toxic effects observed in particular circumstances could be extrapolated to the general population. The main sources of toxicological information are experiments on animals and epidemiological studies (see also Annex 23.).

Some toxic substances act on the liver, an organ with high regeneration capacity, whilst others act on nerve cells. The reaction of the organism can be situated everywhere between these 2 extremes, taking into account that man is exposed to mixtures of chemical substances acting in many ways: *viz*, independent, synergetic, antagonistic, cumulative, or potentiative.

For drinking water, the levels of toxic substances usually found, are too low to produce local effects, at target organ level. In this case the systemic effects could be considered as the key in elucidating the role of drinking water.

The negative results of epidemiological studies correlate to the presence of certain contaminants in drinking water — this should be interpreted with prudence, especially so for carcinogenic substances.

#### 23.7.1.2 Dose Response Assessment

Dose-response assessment describes the relationship between the magnitude of the exposure of any chemical substance and its toxic effect or related disease.

For non-carcinogenic substances, the dose-response assessment means the identification of experimental no adverse observed effect levels (NOAELs). These are used to calculate Reference Doses (RfDs) or Acceptable Daily Intakes (ADI) levels. ADIs are obtained by dividing NOAELs by one of the safety factors (10, 100, 1000, and 10000) depending on specific conditions. There are no means to demonstrate that exposures at estimated RfDs are completely risk-free. Such Reference Doses represent an extremely low risk, which is considered to be acceptable, but they do not guarantee safety. For carcinogenic substances, models such as 'One-hit', Multistage, Multi-hit, Weibull, or Probit', are used often to extrapolate the dose-response curves from the domain of the observable effects to those of the predicted effects. These estimations are adjusted by the results of the studies on animals and by results of epidemiological studies (see also chapter by Wilbourn and Vainio).

#### 23.7.1.3 Exposure Assessment

Exposure assessment estimates the number of exposed persons together with the magnitude, duration and frequency of exposure. A direct possibility to measure the human exposure to toxic substances via ambient air, for example, is the utilization of personal monitors.

There is additional information available concerning the fate and transport between environmental media, in the majority of the cases, *ie*:

i) Information concerning production;

ii) Amounts which enter the environment their location and frequency;

iii) Data relating to a substance's behavior in the environment, including migration, persistence, and degradation;

iv) Enumeration of the principal exposure routes for human beings and the most susceptible population groups; and,

v) Data pertaining to human intake.

The establishment of transport routes, and the levels of the breakdown products, is difficult to accomplish for the complexity of a natural environment. Mathematical models are used many times for these estimates using as a basis the physical and chemical properties of the substance involved. These models are further adjusted with data obtained from the experimental studies under simplified and checked conditions.

Compared with toxicology and epidemiology, exposure assessment science is still in the incipient stage.

#### 23.7.1.4 Risk Characterization

Risk characterization is the final step of the risk assessment process. It is the combination of the information from the previous stages, to estimate the incidence of an adverse effect in any population group.

For non-carcinogenic substances, the risk is characterized generally by the margin of exposure (MOE calculated by dividing the experimental NOAEL by the estimated dose of exposure. MOE is used as a substitute of risk, considering that the extension of an MOE means a smaller risk.

For carcinogenic substances, the risk is estimated by multiplying the dose with the risk per unit calculated from dose-response curves. To establish the range of risk occurrence, different models are used correlating the data from the dose-response curves and the susceptibility of sensitive sub-populations.

Adding to these premises the life style, smoking and alcoholic drink consumption, the risk assessment can become a very complex process that cannot be standardized.

### 23.7.2 Risk Management

Risk management utilizes the results of the risk assessment process and combines them with political, economic, and social information to elaborate by complex analysis, the decision for environmental actions.

Risk management is a tool for setting priorities, determining target levels and standards, and deciding 'how clean is clean?', or 'how safe is safe?', and balancing risk, cost, and benefit [15-17].

### 23.7.3 Risk Communication

Each step in the risk assessment and risk management process requires an explanation relating to initial inputs, the analytical procedure, the assumptions and the uncertainties, in addition to a conclusion based undoubtedly on facts and judgement. In this sense the process itself is a form of communication. The subject is complex, as explaining health hazards to the public is a difficult task. The final target is to create a public level of information and a knowledge of health hazards.

## 23.8 Danube River as a Source for Drinking Water, Evaluation of Human Exposure by Pesticides — A Case Study

The scope of this entire study, for which contamination by pesticides is only a small part, is to promote the population health in the Danube Romanian riverside area by protecting drinking and irrigation water sources against pollution [18]. The urban Romanian population using the Danube river as a source for drinking water increased from 929,000 (1981-1984) to 1,300,000 (1986-1990) as is shown in Table 23.1).

**Table 23.1** Type of source used for drinking water purposes

| Locality | Danube river (only) | Mixed source (ground water and Danube river) | Population x 1000 (1986-1990) |
|---|---|---|---|
| Turnu Severin | X | | 98 |
| Calafat | | X | 18 |
| Turnu Magurele | | X | 52 |
| Zimnicea | | X | 17 |
| Oltenita | X | | 29 |
| Calarasi | X | | 68 |
| Slobozia | | X | 45 |
| Cernavoda | X | | 18 |
| Constanta-Palas | | X | 324 |
| Braila | | X | 235 |
| Galati | | X | 293 |
| Tulcea | X | | 85 |
| Macin | X | | 12 |
| Sulina | X | | 6 |
| Total | | | 1300 |

**Table 23.2** **The basis for the hazards of pesticides used in Romania**

| | |
|---|---|
| Total population | 22,749,000 |
| — Urban | 53.2% |
| — Rural | 46.8% |
| Agricultural land | 62% |
| Total pesticide use in 1989 | 45,000 tonnes $a^{-1}$ |
| — Organochlorinated pesticides | 1,200 tonnes $a^{-1}$ |
| Agrochemical use in 1989 | 1,159,000 tonnes $a^{-1}$ |

Regulations:
- — Ban for DDT and technical use of HCH (in force from 1985)
- — National standard — Drinking Water Quality Criteria — (in force from 1991)

MAC: *0.1 µg $l^{-1}$ for individual pesticide
*0.5 µg $l^{-1}$ for total pesticides

*Source of data: Annual Statistical Book of Romania, 1990

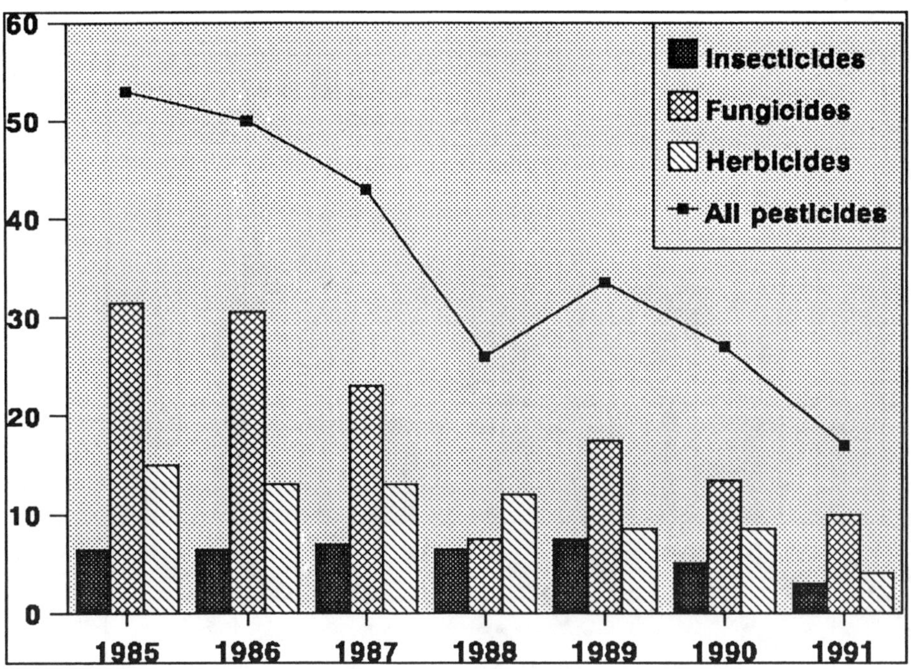


**Figure 23.3** **Pesticide Applications in Romania (1985-1991)**

Source of data: Ministry of Agriculture

Pesticide application in Romania decreased to about 25% compared to that of the European Community (Figure 23.3). However, bad transport, bad management, and the use of existing stocks, have generated continuous application of organochlorine pesticides. This consequence is their presence in the environment and in humans.

A previous study for the evaluation of the organochlorine pesticides' burden in the human body, of a non-occupational-exposed population (WHO Project 'European Cooperation on Environmental Health Aspects of the Control of Chemicals') indicated that human milk levels in the range of 11-12 mg $kg^{-1}$ HCH and 2.8 mg $kg^{-1}$ DDT, were about 5 times higher than in other European countries. The adipose tissue and fat sampled from humans, indicated a mean content in DDT plus DDE in the range of 8-17 mg $kg^{-1}$, the DDE percentages demonstrated over a long period involving the metabolization of DDT and a constant intake of DDE in food.

These data were the basis for a survey study on pesticide contamination of water sources. The study concerning the Danube river water is based on the biannual (spring, autumn) analysis of raw and treated water samples within the location of the water treatment plants along the river.

The present state of the Danube water quality, characterized by classical quality parameters, is generally acceptable but with a slow degradation trend. The levels of organochlorinated insecticides in drinking water of the main riverside localities are shown in Figures 23.4 and 23.5 (gas chromatography with electron capture detection was used as the analytical technique).

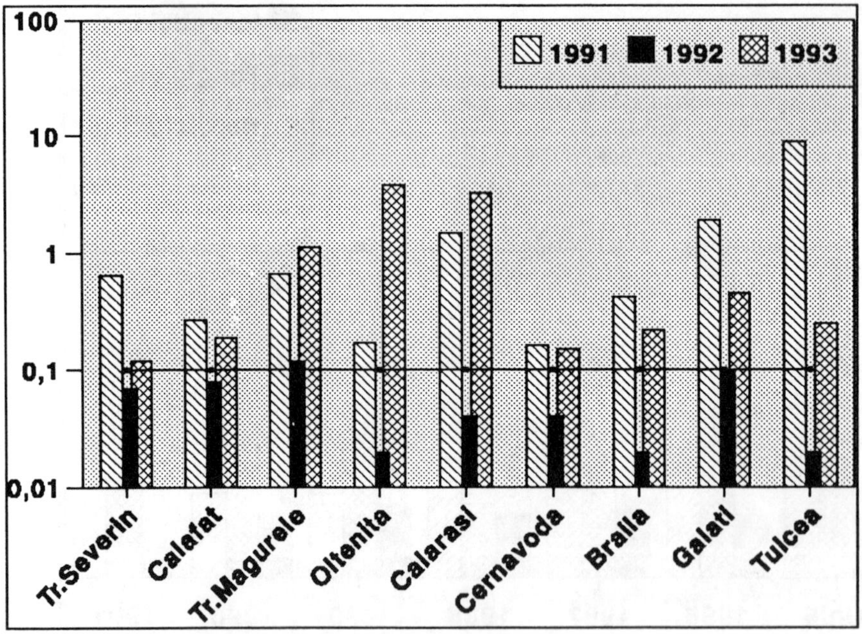


**Figure 23.4** Levels of γ-HCH in drinking water (μg $l^{-1}$)

**Table 23.3** Median value for HCH isomers

| Median value (μg $l^{-1}$) | 1991 | 1992 | 1993 |
|---|---|---|---|
| γ-HCH | 0.65 | 0.04 | 0.45 |
| α-HCH | 0.21 | 0.06 | 0.32 |
| β-HCH | 5.01 | 0.16 | 0.03 |

There were neither significant differences between seasonal samples, nor concomitant samples of raw water and treated water. The results for γ-HCH are in the range of 0.02-8.80 μg $l^{-1}$.

The comparative (1991-1993) median values of γ-HCH shows a decreasing trend. α- and β-HCH have been used in mixtures with γ-HCH (as 'HCH' or 'fortified HCH') in agriculture and in wood protection. Taking into account the inter-conversions in hexachlorocyclohexane isomers and that the rate of degradation of the individual isomers is: $\delta > \gamma > \alpha > \beta$ [19], the results concerning the ratio between 3 isomers suggest the continuous use of technical grade HCH.

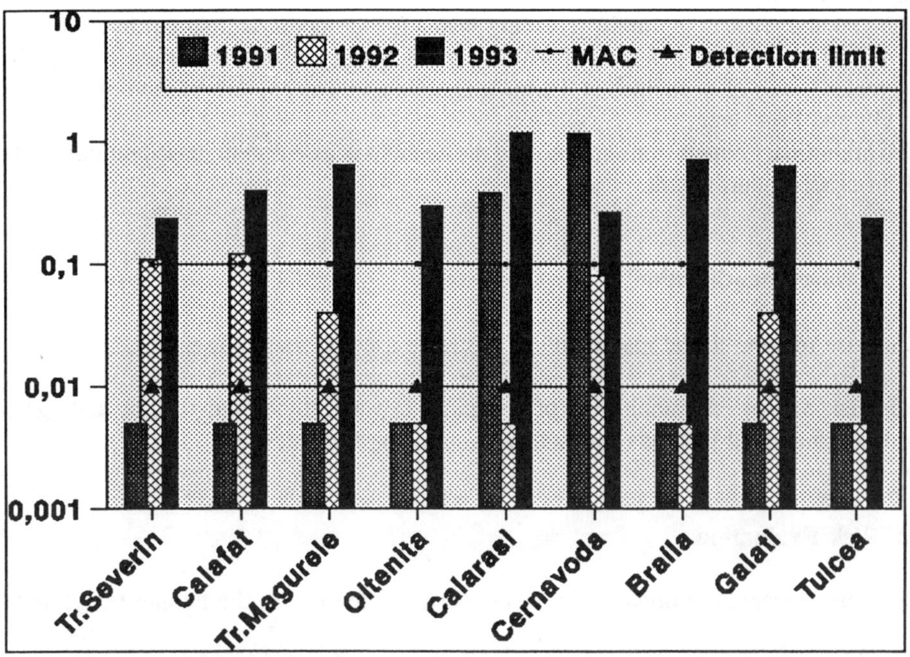


**Figure 23.5** Levels of DDT in drinking water (μg $l^{-1}$)

The concentration of DDT ranges from below the detection limit to 1.20 µg $l^{-1}$. The concentration of the main metabolite DDE, also ranges from below detection the limit to 3.17 µg $l^{-1}$.

**Table 23.4** **Median values DDT and DDE**

| Median value (µg $l^{-1}$) | 1991 | 1992 | 1993 |
|---|---|---|---|
| DDT | *) | 0.04 | 0.40 |
| DDE | 0.37 | 0.01 | 0.12 |

*)=below detection limit

The mean values for DDT shows a slow increasing trend, suggesting a probable use of the existing stocks. The mean values of the metabolite appears to indicate a reduced use of DDT during recent years, as a result of it being banned in 1985.

The sum for all organochlorinated pesticides identified in water (α, β, γ-HCH, heptachlor, aldrin, DDE, dieldrin and DDT) usually exceeds the maximum acceptable concentration (MAC).

The Danube river is the main receiving water for the entire Romanian hydrological basin, and its water quality is related with the water quality of its tributaries. The results show greater levels of pesticides at Turnu Magurele and Tulcea, due to the contribution of the Olt and Prut rivers.

The preliminary conclusions concerning the health risk assessment, based on this study is still in process, but include:

### 23.8.1 Hazard Identification

- Database relating to the magnitude of pesticide use and toxicology; and,
- Adequate survey and monitoring of pesticides in water, food, and soil, by setting up suitable analytical methods for measurement of pesticide levels.

### 23.8.2 Risk Evaluation

- Resuming research to obtain data on the pesticide burden on the human body; and,
- Reliable data on solubility and persistence of pesticides and breakdown products in water and soil.

### 23.8.3 Risk Assessment and Risk Characterization

- Correlation of the data obtained from above items.

### 23.8.4 Risk Management

- Prevention of drinking water pollution by pesticides; and,
- Improving the national strategy for the protection of water resources: legislative regulations, pesticide licences, regulatory measures in occupational areas, and control of pesticides in the environment.
- Public information and education.

## 23.9 Conclusions

The Danube river and its tributaries, running within Romanian and upstream countries, is a vital potable drinking water resource for the people of Romania.

The contamination of the Danube river, with pesticides in particular, is in excess of the criteria of 0.1 μg $l^{-1}$ for individual pestiçides — the EC drinking water directive standard — in a number of areas. This is a matter of great concern for the population's long-term health.

Greater action, within Romania and upstream countries, for stricter control of banned and severely restricted pesticides is a necessity, together with improvements in both monitoring techniques and frequency. Only by adopting these principles can safe and wholesome water supplies for future generations be provided.

## 23.10 References

[1] Moses, M., 'Pesticides', in: *Public Health & Preventive Medicine*, Last, J. M. and Wallace, R.B. (Eds.), 13th edition., Appleton & Lange, 1992, pp. 479-491.
[2] Edwards, C.A., 'Control of pesticide application and residues in food — A guide and directory', in: *Agrochemicals as environmental pollutants*, van Hofsten, B. and Ekstrom, G., (Eds.), Swedish Science Press, Uppsala, 1986, pp. 1-19.
[3] Taber, E.C., *Trans. N.Y. Acad. Sci.*, 1966, **28**, 569-578.
[4] Pavoni, B., Sfriso, A., and Marcomoini, A., *Marine Chem.*, 1987, **21**, 25-35.
[5] Guenzi, W.D. and Beard, W.E., *Proc. Soil Sci. Soc. Am., 1968, **32**, 522-534.*
[6] Gäb, S., Ntiz, S., Parlar, H., and Korte, F., *Chemosphere*, 1975, **4**, 251-256.
[7] Gäb, S., Schmitzer, J., Thamm, H.W., Parlar, H., and Korte, F., *Nature (London), 1977, **270**, 331-333.*
[8] Göthe, R., Wachtmeister, C.A., Akermark, B., Baeckstrom, P., Jansson, B., and Jenson, S., *Tetrahedron Lett.*, 1976, 4051-4505.

[9] Verschueren, K., *Handbook of Environmental Data on Organic Chemicals*, Second edition., VNR, New York, 1983, pp. 433-517, 703-725.

[10] *Fate of Chemicals in the Environment, Compartmental and Multimedia Models for Prediction*, Swann, R.L., and Eschenroeder, A. (Eds.), ACS Symposium Series, 1982.

[11] Mackey, D. and Peterson, S., *Environ. Sci. Technol.*, 1981, **15**, 1006-1014.

[12] *Guidelines for Drinking Water Quality*, WHO, 1984, **1**, 58-77.

[13] *The Risk Assessment Guidelines*, EPA/600/8-87/045, 1986, pp. 1-11 1-10, 3-1 3-15.

[14] Paustenbach, D.J., *The Risk Assessment of Environmental and Human Health Hazard: A Textbook of Case Studies*, 1990, 27-41, 71-90.

[15] *Risk Assessment and Risk Management: Framework for Decision Making*, EPA 600/9-85-00, 1984, 3-18.

[16] 'Risk Assessment of Chemicals in the Environment, Richardson, M.L. (Ed.), The Royal Society of Chemistry, London, 1988, pp. 580.

[17] *Risk Management of Chemicals*, Richardson, M.L. (Ed.), The Royal Society of Chemistry, Cambridge, 1992, pp. 392.

[18] Ursu, L., Berendei, A., Vasiliu, G., Vasilescu, M., and Iacob, I., *Danube River Water Quality and the Influence upon Drinking Water in Riverane Localities*, I.H.P.H., booklet, 1990.

[19] Deo, P.G., Hasan, S. B., and Majumder, S. K., *J. Environ. Sci. Health*, 1981, **16,** (6), 691-701.

# 24. Chlororganic Pesticides and Atrazine in the Environment of Lithuania: Retrospective Analysis and Management Evaluation

Julius Ptashekas, Margarita Barkiene, Genadijus Jonauskas, and Skirmante Zhlabyte

## 24.1 Introduction

Since 11 March 1990, the Republic of Lithuania has become one of the 3 Baltic independent states. Situated along the coast of the Baltic Sea, Lithuania is close to the Scandinavian countries and several central European states (Poland, Germany, Russia, and Belarus).

Modern Lithuania has highly developed energy production facilities, together with chemical, electronics, and other types of industries. However, agriculture is its most intense human activity affecting the environment. In fact Lithuania used to import approximately 10,000 tonnes of pesticides annually involving >60 trade names (Figure 24.1). Average burden to cultivated land used to be 4.0-4.5 kg chemical $ha^{-1}$.

The current state of the environment in Lithuania is characterized by atmospheric pollution, water contamination, acidification of soil, water, and forests; nitrogen leaching as a result of the use of nitrogen containing preparations in agriculture; and, destruction of agricultural soil used for food production (largely due to toxic chemicals and erosion). Approximately 12% of the country's flowing water is heavily polluted. The ammonium and nitrate concentration in flowing water exceeds the maximum allowable limits by a factor of 1.5 to 10. Chromium, zinc, copper, and nickel are the heaviest pollutants in flowing water in Lithuania, and nitrogen-containing compounds continue to have a significant impact on agricultural activity. However, at the same time it is important to stress that since 1961 large quantities of persistent chlororganic compounds and atrazine have been imported and distributed for use in agriculture within the country. This has led to pollution of deep ground waters by 2,4-D type chemicals, HCH and certain other chlorinated organic compounds.

In the period 1985-1988, 2% of all food samples contained residues of different pesticides. However, in the southern area of the former USSR this figure reached 10-15%.

Excess of these preparations in the environment may eventually cause severe impact on health of the human population due to neurotoxic, teratogenic, mutagenic, carcinogenic, and other undesirable properties of chlororganic compounds. It was common practice to set standards and limits for imported banned chemicals (DDT, mercury containing pesticides) particularly in food.

In general, the increasing environmental distress in Lithuania has led to an alarming situation in public health. In many of the larger Lithuanian towns and cities severe environmentally related toxic effects have been observed, such as increased cancer incidence in central Lithuania in the area of Mazheikiai oil refinery, and acute and chronic leukemia in children. (The latter pathology may also be related to the effects of the

Chernobyl nuclear catastrophe.) It is still unknown to what extent the burden of persistent chlororganic pesticides and atrazine could have influenced increase of environmentally-related pathology among the Lithuanian population.

Information on the use of chlororganic preparations had not been analyzed previously, and is still being achieved in many organizations and agencies.

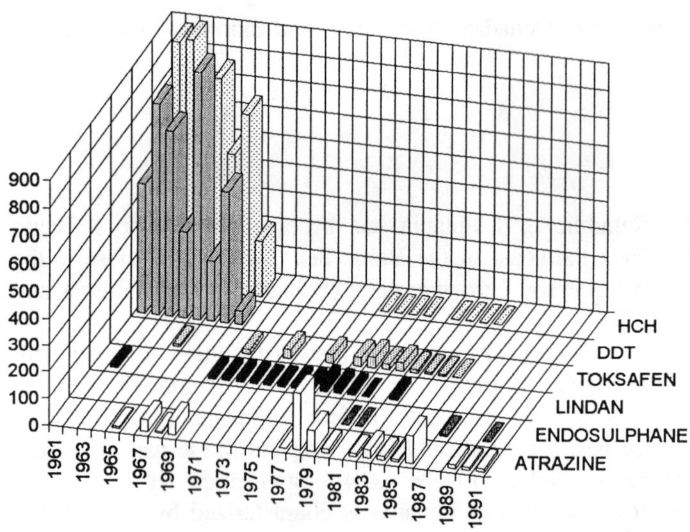


**Figure 24.1** Lithuanian purchases of chlororganic pesticides (in tonnes)

## 24.2 Purpose of the Study

The main aim of this study was to provide an illustration of the use of chlororganic pesticides and atrazine in Lithuania within the period of the last 30 years, with respect to their impact on health and the environment on a country-wide scale.

## 24.3 Objectives

i) To evaluate the burden of chlororganic pesticides and atrazine that had been emitted to the Lithuanian environment since 1961;

ii) To evaluate information on chlororganic compounds and atrazine residues in water, food and soil with respect to possible health impacts; and,

iii) To demonstrate a background for urgent implementation of correcting measures and to propose principles of pesticide management in order to improve the collection of information on persistent chemicals, elaboration of monitoring programmes, and dissemination of the results.

## 24.4 Material and Methods

All data and supplementary information on the use of pesticides investigated and their residues within the period 1961-1991 was provided by a number of institutions in Lithuania:

- Agrochemical Service (Ministry of Agriculture);
- Hydrometeorlogical Service (Department of Environment Protection);
- Plant Protection Service (Ministry of Agriculture);
- Water Supply Service (Ministry of Urban and Commune Affairs); and,
- Hygiene Service (Ministry of Health).

Statistical and graphical data processing was performed in respect to:

- Pesticide residues in surface water;
- Pesticide residues in fish products;
- Pesticide residues in meat products;
- Pesticide residues in milk and egg products;
- Pesticide residues in soil; and,
- Pesticide usage, rates, and costs.

Water sampling was performed for all major rivers and lakes in Lithuania.

Pesticide residues were analyzed in principal types of foodstuffs: milk, meat, vegetables and fruits (Figures 24.2-24.4).

Soil was sampled at 33 control points of the total agricultural area of Lithuania.

In the present study, maximum allowable concentrations for residues of unique chemicals are provided for comparison purposes.

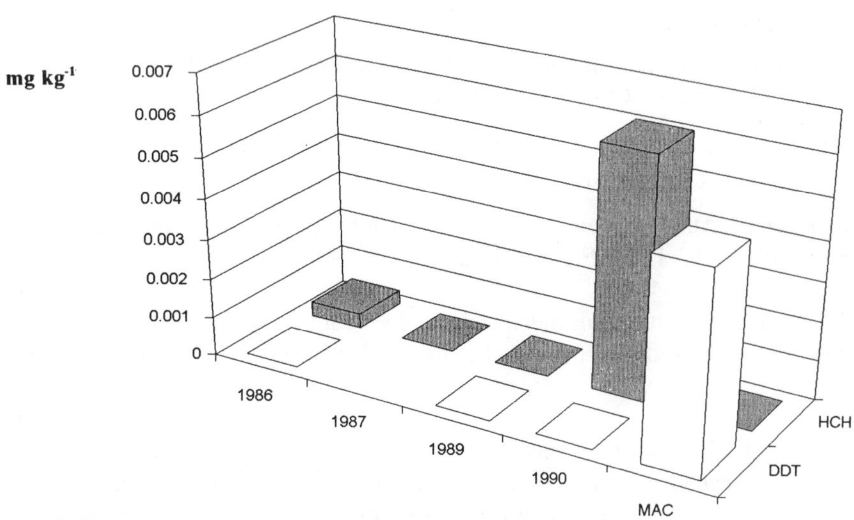


**Figure 24.2** **Pesticides residues in meat products (mg kg$^{-1}$) in 1986-1990**

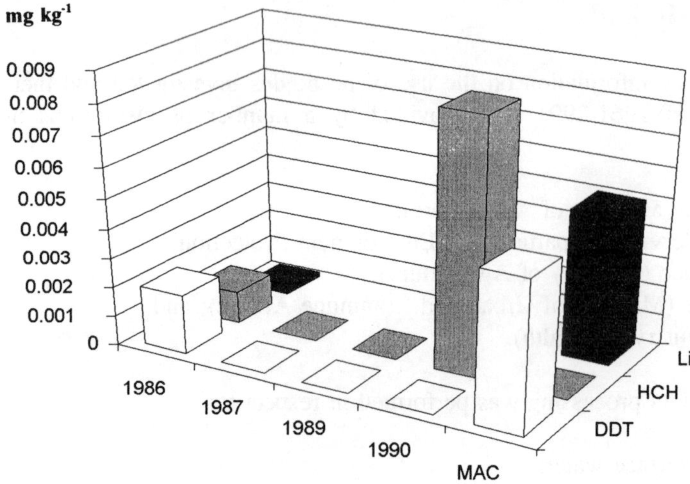


**Figure 24.3** **Pesticides residues in milk products (mg kg$^{-1}$) in 1986-1990**

## 24.5 Results

Import data for the more commonly used chlororganic pesticides and atrazine in Lithuania (1961-1985) are:

i) 3839.4 tonnes of DDT and its metabolites were imported into Lithuania during the period 1961-1958 (Figure 24.4). It was banned for use in 1970. However, in 3 experimental farms DDT had been continued for use against pests in the period 1972-1973;

ii) 5209.475 tonnes of HCH were imported into Lithuania in the periods 1961-1968 and 1977-1985 (Figure 24.5). It was banned in 1982;

iii) 2360 tonnes of Lindane were imported into Lithuania in the years 1962, 1970, 1973, 1976, 1978-1985 (Figure 24.6). It was banned in 1992;

iv) 254.92 tonnes of Toxafen (Figure 24.7) were imported in Lithuania in the years 1965, 1970, 1973, 1976, 1978-1985. It was banned in 1982; and

v) 575,209 tonnes of Atrazine were imported into Lithuania in the years 1965, 1967-1969, 1977-1980, 1982-1986 (Figure 24.8).

Preparations were still in use during the last few years. However, due to climatic conditions these pesticides did not appear to be suitable for Lithuania. Simazine was used latterly.

Data on pesticides residues in water for the period 1986-1990 indicated a trend of enhanced residues of DDT, but relatively lower concentrations of DDE (Figure 24.9). It is evident that these scattered and incomplete data for surface water contamination by chlororganic compounds are not sufficient to provide conclusions on the precise status of surface water in Lithuania.

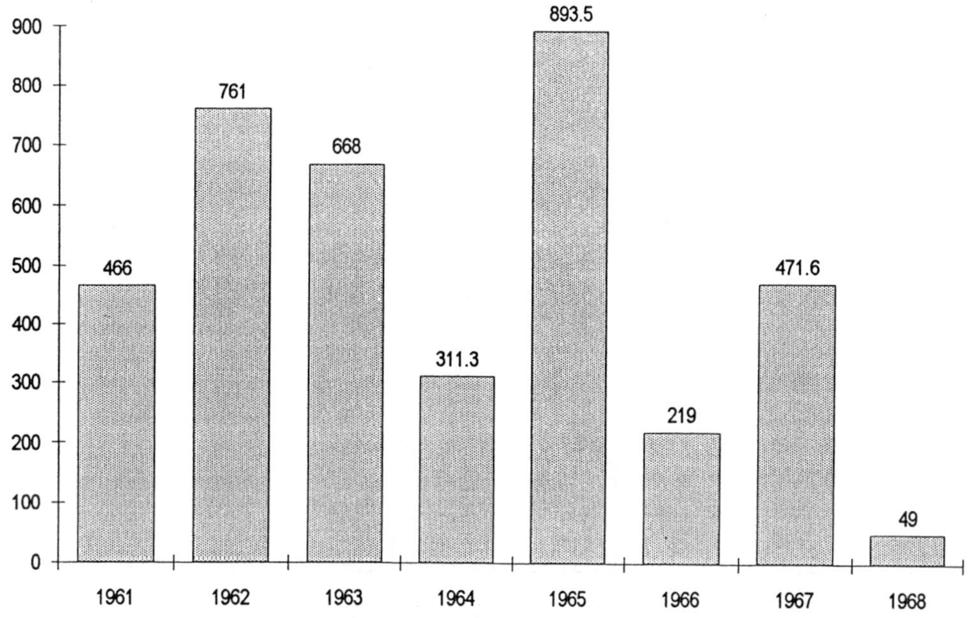


**Figure 24.4** **Total quantity of DDT (in tonnes) used in total agricultural area of Lithuania (1961-1968)**

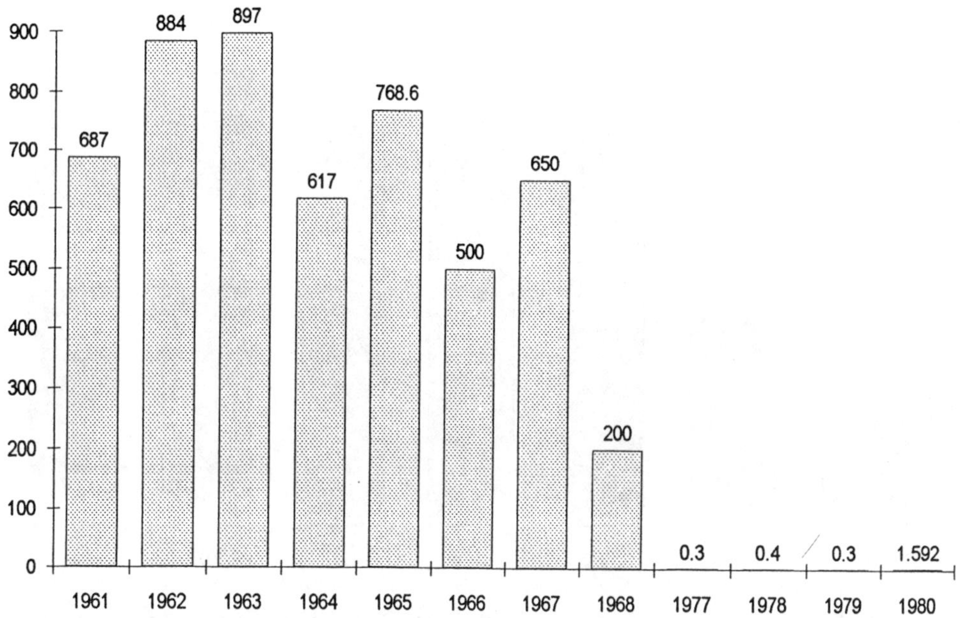


**Figure 24.5** **Total amount of HCH (in tonnes) used in total agricultural area of Lithuania (1961-1980)**

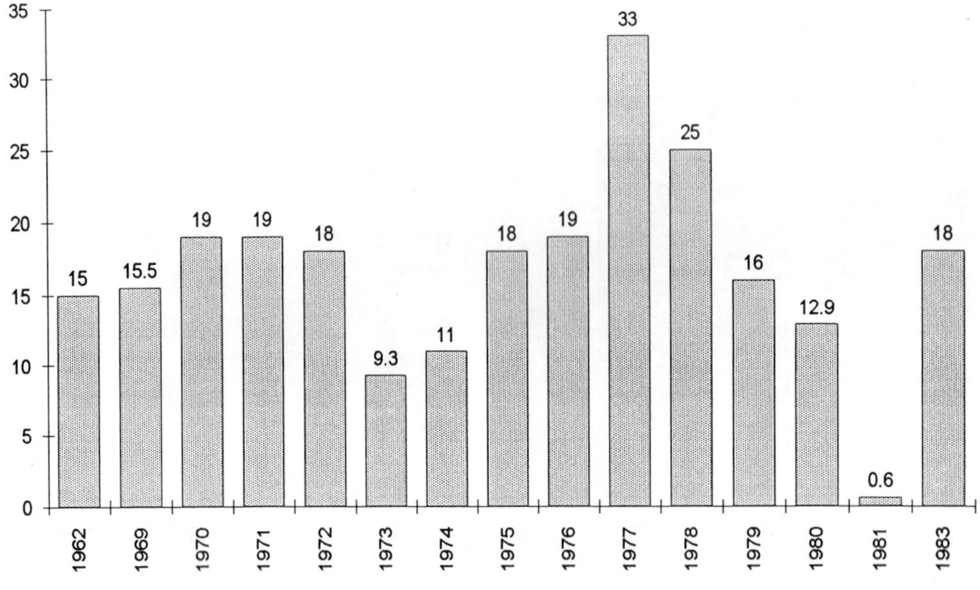


**Figure 24.6** **Total amount of Lindane (in tonnes) used in total agricultural area of Lithuania (1962-1983)**

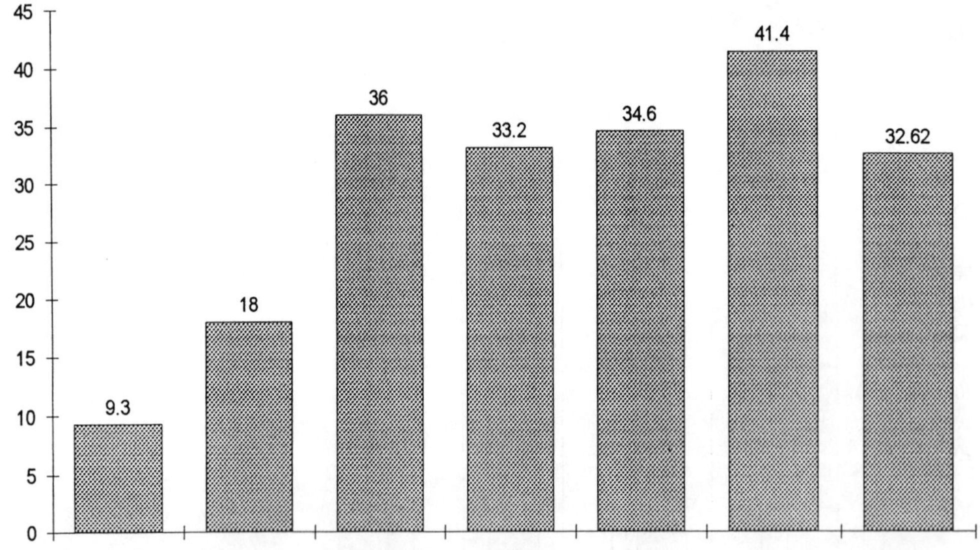


**Figure 24.7** **Total amount of Toxafen (in tonnes) used in total agricultural area of Lithuania (1962-1983)**

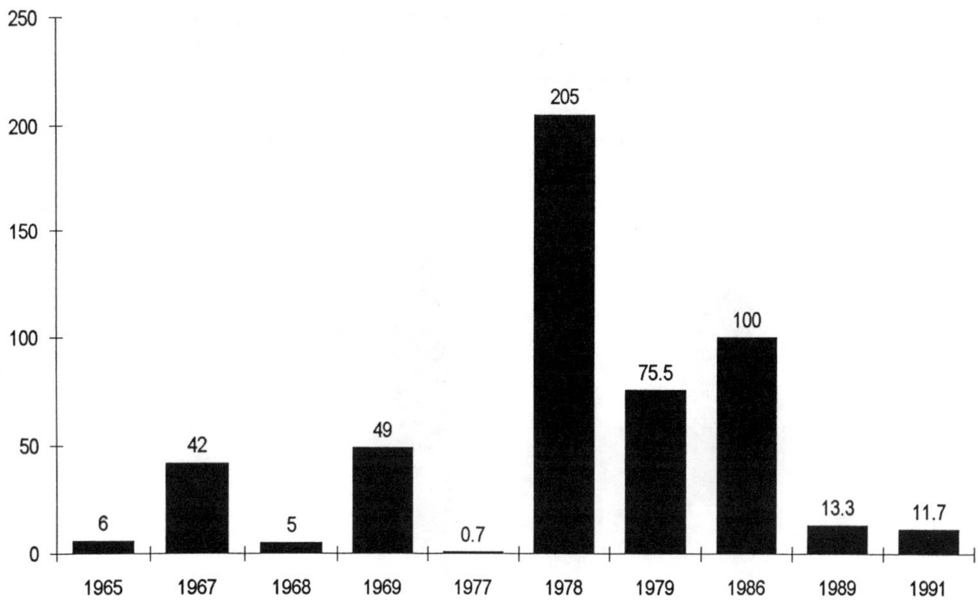


**Figure 24.8** Total amount of Atrazine (in tonnes) used in total agricultural area in Lithuania (1965-1991)

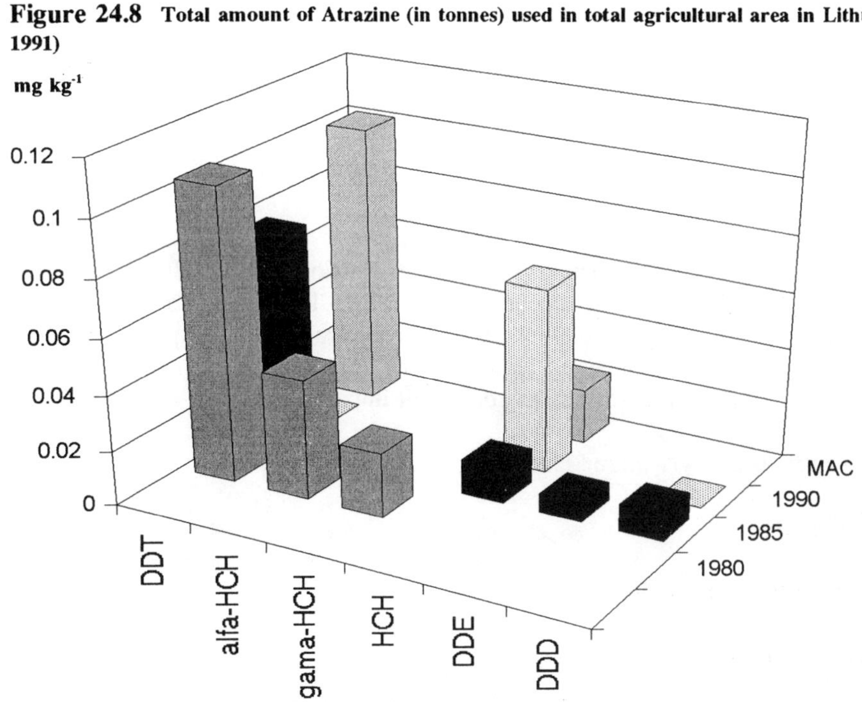


**Figure 24.9** Pesticides residues in water (μg $l^{-1}$) 1986-1990

Information of foodstuffs showed that in the period 1986-1990, there was a trend of increased levels of HCH, Lindane and DDT in fish products for 1986. However, absolute values did not exceed maximum allowable concentrations (MAC) (Figure 24.10); for meat products trends show an increase of HCH, in 1990 (Figure 24.2). The same trend was observed for residues of HCH in milk in 1990 (Figure 24.3).

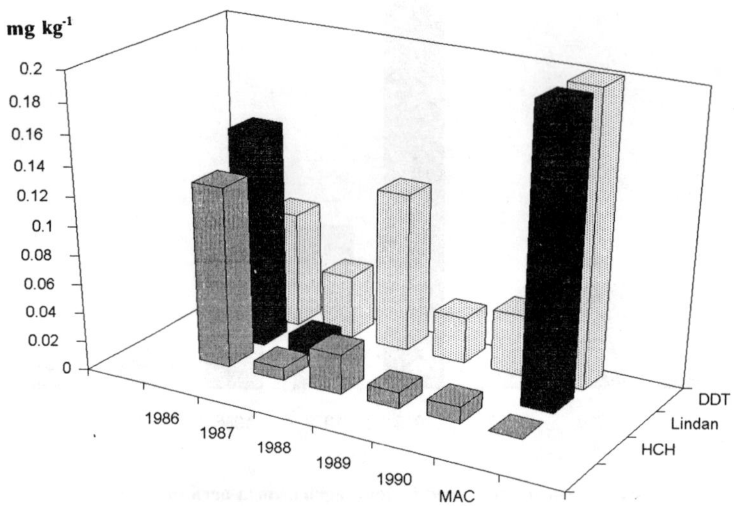


**Figure 24.10** **Pesticide residues in fish production (mg kg$^{-1}$) in 1986-1990**

## 24.6 Discussion

A National Project on the use of chemicals for plant protection, for virtually all pesticides usage was approved by the Government of the USSR. The targets of the National Programme were to produce >700,000 tonnes a$^{-1}$ of chemicals. It was expected to obtain 1500-2000% profit from each invested US$ in agricultural business. However, the only substantial result obtained was severe environmental impacts, *eg*:

i) Low quality of the agricultural chemicals;

ii) High toxicity;

iii) High stability in the environment;

iv) Primitive application technology;

v) Undeveloped control systems of transportation, storage, application, and use of chemicals;

vi) Absence of environmental protection regulations; and,

vii) Absence of legal basis to protect health from impact of environmental chemicals.

The foregoing data shows a relationship from limited and scattered data on residues of chemicals in the environment, including both absence of evaluations on population health and exposure levels to persistent chlororganic compounds.

Registration of agricultural chemicals had been only a matter of book-keeping. Safety testing instructions are available to National Toxicology Units to test every incoming chemical. Safety testing data provided by the importer from abroad were not to be trusted, and had to be rechecked. This practice caused enormous duplication of effort. In practical terms ≤1% of all agricultural preparations underwent safety testing procedures in the former USSR. At the same time, laboratory staff faced severe shortages of adequate analytical equipment and GLP procedures. Therefore, many of the available data have to be carefully considered during the process of evaluation.

In a very formal manner the Government attempted to establish a Commission on the Use of Pesticides under the Ministry of Agriculture of Lithuania, unfortunately according to the scheme that had been functioning in all other Soviet Republics of the former USSR. Some of the experts from the Ministry of Health were invited. This Commission could not work effectively because there was too little participation from its members: they were not paid and there was too much work for the experts in addition to their principal occupation. Conversely, absolute shortage of reliable data on the environmental health impact and related information made it impossible to ensure a rational decision making process.

Existing management is still based on the former USSR model where several ministries and agencies took responsibilities for the control of the use of pesticides: *eg*, Ministry of Agriculture, Ministry of Health, Plant Protection Station, Department on Environment Protection. However, no intersectoral management body has been established.

Another barrier to the effective management of chemicals originated from the policy of secrecy for environmental epidemiology studies. Effects of pesticides on human health was always based on sophisticated studies undertaken in experimental conditions. Population effect investigations or so called 'case-studies' used to be priorities for 'top-secret' or 'for official use only' labelled projects. The general public and even professionals could not obtain access to the results of these findings. This situation should not have been employed for the management of chemicals in any region of the former USSR, including Lithuania.

It became evident that:

i) Exposure tests showed pesticide concentrations in occupational atmospheric air exceeded maximum allowable limits by 12-20 times;

ii) Acute occupational poisoning was extremely rare among pesticide exposed individuals;

iii) 90% of all poisoning cases occurred in home conditions due to a lack of knowledge of how to store, use, and transport of agricultural chemicals during farming;

iv) The last decade saw an end to the use of chlororganic and mercury containing preparations. Notwithstanding, in 1991, there were nearly 700 tonnes of persistent chlororganic compounds illegally stored in Lithuanian agricultural enterprises;

v) Standard setting principles are conflicting with existing experiences on the impact on population health, *eg*, the operational sodium trichloroacetate limit for agricultural use is still 35 kg $ha^{-1}$ for treated areas; and,

vi) Toxicological studies on safety testing during the last 30 years by national institutions had enabled safety limits to be prescribed for <1% of all chemicals in use. Unfortunately, this activity has never been correlated with the existing information on chemicals in international databases (for instance UNEP/IRPTC Data Bank, and Annex 24.). This practice led to an enormous waste of human and material resources.

Further improvement in the environment and health management in Lithuania pesticide management which could be a model has resulted in the following:

i) Elaboration of adequate legislation. 'Umbrella' laws and subsequent By-Law Acts are to be prepared and approved as soon as possible;

ii) Setting correct priorities of action. Information on chemical collection and management, environmental health impact assessment procedures, participation in human exposure studies (*eg*, WHO Collaborative Studies on DDT and dioxins in human milk, UNEP/GEMS/HEAL project, etc.);

iii) Providing adequate training for the Government and professional officers at national level aimed at implementation of rational principles of pesticides management based on the relevant use and provision of information on chemicals.

iv) Establishing a national EIA Monitoring Programme based on relevant chemical analysis technologies supported by Good Laboratory Practice and basic and specialized training;

v) Establishing and budgeting for an Intersectoral Pesticide Management Body in order to ensure effective participation of a number of the relevant agencies and ministries;

vi) Soonest possible implementation of Prior Informed Consent (PIC) Procedures according to the Amended London Guidelines (1989) in exchange for information on chemicals in international trade; and,

vii) Development of publicity and community participation.

## 24.7 Conclusions

Only by means of effective environmental impact studies leading to pragmatic risk assessments and management can safety in the use of chemicals, in particular pesticides, be assured.

## 24.8 References

[1] Report of the Centre of Environmental Medicine, Vilnius, 1993, pp. 2-28.
[2] Epidemiological and Hygiene Status in Lithuania, Vilnius, 1993, pp. 34-67.
[3] National Report of Lithuania to UNCED in Rio, 1992, pp. 12-32.
[4] State of the Environment, Tendencies, Changes, Management of Environment Protection, Report of the Environment Protection Department, Vilnius, 1992, pp. 11-18.
[5] Ptashekas, J., Chemical Management (State of the Art) in the Republic of Lithuania, National Report for the UNEP/IRPTC Sub-Regional Workshop for Users of IRPTC Data Base, Vilnius, 1993, pp. 1-5.

# 25. Management: Halide Mineral Water Discharges

Aga Mamedovich Khojamamedov and Khoja Nepesovich Evzhanov

## 25.1 Introduction

At present in Turkmenistan, underground waters of high mineral content are used as raw materials for the production of iodine and bromine. These waters consist of brines of sodium, magnesium, and calcium chloride in admixtures with a number of rare and valuable elements, *eg*, strontium, boron, etc. The salt content is ca. 200 g $l^{-1}$. The total concentration of iodine and bromine in these waters is $\ngtr$ 0.06% w/w. To extract 1 tonne of iodine it is necessary to process up to 100,000 $m^3$ of brine. After extraction the brines are discharged to the environment as waste and without extraction of the other components.

Hence, in addition to the colossal economic damage from the irrational use of mineral raw materials, irreparable ecological damage is incurred. Further social development in the region of the iodine-bromine industry is impossible without the introduction of the ecologically clean and low-waste technologies. As a result technological processes of complex effluents from the iodine-bromine industry has been developed. This process includes the extraction of all the macro- and micro-components using the natural advantages of the republic, *ie*, a dry and hot climate. The technology is based on the concentration of the brine by water evaporation in open reservoirs using solar energy. The object of the investigation is applied to the effluent from the Nebitdag iodine and the Cheleken chemical plants in Turkmenistan which receive iodine and bromine from the underground high mineral waters. During 1984-1988, experimental systems were investigated at the industrial reservoirs of the Nebitdag iodine plant.

## 25.2 The Characteristics of the Underground Iodine-Bromine Waters (and Their Processing Conditions)

The underground iodine-bromine waters of Turkmenistan are chloride brines, containing a salt mass of sodium chloride of 80-90% w/w. During the extraction of iodine and bromine the chemical compounds of the selected waters is not changed. The characteristics of the effluent are shown in Table 25.1.

The initial iodine-bromine waters transported to the iodine-bromine plants contain hydrogen carbonate ions which are destroyed, together with some organic compounds during sulfuric acid treatment. The process is to adjust the waters to pH 2.0-3.0. The bromine and iodine-ion are oxidized with chlorine and desorbed by air stripping. The dehalogenated effluent is then neutralized. The depleted iodine-bromine waters are drained to fields for evaporation (Cheleken chemical plant) or to a natural cavity (Nebitdag iodine plant).

**Table 25.1** **The chemical composition and some physical-chemical parameters of the effluent from the iodine-bromine plants of Turkmenistan**

| Parameters | Nebitdag iodine plant | | Cheleken chemical plant | |
|---|---|---|---|---|
| Chloride | 118.60 | kg $m^{-3}$ | 135.41 | kg $m^{-3}$ |
| Sulfate | 0.38 | kg $m^{-3}$ | 1.19 | kg $m^{-3}$ |
| Magnesium | 0.65 | kg $m^{-3}$ | 2.37 | kg $m^{-3}$ |
| Calcium | 9.90 | kg $m^{-3}$ | 15.81 | kg $m^{-3}$ |
| Strontium | 0.34 | kg $m^{-3}$ | 0.47 | kg $m^{-3}$ |
| Potassium | 0.55 | kg $m^{-3}$ | 0.40 | kg $m^{-3}$ |
| Sodium | 62.10 | kg $m^{-3}$ | 62.20 | kg $m^{-3}$ |
| Bromide | 85.0 | g $m^{-3}$ | 135.0 | g $m^{-3}$ |
| Iodide | 2.5 | g $m^{-3}$ | 3.0 | g $m^{-3}$ |
| Borate | 120.0 | g $m^{-3}$ | 170.0 | g $m^{-3}$ |
| Ammonium | 45.0 | g $m^{-3}$ | 57.0 | g $m^{-3}$ |
| Lithium | 3.5 | g $m^{-3}$ | 3.0 | g $m^{-3}$ |
| Rubidium | 0.2 | g $m^{-3}$ | 0.6 | g $m^{-3}$ |
| Zinc | 0.2 | g $m^{-3}$ | 0.1 | g $m^{-3}$ |
| Chromium | 0.4 | g $m^{-3}$ | 0.8 | g $m^{-3}$ |
| Iron | 1.4 | g $m^{-3}$ | 4.1 | g $m^{-3}$ |
| Mineralization | 193.8 | kg $m^{-3}$ | 218.3 | kg $m^{-3}$ |
| Density | 1130.6 | kg $m^{-3}$ | 1140.0 | kg $m^{-3}$ |
| pH | 1.60 | | 2.20 | |

## 25.3 Investigation of the Isothermal and Solar Evaporation Processes of the Effluent from the Iodine-Bromine Plant

Considering the significant quantity of the effluent and the concentration of microelements, there is a need to aim at their extraction, and it was of practical and theoretical interest to study the concentration of the effluent and raw brines under isothermal and natural conditions. The possibility of using the natural climatic conditions of the region near the iodine-bromine plants was taken into account, *ie*, the possible use of renewable power sources, viz, solar energy of 80-110 Kcal $m^{-2}$ $a^{-1}$ on the horizontal surface.

In global practice, there are no recorded practical and theoretical experiences of the use of isothermal and solar energy for the evaporation of chloride brines.

The evaporation processes of the brines were studied by means of a physical-chemical analysis of the solubilities in multi-component systems, in the 5 component system:

$CaCl_2$ — $MgCl_2$ — KCl — NaCl — $H_2O$, but restricting this to a 4 component system. Use was made of the isotherm of the 5 component system in the salt tetrahedron. The isothermal evaporation processes was depicted on the projection on the triangles of the salts of the restricted 4 component system. A projection was made for all the poles of the salt components.

This was used for the analysis of the solid phases and the diagrams for the solubility of the multi-component waters-salt system resulting from salt crystallization from the exhaust and raw iodine-bromine brines.

For the Nebitdag iodine plant (NdIP) brines, the salts are crystallized in the following sequence: gypsum ($CaSO_4.4H_2O$), halite (NaCl), carnallite ($KClMgCl_2.6H_2O$), takhhydrate ($CaCl_2MgCl_2.12H_2O$), and calcium chloride tetrahydrate ($CaCl_2.4H_2O$). During further concentration of the brines the co-crystallization of carnallite occurs followed by silvin (KCl), calcium chloride tetrahydrate and salt during the complete drying of the brines.

For the Cheleken chemical plant (CCP) brines, the crystallization occurs as follows: gypsum, halite, takhhydrate, and calcium chloride. Crystallization of carnallite was not observed due to the relatively low content of the calcium ion.

The brine evaporation investigation was conducted under different conditions for different brines:

i) Under laboratory conditions at constant temperature;

ii) Under natural conditions ('solar' concentration) of the raw brine; and,

iii) Acid exhaust brines, including those which had received preliminary neutralization at the expense of the carbonate and the sand and clay in the exhaust waters.

The experiments were conducted for:

i) The clarification of the solar radiation impact on the physical-chemical processes in solution;

ii) Identification of the impact of the brines when in contact with carbonates, sand and clay, including the construction materials (floors and sides) of the working reservoirs;

iii) The receipt of data to provide a material balance on the components of these brines, including water quality testing; and,

iv) Checking of the data at the larger scale and under natural conditions.

The above enabled comparison with laboratory studies where an infrared lamp was used as the source of heat.

The experiments provided information for the sequence of salt crystallization from different brines under different conditions. It was shown that for these brines the crystallization sequence is similar and the quantity of evaporated water prior to commencement of the sedimentation of the salt reaches the eutonic; differences could be explained by the hydrogen ion impact on the crystallizing salt solubility:

i) The possibility of removing an additional quantity of sodium chloride by the introduction of magnesium chloride into the evaporated brine;

ii) The pH of the brines changed during concentration. It was shown that the acidity of the evaporated brines depends upon the initial value of the pH, and exposure of the exhaust brine with carbonate components of the sand.

iii) The possibility of the removal of the iron admixtures from the brine by means of neutralized acid exhaust brines with sand in the form of iron hydroxide. Simultaneously, almost all of the organic substances are removed by means of the absorbtion on the surface of the iron hydroxide, thus enabling easier use of the sorbtive technology for reprocessing the evaporated brines; and,

iv) The process of changes in the micro-components in raw, exhaust and neutralized brines with sand, were established.

It was shown that the bromine ion is accumulated in the brines during sedimentation of the micro-components. Its maximal concentration is ≥1200 g $m^{-3}$. The bromine losses commence with the carnallite sedimentation during the mineralization of the brines at ca. 40% of the mass.

Iodine in the exhaust brines is in the form of the heterohalogenide complex ions $I_2Cl^-$ and $ICl^-_2$. It was found that during the water evaporation from the raw brine iodine ion is accumulated, but that the increase in its concentration is almost twice that of the brine volume reduction. Thus, when the brine volume is decreased 35 times the iodine ion concentration increases by only 17 times and reaches 600 g $m^{-3}$. This is explained by the iodine ion oxidation with atmospheric oxygen and the molecular ion transfer to the gas phase. During exhaust brine concentration under laboratory conditions in glass vessels and at constant temperature, the iodine accumulation takes place in the liquid phase, whereas during solar evaporation of the brines under natural conditions, and with contact with sand, the iodine is lost completely onto the solid the solid phase [1].

During the evaporation of the brines, the toxic element strontium is accumulated in the liquid phase, to a maximum of 6.24 kg $m^{-3}$ $Sr^{2+}$ at the beginning of the calcium-magnesium chloride sedimentation with the strontium decreasing in the brine. During the evaporation process of the exhaust brine at the Nebitdag iodine plant the strontium ion is distributed as follows:

i) 0.3% is co-crystallized in the form of $SrSO_4.2H_2O$ with gypsum; and,

ii) 16% of the total strontium is in the saturated halide salt of the initial brine, 29.9%. This eutonic brine is at a concentration of 53.8%, and in the solid phase is represented by a mixture of takhhydrate, calcium chloride, and salt [2,3].

During the evaporation of the acid effluent, apart from the neutralization, boron is concentrated without losses prior to the sedimentation of the mixed salts. The maximum concentration of boron reaches 6564 g $B_2O_3$ $m^{-3}$ during a 55-fold reduction of the brine volume. During evaporation of the raw brines the loss of boron is observed at the initial stage of the concentration, probably due to the association of part of the boron with volatile organic compounds.

During the concentration of the raw brines and acid effluent the organic compounds are accumulated in the liquid phase to 740 g $m^{-3}$. When evaporated the brine is neutralized with sand at pH 6.0, the removal of the organic admixtures together with the sedimentated iron hydroxide is achieved.

A mathematical model was established for the evaporation of high mineralized brines to permit management of the concentration processes in the effluents in the reservoir in relationship to the rate of the brine evaporation at the Nebitdag iodine plant. The elasticity of the water stream over the brines at different concentrations and at different temperatures (10, 15, 20, 25, and 30 °C) was identified. The data was processed using a computer by the method of the least squares and the deduction of an equation for the calculation of the elasticity of the vapor above the brines during different degrees of concentration in the temperature interval from 5 to 35 °C.

The rate of brine evaporation was determined under natural conditions depending on the chemical composition, the degree of the brine concentration and climatic conditions (wind velocity, humidity and air temperature), at the Nebitdag region, was typical for Western Turkmenia. Simultaneously, with defining the evaporation rate in the experimental industrial sites, seasonal changes of the brine temperature was investigated and the absolute air humidity was measured during 1980 to 1985. On the basis of these data an equation permitting the definition of the most probable brine temperature on any day of the year was deduced:

$$E = 0.198\ [1 + 0.73\ v\ (\tau)]\ \ [P\rho\ (\rho;\tau) - P\beta\ (\tau)]$$

where E = the evaporation rate, kg $m^{-3}$ $d^{-1}$;
$V(\tau)$ = wind velocity depending upon the time of year, m $s^{-1}$;
$P\beta(\tau)$ = absolute air humidity depending upon the time year, Pa;
$P\rho(\rho;\tau)$ = the brine stream elasticity depending upon the time of the year ($\tau$) and its density ($\rho$) or humidity, Pa.

The average monthly wind velocity at a height of 2 m was obtained by averaging the data for 20 years from the Nebitdag meteorological station (4.8 m $s^{-1}$). The adequacy in relationship to the real conditions in the deduced mathematical model was tested in the reservoirs with areas of 80, 100, and 2400 $m^2$. The divergency of the calculated and experimental data was 2 days. On the basis of the experimental data and equations, the programme and programme documentation of the evaporation process model for the brines under Western Turkmenistan conditions were elaborated. The optimum area of the reservoirs, the depth for brine, and the routine work prior to the commencement of sedimentation of the sodium chloride was defined.

## 25.4 Details for Low Waste Reprocessing of Effluent from the Iodine-bromine Plants

The relationship of the brine concentrations provided reasons to seek probable means for the relocation of the iodine-bromine plants located in the regions having an arid climate appropriate to the principles involved in the new technology, *ie*, the complex and low waste reprocessing of brines aimed at the rational utilization of natural resources and environmental protection.

### 25.4.1 Sodium Chloride Extraction

It was shown that the chloride brines which do not contain sulfate ion after preliminary processing in the reservoirs, where the mixtures of iron, gypsum, organic compounds, are removed, are suitable raw materials to produce sodium chloride for foodstuffs. The calculations showed that the potential possibility to receive sodium chloride from East Turkmenian brines exceeds the best deposits in the former Soviet Union and the resulting raw salt contains only small quantities of calcium and magnesium ions.

### 25.4.2 Borate Extraction

Borate extraction from high mineralized brines is a difficult technological problem. Traditional methods for the extraction are not appropriate because of the low borate concentration, and sorbtive methods were investigated. A number of local organic and semi-organic sorbents were tested which resulted in the selection of the organic anionite SB-1 which was found to have selective sorbtion for borate ions. To define the optimal conditions for the borate extraction processes, the dependency of the borate extraction rate on the borate concentration was investigated. Facts included mineralization (the degree of the concentration) of the brines, pH, the height of the sorbent layer, etc. The experiments resulted in the defining of material balances, and kinetic parameters of the sorbtion step. The optimum conditions for boron desorbtion from the sorbent phase in alkali brine were defined. This enabled the manufacture of sodium perborate for use as the bleaching component of synthetic detergents under factory conditions [4,5].

### 25.4.3 Strontium Extraction

Worldwide, there are no methods for the selective extraction of strontium from substrates containing high concentrations of calcium. An effective method for extraction of strontium from exhaust iodine-bromine plants consists of the sequential sedimentation of alkali earth elements. For this purpose the solubility of a multi-component system such as $Na^+$, $k^+$, $Mg^{2+}$, $Ca^{2+}$, $Sr^{2+}$ // $Cl^-$, $OH^-$ -$H_2O$; $Na^+$, $K^+$, $Ca^{2+}$, $Sr^{2+}$ // $Cl^-$, $CO_3^{2-}$ -$H_2O$, was investigated at different temperatures. The experiments resulted in the design of a new method for the isolation of strontium from natural brines by preliminary removal of the alkali earth elements [6-10].

### 25.4.3.1 The Isolation of Calcium and Strontium

A 2-staged process for extracting calcium ion in the form of $CaCO_3$ and $CA(OH)_2$, with subsequent isolation of the strontium carbonate concentrates from effluents from the iodine-bromine production was investigated:

$$Na^+, K^+, Ca^{2+}, Sr^{2+} // Cl^-, CO_3^{2-}, H_2O \text{ at } 25\ °C.$$

Experimental modelling solutions from the Nebitdag and Cheleken effluents and concentrated effluents after magnesium hydroxide sedimentation were used.

It was shown that when the stoichiometric multiplicity factor is the same, the concentration of the strontium ion is less in the concentrated brine.

Judging from these experimental data for the Nebitdag and Cheleken effluent during calcium carbonate sedimentation, the optimum stoichiometric multiplicity is $n = 0.5$, and for the concentrated brine $n = 0.7$. At $n = 0.5$ the extraction is 47.7 and 49.2%, at $n = 0.7$, 65.5% $Ca^{2+}$ of the initial concentration.

### 25.4.3.2 Sodium Hydroxide, Calcium and Strontium Isolation

The process for subsequent extraction of alkali earth elements from mineralized effluents rom the iodine-bromine production in Turkmenistan includes the investigation of the possibility of isolating calcium and strontium from sodium hydroxide solutions.

From the literature available, there is no information on the solubility of the system of $Na^+$, $Ca^{2+}$, $Sr^{2+}$ // $Cl^-$, $OH^-$ $H_2O$. There is some information on the $Ca(OH)_2$ solubility in sodium chloride solutions at different mineral levels. In this connection, the impact of temperature of the calcium ion on the initial concentration was investigated in addition to the mole ratio of $NaOH/CaCl_2$ in the initial mixture, the pH value on the suspension on the sedimentation process of $Ca(OH)_2$ in solutions of $Na^+$, $Ca^{2+}$ // $Cl^-$, $OH^-$ - $H_2O$ system, and also $Ca(OH)_2$ in brines in the $Na^+$, $CA^{2+}$, $Sr^{2+}$, // $Cl^-$, $OH^-$ - $H_2O$ system.

#### 25.4.3.2.1 The Interaction of the $Na^+$, $Ca^{2+}$, $Sr^{2+}$, // $Cl^-$, $OH^-$ - $H_2O$ System at 25, 50, and 75 °C

The reproduction of the experiments during calcium hydroxide sedimentation showed that calcium losses in the form of $CaCO_3$ do not have an influence on the value of the residual concentration of $Ca^{2+}$ in the filtrate.

It was shown that the calcium chloride solutions decreases with an increase in the excess in the sedimenter and the temperature of the reaction mixture. In the solution with the higher calcium initial concentration, the pH value of the suspension is accordingly greater.

From an examination of the literature data the reverse is noted between calcium hydroxide solubility and mineralization in the solutions when the sodium chloride concentration is 1.75-3.96 g-eq $l^{-1}$.

The dependency of the degree of the calcium sedimentation was investigated in relation to time. The balancing conditions in the $Na^+$, $Ca^{2+}$ // $Cl^-$, $OH^-$ - $H_2O$ system at 25 and 75 °C and the mixing of the suspension is achieved within 1 h.

#### 25.4.3.2.2 Investigation of the Solubility in the $Na^+$, $K^+$, $Ca^{2+}$, $Sr^{2+}$, // $Cl^-$, $OH^-$ - $H_2O$ System at 25, 50, and 75 °C

It is stated that the solubility of $Ca(OH)_2$ in the solutions containing $Sr^{2+}$ is the same as for $Na^+$, $Ca^{2+}$ // $Cl^-$, $OH^-$ - $H_2O$ solutions.

The impact of the initial concentration of the calcium ion (5-15 g $l^{-1}$) in the mole ratio of $NaOH/CaCl_2$ was investigated in an initial mixture of the strontium ion at 25.5 and 75 °C.

It was determined that the interval of $Ca^{2+}$ concentration and the degree of extraction of $Sr^{2+}$ increases with an increase in temperature, and the mole ratio of the reagents and pH in the reaction mixture. In solutions with high initial concentration of calcium ions the strontium hydroxide solubility decreases. Hence, in solutions with $C_{Ca}{}^{2+}$ and a 5-15 g $l^{-1}$ mole ratio, it was found to be appropriate for the stoichiometric multiplicity factor of n = 1.4, $Sr^{2+}$ is recovered at 3.2-13% at 25 °C, 5.5-27% at 50 °C, and 8.4-29.7% at 75 °C into the solid phase. In solutions with the $C_{Ca}{}^{2+}$ 68.9 g $l^{-1}$ at n = 1.3 and 75 °C the extraction is 32.5% $Sr^{2+}$.

The degree of strontium ion sediment is determined with the $Sr(OH)_2$ solubility in the sodium chloride/calcium chloride solution in addition to strontium chloride with $Ca(OH)_2$ co-sedimentation with the formation of the *solid* solutions.

With an increase in the mineralization of the background electrolyte from 2.5 to 3.4 g-eq $l^{-1}$ in solutions with $C_{Ca}{}^{2+}$ 15 g $l^{-1}$ and $C_{Sr}{}^{2+}$ 1.4 g $l^{-1}$ the quantity of the isolated strontium ion into the solid phase is practically equal. The degree of the $Sr^{2+}$ sedimentation at n = 1.2 and 75 °C respectively equals 14.4 and 5.7%.

It was calculated that the sedimentation of the concentration of the strontium carbonate with minimum $CaCO_3$ admixture with accepted strontium losses ($\ngtr$ 15%) could be isolated from the initial calcium hydroxide brine with a residual concentration of $Ca \leq 0.1$ g $l^{-1}$. The quality of the strontium carbonate thus recovered meets the specified standards.

#### 25.4.3.2.3 The Interaction in the System of $Na^+$, $Sr^{2+}$, // $Cl^-$, $OH^-$ - $H_2O$ at 25 and 75 °C

It is known than in liquid solutions the solubility of $Sr(OH)_2$ increases with an increase in temperature. It was observed that the reverse dependency is observed in sodium chloride calcium chloride solutions when the temperature increases from 25 to 75 °C.

The experimental data showed that at 25 °C, the residual strontium concentration is approximately the same in the 2.5 M sodium chloride solutions in the system $NaCl$-$SrCl_2$-$NaOH$-$H_2O$, and $NaCl$-$SrCl_2$-$CaCl_2$-$NaOH$-$H_2O$. At 75 °C the degree of strontium extraction is twice that of the sodium calcium chloride solutions.

From the results of the sedimentation method in the system $NaCl$-$SrCl_2$-$NaOH$-$H_2O$, and the 'co-sedimentation' method in the system $NaCl$-$SrCl_2$-$CaCl_2$-$NaOH$-$H_2O$, it follows that the increase in the degree of the strontium sedimentation with an increase in temperature from 25 to 75 °C is probably associated with the process of isomorphic co-sedimentation, with the formation of *solid* solutions of $Sr(OH)_2$ in $Ca(OH)_2$ in the equilibrium conditions of the system.

## 25.5 Conclusions

In Turkmenistan the extraction of bromine and iodine from brines produce effluents which caused considerable environmental damage.

Experimental work and the application of management techniques showed that these waste liquors could be treated and thus improve the chemical safety of the operation. Additionally, it was possible to recover sodium chloride for use in the foodstuffs industry; together with borate and strontium salts for use by industry.

These processes make extensive use of natural resources, especially solar energy.

## 25.6 References


[1] Ksenzenko, V.I., Khojamamedov, A.M., Kuliev, Ch.A., and Ovezova, O., 'The behaviour of rare and isolated elements during the isothermic evaporation of underground mineralized waters at the Gaurdak deposit', Izvestia AS TSSR, *Series of Physical-technical chemical and geological sciences*, 1978, (3), 104-107.

[2] Evzhanov, Kh., Andryasova, G.I., Veisov, B.K., and Javakov, R.S., 'The process of salt crystallization and strontium behaviour during the evaporation of the effluent from iodine-bromine production', Izvestia AS TSSR, *Series of Physical-technical, chemical and geological sciences*, 1980, (4), 64-72.

[3] Kuliev, Ch.A., Khojamamedov, A.M., and Ksenzenko, V.I., 'Strontium behaviour in the process of the concentration of secondary brines', Izvestia AS TSSR, *Series of Physical-technical, chemical and geological sciences*, 1980, (3), 73-76.

[4] Khojamamedov, A.M., Boltenkova, L.I., and Kazantseva, N.N., 'Researching of a process for borate sorbtion from waste iodine-bromine waters', *Magazine of the Neorganic Chemistry*, 1986, **31**, (Ed.11).

[5] Volkhin, V.V., Khojamamedov, A.M., Jumamuradov, B., Zylberman, M., and Lavrova, J.V., 'Ion exchange borate extraction from high mineralized solutions', Izvestia AS TSSR, *Series of Physical-technical, chemical and geological sciences*, 1987, (5), 96-98.

[6] Evzhanov, Kh., and Veisov, B.K., 'Examination of combinations of strontium and other macro-components from the iodine-bromine industrial effluent', Izvestia AS TSSR, Series of Physical-technical, chemical and geological sciences, 1979, (6), 73-75.

[7] Andryasova, G.I., Evzhanov, Kh., and Veisov, B.K., 'The extraction of alkali earth metals from iodine-bromine industrial brines', Izvestia AS TSSR, *Series of Physical-technical, chemical and geological sciences*, 1983, (2), 67-71.

[8] Evzhanov, Kh., Andryasova, G.I., and Berkelieva, L.K., 'Conditions of the isolation of calcium and strontium with sodium hydroxide in the high mineralized chloride based waters', *Chemistry and Water Technology*, 1986, (4), 36-38.

[9] Evzhanov, Kh., Andryasova, G.I., and Berkelieva, L.K., 'Conditions for the isolation of calcium and strontium with soda in highly mineralized chloride based solutions', Izvestia AS TSSR, *Series of Physical-technical, chemical and geological sciences*, 1986, (6), 78-81.

[10] Andryasova, G.I., Evzhanov, Kh., and Berkelieva, L.K., 'The recovery of the strontium carbonate in combination with other macro-components from concentrated waters during iodine-bromine production', Izvestia AS TSSR, *Series of Physical-technical, chemical and geological sciences*, 1987, (5), 104-107.

# 26. Safety in the Use of Chemicals at the Workplace

Nabil T. Watfa

## 26.1 World Production and Use of Chemicals: An Overview

The magnitude of the production and use of chemicals worldwide is not known with any degree of certainty. However, it is estimated that the world annual production of chemicals is close to 400 million tonnes, and that of the 6 to 7 million chemical substances known in the industry and scientific research, close to 70,000 substances were produced for regular use in the industrial sectors, agriculture and services. Of this number only a few 1000 are produced in substantial quantities for industrial use. Of the marketed chemical substances 5-10% were considered hazardous, of which 150-200 chemicals are known carcinogens [1].

At the European Communities (EC) level, Council Directive 92/32/EEC (which is the 7th Amendment of the original Directive 67/548/EEC), on Classification, Packaging and Labeling of Dangerous Substances contains approximately 2000 substances in its Annex I entitled the List of Dangerous Substances. The provisions of this Directive aim at ensuring health protection of the workers, the public and the environment [2] (see also chapters by Campbell, Knight, Kulkarni and Nangle).

The mechanism of approval for the use of chemicals has in part been hampered by a set of requirements involving prohibitive cost of testing and a complicated system of test protocols that resulted in a delay of a number of years before such testing covered the substances intended for use. This problem was further aggravated by the potential carcinogenicity, mutagenicity and teratogenicity of many chemical substances, a number of which possessed known synergistic effects. These problems compelled chemical legislation in several countries to opt for systems of *notification* rather than *approval*, thus leaving the chemical manufacturers with the responsibility of liability in case of any future harmful effects related to the use of their marketed products (see also chapters by Devos and Ekroos). Within the EC, notified chemicals are listed in the European Inventory of Existing Commercial Chemical Substances (EINECS). Excluded from this inventory are pesticides, pharmaceuticals, cosmetics, and food additives. The number of notifications received each year for substances produced in quantities of greater than one tonne has increased significantly since 1982, as shown in Table 26.1 [3]. In the United States, 2000-3000 substances are notified each year under the Toxic Substances Control Act (TOSCA) of 1976. The process provides for the compilation of information on all chemicals, including the testing of those suspected of being harmful, the screening of chemicals and the control of chemicals with proven risks. The chemicals are listed under the Inventory of Chemical Substances. There are a number of reasons for the parity in the number of notification of new chemicals in the EC and the United States. In the EC, a number of chemicals were not listed under the EINECS prior to its establishment in 1982. The cost of notification under TOSCA is much less than that of the EC since the former does not require the provision of toxicological data. Moreover, at the EC level, the notification procedure is pre-marketing and not pre-manufacturing, as is the case in the United States. The number of notifications of new substances in the EC however, is expected to mount to 1000 $a^{-1}$ once the Council Directive 92/32/EEC (7th Amendment) is in force.

**Table 26.1** **Number of notifications of new chemicals received each year by the Commission of the European Communities**

| Year | Number of notifications | Year | Number of notifications |
|---|---|---|---|
| 1982 | 1 | 1988 | 199 |
| 1983 | 15 | 1989 | 240 |
| 1984 | 45 | 1990 | 343 |
| 1985 | 68 | 1991 | 363 |
| 1986 | 83 | 1992 | 202 |
| 1987 | 136 | | |

Of all the chemical substances in use today, close to 2100 only have occupational exposure limits (OELs), also known as Threshold Limit Values (TLVs) or Time Weighted Averages (TWAs). These limits, adopted in several countries, differ in value from one country to another, as illustrated by Table 26.2 [4]. The absence of internationally accepted occupational standards for toxic agents has resulted in serious difficulties in evaluating industrial hazards [5]. Moreover, there is a need to develop TLVs on the basis of scientific guidelines without manipulation by vested interests [6]. In this regard, a number of countries are setting their OELs under the mechanism of tripartism. Universally, the application of the chemical substances involves the following sectors [7]:

i) Acids, alkalis and their salts, and industrial gases used in the chemical industry or other industries;

ii) Organic feedstocks for plastics, resins, synthetic rubbers and fibers, solvents, detergents, dyestuffs and pigments;

iii) Fertilisers and pesticides (including herbicides, fungicides, insecticides, etc.);

iv) Final products of ii) above;

v) Pharmaceuticals;

vi) Paints, varnishes, lacquers;

vii) Soaps, detergents, cleaning preparations, perfumes, cosmetics, etc.; and,

viii) Miscellaneous chemicals (explosives, adhesives, solvents, etc.).

**Table 26.2** **Occupational exposure limits adopted in different countries [4]**

| Substances (TWA mg/m$^3$) | former USSR | United States (NIOSH/ OSHA) | Czecho-slovakia | Poland | Germany | United Kingdom | Switzer-land |
|---|---|---|---|---|---|---|---|
| Acetone | 200* | 1800 | 800 | 200 | 2400 | 2400 | 1780 |
| Lead and compounds (inorganic) | 0.005 | 0.15 (ACGIH) | 0.05 | — | — | 0.15** | 0.1** |
| Styrene | 10 | 215 | 200 | 100 | 85 | 420 | 215 |
| Toluene | 50* | 375 | 200 | 100 | 380 | 375 | 380 |
| Xylene (all isomers) | 50* | 435 | 200 | 100 | 440 | 435 | 435 |
| Xylidine (all isomers) | 3* | 10 | 5 | — | — | 10 | 10 |

*Short Term Exposure Limit (STEL)
**Lead and compounds (except tetraethyl lead)

## 26.2 Hazards Associated with the Use of Chemicals

Hazardous chemicals at the workplace may be classified under 3 groups:

i) The toxic chemicals which cover simple and chemical asphyxiants, irritants, narcotics, systemic poisons, carcinogens, teratogens, mutagens and chemicals with dermatological effects;

ii) Flammables; and,

iii) Explosive substances.

These chemicals are used in virtually all process and manufacturing industries. Table 26.3 enumerates the chemicals used in a selected sample of such processing and manufacturing industries [7].

**Table 26.3** The use of chemicals in processing and manufacturing industries [7]

| Process/operation | Examples of contaminants |
|---|---|
| Abrasives (manufacture and use) | Dusts: aluminium oxide, silicon carbide, silica, energy,carborundum<br>Gases/vapors: carbon monoxide, solvents, vaporised resins |
| Adhesives (manufacture and use) | Solvent vapors, resins |
| Agriculture | Fertilisers (organic and inorganic), pesticides, fungicides, hormones, pathogens, solvents |
| Asphalt | Silica dust, aromatic and aliphatic hydro-carbons and solvents |
| Battery manufacture | Lead, cadmium, formaldehyde, PVC, antimony, acids and alkalis |
| Blasting (abrasive) | Silica, lead, cadmium, zinc, etc. |
| Boiler-making | Silicates, fluorides, welding and metal fumes |
| Brick and tile manufacture | Silica, silicates, carbon monoxide |
| Canning | Metal fumes, solvent vapors |
| Cement (manufacturing and products) | Silica, welding fumes, solvents, asbestos |
| Chemical manufacture | Full range of contaminants |
| Coking | Carbon monoxide, ammonia, hydrogen sulfide, sulfur dioxide, phenols, cyanides, naphthalene, benzene, carbon disulfide, etc. |
| Dairy industry | Acids and alkalis |
| Detergents (manufacture and use) | Proteolytic enzymes, phosphates, sodium perborate |
| Drink | Ammonia, carbon dioxide, refrigerant gases, ethanol |
| Dry-cleaning | Perchloroethylene, trichlorethylene, other solvents |
| Electrical components | Metal fumes (lead, cadmium, tin), solvents |
| Electroplating | Acids: chromic, sulfuric, hydrofluoric, nitric, perchloric<br>Alkalis: formaldehyde, ammonia<br>Metals: lead, zinc, metal oxides, cyanide, arsine |
| Foundries | Metal dusts and powders: sulfur dioxide, carbon monoxide, carbon dioxide, acrolein, aldehydes, phenols, isocyanates, polycyclic aromatics |
| Frozen food | Ammonia, methyl chloride, freons |
| Glass fiber | Asbestos, mineral fibre, resins, acetal styrene, alcohols, phthalates, methyl ethyl ketone, toluene, phenol, isocyanates |

| Process/operation | Examples of contaminants |
|---|---|
| Glass manufacture | Silica, lead, potash, vanadium, arsenic, sulfur dioxide, hydrogen fluoride |
| Insulation | Silica, mineral fibres, asbestos isocyanates |
| Metal treatment | Abrasives, acids, alkalis, solvents (petroleum and chlorinated hydrocarbons), cyanides |
| Motor vehicle manufacture | Abrasives, paints, solvents, metals, welding fumes |
| Office work | Ammonia, ozone, methanol, chlorinated hydrocarbons, petroleum solvents |
| Paints | Lead, mercury, solvents, isocyanates, polyurethanes, insecticides, fungicides |
| Petroleum/oil refining | Full range of hydrocarbon vapors, mercaptans, etc. |
| Plastics and resins | Isocyanates, monomers (*eg*, styrene), vinyl chloride, asbestos, silica |
| Plumbing, etc. | Welding fumes, lead, asbestos, solvents |
| Pottery | Silica, lead, cadmium, copper |
| Printing | Lead, chrome, antimony, nickel, solvents (toluene, xylene, alcohols) |
| Paper and board | Chlorine, chlorine dioxide, sulfur dioxide, sulfuric acid, methyl mercaptan, hydrogen sulfide, caustic soda |
| Roofing | Asbestos, metal oxides, solvents, bituminous products |
| Rubber | Acrylonitrile, butadiene, isocyanates, organic solvents, carbon black |
| Scrap metal processing | Metal fumes (lead, cadmium, mercury, zinc), welding fumes, solvents |
| Shipbuilding | Asbestos, metal oxides, lead, anti-fouling paints, welding fumes |
| Soldering | Metal fumes (cadmium, lead, tin), formaldehyde, aldehydes, etc. |
| Sterilisation processes | Ozone, ethylene oxide, halogenated hydro-carbons |
| Timber | Wood dust, adhesives, solvents, resins, asbestos, arsenic and compounds, chrome compounds, formaldehyde, isocyanates, phenol, terpenes, aldehydes, esters, ketones |
| Water supply and treatment | Chlorine, ammonia, sulfur dioxide, ozone |

### 26.2.1 Toxic Hazards

For a better appreciation of the mode of action and control measures against toxic chemicals, it is essential to recognise the route of entry of the chemicals into the human body. Inhalation is the commonest route of entry, especially if it is assumed that an average worker under normal conditions breathes at an average rate of 5 l air $min^{-1}$, which amounts to a total intake of ambient air of 7,200 l $d^{-1}$. Skin absorption is another route of entry, and accounts for one of the commonest occupational diseases, namely dermatitis. Although infrequent as a route of entry into the body, ingestion becomes significant as a cause of occupational poisoning in the absence of personal hygiene. The transmission of toxic substances from the pregnant woman to the foetus through the placenta may also be listed as a 4th route of entry.

The health effects of chemicals on workers at the workplace are well documented. Recognising the risks associated with the use of chemicals, the chemical industry has emerged as one of the pioneers in the field of prevention and control of occupational accidents, injuries and diseases, and has contributed significantly to the establishment of sound principles in occupational safety and health in general. However trends continue to demonstrate the need for more action. For example, although the accident rate in the Swiss chemical industry which employed 80,000 full-time workers in 1988 was below the average for all industries, the incidence of occupational diseases was higher for that period according to the national insurance programme (SUVA). Besides the chemical hazards, other hazards such as mechanical hazards, noise and radiation were also taken into account [8].

Health effects due to the exposure of workers to organic solvents have also been reported. In the printing industry, the more serious toxic hazards are teratogenicity and carcinogenicity of the solvents and other chemicals present in printing plants [9]. In one of the studies, neurological symptoms including persistent central nervous system deficits and respiratory systems including persistent coughing are also attributed to exposure to organic solvents [10]. In another study, neurobehavioral tests consisting of reaction time (simple and choice), tweezer dexterity, hand precision, and memory (forward and backward) were administered to a group of painters before and after work. The results showed deterioration of performance on reaction time (choice), tweezer dexterity (accuracy), hand precision (accuracy) and memory (backward) among the painters at the end of their work shift. The degree of deterioration of performance was associated with the duration of exposure, which was also shown to lead to headaches and to affect mental alertness and sleepiness [11].

Exposure to solvents was also responsible for an increased accident risk among painters [12]. More specifically, exposure to the organic solvents xylene and toluene in varnishing processes in a major heavy electrical industry was found to lead to behavioural disturbances such as immediate and delayed memory, visual ability, visual learning and psychomotor skills [13]. In another study statistically significant differences were demonstrated between workers exposed to toluene (TWA = 88 ppm) and controls (TWA = 13 ppm) in neurobehavioral tests measuring manual dexterity (grooved peg board), visual scanning (trail making, visual reproduction, Benton visual retention, digit symbol), and verbal memory (digit span) [14]. Exposure of pregnant women in their first trimester to solvents in the electronics industry was significantly associated with spontaneous abortion. Work in electronics assembly was significantly associated with delivering a low birth weight infant but was not associated with spontaneous abortions [15]. Significant deterioration in mental ability has also been attributed to the exposure to aluminium dust (4.6 to 11.5 mg $m^{-3}$) over a period as short as 6 years in an aluminium foundry in Italy. [16].

The hazards of freon including skin toxicity, chemical burns, eye irritation, asphyxia due to inhalation, have been observed [17]. The chemical 1,3-butadiene (BD), which is present in synthetic rubber and motor fuels (gasoline), is reported to cause an increase in lymphomas, leukemias, and other cancers of hematopoietic systems and organs in humans. Being a potent alkylating agent, BD is toxic to developing embryos and damages progeny after parental exposure [18].

A study on workers in a bearing manufacturing plant revealed significant excesses in proportional mortality ratios (PMR) from stomach cancer (PMR=2.0) and rectal cancer (PMR=3.1) among white male workers. Significant association was established between stomach cancer with precision grinding chemicals such as the water-based cutting oils and their aerosols [19].

In a questionnaire survey covering 4008 male and female hairdressing apprentices in Germany, over 70% reported skin problems and nearly 30% encountered severe skin problems since they started their work. The survey also revealed that 20% gave up the profession due to a skin disease and that 11% suffered from skin problems prior to becoming an apprentice [20].

It has been reported that although pharmaceutical workers faced a potential risk from exposure to carcinogenic agents, little is known about the health problems of those employed in the manufacture and formulation of pharmaceutical products [21]. In a retrospective questionnaire study involving 8032 personnel exposed to anaesthetic gases in operating and recovery rooms in hospitals in Ontario, Canada, and 2525 non-exposed hospital staff over the period 1981-1985, women in the exposed group had significantly increased frequencies of spontaneous abortion. Their children also had significantly more congenital abnormalities [22] (see also chapter by Vergieva).

In agriculture it has been demonstrated that the mortality among workers due to some types of tumors (lymphoma, leukemia, myeloma, soft tissue sarcoma, skin, prostate and encephalous and stomach tumors) is higher compared with other occupational categories (see chapter by Wilbourn and Vainio). The only chemical substances used in agriculture which the International Agency for Research on Cancer (IARC) Monographs listed as human carcinogens are arsenical compounds and mineral oils. The carcinogenicity of other agrochemicals such as phenoxyacetic herbicides has been reported in some studies but not in others. Cohort studies which were performed among sprayers and workers employed in insecticide production showed evidence of excesses of lung tumor, and those performed among grain processing workers showed evidence of excesses of non-Hodgkin lymphoma in particular. Other agrochemicals have exhibited carcinogenic effects in experimental animals [23]. Another study in Quebec, Canada, has also supported the hypothesis of a potential relationship between the use of pesticides in agriculture and cancer of the lymphatic tissues [24]. In a follow-up study of 1583 workers employed in a chemical plant which produces herbicides in processes using tetrachlorodibenzodioxin (TCDD), cancer mortality was found to be higher among men with 20 or more years of employment. Similar findings were also reported among men who started their employment with the company prior to 1955 when the production of TCDD was reduced following an outbreak of chloracne. Among the 7% of cohort women with high exposure in the plant, no increased risk of cancer mortality was observed, but breast cancer mortality was raised [25]. In another study on the effects of exposure to cholinergic pesticides (organophosphates and carbamates) on a group of 86 female university workers without known exposure to this group of chemicals and with no other influencing factors, it was found out that the mean plasma and erythrocyte cholinesterase (ChE) levels among a group of 16 females who were using oral contraception were significantly lower than those levels among a group of 70 females who were not using oral contraception [26] (see also chapter by Franekić). This indicated that in assessing exposure to cholinergic pesticides the effect of drug therapy on blood ChE activity deserved to be considered. The same study also investigated the exposure to noise and heat as factors aggravating the effects of exposure to pesticides and organic solvents.

### 26.2.2 Fire and Explosion Hazards

Chemicals may be considered flammable if they combust and continue to burn after being ignited. Most flammable and explosive liquids, gases and dusts have *flammable or explosive range*. This expression refers to the range of concentration below or above which the propagation of flame does not occur when the chemical is in contact with a source of ignition. Sources of ignition can be open flames, hot surfaces, cigarette smoking, electric plug sparks and others. Certain chemicals may undergo auto-ignition under specific circumstances. Highly flammable chemicals are those which readily ignite upon brief contact with low-energy ignition sources. Poorly flammable chemicals require the prolonged action of high-energy ignition sources.

Industrial fires are known to cause disasters, affecting both life and property. Literature is rich on this subject. If the loss of human life is not caused as a result of convected and radiant heat or direct contact with flames, it may be caused by suffocation due to the inhalation of toxic combustion products or to lack of oxygen. In an explosion workers may by injured by direct impact from debris or by the blast or over-pressure generated by the explosion. Some chemicals are specifically formulated to explode and are referred to as explosives. Others such as the organic peroxides and some azo and nitro compounds, explode because they are unstable. These may be formed as intermediates in chemical reactions or as the result of a reaction between incompatible chemicals. Table 26.4 lists examples of major industries associated with explosion hazards [27].

### 26.2.3 Other Hazards

The reactivity of chemicals is another factor to consider in assessing their health hazards. This is particularly important in view of the undesirable release of toxic products and energy that may ensue when 2 or more chemicals are combined.

**Table 26.4 Explosion hazards in major industries [27]**

| Industry | Examples of explosion hazards |
|---|---|
| Woodworking | Wood dust from sanding machines, etc. |
| Oils, fats and waxes processing | Unsaturated oils (hydrocarbons) |
| Solid and liquid fuels processing | Pulverized coal, hydrocarbons and alcohols |
| Lacquer and varnish | Alcohols, esters, ethers, glycols and petroleum naphtha |
| Viscose and rayon | Carbon disulfide |
| Rubber | Aromatic hydrocarbons |
| Pharmaceutical | Alcohols, ethers, esters, unstable substances, finely pulverized drugs |
| Alkalis and heavy chemicals | Hydrogen |
| Plastics | Formaldehyde, solvents, nitrocellulose, casein and moulding powders |
| Paint | Aluminium powder, phthalic anhydride and solvents |
| Metal spraying | Zinc or aluminium in a finely divided state |
| Paper | Cellulosic material, volatile solvents |
| Printing | Ink solvents |
| Linoleum | Cork and wood floors, unsaturated oils and petroleum naphtha |
| Textile | Waterproofing with oils such as linseed oil in petroleum naphtha, and coating with flammable rubber and plastics solutions |
| Dyeing and bleaching | Degreasing solvents |

Chemicals that are released into the environment outside the worksite may cause health hazards to the general public. The released chemicals may react with the ambient oxygen and ozone in the presence of sunlight to form other chemicals such as acids, aldehydes, nitrates and other irritant and/or noxious chemicals.

The generation of toxic gases and fumes from industrial waste dumps is a further source of public health hazards. Chemical wastes are also known to cause serious health threats to scavengers and other exposed persons, sometimes long after the time of disposal.

## 26.3 Safety in the Use of Chemicals

Chemicals have constituted an essential ingredient in our life. The contribution of agrochemicals to increased food production in a world part of which is plagued with famine is a blessing. Without chemotherapy a number of deadly diseases will have remained untreated. The list of technological advances with which chemicals are associated is too long to mention in this chapter. Therefore, chemicals are with us to stay. The challenge is to learn how to use chemicals safely with the prime objective of controlling exposure to them to levels which manifest little or no risk to safety or health. In dealing with the problems associated with the use of chemicals at the workplace, the following components are worth discussing.

### 26.3.1 Classification

Information concerning the hazard potential of chemicals and their products is one of the pre-requisite components of a comprehensive control system. This requirement calls for setting of appropriate toxicity testing, a notification scheme and the setting up of an inventory of chemical substances.

Several classification systems exist at present. Some of these take into account the acute and immediate types of effects of the chemicals, thus addressing the problems inherent in the transport of the chemicals. Examples of these systems include the United Nations Committee of Experts on the Transport of Dangerous Goods (UNCETG), which reported to and was endorsed by the Economic and Social Council (ECOSOC) in 1957. Other systems are based on both the acute and immediate as well as the chronic type of effects. These types of systems are therefore intended for the use of chemicals at the workplace. Besides some of the national systems, the only international system known for classification and labelling of chemicals is that developed and introduced in the member States of the European Communities as Council Directive 92/32/EEC, which is the 7th Amendment of the original Directive 67/548/EEC referred to previously [2]. Under the United States Occupational Safety and Health Act (OSHA), the Hazard Communication health standard 29 CFR 1910.1200 ensures that chemical hazards are evaluated and that related information is communicated to employers and workers by comprehensive hazard communication programmes such as material safety data sheets (MSDS). The United States Federal Hazardous Substances Act Regulation (FHSA) is yet another classification system which aims at consumer protection. In Canada, the Workplace Hazardous Materials Information System (WHIMS) protects the workers by providing information on chemical hazards and highlights labelling and the provisions of MSDS. In Japan, hazardous materials are regulated by the Hazardous Material Regulations.

For an effective and comprehensive control and safer use of chemicals, there should therefore be criteria and systems for the classification of chemicals according to the type and degree of their hazards. The criteria and systems for such classification should be established by the competent authority or an approved body and based upon the characteristics of chemicals including: toxic properties; flammable, explosive and oxidizing properties; corrosive and irritant properties; carcinogenic effects; allergenic and sensitising effects; teratogenic and mutagenic effects; and, effects on the reproductive system.

A national inventory of the chemicals used at work and their classification should be compiled and updated by the national authorities. It is the responsibility of the manufacturers and importers of chemicals not yet included in the national inventory to transmit to the national authority the information that is needed to maintain the inventory.

### 26.3.2 Labelling and Identification

Catastrophes due to mistakes in labelling and identification of chemicals have occurred. Many countries have adopted or are in the process of adopting new regulations concerning labelling and identification of chemicals. Most of these are based on the United Nations Recommendations on the Transport of Dangerous Goods. The use of internationally accepted systems has many advantages, namely the consistency and savings in unnecessary testing of chemicals. In supplementing the more general legislations, several EC Directives have been set requiring the following information in label form: a symbol or sign; risk and safety advice phrases for added information; and, the name of the substance, the name and address of the supplier, and a substance identification number.

In order to ensure harmony with chemical nomenclature, there is available a number of international and national listings. Some of these are: the International Union of Pure and Applied Chemistry (IUPAC); the Classification of Chemicals in the Customs Tariff of the European Communities; the Chemical Abstracts Service List; International Standard ISO 1750 (pesticides and other agrochemicals); and, British Standard 2472: 1965 recommended names for chemicals used in industry.

EINECS may also serve as an appropriate service for terminology. To accompany the above information on the label, the EC have also devised the *risk phrases* which are general phrases clearly indicating the general nature of the risk involved and confirming the accompanying symbol, and the *safety phrases* which are general phrases giving appropriate advice about the necessary precautions to be taken. Further information about the chemical is supplied by MSDSs, technical data notes, leaflets, or information sheets.

With the above introduction, it becomes clear that chemicals which have been classified as hazardous should be labelled so as to provide the essential information regarding their properties, hazards and the safety precautions observed. The national authorities should establish the requirements for labelling in accordance with national or international standards. Technical data notes and information sheets should contain essential information regarding the properties of chemicals and methods on their safe use. The labels of chemicals should enable the employer to recognise and distinguish between chemicals both when ordering and when using them. Labelling requirements should cover the following aspects:

i) Information to be contained on the label, viz:

- Trade names;
- Name of chemical;
- Name, address and telephone number of the supplier;
- Danger symbols;
- Nature of the special risks;
- Safety advice;

ii) Legibility, durability and size of the label; and,

iii) Uniformity of labels including colors.

If the chemical container is too small to carry a label, provisions should be made for such a container to be accompanied by the necessary information.

When technical information notes, sometimes referred to as chemical safety data sheets are to be used, they should ensure to contain essential information such as:

i) Name of the chemical;

ii) Physical and health hazards;

iii) Routes of entry into the body;

iv) Surveillance of workers' health;

v) Exposure limits;

vi) Generally applicable precautions for safe use;

vii) Engineering controls and safe work practices;

viii) Personal protective equipment and clothing;

ix) Procedures for dealing with spills and leaks;

x) Emergency measures;

xi) First aid procedures;

xii) Sources of additional information.

### 26.3.3 Operational Control Measures

There are several measures which should be taken at the enterprise level to ensure safety in the use of chemicals. These measures are the sole responsibility of the employer. They include the following:

#### 26.3.3.1 Handling and Use of Chemicals

Safe handling and use of chemicals is one of the major components of a system aiming at reducing the occupational exposure levels to levels which are with little or no risk to the safety and health of the workers. Criteria for safety in the production, handling and use of hazardous chemicals should be established by the national authorities. The criteria should cover the following aspects:

i) The risk of entry into the body by inhalation, skin absorption, ingestion or other routes;

ii) The risk of injury from skin contact;

iii) The risk of injury from fire and explosion; and

iv) The following engineering and operational control measures:

- Substitution of the chemicals by the least hazardous chemicals;
- Substitution of the process by the least hazardous process;
- Limitations on quantities of chemicals stored at the workplace;
- Choice of safe technology and safe installations;
- Adoption of safe work systems and practices;
- Use of signs and notices;
- Use of ventilation, isolation techniques and wet methods technology;
- Use of personal protective equipment and clothing.

#### 26.3.3.2 Transport of Chemicals

Criteria concerning transport of chemicals within the enterprise should be established by the national authority according to the following:

i) The properties and quantity of chemicals to be transported;

ii) The nature, integrity and protection of the containers used in the transport;

iii) The specifications of the vehicle used in the transport;

iv) The routes to be taken;

v) The training and qualifications of the transport workers;

vi) The labelling requirements;

vii) Loading and unloading; and,

viii) Procedures in case of spillage.

#### 26.3.3.3 Storage of Chemicals

Storage of chemicals may cause serious hazards to the workers as well as the neighbouring population within the vicinity of the workplace. Storage of chemicals may take place at the workplace, at the manufacturers' or suppliers' of the chemicals or in transit stations. The incidences involving flammable, explosive and toxic materials are numerous. They range from small events to disastrous tragedies. Criteria for storage of hazardous chemicals should be established by the national authorities and cover the following principles:

i) The compatibility of stored chemicals;

ii) The properties and quantity of chemicals to be stored:

iii) The security and siting of and access to the storage;

iv) The construction, nature and integrity of the storage containers;

v) Loading and unloading of storage containers;

vi) Labelling requirements;

vii) Precautions against accidental release, fire and explosion;

viii) Temperature, humidity and ventilation; and

ix) Precautions and procedures in case of spillage.

#### 26.3.3.4 Waste Disposal

Since the disposal of waste is an essential part of the industrial process, it deserves the same attention given to other processes. The criteria covering this operation should be based on the following principles:

i) The method of identification of waste products;

ii) The quantity to be disposed of;

iii) The handling of contaminated containers;

iv) The identification of waste containers;

v) The effects on the working environment;

vi) The demarcation of disposal areas; and

vii) The use of personal protective equipment and clothing.

### 26.3.4 Other Issues to be Considered

The subject of the safe use of chemicals at the workplace involves other issues, such as the monitoring of exposure of the workers to the chemicals. In this regard, it is the responsibility of the employer to ensure that workers are not exposed to chemicals in excess of recognised occupational exposure limits. This responsibility calls for measuring and recording the concentration of airborne chemicals at the workplace, as well as the monitoring and recording of the exposure of workers to chemicals. In addition, surveillance of the workers is necessary for the assessment of their health and the diagnosis of work-related diseases and injuries caused by exposure to chemicals.

Employers also have the responsibility of maintaining first-aid facilities in order to deal with emergencies and accidents resulting from the use of chemicals.

A close cooperation between workers and employers is needed for the most effective application of measures. Employers have several responsibilities to fulfil and workers are required to take care of their own safety and that of other persons. This means instruction on safe practices and use of personal protective equipment should be adhered to. At the same time, workers should have the right to obtain information from the employer so as to enable them to take adequate precautions and protect themselves from hazards. This includes the provision of information, training and education.

## 26.4 The Activities of the International Labour Office (ILO) in Chemical Safety

The ILO activities in general are in the form of standards setting (Conventions and Recommendations), information dissemination (publications, technical advice, training) and technical cooperation.

Chemical safety is a major area of concern under the core programme of occupational safety and health within the ILO. The Chemicals Convention (No. 170) and its accompanying Recommendation (No. 177), which were adopted by the 1990 International Labour Conference in Geneva, aim at the protection of workers against the risk associated with the use of chemicals at their workplace. The Convention applies to all branches of economic activity in which chemicals are used, and covers all hazardous chemicals. In addition, the Convention specifies the responsibilities of suppliers with respect to labelling and data sheets and those of employers , which are to be discharged in cooperation with the workers and their representatives as regards the identification of substances, operational control, including monitoring of exposure to chemicals, waste disposal, information and training of workers. It also details the duties and rights of workers and holds chemical exporting states responsible for supplying information to states which import the chemicals. The Recommendation gives additional details on the provisions together with guidelines on how the Convention should be translated into national legislation. States which ratify the Convention are required to work out a national policy for safety in the use of chemicals at work in accordance with the general principles it sets forth, adopt classification and labelling systems for all hazardous substances and introduce chemical safety data sheets [28]. In addition, the ILO has also published a Guide on safety and health in the use of agrochemicals in 1991 [29], which was followed by a Code of Practice in 1993 on Safety in the use of chemicals at work [30].

Following major industrial accidents such as those in Bhopal, Seveso and Mexico City, the ILO has undertaken a series of activities for the prevention of such disasters. In addition to the development of major hazard control systems in a number of developing countries, the Office published a manual on major hazard control [31] and a Code of Practice on the prevention of major industrial accidents [32]. A new Convention concerning the Prevention of Major Industrial Accidents (No. 174) and its accompanying Recommendation (No. 181) were also adopted by the 1993 International Labour Conference in Geneva [33]. The new instruments set provisions which aim at the protection of the workers, the public and the environment from major industrial accidents.

Specifically, the purpose of Convention No. 174, adopted by the International Labour Conference (1993), is the prevention of major accidents involving hazardous substances and the limitation of the consequences of such accidents. It applies to major hazard installations with the exception of nuclear installations and plants processing radioactive substances except for facilities handling non-radioactive substances at these installations, military installations, and transport outside the site of an installation other than by pipeline.

States ratifying the Convention are required to work out, in consultation with the most representative organisations of employers and workers and with other interested parties who may be affected, a national policy for the prevention of major industrial accidents in accordance with the general principles it sets forth. The policy shall be implemented through preventive and protective measures for major hazard installations and, where practicable, shall promote the use of the best available safety technologies.

The Convention specifies the responsibilities of employers with respect to identification of any major installation within their control, notification of the competent authority of any major hazard installation which they have identified, establishment and maintenance of a documented system of major hazard control, preparation of safety reports including their revision, update and amendment, and reporting of major industrial accidents to the competent authority.

The Convention also outlines the responsibilities of competent authorities regarding on-site emergency preparedness, siting of major hazard installations and inspection of those installations. In addition, the Convention outlines the rights and duties of workers and their representatives. Lastly, when, in an exporting member State, the use of hazardous substances, technologies or processes is prohibited as a potential source of major accidents, the information on this prohibition and the reasons for it shall be made available by the exporting member State to any importing country.

The Recommendation provides for an international exchange of information on good safety practices, major accidents, near misses, prohibited technologies and processes, and the mitigation of the effects of major accidents. It also encourages workers' compensation in cases of major accidents and the consideration of the effects of such accidents on the public and the environment and calls on national and multinational enterprises to provide safety measures, without discrimination, to the workers in all its establishments, regardless of the place or country in which they are situated. The Recommendation further states that the implementation of the provision of the Convention should, as appropriate, be guided by the ILO Code of practice on the Prevention of major industrial accidents, published in 1991.

The ILO has also been active in the area of exchange of information on chemical safety and toxic chemicals and risks within the framework of the International Occupational Safety and Health Information Centre (CIS). Within the framework of the International Programme on Chemical Safety (IPCS), the ILO is also active in the dissemination of evaluations of the effects of chemicals on human health and in the preparation of health criteria documents, guides and chemical safety data sheets. Within IPCS, the ILO is also responsible for the harmonisation of the classification systems of chemicals, as stressed in Chapter 19 of Agenda 21 of the United Nations Conference for Environment and Development (UNCED).

The technical cooperation programme is a major instrument employed in the translation of the ILO's social policy into practice. This programme is reinforced by ILO Conventions and Recommendations; collection, analysis and dissemination of information and the work by standing industrial and sectoral committees. In the field of chemical safety and the control of major industrial accidents, the ILO has so far executed a number of projects in Africa, Asia, Latin America and the Pacific with the objective of strengthening national institutions and enforcing the employers and workers capabilities in the promotion of chemical safety at the enterprise level. The ILO also continues to be active in the organization of a number of seminars, symposia and workshops at the national, sub-regional and regional levels in several countries.

## 26.5 References

[1] ILO, Report of the Meeting of Experts on Harmful Substances in Work Establishments, ME/UCW/1987/7 (Rev. 1). Geneva, Switzerland, 1987, pp. 2-3.

[2] Council Directive 92/32/EEC (7th Amendment) on Classification, Packaging and Labelling of Dangerous Substances, *Off. J. Eur. Comm.*, L 154, Brussels, Belgium, 1992, [35], pp. 1-29.

[3] Personal communication with Dr. P. Murphy, Directorate General for Environment, Nuclear Safety and Civil Protection DG XI, Commission of the European Communities, 200, rue de la Loi, B-1049 Brussels, Belgium.

[4] ILO, Occupational Exposure Limits for Airborne Toxic Substances, Occupational Safety and Health Series, No. 37, Geneva, Switzerland, 1991.

[5] Maltoni C., *Am. J. Ind. Med.*, 1988, **13**, (5), 529-530.

[6] Castleman, B.I., Ziem G.E., *Am. J. Ind. Med.*, 1988, **13**, (5), 531-559.

[7] ILO, Safety in the Use of Chemicals at Work, PIACT/1987/1, Geneva, Switzerland, 1987, pp. 3.

[8] SUVA SBA 151, Occupational Safety and Health in the Chemical Industry, Schweizerische Unfallversicherungsanstadt, Fluhmattstrasse 1, Postfach 4358, 6002 Luzern, Switzerland, 1990, pp. 52.

[9] Gennart, J.P. and Lauwerys, R., *Arch. maladies professionnelles*, 1991, **51**, (1), 47-54.

[10] Houck, P., Nebel, D., and Milham, S., *Am. J. Ind. Med.*, **22**, (1), 109-115.

[11] Tripathi, S.R., Bhattacharya, S.K., Chattopadhya, P., and Kashyap, S.K., *J. Human Ergology*, 1989, **18**, (2), 191-198.

[12] Hunting, K.L., Matanoski, G.M., Larson, M., and Wolford, R., *Am. J. Ind. Med.*, 1991, **20**, (3), 353-370.

[13] Gupta, B.N., and Kumar, P., *J. Soc. Occ. Med.*, 1990, **40**, (3), 94-96.

[14] Foo, S.C., Jeyaratnam, J., and Koh, D., *B. J. Ind. Med.*, 1990, **47**, (7), 480-484.

[15] Lipscomb, J.A., Fenster, L., Wrensch, M., Shusterman D., and Swan, S., *J. Occ. Med.*, 1991, **33**, (5), 597-604.

[16] Hošovski, E., Mastelica, Z., Šunderic, D., and Radulovic, D, *Medicina del Lavaro*, 1990, **81**, (1), 119-123.

[17] Voge, V.M., *Aviation, Space Environ. Med.*, 1989, **60**, (10), 27-B28.
[18] Mehlman, M.A., and Legator, M.S., *Tox. Ind. Health*, 1991, **7**, (3), 207-220.
[19] Park, R.M., Wegman, D.H., Silverstein, M.A., Maizlish, N.A., and Mirer, F.E., *J. Ind. Med.*, 1988, **13**, (5), 569-580.
[20] Budde, U. and Schwanitz, H.J., *Dermatosen in Bernf und Umwelt*, 1991, **39**, (2), 41-48.
[21] Teichman, R.F., Fallon, L.F., and Brandt-Rauf, P.W., *J. Soc. Occ. Med.*, 1988, **38**, (3), 55-57.
[22] Guirguis, S.S., Pelmear, P.L., Roy, M.L., and Wong, L., *Brit. J. Ind. Med.*, 1990, **47**, (7), 490-497.
[23] Vineis, P., Settimi, L., and Seniori Constantini, A., *Medicina del Lavaro*, 1990, **81**, (5), 363-372.
[24] Godon, D., Lajoie, P., and Thonez, J.P., *Can. J. Publ. Health*, 1991, **82**, (3), 174-180.
[25] Manz, A., Berger, J., Dwyer, J.H., Flesch-Janys, D., Nagel, S., and Waltsgott, H., *Lancet*, 1991, **338**, (No. 8773), 959-964.
[26] Watfa, N.T., Assessment of Exposure of University Students and Staff to Organic Solvents and Cholinergic Pesticides. Ph.D. Thesis, University of London, United Kingdom, 1981.
[27] ILO: Encyclopaedia of Occupational Health and Safety, Geneva, Switzerland, 1985, Vol. 1, 810.
[28] ILO: Convention Concerning Safety in the Use of Chemicals at Work (No. 170) and Recommendation Concerning Safety in the Use of Chemicals at Work (No. 177), Geneva, Switzerland, 1990.
[29] ILO: Safety and Health in the Use of Agrochemicals: A Guide, Geneva, Switzerland, 1991.
[30] ILO: Safety in the Use of Chemicals at Work, a Code of Practice, Geneva, Switzerland, 1993.
[31] ILO: Major Hazard Control: A Practical Manual, Geneva, Switzerland, 1988.
[32] ILO: Prevention of Major Industrial Accidents, a Code of Practice, Geneva, Switzerland, 1991.
[33] ILO: Convention Concerning the Prevention of Major Industrial Accidents (No. 174) and Recommendation Concerning the Prevention of Major Industrial Accidents (No. 181), Geneva, Switzerland, 1993.

# 27. Poisoning and Safety

Wayne A. Temple and Nerida Smith

## 27.1 Introduction

Although >10 million chemicals have been identified, about 100,000 are in common use globally. Approximately 2000 new chemicals are added to the market each year, and some 1500 chemicals account for 95% of the total world production.

The misuse of chemicals causes significant morbidity and mortality throughout the world, and may involve therapeutic agents, industrial chemicals and agricultural compounds. Around 5 million tonnes of pesticides are applied annually throughout the world. A World Health Organization (WHO) consultation on planning strategy for the Prevention of Pesticide Poisoning estimated that globally the annual pesticide poisoning rate was 1 million accidental cases and 20,000 deaths [1].

In developing countries, acute pesticide poisoning is a major public health problem because it is so frequent. This chapter will focus on pesticide use in the Asian Pacific region, to illustrate both the causes and extent of pesticide misuse. The role of poisons information centres in poisoning surveillance, management and prevention activities will also be described.

## 27.2 Pesticide Misuse in the Asia Pacific Region

### 27.2.1 Thailand

Khonkaen (central province, North East region of Thailand) is agriculturally based with crops of rice, kassava, corn, sugar cane, and beans. Cattle and poultry are also reared. The people of the region are poorly educated compared to other parts of Thailand, and are mostly farmers. A recent prospective study of poisoning incidents in this region revealed that from a total of 257 acute poisoning cases, 70 incidents involved agricultural chemicals [2]. More than half (41) of the cases involved intentional poisoning, and the remainder included 19 cases of occupational exposure. Lack of knowledge was the main cause of unintentional poisonings. Organophosphates (parathion, malathion) and paraquat were commonly involved. Chemicals were not kept in safe places and consequently small children who were often left in the inadequate care of slightly older siblings were able to access the contents of agrochemical containers.

Most of the poisoning cases involved people with little education, with 68.5% having no more than primary school education and 92.2% of all cases had not exceeded the secondary school education level.

The peak poisoning time for agricultural chemicals was June — September. This coincided with the rainy season (May — October) and the planting time, when pesticides were applied in heavy quantities.

### 27.2.2 Sri Lanka

In Sri Lanka, ~700,000 kg $a^{-1}$ of pesticides are imported to be used in food production. In 1986, pesticide poisoning was the 6th leading cause of mortality in major hospitals and accounted for 57% of hospital admissions [3]. Approximately 13,000 people $a^{-1}$ present to government hospitals for treatment of pesticide poisoning (the number of deaths is around 1000 $a^{-1}$). Among these, nearly 25% are occupational or unintentional exposures.

Pesticides are widely distributed, freely available, and used often by people who fail to appreciate the importance of the cautions given on the label or accompanying literature. Cases recorded in Sri Lanka have involved containers damaged in transit causing contamination of food or affecting those handling the consignment. Workers have been splashed by, or otherwise exposed to, the concentrated materials when opening the container or filling up spraying equipment. Exposures have also occurred from absorbing some of the chemical from repeated or prolonged skin contamination by the diluted material during spraying. Inhaling the mist or dust, or swallowing traces of the material by conveying it to the mouth via fingers, food, drink or sucking or blowing out blockages in spray jets have also led to poisonings.

### 27.2.3 China

Chinese investigators have reported a large number of both occupational and accidental poisonings involving pyrethroids [4-6]. This relatively new class of pesticide based on the naturally occurring pyrethrins contained in the chrysanthemum flower is being used more extensively globally for the control of both household and agricultural insects. The relatively low mammalian toxicity of synthetic pyrethroids together with their stability in the natural environment and improved biological activity over the natural compounds have contributed to their widespread use [7].

While they commonly cause characteristic reversible facial paraesthesia, their safety record with occupational usage has been relatively good. This has been attributed to their low skin absorption, effective hepatic metabolism and relatively low concentrations in most formulations [8]. However, findings from China warn of their significant toxicity at high exposures either from careless usage or deliberate ingestion.

A review of 573 cases of acute pyrethroid poisoning reported in the Chinese medical literature (1983-1988) included 325 cases of deltamethrin poisoning (158 occupational cases and 167 accidental), 196 cases of acute fenvalerate poisoning, 45 cases of acute cypermethrin poisoning, and 7 cases of other pyrethroid poisoning [4].

One report included a cross-sectional survey on the prevalence of pyrethroid poisoning in 3113 Chinese cotton farmers [5]. Adverse effects of pyrethroid exposure were found in 834 of them (26.8%), including abnormal facial sensations, central nervous system and systemic effects. Ten subjects were diagnosed as having mild occupational acute poisoning. Measurements of pyrethroid concentrations in the air of the worker's breathing zone, in skin pads, and in urine samples showed that dermal contamination is the main route of exposure to pyrethroids in cotton growers [6] (see also chapter by Shen Li).

### 27.2.4 Australasia

In Australia, pesticide poisoning enquiries directed to the New South Wales Poisons Information Centre constituted almost 8% of a total of 74,351 telephone enquiries. Organophosphates were the most prevalent group of pesticides (19%), followed by pyrethrins (10%) [9].

Enquiries to the New Zealand National Poisons Information Centre concerning pesticide poisoning exposures accounted for 15% of total telephone enquiries for the year ended June 1993 (see Table 27.1). The breakdown of enquiries with respect to type of agricultural agent is shown in Table 27.2 [10].

During the past decade the New Zealand National Poisons Information Centre accumulated a number of poisoning cases involving glyphosate (an agricultural herbicide) [11]. The majority of poisoning incidents involved accidental exposures; mostly whilst spraying glyphosate-containing herbicides using faulty equipment or inadequate protective clothing. In general, these cases exhibited minor local irritant effects which were self-limiting and responded well to symptomatic and supportive care.

Approximately half of the cases involved intentional ingestion of glyphosate, often concomitantly with other substances including alcohol or medicines. The remaining cases involved individuals who were spraying glyphosate containing herbicides in normal use situations. Normal use does not necessarily equate with recommended use, since it may also involve minor and predictable deviations from recommended use. These deviations include blowing out blockages in nozzles, leaking sprayers or spillages. Furthermore, normal use does not always involve the use of protective clothing or equipment.

The most significant problem described was temporary irritation of the mucous membranes from inhalation of the spray mist. In addition, some varying degrees of skin irritation were occasionally seen from prolonged exposure. None of these routes of exposure cause systemic effects. As with many other cases associated with the use of pesticides, a range of non-specific symptoms has been attributed to the use of glyphosate. Clearly, if individuals follow the recommended procedures as provided by the manufacturers or the distributors of pesticides, most if not all of these unnecessary exposures would be eliminated.

The transfer of pesticides to beverage containers also appears amongst cases of accidental poisoning, and may have particularly disastrous sequelae, especially in the case of paraquat. Decanting paraquat into soft drink or beer bottles has featured in New Zealand paraquat fatalities. The addition of both a stenching agent and an emetic in paraquat formulations was introduced to minimize unintentional exposures of this nature.

A rather unusual case of pesticide exposure reported to the New Zealand Poisons Information Centre concerned a helicopter pilot who was involved in the aerial application of a carbamate insecticide onto crops. Foolishly, he mixed the dry powder formulation under the still rotating blades of his helicopter, which caused the powder to disperse into his face. The resulting classical features of carbamate poisoning responded to prompt medical intervention.

**Table 27.1** **Total telephone enquiries received (July 1992-June 1993)**

| | Adults | Children | Animals | Other* | Unknown | Total |
|---|---|---|---|---|---|---|
| Agricultural agents | 536 | 495 | 189 | 288 | 78 | 1586 |
| Cosmetics | 29 | 418 | 0 | 3 | 8 | 458 |
| Household agents | 471 | 1941 | 31 | 87 | 68 | 2598 |
| Industrial agents | 395 | 251 | 25 | 334 | 61 | 1066 |
| Plants | 120 | 850 | 23 | 104 | 29 | 1126 |
| Pharmaceuticals | 992 | 1972 | 23 | 148 | 98 | 3233 |
| Miscellaneous | 98 | 106 | 8 | 85 | 25 | 322 |
| Total | 2641 | 6033 | 299 | 1049 | 367 | 10389 |

**Table 27.2** **Telephone enquiries concerning agricultural agents (July 1992-June 1993)**

| Agricultural agents | Adults | Children | Animals | Other* | Unknown | Total |
|---|---|---|---|---|---|---|
| Animal products | 71 | 70 | 7 | 9 | 4 | 161 |
| Fertilizer | 7 | 39 | 6 | 9 | 2 | 63 |
| Fumigant | 5 | 2 | 1 | 4 | 2 | 14 |
| Fungicide | 22 | 18 | 10 | 14 | 2 | 66 |
| Herbicide | 186 | 67 | 40 | 83 | 37 | 413 |
| Insecticide | 193 | 168 | 31 | 102 | 23 | 517 |
| Molluscicide | 8 | 48 | 20 | 3 | 2 | 81 |
| Rodenticide | 32 | 70 | 73 | 51 | 5 | 231 |
| Miscellaneous | 12 | 10 | 4 | 13 | 1 | 40 |
| Total | 536 | 495 | 189 | 288 | 78 | 1586 |

*Other includes Hazchem (spillages of hazardous chemicals, disposal methods, preventive procedures, MSDS request, etc.), labelling and scheduling queries, plant identification, etc.

## 27.3 Poisons Information Centres

The primary function of poisons information centres is to provide clinical advice on the management of poisoning exposures. The poisonings may be in an acute or chronic context, and thus poisons centres are able to gather case data on human exposures to a wide range of chemicals.

Data from both human and animal exposures are frequently used in the risk assessment of chemical exposures [12]. Most toxicity data are obtained from animal studies. Human data sources are often not recognized, and internationally there is a lack of systematic experimental and clinical (human) observational data. Available data are often of poor comparability and frequently include inadequate follow-up. A number of institutions and services have the ability to collect human health data, and these include poisons information centres, clinical toxicology centres, pre- and post-natal surveillance programs, occupational health services and hospital out-patient services.

Priority should be placed on collection of a minimum of relevant local data. This can be done at little cost and within a reasonable time utilizing:

i) Case data from inquiries to the Poison Centre. These may provide valuable qualitative and quantitative information on poisonings and can be used for evaluation of prevention activities;

ii) Case data from emergency rooms, forensic departments, country hospitals or occupational medicine; and,

iii) Technical information on toxic products and their effects which can be obtained from the literature and other direct sources such as from manufacturers and importers of chemicals.

The collected data should allow identification of local populations at risk, harmful substances and dangerous circumstances with respect to local poisonings. This should thus help initiate planning of targeted preventive measures.

Computerization may aid the storage, access and rapid analysis needed for toxicovigilance assessment. It is therefore necessary to promote:

i) A system for centralized registration of poisoned patients treated in hospitals (with diagnosis codes, such as the International Classification of Diseases established by the WHO, with accident details encoded by the E Code or Supplementary Classification of External Causes of Injury and Poisoning);

ii) Regulations for notifications of intoxications, *eg*, obligatory anonymous reporting of all cases of poisoning;

iii) Collection of good quality morbidity and mortality statistics with improved certification of death by cause; and,

iv) Pooling of information collected in areas of mutual interest, *eg*, experimental toxicology, analytical toxicology, occupational medicine, and toxicology research.

Poison centres have a fundamental role in relation to toxicovigilance and prevention. Toxicovigilance is a function which consists of the active observation and evaluation of toxic risks and phenomena in the community; an activity which should result in measures aimed at reducing the risks. Prevention is the main goal of toxicovigilance: the actions proceeding from toxicovigilance are intended to reduce or remove toxic risks in the community.

From the perspective of agricultural and industrial chemicals, the toxicovigilance role of poison centres includes:

i) Monitoring their toxicity by all routes for acute and chronic effects, particularly with regard to new products and formulations;

ii) Identification of changes in the incidence of poisoning, (*eg*, application of new pesticides) and seasonal variations in the incidence of poisoning (*eg*, agricultural practices); and,

iii) Calling alerts in cases of sudden, unexpected major rises in the incidence of particular poisonings in specific regions.

Preventive measures for both individual and multiple poisonings are established on the basis of data available concerning high risk factors such as circumstances, substances and potential victims. The preventive actions that may be initiated by poison centres, particularly with regard to agricultural and industrial agents, are principally:

i) Education aimed towards particular occupational groups at risk, and additionally the general public and health care professionals; and,

ii) Reports to, and collaboration with, various organizations and institutions; perhaps leading to the development of less toxic products, improved measures concerning safer packaging, design, labelling, transportation, handling and use of hazardous products, and limited availability, or withdrawal, of selected toxic substances.

The International Programme on Chemical Safety (IPCS) was established in 1980 and is a cooperative venture of the World Health Organization, International Labour Office, and the United Nations Environment Programme. The IPCS was formed to respond to the needs of Member States for ensuring that chemicals are used in such a way that they do not destroy or undermine the integrity of either human health or the environment but, rather, enhance them. The IPCS assess the chemical risks to health and the environment. One of the objectives is to support national programs for the treatment and prevention of poisonings. This has particular relevance in developing countries, where poisons control programs may be weak or non-existent [13].

The IPCS is preparing a poisons information package called INTOX. Evaluated information on the toxicological properties of chemicals, on how to diagnose and treat victims of poisoning, and on how to prevent poisoning, is published as Poisons Information Monographs. The Monographs are prepared with the assistance of poison information centres and other experts throughout the world who collaborate through the IPCS as a network of centres. INTOX has a training function for developing countries and is providing a twinning arrangement between established and new poisons information centres in order to encourage more effective international cooperation [13-14].

Despite the widespread use of chemicals, information on health and safety aspects associated with their use remains lacking. These data are needed for the risk assessment process.

Official recognition by the authorities of the toxicovigilance and prevention roles of poison information centres, would add credibility to the preventive actions generated by the centre. This could also enhance availability to the centre of the complete formulae of toxic and potentially toxic products.

At the United Nations Conference on Environment and Development (2-14 June 1992, Rio De Janeiro) the IPCS had been designated as the nucleus for strengthened international cooperation on environmental and sound management of chemicals. The role of poisons information centres in areas such as chemical risk reduction had been recognized, and governments were urged to establish poisons information centres in their countries.

In some cases, legislation allowing the disclosure of the chemical components of products to poison centres, while guaranteeing confidentiality, would be of utmost value. Authorities should seek the recommendations and advice of their poison centres concerning legislation relevant to poisoning.

## 27.4 Preventing Chemical Exposures

Preventive and educational actions directed towards the whole community (*eg*, poison prevention campaigns, posters demonstrating the dangers of poisonings from chemicals) for specific groups at risk (*eg*, safe use of pesticides for rural workers, risks of contact with specific chemicals in the workplace). The methods and techniques employed for the prevention and generating awareness about poisonings should be adapted to each nation's situation and circumstances.

For example, the authors of the recent poisoning review in Khonkaen, Thailand [2], recommended that pictograms of essential safety information be placed on the labels of chemicals, since the majority of occupational poisoning exposures involved people with low levels of education and that improving the level of education could only be a long-term solution.

These authors also recommended that where the use of child resistant packaging was not possible, that substances be secured safely, in places inaccessible to children.

Overseas studies have shown that child resistant packaging (CRP), especially child resistant closures (CRCs), is an effective means of reducing the unnecessary morbidity and mortality associated with childhood poisoning [15,16].

'Child resistant packaging' means packaging that is designed or constructed to be significantly difficult for most children under 5 years of age to open or obtain a toxic amount of the substance within a reasonable time. It is not childproof packaging. The packaging should not be difficult for normal adults (those with no overt physical handicaps) to use properly. Child resistant packaging includes packaging such as:

i) Child resistant closures that can, after opening, be reclosed with a similar degree of security; or

ii) Non-reclosable packaging, such as strip foil or plastic blister unit packaging.

Until recently, there was little evidence as to whether blister packs were as effective in preventing poisonings as child resistant closures. However, a recent study in the United Kingdom found that medications involved in poisonings were most frequently packed in containers without child resistant closures (63%) or transparent blisters (20%). Conversely, child resistant closures, foil strips, sachets and opaque blister packs had low associations with poisoning incident [17].

In 1970, the Poison Prevention Packaging Act was passed in the USA and since that time has steadily increased the number of substances covered by safety packaging to include all prescription medicines, and an increasing number of non-prescription and household products.

A comprehensive review estimated that child resistant closures on prescription medicines have prevented over 200,000 accidental ingestions during 1974-1978 and saved, on average, 26 children's lives $a^{-1}$ in the United States. The ingestion rate per thousand children has declined from 5.7 cases to 3.5 during the same period. Child resistant closures are now accepted and widely used in the USA [18].

It has been estimated by American researchers that the widespread use of child resistant packaging on medicines and toxic substances found in and around the home could reduce hospital admissions and the need for medical treatment by up to 80% (see Table 27.3 [15,18,19].

**Table 27.3 Number of ingestions of some regulated non-pharmaceutical substances reported in the USA for children under the age of 5: a comparison of the effective year of regulation and 1982 [19]**

| Regulated substance | Effective year | Ingestions in effective year | Ingestions in 1982 | Decrease |
|---|---|---|---|---|
| Furniture polish | 1972 | 697 | 229 | 67% |
| Turpentine 1973 | 777 | 110 | | 86% |
| Lye products | 1973 | 508 | 69 | 86% |
| Paint solvents | 1977 | 641 | 180 | 72% |

The United Kingdom introduced legislation in 1974 requiring some pharmaceutical products, such as junior aspirin, to be fitted with child resistant closures. One year later the legislation was extended to cover adult aspirin. Admissions to hospital for children under 5 years with aspirin poisoning showed a dramatic reduction of 85% during the period 1975 to 1978 [16].

In 1982 the legislation was extended to include toxic substances found in and around the home, and in January 1989, it was made a professional requirement for United Kingdom pharmacists to use child resistant closures for dispensed medicines.

Other countries, such as The Netherlands, France, Germany, and Canada, also use standards-approved forms of child resistant packaging as a means of reducing the incidence of poisoning of young children.

In New Zealand, the 1984 Medicines Regulations require that the 6 types of medicines that were most frequently associated with potentially serious poisoning incidents in children be supplied in strip or blister packaging which is 'reasonably resistant' to attempts of young children to gain access to contents. These medications are aspirin, paracetamol, iron salts, barbiturates, phenothiazines, and antidepressants. Liquid forms of those medicines may be dispensed with a container fitted with a CRC. It should be noted that this list is now somewhat dated, given that barbiturates are not now generally available in New Zealand.

A technical standard dealing with the quality of reclosable packaging was prepared and adopted in 1983, and further updated in 1991, but has never been used. Instead, packagings on medications are subjectively examined by Ministry of Health staff during their assessments of medicines prior to market release.

The Ministry of Health has recently undertaken a campaign promoting the use of child resistant containers for prescribed medicines. In the past, such campaigns have not met with success, principally due to the erratic supply of child resistant closures to pharmacies. However, the Ministry has taken cognizance of this experience and has gained assurance from suppliers of closures that adequate stocks will be available. This campaign is intended to encourage consumers to request child resistant containers from their pharmacists when obtaining their medicines. Thus, it is consumer driven rather than by legislation as is common overseas.

Unfortunately, this campaign does not address the issue of child resistant packaging for scheduled toxic substances. The Toxic Substances Board (an advisory committee to the Minister of Health) recommended that the Ministry adopt their proposed draft legislation amending the Toxic Substances Regulations such that child resistant closures would be required for certain *scheduled* chemicals including pesticides with container capacities <2.5 l. Currently, this remains unactioned.

## 27.5 Concluding Remarks

The activities of poisons information centres that have been operating in developing countries for several decades have demonstrated their role in the active observation and evaluation of toxic risks and phenomena in the community. The main goal of this activity is to reduce the risks of chemical exposure. Developing countries, through international cooperation such as the IPCS, can establish or strengthen the capabilities of their own poisons information centres which in turn can have a significant impact on reducing unintentional chemical exposures.

## 27.6 References

[1] *Handbook of Pesticide Toxicology, General Principals*, Hayes, W.J. and Laws, E.R. (Eds.), Academic Press, Inc., San Diego, California, 1991, Vol. 1, pp. 282.

[2] Chirasirisap, K., Ussanawarong, S., Tassaneeyakul, W., Reungsritrakool, W., Prasitwatanaseree, W., Sripanyawit, U., Premkamol, A., and Patitas, N., *Vet. Hum. Toxicol.*, 1992, **34**, (6), 489-492.

[3] *Pesticides in Sri Lanka*, Documentation of selected literature and legal aspects, Fernando, R, (Ed.), Friedrich-Ebert-Stiftung, Colombo, 1989, pp. 255.
[4] He, F., Wang, S., Liu, L., Chen, S., Zhang, Z., and Sun, J., *Arch. Toxicol.*, 1989, **63**, 54-58.
[5] Chen, S.Y., Zhang, Z.W., He, F.S., Yao, P.P., Wu, Y.Q., Sun, J.X., Liu, L.H., and Li, Q.G., *Br. J. Ind. Med.*, 1991, **48**, (2), 77-81.
[6] Zhang, Z.W., Sun, J.X., Chen, S.Y., Wu, Y.Q., and He, F.S., *Br. J. Ind. Med.*, 1991, **48**, (2), 82-86.
[7] Dorman, D.C. and Beasley, V.R., *Vet. Hum. Toxicol.*, 1991, **33**, (3), 238-243.
[8] WHO, *Environmental Health Criteria 97 Deltamethrin: A General Introduction*, World Health Organization, Geneva, 1990, pp. 133.
[9] New South Wales Poisons Information Centre, 1992 Annual Report, Children's Hospital, Camperdown, Australia (1992), pp. 22.
[10] National Toxicology Group, National Poisons and Hazardous Chemicals Information Centre — Twenty-eighth Annual Report, 1992-1993, University of Otago, New Zealand, ISSN 0112-853 1 (1993), pp. 17.
[11] Temple, W.A., and Smith, N.A., *NZ Med. J.*, 1992, **105**, 173-174.
[12] Temple, W.A. and Ferry, D.G., 'Solvent exposures and risk assessment', in: *Risk Assessment of Chemicals in the Environment*', Richardson, M.L. (Ed.), The Royal Society of Chemistry, London, 1988, Ch. 13, pp. 222-241.
[13] Haines, J.A., *Clin. Toxicol.*, 1992, **30**, (2), 239-243.
[14] Mercier, M., 'Risk assessment of chemicals: a global approach', in: *Risk Assessment of Chemicals in the Environment*, Richardson, M.L., (Ed.), The Royal Society of Chemistry, London, 1988, Ch.5, pp. 73-91.
[15] Maroncelli, R., Kaun-Till, G., and Rauber, A., *Vet. Hum. Toxicol.*, 1984, **26**, 16-17.
[16] Sibert, J., *Pharm. J.*, 1988, **60**, 1155-1157.
[17] Wiseman, H., Guest, K., Murray, V., and Volans, G., *Hum. Toxicol.*, 1987, **6**, 303-314.
[18] Walton, W., *Pediatrics*, 1982, **69**, (3), 363-370.
[19] CPSC Directorate for Economics, US Consumer Product Safety Commission, Study of Poisoning Packaging Prevention Act, Washington, D.C., 1989, pp. 12.

# 28. Some Information Regarding Chemical Safety Both in Occupational and Environmental Medicine in China

Shen Li

## 28.1 Introduction

Human society is currently an informative society; information in a similar manner to natural resources and to property necessitates significant attention. An *informative idea* is an important characteristic of every person, one should possess more information, and thus generate more initiatives and activities.

This chapter provides an overview of certain principal information techniques relating to chemical safety on occupational and environmental medicine in China, particularly stressing some of the national strategic objectives of environmental hazards for the year 2000.

This chapter also provides information on the general introduction to regulations and health standards pertaining to toxic chemicals in China, the situation relating to occupational and environmental medicine, and major institutions and journals concerning occupational and environmental medicine.

## 28.2 Strategic Objectives

### 28.2.1 Health Status Objectives [1]

#### 28.2.1.1 Controlling Dental Fluorosis and Skeletal Fluorosis due to Atmospheric Fluorine Pollution

The objectives are:

i) In areas burning high fluorine coal, prevalence of new dental fluorosis patients caused by atmospheric fluorine should be <15%, and simultaneously, no new skeletal fluorosis patients will be detected; and,

ii) In the year 1995 the prevalence of new dental fluorosis patients shall not exceed 40%, and the prevalence of new skeletal fluorosis patients shall not exceed 15%.

There are no base-line data for these objectives within the whole of China. However, according to a survey taken in the 3 Gorges area, the population in the area surveyed was 4,470,000 and 1,500,000 dental fluorosis patients were recorded. In the typical disease areas, prevalence of dental fluorosis was 90%; and prevalence of skeletal fluorosis was 40%.

#### 28.2.1.2 Improvements to Air Quality, Decrease in Mortality, and Prevalence of Respiratory Diseases in the Cities

The aim is to reduce mortality by 15% by the year 2000 in comparison with data collated for 1990.

For children 10 years old, the mortality of respiratory diseases and the prevalence of chronic tracheitis, asthma, etc., will be reduced by 30% from that recorded in the year 1990. This indicator in polluted areas will be ≯50% compared with that in control areas, and similar prevalence for persons aged 40-60 years in polluted areas shall not exceed 80% compared with control areas.

The base-line showed the following data for the mortality of respiratory diseases (including cardio-pulmonary): In 39 Chinese cities in 1981, 1986, and 1989 were 107, 109, and 109 respectively per 100,000. In 1986, the mortality of respiratory diseases for children was 27.5 per 100,000, and in polluted areas the prevalence of the above indicator for the 40-60 year age group was more than double or triple for control areas.

#### 28.2.1.3 Decreasing the Total Number of New Patients Suffering from Occupational Diseases

The aim will be 22,500 new patients in 1995, and 20,000 new patients in the year 2000. Some information on new patients suffering from occupational diseases during the 1980s are shown in Table 28.1.

**Table 28.1** **Numbers of the new patients of occupational diseases in China 1985-1989**

| Disease | 1985 | 1986 | 1986 | 1988 | 1989 | Average | New Patients Total |
|---|---|---|---|---|---|---|---|
| **Pneumoconiosis** | 17645 | 19335 | 15784 | 14965 | 16551 | 16856 | 84280 |
| **Chronic occupational diseases** | 3461 | 3972 | 3017 | 2813 | 2821 | 3217 | 16084 |
| **Acute occupational diseases** | 2781 | 2131 | 1796 | 1639 | 2259 | 2121 | 10606 |
| **Others (include eye, ear, nose, throat and skin diseases caused by occupational agents)** | 3126 | 2627 | 2824 | 2777 | 2126 | 2696 | 13480 |
| Total | 27013 | 28065 | 23421 | 22194 | 23757 | 24890 | 124450 |

#### 28.2.1.4 Decreasing Detectable Chronic Occupational Patients

The objective will be a reduction of 5% every 5 years. It is estimated that in 1995 there will be 2500 patients, and by the year 2000 it will have decreased to 2250 persons. Between 1985 and 1989, the average number of such patients was 3217.

#### 28.2.1.5 Decreasing Detectable Acute Occupational Poisoning Patients and Associated Mortality

In the year 1995 it is predicted there will be 2000 cases, with a mortality of 6%, and by the year 2000 these will be reduced to 1800 cases and 5.6%, respectively.

The base-line of this objective indicated that in the 1985-1989 period the average number of acute poisoning cases $a^{-1}$ was 2121, with a mortality of 6.6% [1].

### 28.2.2 Objectives for Reducing Risk Factors [1]

#### 28.2.2.1 Reduction of Blood Lead Concentrations in Woman in Cities

The lead concentrations in women's blood in the year 2000 is predicted to be 50 µg $l^{-1}$, and for women of reproductive age, the concentration >100 µg $l^{-1}$ shall not exceed 5%. For 1995 the recommendations are 55 µg $l^{-1}$ and 6%, respectively.

In 1988 the lead concentrations for women non-smokers in 16 cities in China were 59 µg $l^{-1}$, of which 7.3% were >100 µg $l^{-1}$, and 2% >150 µg $l^{-1}$.

#### 28.2.2.2 Decrease in Children's Blood Lead Concentrations in Polluted Areas

Less than 1% of children aged between 1 and 6 have a lead concentration in blood >250 µ $l^{-1}$, and a concentration >150 µg $l^{-1}$, <5% in the year 2000. By 1995 the concentration of >250 µg $l^{-1}$ will be <10%.

The base-line for blood lead concentrations in children showed that in the industrial areas of Shanghai in 1988, 60% of 12 year old girls had levels of >150 µg $l^{-1}$, and in the Shenyan industrial areas 39% were >250 µg $l^{-1}$.

#### 28.2.2.3 Reducing the Content of Organophosphorus Pesticides in Mother's Milk

The content of organophosphorus pesticide in human milk by the year 2000 should be <1 mg $kg^{-1}$ (calculated as milk fat), hence the level for infants will approximate to safety, and by 1995 it is predicted to be 2.0 mg $kg^{-1}$ in human milk.

The base-line of this indicator in 1988 for the content of these pesticides in mother's milk in 31 major cities of China was 4.93 mg $kg^{-1}$, and the concentration of DDT in mother's milk was 6.06 mg kg $l^{-1}$.

#### 28.2.2.4 Increasing the Rate of Monitoring for Occupational Adverse Factors

Monitoring objectives are planned to increase to 3-5% every 5 years, by the year 1995 the qualified rate will be 65%, and by the year 2000 it will be 70%.

In 1989, it was 62.05%. Information on monitoring is shown in Table 28.2.

**Table 28.2** Information on monitoring in enterprises during 1986-1989

| | 1986 | 1987 | 1988 | 1989 |
|---|---|---|---|---|
| Monitoring points | 486522 | 514603 | 639020 | 689714 |
| Pass points | 246015 | 291760 | 342275 | 427796 |
| Pass rate (%) | 50.57 | 56.70 | 53.56 | 62.05 |

#### 28.2.2.5 Increase in the Coverage of Preventative Sanitary Surveillance

The predicted increases in the coverage in 1995 and 2000 are shown in Table 28.3.

**Table 28.3** Predicted coverage of preventative sanitary surveillance in the years 1995 and 2000

| Enterprise | 1995 | 2000 |
|---|---|---|
| County level and above | 90% | 95% |
| Village and town level | 30% | 40% |
| Cooperation (by Chinese and foreign companies) | 95% | 100% |

According to estimators in the relevant departments, the qualified rate for enterprises at county level and above should be about 80%. Data are not available for village and town levels.

#### 28.2.2.6 Decrease in the Concentration of Carbon Monoxide and Sulfur Dioxide in Indoor Air

By the year 2000 the days during winter in which concentrations of these pollutants are likely to exceed their health standards will be reduced by 50% as compared to that for 1990. (The health standard for sulfur dioxide (daily average) is 0.15 mg $m^{-3}$ and for carbon monoxide 3 mg $m^{-3}$.) By the year 1995 the relevant days will be reduced by 30%.

The results of monitoring data collected during the winter of 1988 for 4 typical cities are indicated in Table 28.4.

**Table 28.4** **Results of concentrations of sulfur dioxide and carbon monoxide in indoor air of 4 major cities in China**

| City | Fuel | Sulfur dioxide | Carbon monoxide |
|---|---|---|---|
| **Chengde** | | | |
| Kitchen | coal | 0.48 | 7.4 |
| Bedroom | | 0.27 | 7.1 |
| Kitchen | gas | 0.16 | 5.2 |
| Bedroom | | 0.14 | 4.9 |
| **Shenyang** | | | |
| Kitchen | coal | — | 7.5 |
| Bedroom | | — | 6.2 |
| Kitchen | gas | — | 4.7 |
| Bedroom | | — | 4.3 |
| **Shanghai** | | | |
| Kitchen | coal | 0.86 | 14.1 |
| Bedroom | | 0.50 | 13.7 |
| Kitchen | gas | 0.065 | 3.4 |
| Bedroom | | 0.037 | 3.6 |
| **Wuhan** | | | |
| Kitchen | coal | 0.14 | 13.5 |
| Bedroom | | 0.087 | 9.9 |
| Kitchen | gas | 0.07 | 4.8 |
| Bedroom | | 0.041 | 4.4 |

According to the data from the Global Environmental Monitoring System (GEMS) December 1989 to February 1990 (total 90 d), information indicated that the number od days which exceeded the Chinese Health Standard were 88 d in Beijing, 30 d in Shanghai, 53 d in Shenyang, and 2 d in Guangzhou [1].

### 28.2.3 Social Participation [1]

#### 28.2.3.1 Increase in the Ability to Understand the Adverse Effects of Indoor Air Pollutants for Adult Residents

By the year 2000 at least 50% of adult residents should understand the adverse effects of indoor air pollutants on human health, and might take appropriate protection to decrease the concentration of indoor air pollutants to allowable levels. In 1995 the aim of the above objective will be 30%.

#### 28.2.3.2 Strengthening the Level of Knowledge of Toxicity of Major Pesticides for the Human Health of Peasants

In the year 2000 at least 50% of adult peasants will be aware of the toxicity of major pesticides on human health, and will have been taught many of the protective and emergency measures required. By the year 1995 the figure will be 30%.

#### 28.2.3.3 Residents able to Understand the Harmful Effects of Domestic Chemicals (such as cosmetics) on Human Health and able to take Protective and Preventive Measures

At least 20% of adult residents will be able to understand the potentially adverse effects on humans and be taught relevant protective measures. For 1995 these objectives are:

i) At least 10% of adults will understand how to select and use cosmetics properly;

ii) At least 15% of adults will learn the harmful effects associated with paints and decorative materials (such as formaldehyde, lead, etc.) in indoor atmospheres, and understand how to take protective measures; and,

iii) At least 15% of adults will learn of the adverse effects of surface active materials (for example detergents) on human health such as allergic reactions to skin, and understand how to take preventive and protective measures.

#### 28.2.3.4 Increasing the Coverage of Occupational Medicine Education

By the year 2000 at least 80% of the municipalities at different levels will be provided with relevant public knowledge of the toxicity, prevention of accidents, and emergency measures for chemical substances. By 1995 the target is 30% [1].

### 28.2.4 Services [1]

#### 28.2.4.1 The Proposed Increase in the Physical Examination Rate for Workers Whose Work Brings Them into Contact with Adverse Occupational Factors

The objective for the physical examination rate for workers for the period 1995-2000 is shown in Table 28.5.

**Table 28.5** Physical examination rates for workers in 1995-2000 (%)

| Industrial enterprises | 1995 | 2000 |
|---|---|---|
| In county level and above | 30% | 40% |
| In village level and above | 15% | 20% |
| Average | 22.5% | 25% |

#### 28.2.4.2 The Proposed Increase in the Coverage of Occupational Health Records

The objectives are shown in Table 28.6.

**Table 28.6** Coverage of Occupational Health Records

| Level | 1995 | 2000 |
|---|---|---|
| Enterprises in county level and above | 80-95% | 95-100% |
| Enterprises in villages and towns | 30-60% | 60-70% |

There are no available data for the whole country in 1990.

#### 28.2.4.3 Promoting the Reporting System and Network of Occupational Diseases

In the year 2000, in the whole of China (*eg*, 30 provinces), autonomous regions and municipalities controlled directly by Central Government will establish the above systems and networks. By 1995 this objective will be >90%.

In 1991 a computer software system for occupational medicine (including registers and reporting systems for occupational medicine) was available as a base-line. It is assumed that the non-available report rate for pneumoconiosis for the whole country was approximately 40% in 1986, and for 1989, the average non-available report rate for occupational diseases was 10% [1].

### 28.2.5 Training [1]

#### 28.2.5.1 Training and Expansion of Professional personnel in the Field of Community Hygiene (Environmental Health)

By the year 2000, 30,000 more professional personnel must be trained and a further 5000 new persons engaged in community hygiene work. By 1995 30% of this objective is scheduled to be accomplished. As a base-line in 1991 there were approximately 8000 professional personnel involved in community hygiene (or environmental health).

#### 28.2.5.2 Training Professional Personnel for Labor Hygiene and for Control and Treatment of Occupational Diseases

In 1995 the percentage of trainers for personnel engaged in labor hygiene and occupational medicine will reach 60% of the target, and by the year 2000 the target will be 90%.

Currently there are 150 institutions for occupational medicine, and approximately 300,000 professional personnel engaged in occupational medicine. In the whole country, there are 34 departments of occupational medicine in medical universities or colleges, plus 6 national training centers for occupational medicine. At the present time in China postgraduate students for Master and Doctorate degrees are enrolled by the Institute of Occupational Medicine, the Chinese Academy of Preventive Medicine, the Shandong Provincial Academy of Medical Sciences, and 15 medical universities.

In order to improve in the examination and professional accreditation of personnel in the fields of labor hygiene monitoring and the diagnosis of occupational diseases the coverage must be increased.

In 1995 80% of the above objective will be reached, and 95% by the year 2000.

At present in China there are diagnostic groups for occupational diseases at the national provincial and municipal levels, and their quality control must be undertaken.

#### 28.2.5.3 Training Technicians for Safety in Factories

By 1995 the training coverage for enterprises at the county level and above will reach 50%, and 70% by the year 2000. There are no current data available for this objective [1].

### 28.2.6 Data and Monitoring

#### 28.2.6.1 Establishment of Quality Monitoring Points for Indoor Air

By the year 2000, selective monitoring points for indoor air at various types of residences involving different fuels is to be undertaken. By 1995 10-20 representative monitoring points for cities and rural areas will be selected to carry out this work.

In 1991 the monitoring points for indoor air had not been established.

#### 28.2.6.2 Establishment of a Reporting System for Poisoning Resulting from Toxic Chemicals

In the year 2000, in the whole of China, *eg*, every province, autonomous region and municipality, the reporting system for poisoning will be established.

In 1995 50% of the above objective is to be accomplished.

By 1991 a few reporting systems for poisoning resulting from toxic chemicals had been established.

#### 28.2.6.3 Enhancement and Perfection of the Reporting Systems for Accidents Resulting from Environmental Pollutants

By the year 2000 the above system will have been completed in all provinces, autonomous regions and municipalities, with a reporting rate of >80%.

In 1990, the relevant reporting system was established in 29 provinces, autonomous regions and municipalities, but the system was not perfected and there were a number of missing reports.

#### 28.2.6.4 Undertaking Biological Monitoring Systems

In 1995, all major cities and important polluted areas will undertake regular biological monitoring for lead, cadmium, arsenic, mercury, and organic chlorine substances. The total population involved in this monitoring program will be 60 million. Currently, 28 capitals directly under the control of the Central Government are carrying out such monitoring.

#### 28.2.6.5 Establishment of Monitoring Points for Occupational Diseases

Monitoring points for occupational diseases will be conducted in 2 steps, and focused on the most severe areas suffering from occupational problems.

In 1995, 6 provinces (Liaoning, Shanghai, Shanxi, Sichuan, Hunan, and Jiangsi), and by 2000, 5 provinces (Hubei, Heilongjiang, Guangdong, Hebei, and Jilin) will establish the relevant monitoring systems. The requirements for labor hygiene management will be established by 1995 and 2000, respectively.

In 1991, there were no available data for this objective.

#### 28.2.6.6 Establishment of a National Center for Poisoning Control and a Data Bank

In 1995 the National Center for Poisoning Control and the Data Bank of Emergency Action for Acute Poisoning will be established and by 2000 some regional areas will also establish such centers. A national network for these centers will be established.

## 28.3 Regulations and Health Standards for Occupational and Environmental Medicine

Since the 1970s environmental protection programs have become a global project. China and a number of other countries have provided challenges for these programs. Since the foundation of the People's Republic of China some 44 years ago, China has developed industrially with great speed resulting in an increase in environmental pollution.

At present, the environmental programs are one of the most important national policies in China; the Government pays significant attention to these programs which are related to potentially hazardous environmental factors. These include chemical and physical factors (*eg*, noise, radiofrequency, microwaves, infrared radiation, etc., and biological pollutants in air, water and soil.

It is clear that chemical pollutants have a serious significance in all aspects of environmental protection requirements. The major chemical pollutants which are known to incur adverse effects to human health and to the environment include: sulfur dioxide, carbon monoxide, nitrogen oxide, heavy metals (*eg*, mercury, including methylmercury, cadmium, lead, etc.), pesticides, environmental carcinogens, (*eg*, asbestos, polychlorinated aromatic hydrocarbons (PAHs), etc.

Some information relating to the annual total emission quantity of wastewater, effluent gases and industrial solid waste were provided in the 1992 China Environment-Statistical Bulletin. For example, the annual total emission quantity of wastewater was 36.6 billion tonnes (except for rural and town enterprises, etc.); industrial effluent wastewater was 23.9 billion tonnes; the annual total emission quantity of effluent gases resulting from fuel combustion was 1050 billion $m^3$, including smoke 14.14 billion tonnes; sulfur dioxide was 16.85 million tonnes and the annual total quantity of effluent industrial dust was 5.65 million tonnes. The annual total emission of industrial solid waste was 30 million tonnes [2]. Thus environmental protection programs evoke important questions and effective steps must be taken for control and management measures.

The Environmental Protection Law of the People's Republic of China was adopted in 1979 and stipulated that 'prevention and control of noxious substances from factories, mines, enterprises, and urban life, *eg*, waste gases, waste waters, waste residues, dusts, garbage, radioactive materials, etc., as well as noise, vibration, and foul odours from pollutants must not damage the environment' (Article 16) [3], and 'provision is to be made to undertake experiments and adopt new technologies, techniques and devices which are pollution-free or cause less pollution. Business management and carrying out of production techniques have to be strengthened to make the best use of the environment; polluting substances such as waste gases, waste waters and waste residues, should be considered for transformation into useful materials. Discharge of such substances, where necessary, shall comply with the standards laid down by the State. Where such national standards cannot be met in the short term, a subsequent date will be set for their compliance with Article 18 [3].

It is well known that environmental protection programs are comprehensive and multidiscipline, involving coordination and cooperation for realization of the program targets. In China, the Ministry of Public Health is responsible for the medical and biological aspects in the field of environmental protection. Within the Ministry of Public Health there are various institutions established at different levels, such as the Chinese Academy of Preventive Medicine (CAPM). CAPM is a national research and technical institution and was set up in 1983. The primary purpose of this Academy is to promote and facilitate the implementation of the health policy, in turn promoting the concept of prevention first and thus making the public health service in China more efficient. Scientists at the Institute of Environmental Health and Sanitary Engineering (CAPM), the Institute of Occupational Medicine (CAPM), and the Institute of Environmental Health Monitoring (CAPM) are engaged in environmental and occupational medicine, including environmental health criteria, environmental health monitoring, environmental and industrial toxicology, etc. In order to carry on the policy of 'put prevention first' within the Ministry of Public Health there are sanitary and anti-epidemic stations at provincial, municipal and county levels. In 1990 there were a total of 3618 stations [4]. These institutions assist each other in investigating and monitoring the adverse effects of potentially harmful chemicals on man, for the supervision of the implementation of health standards, and in the prevention and treatment of chemical poisoning due to environmental pollution.

At present, in China, there are Environmental Protection Agencies (EPA at different levels, *eg*, at provincial, municipal and county levels.

The Chinese Academy of Environmental Sciences, directly under the NEPA, is a national research and technical center for environmental protection.

Some information concerning health standards for occupational and environmental medicine include:

i) Maximum allowable concentration (MAC) of toxic chemicals in the workplace atmosphere (TJ 36-79);

ii) Additional revised MACs following TJ 36-79, promulgated from 1983 to 1989;

iii) Additional revised MACs intended for promulgation after 1989;

iv) Maximum allowable concentration of toxic chemicals in the atmosphere of population centers;

v) Recommended maximum allowable concentrations for toxic chemicals in surface waters;

vi) Maximum allowable concentration of toxic chemicals in drinking water in China;

vii) Maximum allowable concentration for chemicals used in cosmetics;

viii) Classification of health hazards from occupational exposure to toxic substances; and,

ix) Classification of health hazards resulting from occupational exposure to toxic substances and include examples from different manufacturing processes. Details of these are described in reference [5].

The Chinese Academy of Environmental Sciences, directly under the NEPA, is a national research and technical center on environmental protection.

Approximately 263 environmental standards have been promulgated and issued by the NEPA by the end of 1992 [2], and these include:

i) Ambient Air Quality Standards;

ii) Marine Water Quality Standards;

iii) Surface Water Quality Standards; and,

iv) Standards for Irrigation Water Quality; etc.

These standards play an important role for the prevention of chemical pollution in China.

## 28.4 Data on the Present Situation Pertaining to Occupational and Environmental Medicine

### 28.4.1 Occupational Medicine

The *Annual Bulletin of Health Inspection* (1992), issued by the Department of Health Inspection, Ministry of Public Health, China, indicates that the total occurrence of occupational disease, nationwide, in 1991 was reduced by 9.5% when compared with 1990.

A total of 2359 new cases of acute occupational poisoning were reported in 1991, which was an increase when compared with 1990. Organophosphorus pesticides poisoning increased from being second in rank to first.

In 1991, 2390 new cases of chronic occupational poisonings were reported, with lead, benzene and trinitrotoluene continuing to be the 3 foremost causative agents [6].

The reported occurrence of occupational diseases in 1991 and their distribution by industry are presented in Tables 28.7 and 28.8.

**Table 28.7** **Reported Occurrence of Occupational Diseases, 1991 [6]**

| Classification of Diseases | No. of cases | % | No. of Deaths | % |
|---|---|---|---|---|
| Total | 21353 | 100.0 | | |
| Pneumoconioses | 14294 | 66.9 | 5128 | 1.4 |
| Coal Worker's Pneumoconiosis | 6300 | | 2032 | 1.3 |
| Silicosis | 5288 | | 2570 | 1.5 |
| Chronic poisoning | 2390 | 11.2 | | |
| Lead and its compounds | 1413 | | | |
| Benzene | 485 | | | |
| Trinitrotoluene | 90 | | | |
| Acute poisoning | 2359 | 11.0 | 179 | 7.6 |
| Organophosphorus pesticides | 773 | | 5 | 0.7 |
| Carbon monoxide | 633 | | 93 | 14.7 |
| Hydrogen sulfide | 92 | | 28 | 30.4 |
| Ammonia | 24 | | 0 | |
| Phosgene | 5 | | 2 | 40.0 |
| Cyanogen and organocyanogens | 5 | | 1 | 20.0 |
| Occupational eye and ear diseases | 1288 | 6.0 | | |
| Noise-induced diseases | 634 | | | |
| Occupational cataracts | 226 | | | |
| Occupational dermatoses | 438 | 2.1 | | |
| Physical factor-induced diseases | 94 | 0.4 | | |
| Occupational communicable | 212 | 1.0 | | |
| All other occupational diseases | 278 | 1.3 | | |

Excludes data from Tibet and Taiwan

Includes chemical burns, metal fume fever, occupational asthma, occupational intrinsic allergic alveolitis, byssinosis, underground coal-miner bursitis, and dental erosion by acids.

**Table 28.8** **Distribution of occupational diseases by industries, 191 [6]**

| Industry | A | B | C | D | E | F | G |
|---|---|---|---|---|---|---|---|
| Total | 21353 | 100.00 | 14294 | 2359 | 179 | 2390 | 482 |
| Coal/coke | 6850 | 32.08 | 6595 | 112 | 20 | 91 | 35 |
| Petroleum | 51 | 0.24 | 17 | 8 | 3 | 20 | 0 |
| Electric power | 274 | 1.28 | 208 | 5 | 2 | 38 | 2 |
| Nuclear | 25 | 0.12 | 14 | 6 | 0 | 0 | 3 |
| Metallurgical | 2648 | 12.40 | 1729 | 259 | 31 | 461 | 7 |
| Non-ferrous metallurgical | 1026 | 4.80 | 567 | 66 | 6 | 325 | 1 |
| Machinery | 1561 | 7.31 | 792 | 106 | 2 | 331 | 21 |
| Electronics | 83 | 0.39 | 22 | 2 | 0 | 33 | 11 |
| Weapons | 43 | 0.20 | 19 | 5 | 1 | 6 | 1 |
| Marine | 46 | 0.22 | 27 | 4 | 0 | 3 | 3 |
| Chemical | 1530 | 7.17 | 295 | 477 | 30 | 258 | 297 |
| Pharmaceutical | 195 | 0.91 | 24 | 22 | 1 | 24 | 35 |
| Railway | 326 | 1.53 | 263 | 16 | 0 | 21 | 3 |
| Communication/transportation | 297 | 1.39 | 205 | 26 | 4 | 48 | 2 |
| Airlines | 1 | 0.00 | 0 | 0 | 0 | 1 | 0 |
| Building materials | 1372 | 6.43 | 1177 | 23 | 5 | 15 | 7 |
| Construction | 155 | 0.73 | 74 | 35 | 7 | 22 | 5 |
| Geological/mineral | 152 | 0.71 | 129 | 14 | 4 | 5 | 0 |
| Hydrographical | 97 | 0.45 | 82 | 0 | 0 | 5 | 1 |
| Agriculture | 774 | 3.62 | 76 | 671 | 5 | 7 | 0 |
| Forestry | 61 | 0.29 | 23 | 30 | 0 | 3 | 0 |
| Light industry | 1182 | 5.54 | 663 | 70 | 6 | 274 | 11 |
| Textile | 211 | 0.99 | 31 | 15 | 1 | 32 | 1 |
| Aviation/aerospace | 29 | 0.14 | 9 | 2 | 0 | 8 | 0 |
| Commerce | 139 | 0.65 | 35 | 71 | 0 | 14 | 1 |
| Post/telecommunication | 9 | 0.04 | 2 | 0 | 0 | 4 | 1 |
| Public security | 70 | 0.33 | 65 | 1 | 0 | 1 | 0 |
| Petroleum chemical | 54 | 0.25 | 12 | 21 | 0 | 4 | 6 |
| Town/village | 1156 | 5.41 | 481 | 246 | 44 | 270 | 18 |
| Owned enterprises/others | 936 | 4.38 | 658 | 46 | 7 | 66 | 10 |

Excludes data from Tibet and Taiwan.
Includes chemical burns, metal fume fever, occupational asthma, occupational intrinsic allergic alveolitis, byssinosis, underground coal-miner bursitis and dental erosion by acids.

| H | I | J | K | L |
|---|---|---|---|---|
| 806 | 94 | 212 | 438 | 278 |
| 13 | 1 | 0 | 1 | 2 |
| 2 | 0 | 0 | 4 | 0 |
| 16 | 0 | 0 | 3 | 2 |
| 1 | 0 | 0 | 0 | 1 |
| 85 | 13 | 0 | 89 | 5 |
| 46 | 5 | 1 | 8 | 7 |
| 218 | 22 | 2 | 59 | 10 |
| 2 | 0 | 0 | 4 | 9 |
| 12 | 0 | 0 | 0 | 0 |
| — | — | — | — | — |
| 61 | 2 | 0 | 63 | 77 |
| 9 | 14 | 34 | 13 | 20 |
| 14 | 3 | 3 | 3 | 0 |
| 3 | 1 | 0 | 10 | 2 |
| 0 | 0 | 0 | 0 | 0 |
| 142 | 1 | 0 | 6 | 1 |
| — | — | — | — | — |
| 4 | 0 | 0 | 0 | 0 |
| 9 | 0 | 0 | 0 | 0 |
| 5 | 0 | 15 | 0 | 0 |
| 0 | 4 | 0 | 1 | 0 |
| 33 | 4 | 17 | 78 | 32 |
| 72 | 5 | 12 | 22 | 21 |
| 1 | 0 | 4 | 2 | 3 |
| 2 | 1 | 12 | 3 | 0 |
| 2 | 0 | 0 | 0 | 0 |
| 0 | 0 | 0 | 0 | 3 |
| 7 | 0 | 0 | 1 | 3 |
| 12 | 3 | 25 | 42 | 59 |
| 20 | 13 | 87 | 17 | 19 |

A=Total number of cases
B=Total %
C=New cases of pneumoconioses
D=Acute poisoning - number of cases
E=Acute poisoning - number of fatalities
F=Chronic poisoning
G=Occupational eye diseases
H=Occupational ear, nose and throat diseases
I=Physical factor-induced occupational diseases
J=Occupational communicable diseases
K=Occupational dermatitis
L=All other occupational diseases

### 28.4.2 Certain Basic Information on Environmental Medicine

The total death rate for 1992 on a nationwide population basis was $66.4 \times 10^{-5}$ which was reduced by 0.9% in comparison with 1991, with malignant tumors being the leading cause for the death rate. The mortality of cancer for the whole population is $125.76 \times 10^{-5}$ which consists of 21.66% of total deaths. In major cities the death ate for cancer for residents is $132.5510^{-5}$, including $99.48 \times 10^{-5}$ for middle and small cities. In addition, the mortality rate for lung cancer is the highest among all malignant tumors, it reached $33.64 \times 10^{-5}$, in major cities is $36.42 \times 10^{-5}$, and in middle and small cities the above mortality is $22.88 \times 10^{-5}$. When compared with 1988, the mortality level for malignant tumors increased by 5.6% in municipal areas including the mortality for lung cancer which increased by 16.6%, and in rural areas it increased gradually with each year, *viz.* it was $95.02 \times 10^{-5}$ in 1988, and by 1992 it had reached $102.53 \times 10^{-5}$ increasing to 16.2% of total death cases, and thus resulted in being the third greatest death cause. At present, in China, respiratory diseases are the foremost death cause, in 1992 their mortality reached to $168.92 \times 10^{-5}$ consisting of 26.6% of total deaths. Environmental pollution and adverse lifestyles are the major etiological causes [2].

## 28.5 Exchange Information Activities

The concept relating to chemical safety for both occupational and environmental medicine is a program similar to *system engineering*, and involves hygiene, toxicology, environmental protection, chemical engineering, etc., it has a requirement for comprehensive measures to be taken, to enable the continued use of chemicals. Hence, it is beneficial to become involved in the exchange of information on both an international and a national basis.

Since the 1980s a fruitful cooperation and contact with the International Programme on Chemical Safety (IPCS) has been established. The optimal use of these UN documents aims, and the involvement of occupational and environmental medicine, plays an important role and has many benefits.

The International Register of Potentially Toxic Chemicals (IRPTC) was established by the United Nations Environmental Programme (UNEP), following a recommendation of the 1972 UN Conference on the Human Environment, held in Stockholm.

IRPTC is a part of UNEP's Earthwatch programme created to observe environmental changes, and attempt to establish their causes and to communicate results. It works alongside the Global Environmental Monitoring System (GEMS) and other information exchange activities of UNEP, such as INFOTERRA. IRPTC maintains a databank of centralized computer files linking a formal network of government-nominated institutions.

The Chinese Government formally joined the IRPTC network in 1979, the Institute of Environmental Health Monitoring (former name of the Institute of Health) is the National Correspondent. In order to carry out the tasks required of the IRPTC national correspondent, the UNEP/IRPTC Chinese Working Group was established in 1980.

The 5 objectives of the IRPTC are:

i) To make it easier to obtain existing information on the production, distribution, release, disposal, and adverse effects of chemicals;

ii) To identify the important gaps in our knowledge of the effects of chemicals and call attention to the need for research to fill those gaps;

iii) To help to identify potential hazards from chemicals and wastes and to improve awareness of these dangers;

iv) To provide information about national, regional and global policies, controls and recommendations on potentially toxic chemicals; and,

v) To help implement policies for the exchange of information on chemicals in international trade [7].

The knowledge and level of English among Chinese people is not widespread or great, hence translated works are of significant importance. The following IRPTC publications have been translated into Chinese and distributed to principal and municipal institutions involved with occupational and environmental medicine:

i) Instructions for the Selection and Presentation of Data for IRPTC with 60 Illustrative Chemicals (IRPTC, 1979);

ii) The Legal Profiles for Selected Chemicals (IRPTC, 1980);

iii) The English-Russian Glossary of Selected Terms in Preventive Toxicology (IRPTC, 1983);

iv) Maximum Allowable Concentrations and Tentative Safe Exposure Levels of Harmful Substances in the Environmental Media (Hygienic Standards Officially Approved in the USSR) (IRPTC, 1984);

v) Some Selected Scientific Reviews of Soviet Literature on Toxicity and Hazards of Chemicals (IRPTC, 1983-1987);

vi) IRPTC Legal File, 1983;

vii) Some Selected IRPTC Bulletins; and,

viii) Selected Compilation on Preventive Toxicology (materials from IRPTC Training Course in Preventive Toxicology.

The International Programme on Chemical Safety (IPCS) was launched formally in 1980, it is a cooperative program of the 3 organizations — WHO, UNEP, and the International Labour Office (ILO). The evaluation of the risks to health and the environment are the responsibility of the IPCS.

The IPCS has 2 overall roles;

i) To provide a forum for the establishment of an international consensus for the assessment of chemicals for risks to health and the environment; and,

ii) To promote the national use of these assessments and to strengthen the capabilities of Member States to deal with chemical emergencies through the IPCS, the scientific basis is provided for Member States to develop and implement their own chemical safety activities.

The IPCS objectives are to catalyze and coordinate activities in relation to chemical safety, and in particular to:

i) Carry out and disseminate evaluations of the risk to human health and environment from exposure to chemicals, mixtures of chemicals, or combinations of chemicals and physical and biological agents;

ii) Promote the development, improvement, validation, and use of methods for laboratory testing and ecological and epidemiological studies, and other methods suitable for the evaluation of health, and environmental hazards and risks from chemicals;

iii) Promote technical cooperation with Member States, in particular, developing countries to:

- Facilitate the use of available evaluations of health and environmental hazards and risks from chemicals;

- Improve the capabilities of national authorities in conducting their own evaluations of health and environmental hazards and risks from chemicals; and,

- Strengthen infrastructures for safety aspects relating to chemicals, their production, importation, transportation, storage, use, and disposal;

iv) Promote effective international cooperation with respect to emergencies and accidents involving chemicals;

v) Support national programs for prevention and treatment of poisoning involving chemicals; and,

vi) Promote training of the required manpower [8].

The IPCS basic scientific risk evaluation documents are published in the Environmental Health Criteria Series (EHC). This series covers evaluation of specific chemicals or groups of chemicals and is designed for scientific experts responsible for the evaluation of the risk posed by chemicals to human health and the environment, enabling relevant authorities to establish policies for the safe use of these chemicals.

Up to August 1983, a total of 148 EHC documents have been published.

China, as a Member State of IPCS, and the Chinese Academy of Preventive Medicine (CAPM), as the IPCS Focal Point attends the IPCS activities via the Institute of Environmental Health and Sanitary Engineering (CAPM), the Institute of Environmental Health Monitoring (CAPM), the Institute of Preventive Medicine, and the Shanghai Medical University are all participating institutions for IPCS.

Great attention is paid to the distribution and use of the IPCS/EHC documents, some EHCs have been translated into Chinese including the first 50 EHCs. In addition, some of the methodological materials from the EHCs, such as: No. 60 Principles and methods for the assessment of neurotoxicity associated with the exposure to chemicals; No. 70 Principles for the safety assessment of food additives and contamination in food; No. 104 Principles for the toxicological assessment of pesticide residues in food; No. 109 Summary report on the evaluation of short-term *in vitro* tests for carcinogens; No. 141 Quality management for chemical safety testing, and No. 144 Principles for evaluating chemical effects on the aged population, have all been translated into Chinese and will be issued in 1994.

Health and Safety Guides (HSG) are another source of important documents from IPCS which are available and useful for administrators, managers and decision makers in various ministries and governmental agencies, as well as in commerce, industry, and trade unions who are involved in various aspects of using chemical safety and preventing environmental health hazards. There are short documents summarizing the toxicity information in non-technical language, and providing practical advice on matters such as safe storage, handling, and disposal of the chemicals, accident prevention and health protection measures, first aid and medical treatment in case of exposure leading to acute effects and clean-up procedures [9]. For optimal use of HSGs, some selected IPCS/HSG documents have ben translated and issued in China.

The International Chemical Safety Cards (ICSCs) which summarize essential product identity data and health and safety information on chemicals, are designed to provide evaluated information fur use at the shop floor level, in factories, agriculture, and other workplaces, bearing in mind that they have no legally binding status, and are not intended to be used in the regulatory process in a specific country. A standard format, including space for information of local significance such as legal restrictions, labelling provisions and first aid measures, will ensure wide acceptability and ease of use. The development of the ICSCs is based on the use of standard phrases with a view to facilitating the preparation, translation, and comprehension of these cards.

The Scientific Information Center (CAPM), actively joined the IPCS/ICSC project (1989-1992); it consists of 3 steps which have been completed as follows:

i) A Chinese word processor has been used to create a master TEXT File of Chinese standard phrases using blank brackets;

ii) The phrase Subfile for each chemical with data, in the brackets, for the corresponding English phrase have been compiled; and,

iii) Using other routines on diskettes to create and print CADR files. As a result 400 ICSCs (in Chinese) have been translated and issued [9].

Furthermore, the Computerized Registry of Chemicals being Tested for Toxic Effects (CCTTE), which is an IPCS/IRPTC joint project have also been attended to. This joint activity aims at developing and maintaining a data system, in addition to listing critical reviews of chemicals undertaken worldwide, and which serve as a center for information exchange to encourage better utilization of resources by minimizing duplication. Costs of toxicity testing are high and increasing, largely due to demands for more long-term studies in several species and examination of many organs. Some Chinese information resources are registered in CCTTE compilations, provided by the Scientific Information Center (CAPM).

In order to strengthen the exchange of information regarding occupational and environmental medicine, the cooperation and contact with The Royal Society of Chemistry, especially with Mervyn Richardson, has resulted in chapters being published, *eg, An Epidemiological Approach for the Risk assessment of Chemicals Causing Human Cancer and Other Disorders* [10], *Pesticides, Environmental Pollution and Human Health in China* [11], *Regulations and Health Standards in the Management of Risks in the Chinese Chemical Manufacturing Industry* [5], and *Reproductive Toxicology in China* [12].

At present, the Society of Preventive Medicine and Information was established, and is available for exchanging information. Additionally, there is the Society of Occupational Medicine, the Society of Environmental Health, and the Society of Toxicology. These societies belong to the Chinese Preventive Medicine Society, and each play an important role for information exchange.

## 28.6 Some Major Institutions and Journals Concerned with Occupational and Environmental Medicine in China

### 28.6.1 Major Institutions having Responsibilities for Occupational and Environmental Medicine

Institute of Occupational Medicine (CAPM), Beijing;
Institute of Environmental Health and Sanitary Engineering (CAPM), Beijing;
Institute of Environmental Health Monitoring (CAPM), Beijing;
Scientific Information Center (CAPM), Beijing;
School of Public Health, Beijing Medical University, Beijing;
Beijing Institute of Labour Hygiene and Occupational Diseases;
Beijing Sanitary Anti-epidemic Station;
School of Public Health, Shanghai Medical University;
Shanghai Institute of Occupational health;
Shanghai Sanitary Anti-epidemic Station;
School of Public Health, Tongji Medical University, Wuhan;
Institute of Environmental Medicine, Tongji Medical University, Wuhan;
Institute of Environmental Medicine, Zhejiang Medical University, Hangzhou;
School of Public Health, Sun Yatsen University of Medical Sciences, Guangzhou;
School of Public Health, Harbin Medical University, Harbin;
School of Public Health, West China Medical University, Chendu;
School of Public Health, China Medical University, Shenyang; and,
Shenyang Institute of Occupational Health.

### 28.6.2 Some Principal Journals Concerned with Occupational and Environmental Medicine

Chinese J. Preventive Medicine, Beijing;
J. Hygiene Health, Beijing;
J. Health Toxicology, Beijing;
Chinese J. Pharmacology and Toxicology, Beijing;
Biomedical and Environmental Sciences (in English), Beijing;
Environmental Sciences in China, Beijing;
J. Environment and Health, Tianjin; and,
Chinese J. Industrial Hygiene and Occupational Diseases, Tianjin.

## 28.7 Conclusions

Currently, the program of environmental protection is a national policy, and occupational safety aspects are of significant importance. The Chinese Government pays great attention to these affairs. Strategic objectives are important targets and aims to strengthen and to improve the quality of occupational and environmental medicine.

The aspects of information exchange are not limited and isolated by national boundaries. They should be beneficial and available for everyone on a global basis.

## 28.8 References

[1] Dai, Z.C. and Kan, X.G., *The Study on the Formulation of China's Strategic Objectives of Disease Prevention and Health Care for the Year 2000 A.D.*, (formulated by the joint organization formed by the Department of Hygiene and Epidemic Prevention, the Department of Sanitary Surveillance and the Office of Foreign Loans, Ministry of Public Health, China), published by Chine People's Health Publishing House, 1991, pp. 58-92.

[2] EPA, China Environmental Status Communique, 1992, pp. 1-7.

[3] Sun, G., Wang, S., and Li, S., *Environmental Medicine*, Sciences and Technology Publishing House, Tianjin, 1987, pp. 408-429.

[4] 1990 Statistic Communique on Chinese Public Health, promulgated by Statistic-Information Center, Ministry of Public Health, China, *China Daily*, No. 3386), April 11, 1991.

[5] Li, S., 'Regulation and Health Standards in the Management of Risks in the Chinese chemical Manufacturing Industry', in: *Risk Management of Chemicals*, Richardson, M.L. (Ed.), The Royal Society of Chemistry, Cambridge, 1992, pp. 167-190.

[6] Annual Bulletin of Health Inspection (1992), Department of Health Inspection, Ministry of Public Health, China, 1992, pp. 3-6.

[7] International Register of Potentially Toxic Chemicals (IRPTC/UNEP) (brochure), prepared by Peter Hulm with IRPTC staff; design and illustrations by Nikki Meith, printed in France, 1990, 4.

[8] The International Programme on Chemical Safety (IPCS) (brochure), 1990, 8.

[9] WHO/IPCS, Workplan of the Central Unit of IPCS for the Period 1992-1993, (IPCS/92.15), Feb. 1992, pp. 14-17.

[10] Li, S., 'An Epidemiological Approach for the Risk Assessment of Chemicals Causing Human Cancer and Other Disorders', in: *Risk Assessment of Chemicals in the Environment*, Richardson, M.L., (Ed.), The Royal Society of Chemistry, Cambridge, 1989, pp. 207-221.

[11] Li, S., 'Pesticide, Environmental Pollution and Human Health in China', in: *Chemistry, Agriculture and the Environment*, Richardson, M.L., (Ed.), The Royal Society of Chemistry, Cambridge, 1991, pp. 389-409.

[12] Li, S., 'Reproductive Toxicology in China', in: *Reproductive Toxicology*, Richardson, M.L., (Ed.), VCH Publishers, Weinheim, 1993, pp. 63-71.

# 29. Environmental Chemical Safety

Aysen Müezzinoğlu, Oya Gürel, and Mustafa Odabaşi

## 29.1 Chemical Contamination in the Environment

Today, the role played by chemicals in the life of both urban and rural people is so important that we can literally describe this world as a 'world of chemicals'. Consumption of more and more chemicals as societies develop is the reality of our civilization. Indeed, without the aid of certain critical agents such as agricultural chemicals and some medicines, undoubtedly we would not have the same quality of life.

Molecular biology shows that the molecules of some chemicals when reacting with each other in certain ways are upbringing the 'life' and many others surrounding these reactions are known as the non-living matter. In many cases the non-living materials interfering with these reactions support life. All substances both taking part in life forms and in non-living components that are coexisting in a certain unit section of the environment make up an 'ecosystem'.

Increasing use of chemicals has always been a trend in our civilization throughout the history of mankind, but the rate of this trend has become remarkable during recent decades. A continually increasing diversity of chemicals are being used in everyday life as pharmaceuticals, cosmetics, plastics and other polymeric substances, cleansing agents, agricultural materials, etc. Introduction of new 'synthetic' molecules or new methods utilizing the existing 'natural' ones by the mankind is aimed at an easier, more convenient, prosperous and healthier life. Nevertheless, due to this introduction, residues of these emerging new chemicals contaminate ecosystems by various mechanisms. When interference problems of such chemicals with the 'life' and 'life-support' reactions are considered, we can understand easily how critical this contamination may become in some ecosystems. This new problem is especially critical for some chemicals. In many cases not only the mere presence, but also the built-up concentrations of the chemicals are of importance. This relatively newly realized ecological disorder is known as 'pollution'. In more precise terms, the *presence of chemicals (or sometimes forms of energy) in parts of an ecosystem that would not normally contain that chemical (or energy), at least not in the quantities that they have built-up, is known as pollution.*

Mechanisms of chemical contamination in the environment has developed mainly due to the development of complex sampling methods and very sensitive techniques and instruments for chemical analysis. Without the aid of these laboratory instruments capable of detection of very low detection limits, many examples of the environmental contamination risks would remain unveiled today. Example include problems of pesticide residuals in a water body; the dioxins, furans and TCDD compounds in air originating from the incineration of solid wastes containing chlorinated polymers are all detected in ecosystems by means of such sophisticated research techniques and equipment. By example, with the help of a GC/MS system, both the identity of an organic chemical in the environment can be found and its concentration as low as a few parts per billion (ppb, $10^{-9}$) and sometimes even one thousandth ($10^{-12}$) can be found. There are several very sensitive techniques to measure and monitor such low level concentrations of chemicals.

Lists of chemicals in use, such as listing of CAS numbers with corresponding identifications often include toxicity ratings of pure chemicals. New legislation to control their usage in many countries in Europe and USA including Turkey has been issued by taking such lists as a basis [1]. Besides these legislations, strict rules are established in many countries with regard to commercialization of new chemicals to follow their fate in the environment. According to these rules, it is necessary to undertake several tests prior to commercial handling of new chemicals. These tests usually assist in the generation of data to estimate the behavior of a particular substance or its derived products in the environment.

Commercial materials are usually not pure in the active chemicals, but are a mixture of several impurities and filling materials in continuation with the active ingredient. These secondary substances are either other chemicals to modify the effects of the active substance or some filling materials added for commercial and other practical reasons. In many cases it is supposed that these secondary substances are safe for the environment. However, although they may not be so active chemically, it must not be forgotten that these materials may sometimes be perilous to the environment during their production, utilization, or during final disposal. Recently, this has been found to be particularly important for some organic solvents being used to apply paints, pesticides, etc. It has to be noted that some of these solvents evaporating into the atmosphere (indoor or the ambient) are known to be hazardous either to health or to delicate environmental balances.

Yet, in many cases chemicals are used in a satisfactory manner, in spite of their unwanted effects in the environment. That is why their risks must be assessed carefully and weighted for a trade-off between the benefits of using that substance at active concentrations against its harmful effects in the environment.

## 29.2 Transport Mechanisms for Pollutants

Environmental substances such as water and air are fluids capable of displacement over long distances. While they are flowing, they carry other materials either by simple drag action or convey them in a mixture or solution. These mass movements of fluids begin in one physical medium, but may progress and terminate in others. A good example of this is rain; as raindrops are falling from the sky, they dissolve atmospheric gases and carry them to the surface waters (rivers, lakes or the oceans) or to the soil through which they percolate. In all of these pathways, dissolved gases transform into other ionic forms and the latter react with many other chemical substances they transgress on their trajectories.

Flowing masses of environmental fluids cross not only physical environmental media or ecosystems, but also may originate in one country and progress through others and terminate in a different country. Sometimes even continents are trespassed. During these migrations of flowing matter, more chemicals are encountered, incorporated into the flowing masses and are carried from medium to medium, from ecosystem to ecosystem and from country to country.

During these 'transport' processes, changes occur in both the carrying masses and the chemicals being carried. These changes are seen in:

i) *Molecular forms* — by chemical reactions, biological or radioactive transformations;

ii) *Concentrations* — by way of dilution due to dispersion or simple diffusion, or by way of accumulation due to fractional distillation, condensation, etc.; and,

iii) *Movement pathways* — by way of intersecting these initial pathways by various others such as leaching, sedimentation, deposition, adsorption, absorption, desorption, evaporation, condensation, nuclear fission, retention in biomass, etc.

Such transport mechanisms are physical or chemical mechanisms in an ecosystem and obviously they do not include commercial transport of chemicals. In reality, national and international trade is responsible to a large extent from movement of many dangerous chemicals. Sometimes unwanted chemicals of some countries appear in less conscious countries, international seas or no-man's lands. Sometimes not only the chemicals or the wastes that contain them, but technologies producing such products and wastes are transferred to other countries. This has been subject to a special decision taken at the Rio-UNCED conference in June 1992 when the establishment of international rules and technology transfer organizations were promulgated.

## 29.3 Effects of Transported Chemicals on Local Ecosystems

Textbooks addressing environmental problems (for example [2]), use 2 complementary approaches to describe these transport processes:

i) The Lagrangian approach to study the fate of fluids using the conscience of an imaginary observer residing within one parcel of this fluid. While traveling with the flowing mass, this observer witnesses the physical mechanisms these fluids undergo and generate enough information to enable a calculation of the efficiency and time rate of change of each event; and,

ii) The Eulerian method is to assume an observer situated at a fixed point with given coordinates on the trajectory of the moving fluid cloud. This second observer notes the changes due to the cloud of fluid passing by with respect to time (*ie*, prior, during and after the cloud).

Expectations at a receptor site can only be comprehended when both of these approaches are followed fully.

To discuss effects of transported chemicals at a fixed location, methods of thinking similar to the Lagrangian and Eulerian methods should be followed. In other words they must cover:

i) Tracing the pollutants or polluted streams of fluids from their origin, over their trajectories, to their final sink; and,

ii) Make budgets of chemical substances (or other polluting agents) over an area of interest.

The first method which resembles the Lagrangian concepts, also can be followed by tracing the chemicals from their early stages of production to packaging, transport, storage, marketing, sale, consumption (to the end-use) and final disposal steps. This methodology can be summarized as 'from-cradle-to-grave' concept [3]. At each stage or step, minimizing the risks of escaping, seepage or leakage from the main line of transfer is the essential goal in this method. This, of course, necessitates a full knowledge of intercepted migration pathways.

Conversely, the second method can be best simulated by devising a planning instrument called 'Environmental Impact Assessment' (EIA) to planned activities at predetermined alternative locations. EIAs will be considered later in this chapter.

Examples combining both of these methods in long range transport phenomena are given below. The first example is to study the calculated air pollutant depositions over Turkish land due to emissions originating in the Central and Eastern European countries. This is mainly by the action of permanent weather systems prevailing on the Balkan peninsula. According to the data of European Monitoring and Evaluation Program (EMEP), Central and Eastern European countries emit high quantities of sulfur dioxide (Table 29.1).

**Table 29.1 Sulfur dioxide emissions from some Central, Eastern European, Balkan countries and ex-USSR European part in 1991 according to EMEP [4]**

| | x 1000 tonnes $SO_2$ per year |
|---|---:|
| Albania | 25 |
| Bulgaria | 515 |
| Czechoslovakia | 1282 |
| East Germany | 2621 |
| Hungary | 505 |
| Poland | 1605 |
| Romania | 900 |
| Ex-USSR (European) | 4455 |
| Ex-Yugoslavia | 740 |
| Total | 12 648 |

Emissions originating from these countries are dispersed over a trajectory intersecting the Balkan peninsula to reach Turkey by the use of a long range transport model. This study is taken from Pervan, T., *et al.* [5]. A mathematical model (SERTAD, Statistical

Estimates of Regional Transport and Acidic Deposition) which is known to be deviced by Fisher [6] has been used in this study and its results are summarized in Figure 29.1 [5]. İsolines in Figure 29.1 indicate both dry and wet sulfur dioxide plus the wet sulfate deposition at ground level in (kg $SO_2$ $ha^{-1}$ $a^{-1}$) units. These deposition figures indicate a very high background value upon which depositions due to local emissions must be added. Calculated background sulfur dioxide depositions of Turkey due to external sources are very high and they exceed the deposition limits for year 2000 of some countries such as Denmark (10.0 kg $SO_2$ $ha^{-1}$ $a^{-1}$, natural deposition excluded) and the Netherlands (25.6 kg $SO_2$ $ha^{-1}$ $a^{-1}$, natural deposition included) within several isolines in western part of Turkey. In contrast to this 12,648 million tonnes of sulfur dioxide emissions from these countries, Turkey emitted approximately 1.3 million tonnes of sulfur dioxide in 1991 according to the authors' own calculations.

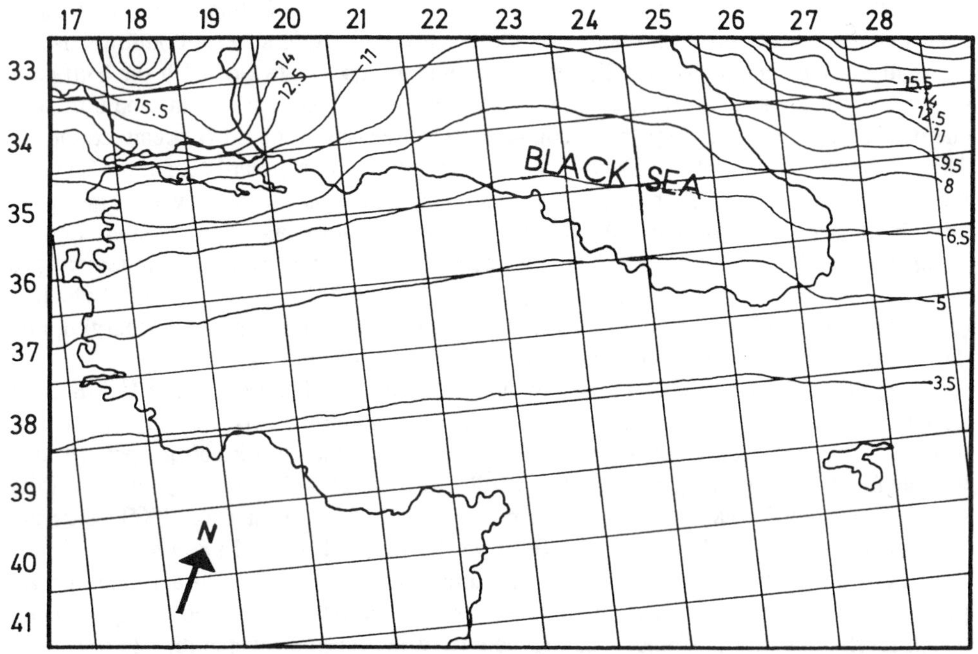


**Figure 29.1** **Dry and wet sulfur dioxide plus the wet sulfate deposition at ground level due to emissions from Eastern, Central and ex-Soviet European countries in (kg $SO_2$ $ha^{-1}$ $a^{-1}$)**

In spite of 1000s km in between, model calculations show that the imported part of the deposition from Eastern, Central and ex-Soviet European countries is more effective in Turkey than the self-emitted sulfur dioxide in a general framework. Obviously this may not hold true at some local problem areas within the country, where high emission sources are effective at a smaller scale .

Kantarcì [7] underlines the evidences of acidic depositions due to such extraneous pollutants which may be affecting the high mountain vegetation in western Turkey. He claims that at remote forest areas at high altitudes away from any significant local effect, hazards of acidic depositions are observable. He is also collecting data on the pH of high mountain ice to note this kind of transportation effects. Especially at the Trace part of Turkey (which is a continuation of Balkan Peninsula) and at the western part of Anatolia high altitude ice and some symptoms of injuries in trees indicate the importance of acidic depositions, however low and middle altitude trees in the same mountains do not exhibit such impacts [7].

Other good examples related with transboundary migration of chemicals can be taken from evaluations of pollution data in rivers which are crossing several countries. Many rivers in Europe such as Rhine, Elbe rivers are under close control of both the European Community and special international organizations to prevent contamination with chemicals originating from upstream countries to cause risks at the downstream countries. The European Community (EC) has set very strict common standards for today and for the near future to control chemical contamination of such trans-national rivers. Among the cross-boundary European rivers, the Danube has a unique place, as it crosses many Central European and Balkan countries which are known to pollute the river with municipal and industrial wastes. However, these strict EC standards do not apply to Danube which is originating from EC countries but flowing towards non-EC countries and discharging into the Black Sea which is also encircled with non-EC countries.

In combination with the Danube case, another example related with the Black Sea for studying the long range migration of chemicals is given below. This sea is a very critical receptor for many polluted streams as it has a unique stratification pattern and hydrologically is a (nearly) closed-sea. Hydrological box model studies based on salinity gives an age <400 years of residence time, from $^{14}C$ data the age of 2000 years are calculated for the deep layers below 100 m in the Black Sea [8]. Its main outlet is the Bosphorus which has a double layered structure; a deeper layer which acts like a river pouring the Aegean origin high salinity waters into the Black Sea, and an upper layer which discharges into the Black Sea low salinity waters in the reverse direction.

The Black Sea has a unique stratification pattern consisting of 2 layers. The oxygen containing upper layer occurs between 80-120 m, and below this layer there is no oxygen. These anoxic conditions are coupled with a high level of hydrogen sulfide. This oxic upper layer originates from the freshwater discharges into the sea, therefore, higher levels at the coastal zone and lower figures of the range coincide with the middle part of the Black Sea. The Knorr expedition at 1988 indicated the existence of a suboxic zone between where the dissolved oxygen reaches zero and where sulfide sharply increases, and that this suboxic zone was located at a depth of about 50-90 m in the central regions of the Black Sea. This is in contrast to the historical data from the same region indicating the depth of the region where oxygen and sulfide overlapped to be at -125 m. Similar dramatic changes are shown in the anoxic interface region [8]. It is probable that the stratification of the sea is being affected as land-origin oxygen-consuming pollutants continue to flow into the Black Sea. These rivers are impounded on land and clean fresh water supplies are diminishing. Therefore depths of layers may be changing due to the water budget limitations. [8]

The Black Sea is receiving an appreciable portion of the pollution originating from Central and Eastern Europe as atmospheric deposition and as water pollutants collected from the catchment areas of the big rivers, *eg*, the Danube and the Dnyeper, discharging at the west and north. However, not only the countries having rivers discharging into the Black Sea but many other countries consider this sea to be a dumping ground for their dangerous chemical wastes. For example, in the Turkish Black Sea coasts many floating barrels containing hazardous chemical wastes have been found a few years ago. Originally the barrels were certainly anchored to the bottom at locations outside of the territorial waters, but later their ropes or chains have corroded, broke and the barrels floated towards the Turkish coastline [9]. Although these barrels were found to be carrying the name and address of a foreign company (belonging to a country far away from the mentioned rivers and the Black Sea coastline), legally it was not possible to sue or punish this company for the unethical dumping of their wastes. This incident is an indicator of the situation of violation of international law and ethics related with protection of the seas. The Turkish 'barrels story' is very well known and is still being held alive among the public by the media. The story continues with the collected barrels which contained an unmarked chemical inside, villagers did not want them in their beaches, the Turkish Government had to expend significant funds to dispose of them with disposal methods still under discussion, and finally, everybody is satisfied partially after the burial of the barrels in special landfill sites.

The Black Sea coastal region of Turkey is an unfortunate area as it also received an appreciable dose of radioactive fall-out after the Chernobyl accident. After this accident almost a whole years' crops (mainly nuts and tea leaves) had to be collected and destroyed. So this 'barrels story' was only an additional incident to the misfortune in that part of the country. In both of these almost concurrent occurrences, the Black Sea coast people in Turkey suffered economically, ecologically, socially and perhaps paid with their health for the mistakes of others. Such incidents may happen to any nation or community anytime, perhaps even with more drastic end-results. This shows that the scientists and politicians of the world must work together to stop illegitimate transport of dangerous chemicals, and minimize risks of accidents which may create environmental disasters with transboundary transport possibilities.

## 29.4 Risk Assessment for Chemicals in the Environment

Among a few specific methods of handling pollution problems, quantitative techniques for assessing environmental risks due to contamination of environmental media by unwanted chemicals are becoming increasingly popular. Many papers and presentations such as [10] mention application of this type of risk assessment studies being carried out in the USA, Canada and Western European countries.

Quantitative risk assessment techniques are developed for the environmental presence of chemicals, and these techniques appears to be originating from ordinary insurance systems (see also chapter by Devos and Ekroos). It is hoped that in the near future, calculated risks of contamination during the production, storage, transport, use and final disposal of chemicals are to be balanced with the costs of loss of health, welfare, natural resource, and if possible remediation of the environmental media if pollution occurs, whence it will be covered by special policies to be issued by commercial insurance companies. At present, there is only one commercial system for insuring such risky incidents, and it covers oil spill hazards in the marine environment [11]. Many countries and big ports in the world do not permit uninsured tankers carrying petroleum and its derivatives to sail in their territorial waters, reach their ports or discharge their cargo unless they are insured against oil pollution risks. The authors believe that a good environmental management scheme for the near future must incorporate environmental insurance services to be based on realistic risk assessment reports. These services will need to cover all hazardous chemicals throughout their life spans (*ie*, 'from-cradle-to-grave') against damage to the environment at inadmissible levels.

## 29.5 Environmental Impact Assessment Studies

The Environmental Impact Assessment (EIA) is a systematic approach developed to predetermine and prevent the possible environmental degradations that may occur as a result of any activity. Earliest EIA applications were seen in USA (1970) and subsequently they were applied in Canada (1973) and European countries (1973). In Turkey, the EIA applications officially started after promulgation of Environmental Impact Assessment Regulation in Official Gazette on 7 March 1993. Presently in Turkey, there are 4 EIA reports at different stages of preparation by different groups; the first one was completed by a group of 30 scientists and coordinated by the authors.

EIA is a method based on preestimation-synthesis-prevention trio and in one sense it is a defense mechanism based on scientific grounds against the environmental degradations created as a result of man-made activities. Hence, in order for this mechanism to be effective it should be flexible and adequately extensive to enable the estimation of multi-directional effects that may develop as a result of different types of activities [14].

Even though the EIA approach appears to be a very logical and necessary procedure, there are many complicated economic, official, social, political, scientific and technological problems behind this technique.

In the 1950s and 60s, as a result of the recognition of the negative environmental effects of various projects, an environmental consciousness had formed in the world and it was accepted by wide social groups. Hence environmental studies gained importance and several environmental impact studies were carried out. At the beginning, environmental impacts were evaluated by cost-benefit analysis. But after various trials, the weaknesses of this system was realized and resulted in efforts being made to find a more suitable method; as a result of the current 'Environmental Impact Assessment' approach was originated. From the first applications of EIA, this technique was seen as a complementary tool for cost-benefit analyses and as a result it was used in a very narrow range, primarily for systematic data collection and evaluation. Currently it is used in a very broad sense to determine if a project can be realized or otherwise with its proposed design; to find if other project alternatives are present both providing the same benefits and being more secure from an environmental viewpoint; to determine the environmental risks as a result of the technological developments; to determine the environmental protection measures that should be taken at the realization stage of the project alternatives, etc. [16].

On examining the definition of EIA in different countries it is noted that it does not have a unique interpretation even though their objectives are similar. But there is one matter concerning EIA reports which should not be neglected, *viz*, EIA must not be the final stage of decisive project design and planning. An EIA study is an approach which provides alternatives and shows the favorable and unfavorable ways for these alternatives to the decision-makers to enable them to formulate sound decisions. Because of these reasons an EIA study should conclude with a list of logically consistent proposals. The final decision is given by the authorized persons and not by the people preparing the EIA report.

As can be seen in almost every new technique, initial EIA studies were perceived with suspicion especially in under-developed and developing countries. Many politicians and decision makers in these countries believe that environmental considerations in general and EIA formulations in particular hinder project development and think that developed countries are playing a new game on under-developed ones [12,15]. These people oppose EIA studies by saying EIA studies are time consuming and very costly. If one has a one track mind for economic development these may seem true. But today, our world is in a situation where everybody should enlarge their sight and evaluate every new thought and system from different points of view if we wish to continue to live in a clean and modern environment. Hence if we evaluate EIA studies for these 2 goals, it can be realized that consumption of time and money are not actually disadvantages if the EIA instrument is used properly and in time.

For example, if we take the time factor it is appreciated that an EIA study needs a long period of time. So at first sight, the result of delayed projects appears as an economic loss. But in this evaluation there is one matter that is being overlooked, and that is the commencement date of EIA studies. An administration that knows and believes the advantages of this approach will start the environmental evaluation of a particular activity or project as soon as possible and will continue with other planning studies related with this activity in parallel with an EIA preparation.

This means that the EIA is a very powerful planning instrument if used properly. The time taken to prepare an EIA report depends on the type of the project and also on the quality and quantity of the data that is present. Typical study periods take from 8 months to 18 months in the USA. But this should not be taken as a base for all countries because especially for the developing countries normally national development plans are not prepared for long periods of time. Hence in these countries EIA reports may be prepared in shorter time periods and then supported by follow-up studies. The important issue in the preparation period of EIA reports is that they should be in coordination with the planning stages of the country.

When the cost of these studies is investigated it is seen that they are built up from the costs of investigations and the cost of report preparation. Especially for projects in which the necessary data is not present, investigation costs rise considerably. Hence, for the sake of less costly but more dependable EIA report preparation, databanks should be formed in the countries. Thus, all the data that is present for different regions of the country which can be used in determining the present situation in EIA reports, should be collected in these data banks [12]. Additionally, to keep the costs low, at the beginning, the EIA study area should geographically be well framed and instead of an academic research approach the report should be prepared by giving concrete answers to concrete problems [13].

As an application example, the EIA preparation and permission procedures in Turkey are shown schematically and at different stages in Figure 29.2.

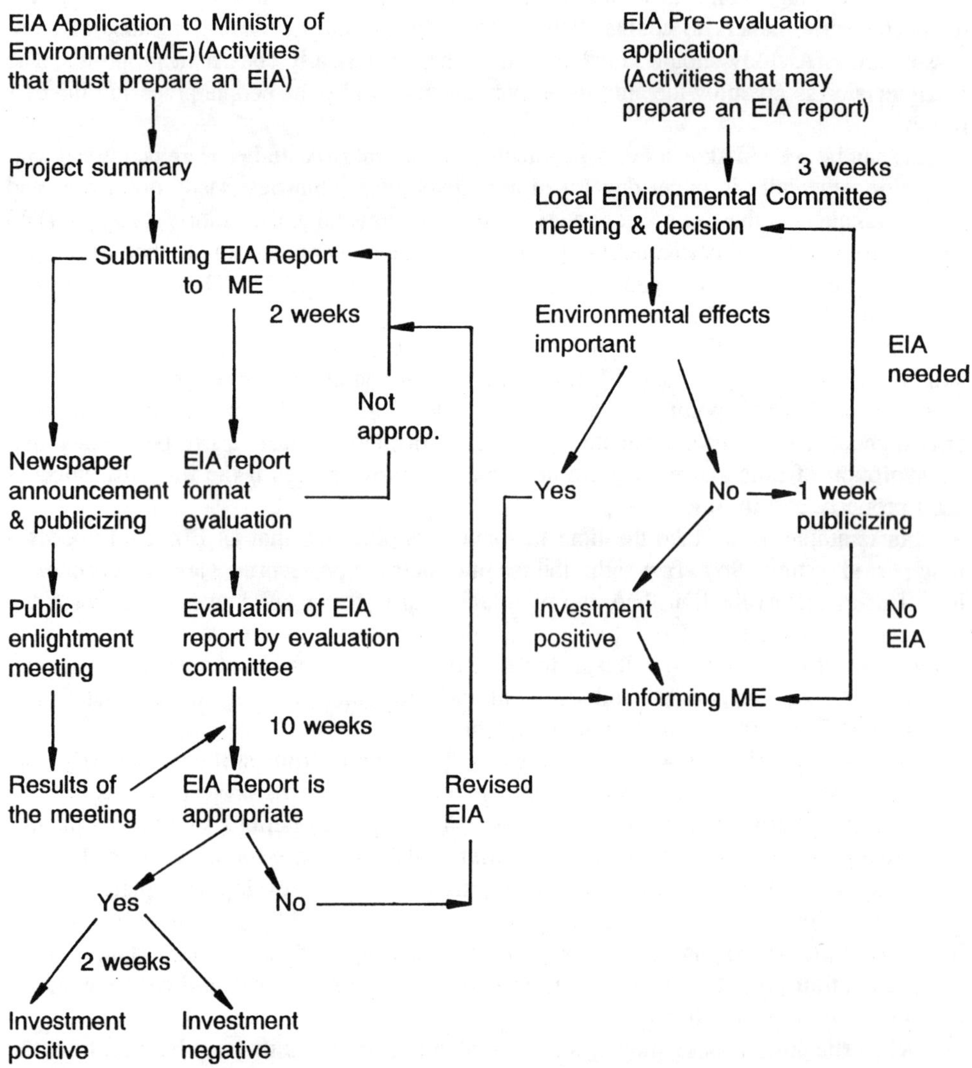


**Figure 29.2** Stages and timetables for EIAs in Turkey (ME, Ministry of Environment) [17]

In this chapter the authors do not wish to detail the preparation of an EIA report because this can be obtained from the literature. Instead, the authors will attempt to summarize some of the important problems that are faced during procedures of obtaining EIA statements and at the approval stage of the activity.

### 29.5.1 Public Participation

Generally in all countries public participation plays an important role in the approval or disapproval of any activity, and this is equally true for the activities in which EIA reports are prepared.

Authorities arrange public hearings to facilitate public consultation prior to irrevocable decisions being made.

EIA is a democratic method and is very helpful from both the environmental and economic developmental viewpoints. But the public involvement in EIA reports has been the subject of many discussions as to whether it is helpful or time consuming.

However, it has been argued that the scientific expertise necessary to determine the environmental impacts of any activity was the task for a limited number of people in government, industry and academia.

Disadvantages of public involvement and include:

i) Leads to unnecessary project delays because most of the public does not understand the technical language in the EIA reports, and further thinks that an EIA report is the final decision stage of any project. Hence the public, on grounds of environmental discontent, in general, may reject the application of any investment in their region even though the latest non-polluting technology to be used in that investment; and,

ii) Does not work as planned because those who raise issues at hearings are political lobby groups which do not reflect the actual view of the general public. This is true especially for developing countries where environmental conscience is recently developed. In these countries since environmental protection gains increasing importance on a daily basis, politicians who wish to become popular, and who do not have any other power in the government use such public hearings as a lifeline to try to climb higher in their political careers by appearing to reject industries for the sake of environmental protection. Naturally, if their rejection is based on sensible grounds this will be helpful for that region from environmental protection viewpoint.

Even though public participation is a tiresome procedure in EIA determinations, it is required. Otherwise, how can governments say that their decision truly reflects the public interest? Public involvement helps widen the scope of efforts associated with the initial assessments. To not involve the public will cause the formation of an anti-trust feeling among citizens as if some issues are being covered up by the government.

Since public participation is a very important part of in EIA studies, care should be taken by the decisive authorities, to include the varying ideas of many of the related public and not to be affected only from the ideas of the political lobbies, and to be able to distinguish real public concerns.

### 29.5.2 Bureaucratic Opposition

At the initiation of EIA procedures, government offices that previously gave permission to projects, fear that they will lose their power and may behave very sceptically against the EIA in the content commission. Unless the new EIA legislation clearly offsets their power for giving permission to projects, they may produce challenging decisions in the content committee and on the granting of permits.

### 29.5.3 Political Objections

Some local politicians act as 'cheap' heroes and try to become popular by just saying 'No', which is obviously the easiest method to safeguard the environment. This is a kind of 'power game' which they play with their voters. Although this harms people living in that region, as their region may lose the opportunity of receiving new non-polluting technologies together with any economic benefit, it may enhance the future of an 'heroic' politician near election time. This political gamble may sometimes transgress moral barriers and lead to accusations of the technicians and scientists preparing the EIA report by distorting the facts for the sake of money.

## 29.6 Economic Growth *Versus* the Environment

Economic development and growth for prosperity is the vital goal for the future of humanity. If this goal should not be achieved, there would be no discussion of current environmental problems by reason of human rights and also to guarantee a justifiable future to the whole world. This (perhaps somewhat immoderate) goal must not be overlooked.

Modern societies live on ideals and realities such:

i) More production/more profits;

ii) Population explosion;

iii) Increase in demand of consumption goods;

iv) More and more alternative varieties for goods;

v) Demand for continuous rise in incomes;

vi) Fight against inflation;

vii) Better distribution of wealth between social classes; and,

viii) Individualistic approaches to creation of jobs.

This produces the ideal of a rise in the standards of living. These are the concepts of welfare economics being advocated to the developing world. However, for this dream to be realized, we all need sufficient natural resources; for more production we need raw materials, land, water, energy, air and chemicals. Simultaneously, more wastes are generated due to intensive production, they must be handled in such a way as to ensure the purity of the remaining stocks of resources. In other words, we must protect the earth from being polluted, so that we can continue to use the resources for more production. Under these conditions, if welfare economics with its traditional methods of production, industrialization, trade and consumption are to be benefitted by everybody, it is very doubtful that the world resources will suffice. Therefore, the motto of the modern era 'consume more, so we can produce more and create jobs for you', is to be revised if we all want to survive on this small planet. Revision should commence by placing a limitation on consumption demands; it must be restricted to real necessities for a morally and physically healthy lifestyle and at the same time production methods must be carefully examined so as not to permit undue pollution occur to the ecosystems per unit of production [18].

Currently, in view of the differences in local objectives in the understanding of life necessities, our earth is faced with many problems. The critical problems of the earth today and for the future include:

i) Shortage of food in relation to loss of fertile land, sea and other aquatic resources for food production;

ii) Increasing environmental pollution;

iii) Shortage of (clean) energy sources;

iv) General shortage of resources for the adequate production of goods and services;

v) Lack of means for education to increase the skills necessary for sustainable methods of development;

vi) Depletion of the ozone layer;

vii) Global climatic change; and,

viii) Endangered biological diversity.

Therefore, sound global and national/local resource conservation policies are needed to fulfil the requirements of sustainable development goals.

According to literature sources such as [19], world economy will be 5 times greater if economic growth trends of the near past continues. This expansion will have to answer the demands of a world population about 4 times higher than the in 1950s. For such an expansion in economic growth only within the lifetime of the next generation, the first drawbacks will be seen in the available land resources for agricultural production. This is due to increasing rate of infertility and loss of fertile soil due to deforestation, overuse, overgrazing, consumption of vegetation cover for energy, careless industrial locations, waste disposal problems, acid rain and other acidification problems.

Limiting factors will include both land resources and a lack of many types of raw and auxiliary materials for industrial and services production. A good example is fossil fuels that are the largest portion of commercial energy resources. Such high percentages in fossil fuel use and their projected consumption create serious problems because of local air pollution incidents and certain other global problems such as climate change due to carbon dioxide increases in the atmosphere. On the other hand, in many developed and developing countries, non-fossil energy resources are available and the prerequisite for their wider use is the availability of improved technology in these countries. Geothermal, wind and solar energy are examples for such non-fossil resources waiting for much more wide-spread use with the assistance of technological innovations.

High technology is required for improving energy efficiency and minimizing the unnecessary energy consumption, *ie,* energy saving technologies. Today, in many developing countries including Turkey, carbon oxidation efficiency of medium sized industrial furnaces is as low as 65% for oil-fired, and 57% for mechanical coal fired units [20]. With the use of energy saving technologies these efficiencies may be increased to 85-90% and 75-80% respectively, thus creating a reduction in fossil fuel use and a reduction of pollutant emissions. Increasing the efficiencies in fossil fuel burning is very important when one considers that about 40% of world energy consumption belongs to the developing world.

## 29.7 Sustainable Development

On consideration of the foregoing, a reliable method for development with sustainable characteristics, in other words a development rendering the development realizable for the future, has been defined during the last decade. In order for this to be realized, world resources must be economized so that future generations can continue to use them for their share of development. Economy in resources necessitates some changes in lifestyles, reuse and recycling as well as prevention of pollution in industrial production and services. This is especially important in using scarce resources such as fresh water, energy, etc.

Although sustainable development has been recognized as a societal right for future generations and underdeveloped parts of the world, many administrators from the developing world do not appreciate this new planning philosophy. The simple reason for this is that they do not want to hear any other idea but the traditional development methods they have witnessed in developed countries. To them such new philosophies are invented by developed countries to slow down their 'sacred' efforts for development at any expense. In reality such philosophical approaches are beyond their intellectual capacity, so it is safer for them to refuse any method of development with global objectives and that they make use of every opportunity to exhibit them against their country's national goals.

## 29.8 Conclusions

Environmental problem solving creates major conflict areas with the politicians in developing countries. For example, Environmental Impact Assessment Studies is a good Eulerian approach to predict the effects of transport phenomena and a very convenient planning tool for future activities. However, in its application local politicians may block the scientific opinions from reaching the public. Thus *new technologies such as pollution prevention measures are sometimes refused. Thus they cause local people to lose an economic benefit, although it ensures the future of politicians near election time.*

To make development realizable in the future, and widespread for all nations in the world, sustainable development is the most correct approach for economic development. However, although sustainable development appears to be the only open gate for the near future of human development, many administrators from the developing world do not care much for this new planning philosophy for reasons of their single-mindedness. This indicates the importance of environmental education programs for bureaucrats and administrators.

One must also mention the importance of screening our lifestyles for the prevention of pollutant generation due to unnecessary consumption. Thus, chemicals that are contaminating the environment will be minimized and prevention will be a necessity rather than treatment.

One last conclusion in this chapter is that the scientists and politicians of the world must be brought together to stop illegitimate transport of dangerous chemicals, and minimize risks of accidents which may create environmental disasters with transboundary transport possibilities.

## 29.8 References

[1] Turkish Ministry of Environment, *Regulation for hazardous and dangerous materials,* Official Gazette, Ankara, 11 July 1993.

[2] *Mixing in Inland and Coastal Waters*, Fischer, H.H.B., (Ed.), Academic Press, New York, London, 1979, pp. 1-50.

[3] IUAPPA (International Union of Air Pollution Prevention Associations), *Declaration for the UNCED meeting of Rio de Janeiro, 5 June 1992*

[4] Data from European Monitoring and Evaluation Program (EMEP), UN-ECE.

[5] Pervan, T., Palaoğullarından, G., Tunçel,G., and Alp, E., *Uzun Mesafe Kirletici Taşınım Modelinin Türkiye ve Çevresine Uygulanması, (Application of the Long Range Air Pollutant Transport Model to Türkiye and Its Surroundings)* İstanbul Technical University, İTÜ 1. Air Pollution and Control Symposium'93, İstanbul, Türkiye, 15-16 March 1993.

[6] Fisher, B.E.A., *Atmos. Environ.*, 1983, **17**, 1865-1880.

[7] Personal Communication with Prof. Dr. Doğan KANTARCI, İstanbul University Faculty of Forestry, Büyükdere, İstanbul, Türkiye.

[8] İzdar, E. and Murray, J.W., *Recommendation for Future Studies, Black Sea Oceanography,* İzdar, E. and Murray, J.W, (Eds.), Kluwer Academic Publishers, NATO ASI Series, Series C:Mathematical and Physical Sciences-Vol. 351, Dordrecht/Boston/London, 1991, pp. iv-x.

[9] Turkish Ministry of Environment, *2000' li yillara doğru Çevre (Environment towards year 2000)*, Ankara, 1991, p. 98.

[10] Corey, Richard W., 'Air Toxics Hot Spots: Identifying Potentially High Risk Facilities and Conducting Risk Assessments', in: *Proceedings 9th World Clean Air Congress Towards the Year 2000: Critical Issues in the Global Environment*, Vol. 7, Montreal, IU-24C.10, Canada, Sept. 1992.

[11] Information obtained from TOVALOP, Tanker Owners Pollution Federation, Ltd., London.

[12] Uslu O., *Environmental Impact Assessment,* Publication of Türkiye's Environmental Problems Foundation (TÇSV), Ankara, 1986, pp. 1-15.

[13] Uslu O., *Examples of Environmental Impact Assessment (EIA) Application,* foreword, Publication of Türkiye's Environmental Problems Foundation (TÇSV), Uslu, O., (Ed.), Ankara, 1986.

[14] Environment Canada *Initial Environmental Assessment At Environment Canada, A discussion paper with recommendations: Report EPS 8/FA/1*, Canada, 1987.

[15] Harrison S.R., *Development, Environment and Poverty In Asia:An Economic Policy Perspective*, International Association For Impact Assessment, 1993 Annual Conference, Shanghai, 1993

[16] Anonym., *Methodology, Focalization, Evaluation and Scope of Environmental Impact Assessment*, Report of the first workshop-NATO-CCMS pilot study, Brussels, 1991.

[17] Turkish Ministry of Environment, *Turkish Environmental Impact Assessment Regulation*, Official Gazette No:21489, Ankara, 1993, pp. 62.

[18] Geyer-Allély, E., *OECD Approaches to Cleaner Technology and Technology Transfer, in Proceedings of the Workshop on Pollution Prevention Technologies for Developing Countries, May 21-23 1992*, Çeşme/İzmir, Turkey, Published by the NATO/CCMS Pilot Study Pollution Prevention Strategies for Sustainable Development, pp. 9-17.

[19] *World Resources Institute in collaboration with UNEP and UNDPWorld Natural Resources 1992-93, A Guide to the Global Environment Toward Sustainable Development*, Oxford University Press New York, Oxford, 1992, pp. 1-11.

[20] Bayram, A., *Yakma Tesislerinin Verimliliği ve Hava Kirliliği (Efficiency of Burners and Air Pollution)*, in *Proceedings of Turkish 5th Energy Congress*, Ankara, Oct. 1990, vol. 4, pp. 247-261.

# 30. Approaches to Identifying Adverse Health Effects of Chemicals in Use

John H. Duffus and Morrell H. Draper

## 30.1 Introduction

During the first half of the 20th century most substances that people were likely to encounter in their daily lives were derived with little modification from the earth and the growing things upon it, that is from animal, vegetable, or mineral sources. The tremendous growth of the chemical industry from a production of about one million tonnes to the current 100s of millions of tonnes has meant that today there is an extensive 4th category, synthetic chemicals, a class that had not existed in the environment until their creation by human scientific and industrial effort. These synthetic chemicals play an increasingly dominant role in human affairs throughout the entire world. Their number, importance, and the extent to which they have spread through the biosphere is still not fully appreciated. Notable examples of these chemicals are the pesticides, which have spread world-wide since the introduction of the first generally effective synthetic insecticide, DDT, in the 1940s. Other examples are the plastics which are now found everywhere, in such common items as floor and wall coverings, clothing, wrappings, curtains, insulation materials and furniture: they are also now a major pollutant of the biosphere because they are generally chemically stable and because our waste disposal systems are inadequate. The plastics themselves are the result of the development of 1000s of new chemicals by research laboratories in the chemical industry - now among the giants of all industry.

It soon became evident that the rapid development of new chemicals to meet perceived needs in agriculture, industry, and the household, with all their benefits to society, was accompanied by hazards to human, animal and environmental health. It was the dramatic emergence of some of these hazards and the urgent calls for action by public health authorities and other national and international bodies with responsibilities for health that brought about in the late 1970s and early 1980s the consolidated legislative measures for the control of toxic substances that we know today. At the same time there have been great advances in the understanding of the mechanisms of toxicity. The past 3 decades have seen the evolution of toxicology into a major multidisciplinary area of scientific endeavour.

There is now a general awareness of the necessity and benefits of synthetic chemicals and the need for measures to ensure that the potential dangers of a minority of chemicals are detected and, as far as possible, eliminated from the environment. However, the insidious nature of low level, long term exposures means that the inheritance of some decades of largely unsupervised, wide spread distribution of thousands of chemicals may yet be seen in morbidities or mortalities. Thus, there is now the problem of how to identify adverse effects of chemicals which are already in use. In order to derive a logical approach to solving this problem, it is important to understand the historical development of our current understanding of the situation.

The political will to introduce extensive legislation and to start the international activities that now contribute to the harmonization of efforts in the field of chemical safety arose not only because of considerable advances in science, but also because of a great increase in public awareness of the potential dangers of the newly synthesized chemicals. Perhaps the most significant development has been the explosive growth of knowledge about the molecular basis of genetics, in particular the structure of DNA and the nature of the genetic code. The further development of knowledge about the way that certain classes of chemicals can interact directly with DNA and bring about mutations, led to an understanding that the basic event in the causation of cancer could be a mutation in a somatic cell. Parallel with this was the exploitation of the experimental techniques used in genetic studies as assay procedures for detection of mutagenic chemicals and hence as screening tests for potential carcinogens. Most notable here was the research of Professor Bruce Ames into the use of specially constructed strains of *Salmonella typhimurium* as an assay system, known universally today as the Ames test. The extensive application, too often uncritically, of the Ames test and the many other assay systems that were rapidly developed resulted in the identification of many hundreds of putative carcinogens. This naturally attracted considerable attention, not only in the specialized scientific journals, but also in scientific journals of more general coverage and eventually in the magazines and newspapers available to the general public. Much of the wider discussion about the implications of these obviously important discoveries for human cancers was rather uncritical, often verging on the sensational. However, in spite of distortions and misrepresentations, there is no doubt that the issue of toxic chemicals is now firmly in the public domain as never before.

The issue of carcinogenicity came towards the end of the development of public concern about the environmental impact of potentially toxic chemicals. There had already been the discovery that the pesticide DDT could be found as far afield as the Antarctic in the fat of penguins as well as in the fat of many humans with no obvious agricultural connections. Furthermore, there was growing evidence of adverse effects on some species of birds and fish. There was the further disquieting discovery that purely industrial substances, polychlorinated biphenyls, could also be found in human fat, where no direct exposure could have occurred. The publication in 1962 of Rachel Carson's 'Silent Spring', about her beliefs concerning pesticide misuse, had a wide impact on the public perception concerning the dangers of the unsupervised exploitation of chemicals [1].

## 30.2 Development of Control Measures

Against the background outlined above, many nations introduced legislative procedures for the general control of toxic chemicals, as well as more specific measures for the control of pesticides, for the control of chemicals at the workplace, and for consumer protection. At the international level, there was a recognition of the fact, demonstrated by the discoveries concerning the polychlorinated biphenyls (PCBs), that as far as pollution was concerned, chemicals were not confined by national boundaries. Within the United Nations family, important developments were the institution of the United Nations Environmental Programme (UNEP), the International Register of Potentially Toxic

Chemicals (IRPTC), and the International Programme on Chemical Safety (IPCS) of the International Labour Office (ILO), the United Nations Environmental Programme (UNEP) and the World Health Organization (WHO). Other international organizations, such as the European Economic Community (EEC) and the Organization for Economic Co-operation and Development (OECD) also undertook important activities in the implementation of control measures.

The overall result of these national and international activities was a general agreement on the legal framework that was needed in order to be able to implement a programme of chemical safety. There was also agreement that, as a first step, all new chemicals proposed for marketing should undergo a series of defined toxicity tests [2]. In order to implement this within the European Community, a list of all existing chemicals was compiled called the European Inventory of Existing Commercial Chemical Substances (EINECS) [3]. This list defines those chemical substances which were on the European Community market between 1 January, 1971 and 18 September 1981. Within the European Community if a proposed chemical is not on the EINECS list as finalized,then it is considered to be a 'new' chemical and a legally defined dossier of information must to be supplied to the Competent Authority , where, after careful scrutiny, if found unsatisfactory, it may be rejected as unsuitable for the market. All this has taken a vast amount of effort by hundreds of lawyers, scientists, officials and politicians, at a cost of many 10s of millions of dollars. It is a good foundation but there remain huge tasks. The most obvious problem is the assessment of potential toxicity of those 10 of thousands of untested chemicals that are in the EINECS list and have been in general use for many decades. Much effort has been devoted to this problem and, although this aspect is outwith the remit of this chapter, some indication of the thinking in this area is needed so that proposals for future developments can be viewed against the totality of current endeavours. (See also chapters by Campbell, and Kulkarni and Nangle.)

## 30.3 The Current Chemical Dimension

Attempts to select from the 1000s of potentially toxic chemicals a manageable list of substances that really pose health problems, have never been entirely satisfactory. A number of ranking schemes have been proposed, either with a view to deciding priorities for regulatory action, or in order to identify priorities for research and data collection.

### 30.3.1 Commonly Adopted Approaches That Have Been Tried [4]

#### 30.3.1.1 Cost-risk-benefit Analysis

An attempt is made to quantify costs, risks, and benefits associated with the production and use of specific chemicals. In practice, this procedure is complex, time consuming, and labour intensive.

#### 30.3.1.2 The Delphi ('wise person') Method

A committee of experts establishes priorities on the basis of individual experience and collective judgment. This can be rapid and relatively inexpensive, but it is largely subjective and absolutely dependent on the abilities of the experts involved.

#### 30.3.1.3 Hierarchical Testing and Evaluation

This is the approach currently applied to new chemicals. Usually 3 levels of testing are used. At level 1 there are relatively quick screening tests; at level 2, substances identified as of concern at level 1 are subjected to more detailed laboratory tests. If level 2 tests substantiate the suspicions raised at level 1, level 3 tests involving some form of environmental toxicity assessment may be undertaken. Expert evaluation will be applied to the results at each stage and priorities set in relation to the seriousness of the effects observed and the likelihood of the substance becoming a long term environmental contaminant.

#### 30.3.1.4 Stressor Matrix Systems

Consideration is given to the levels of production, the transport, distribution, and utilization of the product, and the likely persistence and effects of the substance in the light of its potential toxicity. This is a time consuming and labour intensive undertaking.

#### 30.3.1.5 Structure/toxicity Relationships

Some chemical structures are related to known toxic effects and, on this basis, predictive schemes can be constructed for expected toxic effects which can then be ranked in terms of potential hazard to a population.

#### 30.3.1.6 Exposure/toxicity Assessment

An estimate is made of the amount of the chemical likely to be present in the environment and this is combined with a figure representing an index of toxicity. This can be a rapid method of ranking, but it is dependent on the availability and accuracy of data.

#### 30.3.1.7 Comparison of environmental concentrations with concentrations likely to cause harm, or with established permissible levels

Probable environmental concentrations may be calculated using data on production, use, emission rates and physico-chemical properties. These concentrations are then related to concentrations known or calculated to be hazardous and to any environmental standards or quality objectives that may have been set. An index of concern, and hence of priorities, may be established. This index will arrange potentially hazardous substances in inverse relationship to the degree by which actual or estimated environmental concentrations fall below the concentrations which may cause harm. That is, the smaller the difference between the concentrations, the greater the cause for concern.

Because of the great importance of chemicals in world trade, the OECD has invested considerable resources in matters relating to chemical safety, including the question of the identification of hitherto unsuspected toxic chemicals among the 'old' chemicals. In 1986 they carried out what was probably the most thorough and internationally significant exercise that has been attempted to establish methods for establishing priorities for the selection of existing chemicals for toxicity assessment [4]. The essentials of the scheme arrived at are set out below.

### 30.3.2 OECD Scheme 1986

#### 30.3.2.1

Selection from the universe of chemicals of substances to be considered (set A). This set may be selected by deletion from the universe of chemicals of those that are judged to be irrelevant or difficult to review (see [5]), such as:

i) Substances already regulated;

ii) Substances not subject to regulation;

iii) Substances without Chemical Abstract Service (CAS) registry numbers;

iv) Substances difficult to characterize; and,

v) Environmental mixtures.

#### 30.3.2.2

Selection from set A of those substances that may reach the human environment at exposure levels that may be significant (set B). Set B should include substances that may affect environmental processes of immediate importance to human health, such as the activity of sewage degrading organisms. Assessment of probable exposure levels should take into account such data as production, use and disposal quantities, octanol-water partition coefficients and bioaccumulation measurements, volatility, measures of persistence and biodegradability, probable environmental mobility, and major ecological effects.

**30.3.2.3**

Selection from set B of those substances associated with persistent or irreversible adverse effects on human health (set C). Substances likely to cause transient or reversible effects are eliminated at this stage.

- Ranking of substances in set C on the basis of:

  i) Estimated environmental exposure levels; and,

  ii) Severity of possible persistent or irreversible adverse effects in response to estimated exposures.

  Ranking is largely a matter of opinion and its effectiveness is absolutely dependent on the expertise of the people involved. The group carrying out the ranking must include medical, ecological and chemical experts.

- Review stage

  Because of the complexity of the problems and the serious consequences of erroneous decisions, the ranking procedure should be subject to independent review which would pay particular attention to the reliability of the underlying data.

- Implementation of control measures and further studies on selected chemicals as indicated by the ranking process.

- Regular revision of priorities in the light of new information.

  The work of the OECD has progressed to the point of producing a list of about 1500 existing chemicals (the EXICHEM list) which are being given priority for toxicity assessment. The chemicals were selected mainly on the basis of their being in large-scale production, this being regarded as an indication of potential for extensive exposure of human populations. The assessments are being carried out on an international basis by the OECD countries, with co-operation of IPCS and IRPTC. This represents a major step forward in applying limited resources effectively to tackle the problems associated with the use of potentially toxic chemicals.

## 30.4 Chemicals in the Community

It is clear from the above considerations that as far as assessment of chemical hazards is concerned, there is general agreement on how to proceed, even though, because of the obligation to test all new chemicals and the shortages of resources and expertise, many thousands of 'old' chemicals are in the queue for examination. It is evident that it will take many years to clear this backlog.

Scientific studies on chemicals lead to the conclusion that the presence of some chemicals in the community are likely in particular circumstances to cause harm. There are many examples where this conclusion has been amply justified, so much so that it is possible that there is much more ill health in the community brought on by exposure to chemicals than has been suspected. This leads to a basic question — just how much disease in the community is caused by chemical exposure? This in turn poses the question - how should this possibility be investigated? If it is confirmed that there is a significant burden of disease due to chemical exposure, what steps can be taken to alleviate the situation? As will be discussed, there are no adequate answers to these 3 questions but attempting to answer them indicates where action is needed.

Let us consider acrylonitrile and one of the products in which it is incorporated as an example of how a chemical enters the community and may cause problems. A primary chemical producer acquires raw materials from oil or gas and these are processed to produce vinyl chloride monomer and acrylonitrile as stock chemicals. These, in turn, go to a manufacturer who makes stiffened plastic tubs or cartons for margarine, and, in due course, these are filled with margarine by a product distributor, sent to a supermarket, and, hence, to the consumer. It is subsequently discovered that acrylonitrile can leach out of the plastic into the margarine in significant quantities. Thus, for this one chemical, a putative carcinogen, at least 4 populations can be identified as at risk. These are 3 groups of workers and a group of consumers, the latter of possibly enormous extent and covering all age groups and degrees of susceptibility. In fact, as far as the identification of chemical safety issues is concerned, the sequence that actually occurred was as follows:

i) Identification of acrylonitrile as a potential carcinogen towards the end of the 1980s;

ii) Secondly tracking down of populations at risk; and

iii) Implementation of measures to eliminate or, at least, reduce the risk.

In the case of an important industrial chemical such as acrylonitrile, that can be used in quantities of the order of 1000s of tonnes, measures to reduce risk will include defining an acceptable exposure level at the workplace and monitoring the environment to ensue compliance. Ideally, the workers themselves should be monitored to determine the quantities absorbed during exposure, but this is rarely practical. An important parallel contribution to the overall safety assessment of acrylonitrile is an epidemiological study of the mortality figures for the exposed workforce.

As far as the exposure of consumers to acrylonitrile was concerned, this was eliminated by changing the manufacturing process. Acrylonitrile illustrates well the sequence of events that should follow upon the discovery that a chemical can pose a serious hazard to health. It is not the purpose of the present discussion to examine the acrylonitrile sequence in detail, except to note that even in this apparently well defined situation many problems remain. For example, the suspicion that exposure to acrylonitrile can result in brain tumors has not yet been resolved (see [6]).

## 30.5 Chemicals in Industry and Carcinogenicity

It was the issue of chemical carcinogenesis that provided much of the impetus that led to the framework that now exists for toxic chemicals control. There were clear indications of a need for some legislative measures to ensure safety in use of dangerous chemicals from the very earliest developments in the modern chemical industry, namely the dyestuff and coal tar industries of the early part of the century. The few physicians who concerned themselves with the diseases of the workers in manufacturing industries, the pioneers of occupational medicine, had been commenting on the association between chemical exposure and disease since the earliest days of the industrial revolution. The association of bladder cancer with exposure to chemicals in the dyestuff industry was described as far back as 1895 [7]. The skin cancers in the coal industry have been studied for over half a century. The scrotal cancer of the chimney sweep, noted by Percival Pott in the eighteenth century has been replaced by the scrotal cancer of the lathe worker exposed to cutting oil in the 20th century. Lead, arsenic and mercury have been recognized industrial hazards for a long time. Indeed mercury entered the English language in the phrase 'mad as a hatter' because of its effects on those who used it in hat making. However, such manifestations of disease were in general regarded as curiosities rather than indications of an underlying problem. Fortunately, now the situation is quite different.

The developments following the identification of carcinogenic hazards at the workplace need to be considered in some detail because they have set the stage for all future developments in toxic chemicals control. The deliberations of International Agency for Research on Cancer (IARC) expert working groups identified chemicals that were clearly human carcinogens and for which safety procedures were essential. The next step was to try to identify the exposed worker population at risk. This is a complex matter that involves production statistics, factory utilization statistics, the identification within a factory of those processes that involve the handling of the chemical, possible secondary distribution exposures and the like. This is an exercise that has proved to be very difficult, even in a heavily industrialized country such as the USA. Samuels [8], has put together some estimates of exposed work populations in the USA at risk from regulated and unregulated carcinogens or carcinogenic processes. In all, it appears that many millions of workers are at some level of risk.

Epidemiological studies are required to determine the reality of any postulated health hazard for human beings. Such studies provide the definitive evidence underlining the IARC conclusions that a chemical or process should be a group 1 carcinogen. Difficult though epidemiological studies may be, and handicapped as they are by poor records, epidemiological studies are the keystone of the arch of chemical safety, with the science of toxicology as one base and with preventative measures as the other. Epidemiology depends on facts relevant to health and it is essential that facts about health are adequately documented and made available.

The issue of chemical safety in relation to the problem of carcinogenicity has had a powerful influence upon events. The development of the control measures required for the prevention of industrial cancers can now be taken as a model for the prevention of other diseases caused by chemical exposures. A consideration of the classic studies of bladder cancer in the dyestuff and rubber industries can be used to define all the elements that must be put together to establish an effective system for the elimination of a serious chemical hazard.

The problem of bladder cancer in industry was identified following the clinical observation of an increased incidence of the disease in workers in particular industries. Further enquiry established that the affected workers were located in parts of the factory where exposure to a particular class of chemical occurred [7]. In due course, in this case some 60 years, these observations were confirmed and amplified by an epidemiological study showing that in the British chemical industry a high incidence of bladder tumors had developed in men exposed to benzidine, replacing suspicion by statistically significant evidence[9].

Parallel with an increasing clinical, concern among a few physicians about bladder cancer and exposure to certain chemicals, was the development of an experimental approach. In 1938, it was demonstrated that dogs treated with 2-naphthylamine developed bladder tumors [10]. This did not attract much attention because 2-naphthylamine was not at that time accepted as a suspect chemical. However, by 1954, benzidine had been shown to produce bladder cancers in dogs, and the coming together of the epidemiological and experimental findings was to have a powerful influence on future developments [11]. In the same paper, 4-aminobiphenyl was also shown to be a bladder carcinogen in the dog, and this led the authors to predict that this substance would prove to be a human bladder carcinogen. This was proved to be the case in 1958 [12]. Thus the elements of problem identification and evaluation are as follows:

i) An interest in a specific human illness;

ii) An association with a chemical exposure;

iii) An investigation of the association by clinical and epidemiological studies; and,

iv) Exploratory, predictive, or confirmatory toxicological studies.

As far as cancers are concerned, the current situation is that toxicological studies have revealed many chemicals with potential carcinogenic properties. On the clinical side, the early successes with bladder cancer and lung cancer have not been repeated. The cancers of the lymphatic and hematopoietic systems provide a continuing challenge. It has been claimed that pancreatic cancer in particular provides the greatest oncological problem today. It is one of the few cancers on the increase, leaving aside cancers of the lung and the association with cigarette smoking. There are weak links with urbanization and occupational carcinogens [13]. These particular cancers are good examples illustrating a fundamental difficulty that severely limits progress in understanding how chemical exposure may affect health. There is usually no available knowledge about any chemical exposures, often because those concerned with the patient do not seek it.

It cannot be emphasized too strongly that a most significant step forward in toxic chemicals control will occur when all those responsible for health appreciate the fundamental importance of an adequate occupational and environmental health history. In the evolution of the study of occupational cancer, the one great handicap that the epidemiologists have had to face has been the deficiency of exposure data. This is coupled with inadequate workplace records of staff activities and health, particularly data about the actual tasks performed and mortality records. Another difficulty is the tracing of employees who have left the industry or retired. It is a matter of great importance to ensure that zeal for the confidentiality of records does not impede genuine research efforts that are after all very much in the interests of the whole community.

## 30.6 Chemical Exposures and Illness

Moving from cancer to consideration of other diseases, the necessity of an adequate occupational and environmental health history becomes more apparent to those concerned with occupational health, but regrettably not to the general practitioner. There are two important aspects to the problem:

i) There is the problem of communicating the necessity to general physicians and helping them to carry out the task;

ii) There is the problem that the patient may find it impossible to recall adequately the facts of his various work situations.

Before discussing these aspects further, some attention must be given to the developments in toxicology that have led to the realization that the contribution of toxic chemicals to the burden of disease in the community may be quite substantial.

The thalidomide disaster made all those with responsibility for any aspect of toxic chemicals control aware that chemicals, be they industrial or therapeutic, could have serious adverse effects on reproductive functions. Attention was further focused on these possibilities with the discovery of the mutagenic potential of some chemicals. These early discoveries of the harmful effects of chemicals eventually resulted in legislative control, and from this the requirement for a more systematic approach to the testing of chemicals. Thus, in addition to general acute and chronic tests, tests were introduced for teratogenicity, carcinogenicity and mutagenicity. Toxicologists, following up clinical observations of neuropathies and behavioural changes subsequent to exposures to solvents and pesticides, began to study these aspects in animal models, and neurotoxicology and neurobehavioral toxicology began to develop. Following from these developments, a whole range of organ specific toxicologies began to be investigated as it became apparent from clinical and research findings that the harmful effects of chemicals could occur in a wide variety of systems, often appearing to the physician as a common medical condition. In recent years some chemical exposures are being linked with complex entities, such as cardiovascular disease. Rosenman [14] has set out some of the factors that have been associated with work related cardiovascular disease, and Samuels [8] has listed a large number of suspect chemicals together with estimates of the very large numbers of workers that could be at risk. Finally the latest developments in the field of immunotoxicology have revealed the possibilities of subtle long term effects whose ultimate manifestation as a serious disease may be far different from the original insult, for example, an autoimmune disease.

The importance and difficulties of obtaining an occupational and environmental history have been discussed by Goldman and Peters [15] and they have developed a systematic approach to history taking which could greatly assist in diagnosis. Their scheme is set out in Table xx 1. They also considered those signs and symptoms that could arise from an exposure to a toxic chemical and it may be noted that many of them are what are sometimes thought of as the 'ordinary' complaints that a physician would expect to see in his daily work. Goldman and Peters [15] also make the important point that it is not only the factory worker that is exposed to toxic chemicals. Consideration must be given to those chemicals that occur in and around the home, not overlooking the important category of hobby chemicals. Their paper lists household products and activities that can cause problems, usually from improper use.

Problems can arise in the home in most unexpected ways as happened in 1966 in Norway where an outbreak of severe allergic contact dermatitis occurred among housewives. This distressing condition was eventually traced to a particular batch of a dish-washing product that had accidentally been subjected to an abnormal procedure during manufacture with the result that toxic contaminants were unknowingly generated [16]. Similar types of skin disease are common in the community, but, because they do not come to attention in a dramatic way, the victims usually have to put up with a reduction in their quality of life, because treatments are ineffective because there is no real diagnosis. The chemical exposure is rarely pursued, not entirely because the possibility is not considered, but because there is little systematic knowledge in this field. It is at the crucial point of interaction between the patient and the physician that awareness must be fostered about the importance of knowing about chemical exposures.

As has been mentioned, the patient is often an unreliable witness concerning previous experience in industry. However, a solution to this problem lies in new developments allied to the availability of computers in the doctor's surgery. In France and in the United Kingdom experiments have taken place with 'smart cards', small plastic cards with a memory chip embedded in them. A patient's history can be recorded on the card and, when he goes to the surgery, he will present his card to the doctor, who will read it from his computer, update it as necessary during the visit, and return it to the patient. If such a card carried an internationally coded job history as well as the medical facts, this would be a major contribution to chemical safety.

**Table 30.1** **Systematic approach to history taking and diagnosis of occupational or environmental illness (After [15])**

<u>Step 1</u>

Routine Survey of Every Patient
- Jobs
  - List of current and longest held jobs
- Review of Possible Exposures
  - Exposure to fumes, dusts, chemicals, loud noise or radiation?
- Chief Complaint
  - Attention to
    - Any temporal relationships to work or home activities?
    - Any relationship to jobs or review of possible exposure options?
    - Other contributing factors such as cigarette smoking, alcohol use or medications?

<u>Step 2</u>

Sources of Exposure
- Workplace
  - List all jobs
  - Places of employment and product manufacture
  - Similar illness in other workers?
- Home Surroundings
  - Neighbourhood pollution (External)
    - Nearby industry?
    - Work clothes contamination?
    - Neighbours also sick?
    - Acute pollution disaster?
  - Household poisons (internal)
    - Use of household chemicals?
    - Hobbies?

<u>Step 3</u>

Identification and Handling of Hazardous materials
- Chemical or physical form of agent?
- How substance is handled
  - Operating and clean-up practices?
  - Protective equipment?
  - Ventilation?
- Modes of entry
  - Ingestion?
  - Skin absorption?
  - Inhalation?

<u>Step 4</u>

Follow-up, Consultation and Resolution of the Problem

## 30.7 Morbidity Data

The difficulty of disentangling from other diseases illnesses that might have arisen from a chemical exposure arises to a considerable extent because there is no framework for the systematic collection of morbidity data. Rutstein and his colleagues [17] have proposed an elaboration of the Sentinel Health Event (SHE) concept to relate to illnesses that can arise from chemical exposures and, thereby, to develop a framework for the systematic collection of data. An SHE is a preventable disease, disability, or death whose occurrence serves as a warning signal that the quality of preventative and/or therapeutic medical care may need to be improved. Thus, these events serve as negative indices of medical care. For example, a case of poliomyelitis is an SHE, in that it signals a breakdown in the immunization programme.

Applying the SHE concept to the field of occupational and environmental health defines the Sentinel Health Event (Occupational) (SHE/O) as an unnecessary disease, disability, or untimely death which is occupation or chemical exposure related and whose occurrence may:

i) Provide the impetus for epidemiological or industrial hygiene studies; or,

ii) Serve as a warning signal that materials substitution, engineering control, personal protection, or medical care may be required.

If diseases are to be designated in this way, it becomes essential to be clear about the precise identification of each disease entity so that physicians, both nationally and internationally refer to or count the same entity. This can be achieved by the adoption of the World Health Organization's Manual of the International Classification of Diseases, Injuries and Causes of Death [18], usually referred to as the ICD with a number relating to the particular revision, the one in current use being revision 10 [19]. The disease entities in the manual are systematically entered in numbered lines; each entry is known as a rubric; thus, no. 493 refers to asthma and would be referred to as ICD9, 493. This matter of unambiguous reference to disease entities is of fundamental importance for epidemiological work, obviously for the certification of death, but also for the collection of morbidity data. Thus, it is now essential that all those who carry out the first documentation of a disease conform to the ICD definitions, or defined national derivatives. The importance of this matter is still not as widely appreciated as it should be. Rutstein and colleagues [17] have surveyed the occupational health literature and compiled a list of SHE(O)s, each of which meets 3 criteria of scientific proof:

i) Documentation of associated agent(s);

ii) Documentation of involved industries;

iii) Documentation of involved occupations.

Their paper contains a valuable compilation of occupationally related unnecessary disease, disability, and untimely death.

In a survey of permanent or periodic data collection through sentinel networks of general practitioners carried out within the European Economic Community [20], national sentinel networks of GPs were reported to exist in 4 member states, Belgium, France, Great Britain and the Netherlands (Switzerland also has a system); other member states were in various stages of planning for the implementation of similar schemes. The problems that were faced in setting up such a network in Belgium have been described [21]. An International Primary Care Network, a consortium of networks in different countries, has been set up with 9 members so far (organizations from Australia, Belgium, Canada, Israel, The Netherlands, New Zealand, Switzerland, United Kingdom and USA).

Inadequate though past death certification has been because of a lack of a standardised nomenclature, at least it existed, and thus different kinds of death could be counted. Unfortunately the same is not true for morbidities, and it is only recently that some attention has been given to this problem. In the past, for obvious public health reasons, epidemics of infectious diseases were documented. Data collection was achieved by an obligatory notification scheme for specified diseases. Interest in the collection of data on general morbidities is a relatively recent development, and even then, in only a few countries. This is a major obstacle as far as effective progress in chemical safety is concerned. For example, if it is suspected that part of a disease burden in a community is a chemically induced asthma, part of the case would rest on establishing that there has been an increasing incidence of asthma over the years in that community parallel with an increasing use of or exposure to the suspect chemicals. If there is no knowledge of the incidence and prevalence of the disease, unless a unique cluster appears, the suspicion will remain as just another speculation in most eyes and, thus, not worthy of special attention, despite the importance of the disease.

In considering the morbidities of relatively common noninfective diseases, the magnitude of the task of documentation makes extremely difficult any solution based on an overall compulsory notification to a central body. In Europe at present there is only one scheme that reports on the morbidities underlying doctor/patient contact. This is the National Study of the Morbidity Statistics from General Practice [22], that has completed 3 national studies, having reported on the years 1955/56, 1970/71, and 1981/82. From these reports it can be seen, for example, that patients consulting rates for asthma were 9.6 per 1000 persons at risk in 1971/72 and 17.8 in 1980/81, and, for diseases of the skin and subcutaneous tissue, the rates were 105.6 in 1955/56, 110.8 in 1971/72, and 117.8 in 1981/82. It was noted that much of the increase in the latter category was due to rising rates for dermatitis, eczema, and cellulitis. Clearly this kind of information is of great interest to those who suspect that some of this morbidity may have a chemical basis.

Finally in these morbidity considerations, there is a particularly important source of primary data concerning toxic chemicals that should not be overlooked, namely poison information and control centres, especially as these are already linked both nationally and internationally, not only as poison information and control centres, but also with WHO programmes such as the International Programme on Chemical Safety.

## 30.8 Surveys of Industries

So far the discussion has centred around the problem of ascertaining the presence in a community of an excess of morbidities brought about by an unsuspected exposure to some harmful chemical(s). It is likely that a person with an illness due to an exposure to a harmful chemical will consult his family physician. Hence the crucial role of general physicians in future developments in chemical safety, even though at present they are not well informed about the possible effects of exposures to chemicals at the workplace, let alone in and about the domestic environment.

Turning first to the problems at the workplace, 2 major approaches need to be developed. One starts by looking at the problem from the periphery and working to the centre while the other works in the reverse direction. Starting from the periphery means establishing what industries are actually present in the community at risk and considering all the chemicals used by those industries. As was noted earlier, knowledge about the levels of production of chemicals is one method used for establishing priorities for assessment of particular chemicals.

Academic departments and government institutions, such as the Occupational Safety and Health Administration (OSHA) and the National Institute for Occupational Health (NIOSH) of the USA have invested much effort in developing what has been referred to above as the approach from the periphery. This strategy has been adopted because the lack of adequate disease surveillance methods has resulted in a failure to identify workplace related diseases that toxicological investigations indicate must be present. It is suggested that the supplementation of occupational disease surveillance with what can be termed hazard surveillance could greatly improve the detection of situations where an active intervention policy could be successful. There is a great deal of important information available about factories and the chemicals they use in official statistics from departments of trade, from those authorities that are responsible for the implementation of regulations concerning matters such as factory inspection, and from technical literature on the commercial and technical aspects of an industry. The procedure is complex but it offers a systematic approach to the location of situations which call for some kind of intervention [23]. Froines and his colleagues studied an industrial complex in the State of Los Angeles, USA, and the kinds of data that were available to them were, *inter alia* , a standard industrial classification (SIC), a compilation of inspection - based exposure rankings (IBER), an industry risk index (IRI), the results of the National Occupational Hazard Survey (NOHS), and an OSHA weighted index (OWI). Amongst other things, they prepared a list of factories identified by their standard industrial classification number and ranked them by the degree by which they failed an inspection, that is the degree by which they exceeded the permissible exposure level for some designated chemical(s). Other ranking systems for the same factories were applied and they do not agree very well. Nevertheless, an inspection shows that some industries overall have poor ratings. Thus out of the 25 a selection can be made for further study. The analysis is rather more sophisticated than indicated but the above gives a general idea of the approach at the industry level. Quantification of amounts of chemicals, measurements of exposure levels and numbers of workers involved gives an indication of possibilities of health effects, and hence the advisability of intervention.

The above approach comes from an industrial situation where a considerable amount of information was being generated, but not in fact for the purpose of hazard surveillance. The exploitation of similar sets of data along the lines suggested, even if less extensive should at least reveal factories, or processes in factories, that could be said to have a high index of suspicion. Unless some systematic approach along these lines is adopted many hazardous situations will persist to the detriment of the workers, particularly in the small factory.

## 30.9 Toxic Chemicals in the Factory

We turn now from the approach from the periphery, from a global view of an industrial complex, to the consideration of one specific factory, the health of each individual worker, and how it may be affected by the chemicals in that factory environment. Any proposed intervention must be planned with allowance for the fact that a factory is a complex situation where there are a number of conflicting situations. Thus, there is the perception of the purported effect of a chemical exposure by the individuals who are being, or who have been, exposed, their management, their physicians, their unions, public health and occupational health physicians, and the various authorities concerned with chemical safety. These interests may further involve legal, regulatory, ethical, economic, and, last but not least, political aspects. One obvious need is for a much greater effort on the educational side so that all concerned realize the importance of the subject and that investment in safety is likely in the long run to help with profitability.

It might be thought that in order to ensure the health of workers, the obvious step is to organize periodic comprehensive medical examinations of the work force. This confuses the functions of the general practitioner with the specialized functions of those physicians who deal with specific problems of work related diseases, which, after all, are added to the other health problems that the individual may have due to genetic make-up and their particular life style, such as smoking or alcohol consumption. Much has been written about the role of the medical examination in the protection of the health of workers [24], and on the principles of medical screening in the workplace [25]. The purpose of any intervention in a factory is to interrupt the initiation of the disease process (primary prevention) or, failing this, to detect a disease process at a stage before a worker would be aware of a problem and seek medical advice (secondary prevention). If clinical disease is discovered, appropriate care must be arranged (tertiary prevention), obviously the least satisfactory outcome. If, for example, a chemical comes under suspicion as a bladder carcinogen, because the latency of human bladder cancer is measured in decades, it is not much use examining newly exposed workers medically for overt bladder disease. It is, however, a practical matter to minimize or eliminate the exposure, and to make appropriate observations on the workers to see that in fact they are not absorbing any of the chemical. Monitoring of workers can be done periodically, not so much for the health of the worker, but as a measure of the effectiveness of the containment measures. Monitoring activities constitute one of the most important procedures in primary prevention. However, it should be noted that as monitoring is an intrusive procedure and an expensive one, it is important that such activity should be undertaken only when there is a clearly defined purpose.

The procedure of making periodic observations of some specific parameters for a defined health objective comes under the general heading of medical surveillance. In the example chosen, the ultimate outcome of the particular exposure was expected to be a specific cancer and the objective was primary prevention. If however the health effects of exposure were less tangible but there were grounds for suspicion, a more elaborate set of observations might be warranted and this could be referred to as medical screening. Halperin and his colleagues [25] define medical screening as 'the application of an examination, historical question, or laboratory test to apparently healthy persons with the goal of detecting absorption of intoxicants or early pathology before the worker would normally seek clinical care for symptomatic disease.' They would include biological monitoring as a screening activity. Because these activities must be undertaken with due attention to the constraints imposed by the factory situation referred to above, it is essential that any occupational surveillance or screening test or examination should be directed to a specific well defined risk in the particular work situation. Furthermore, all procedures, from questionnaires to testing and any evaluations must be carried out by properly trained staff. One of the main problems in this area is a lack of appreciation of the great difficulties in the design, execution and interpretation of a study. In particular, many well intentioned medical practitioners who take on the additional work of part time adviser to a local factory are often unaware of the complexities of these matters and the need to seek specialist advice. Some idea of the difficulties, both technical and human, that can arise have recently been discussed in relationship to occupational asthma and alveolitis [26-28]. The signs and symptoms may be obvious but, even with an association with a clearly identifiable possible cause such as isocyanates, there can be great difficulty in arriving at a satisfactory conclusion. There is thus a great need for the encouragement of occupational physicians in their efforts to research in these difficult areas and for their advice to be more generally appreciated and available.

The essential element in any consideration of interaction between a subject and a chemical is quantitative knowledge about how much of the chemical has actually been absorbed. Unfortunately such knowledge is rarely available and recourse has to be made to indirect estimations. In primary prevention, it may be satisfactory to establish that the chemical in question is present at a level that has been accepted by some appropriate authority as of insignificant danger to health. The various activities undertaken to establish in a systematic way how much of a chemical is present either within or surrounding a subject are known as monitoring activities. In general, there are 3 categories of monitoring:

i) Ambient or environmental monitoring, where the health risk is assessed by measuring the concentrations in air, food or water;

ii) Biological monitoring, where the health risk is evaluated by measuring the amount of chemical that has been absorbed or by assessing a biomarker of exposure such as a DNA or protein adduct; and,

iii) This is sometimes known as health surveillance or the biological monitoring of effects, where changes in biochemical or physiological functions thought to be due to the chemical exposure are studied, for example lung function tests in suspected occupational asthma or choline esterase activity following possible exposure to certain insecticides.

Although monitoring activities are of great importance, there are many problems to be overcome before establishing a programme with any prospect of success. Each chemical poses a sampling and analytical problem, exacerbated because many of the procedures must be carried out under field conditions. In the case of biological monitoring, there is the added complication of the possible metabolism of the chemical and the necessity to allow for this, if necessary, by special metabolic studies so that the identified metabolites can also be estimated in the samples. Some idea of the many problems in this area can be had from the many studies that have been carried out on the important industrial chemical, acrylonitrile [29]. Unfortunately, information on the metabolic fate of many important industrial chemicals in human beings is insufficient for the purposes of devising methods that are suitable for biological monitoring. There is also the problem of the availability and funding of the required sophisticated technology, a matter that will be discussed later.

## 30.10 Chemical Safety at the Workplace

Many nations now have legislation that requires management to ensure the safety of the worker at his place of work and among these responsibilities are requirements concerning chemical safety. There are also more general requirements concerning such matters as the labelling of chemicals and the provision of safety data sheets. There are also national and international data banks dealing with information on the toxic properties of chemicals. Thus, in theory, any person designated as a safety officer in a factory should be able to inform himself about the potential dangers of any chemicals on the site. Unfortunately, the imposition of these demands only in the past few years has meant that many safety officers have scant knowledge about their responsibilities, often imposed upon them by management because they could be spared from other tasks. This is particularly true in factories employing up to a few 100 workers, and some of these are the very ones that may utilise a variety of highly reactive chemicals. There is a need for educational programmes to deal with the safety aspects of chemicals for designated safety officers in relatively small factories. This should cover all aspects, such as to how to audit a factory to know what chemicals are there, how to ensure that the audit is kept up to date, how to obtain the necessary safety information about specific chemicals, and how to ensure that the factory records of employees should be organised so that early warning of problems is given by, for example, an unusual pattern of sickness leave. In these considerations it must not be forgotten that management also has to be educated to understand the importance of these matters, because the safety officer can only operate effectively with the full co-operation of management. It is here that the backup of those statutory bodies that have responsibilities in these areas, such as the Health and Safety Executive in the United Kingdom becomes so important, and it also becomes a matter of priority to ensure that their resources to do this work are adequate. (See also chapter by Cowie and Richardson.)

Looking to industry as a whole, it can be seen that the really big industries, with their correspondingly large resources have undertaken studies of great value. The petroleum industry was one of the first to undertake an industry wide study. The industry was confronted with a number of problems of suspicious chemical exposures among their workforce. There was a concern about the handling of bulk petroleum products in which there were significant concentrations of polycyclic aromatic hydrocarbons, with an attendant risk of skin cancer. In one way or another, benzene was handled and widely distributed, as were solvents such as n-hexane. There were problems about lead in air and the carcinogenic properties of some cutting oil constituents. After a decade of effort involving the surveillance of 10s of thousands of employees in a series of well planned projects and much attention to 'good housekeeping', it has been established that, with proper handling and containment procedures, the petroleum industry can be regarded as a generally safe industry in which to work. Further details of this important series of studies are available in the industry report [30]. See also the papers by Harrington [31] and Wong and Rahba [32].

The petroleum industry is an example of a large integrated multi-national organization. It is becoming apparent that, in terms of numbers of workers at serious risk, it is in the multitude of firms employing relatively few people that serious problems of chemical safety can arise. As an example, the newly emerging microelectronics industry illustrates well the kinds of problems that must be confronted. This industry is made up of 100s of small independent units, usually employing <200 people. It has an entrepreneurial management concerned with large volume, low cost, precision elements with small profit margins. Although its manufacturing processes are conducted with maximum cleanliness as far as the components are concerned, the workforce may still be at risk. This is causing concern because of the large quantities of toxic metals, chemicals, solvents and gases, many of which, such as arsine, phosphine, and diborane, have never been considered from a long term, low level toxicity viewpoint. Further, although used in relatively small quantities in small factories, they may be transported in bulk from a few centres of production over long distances, for example from Japan to the USA, and thus be a major transport hazard. Another characteristic of the industry is that although the size of an individual factory is relatively small, they tend to congregate together in 'Silicon Valley' conglomerates of 100s of units. The aggregate discharge of solvents alone on one site in the USA is causing serious concern because of the steadily increasing contamination of the ground water. The original 'Silicon Valley' in California USA has become a good example of an evolving health strategy in a conglomerate industrial complex, where initially and understandably, most managements were more conscious of profits and industrial secrets than health issues [33-35]. Thus, it is now apparent that one of the major issues in chemical safety centres around what can be termed the small factory problem. A related area of great concern is what some consider the 'ultimate minifactory', namely the home where many potentially toxic substances are used under less than ideal circumstances.

As has been discussed, an adequate study of any exposure situation needs adequate technical resources and a wide range of chemical safety expertise which are not likely to be available in a hard pressed small firm. An example of one possible solution to this problem is that adopted by the Institute of Occupational Medicine, Edinburgh [36]: in the course of their work and in collaboration with the coal industry management, they have developed a comprehensive set of mobile laboratories that can undertake all the necessary procedures for epidemiological work from interviews to urine tests to complex lung function tests and X-ray examinations. Over the years, they have carried out successfully a number of studies and demonstrated the effectiveness of this approach. The cost of any epidemiological work is high and to add mobile laboratory facilities may appear to be too great an additional financial burden. However, in terms of value, one must consider that proper observation of exposed subjects is the most effective way to make progress in reducing chemically induced diseases which are a source of a considerable reduction in the quality of life for many and a cause of premature death for some of those affected. In view of the above considerations, it is perhaps pertinent to reflect on the fact that one bioassay for carcinogenicity on one chemical in the rat costs upwards of US $500,000, the result being in many cases of dubious value to human problems. Such a sum can finance a series of epidemiological studies of direct value to human health. Here is one aspect where priorities in the allocation of resources need re-evaluation.

## 30.11 Toxic Chemicals and the Environment

So far consideration has been directed to the 'flow of chemicals' through society, affecting in their passage the lives of factory workers and consumers, mostly with benefit but sometimes causing harm. As far as the latter is concerned, there are many actions that can be taken within local resources to reduce the adverse effects of chemicals, particularly through the work of general practitioners. However, there is one aspect of this flow of chemicals that has by the default of previous generations, now become so large that it needs the concerted actions of governments to solve the resultant problems. This is the matter of waste and sewage disposal with their burden of toxic substances. This is an enormous problem that has scarcely begun to be tackled. In rounding off this survey of approaches to identifying adverse health effects of chemicals in use, which has concentrated in the main on the direct human/chemical interaction, some reference is needed to the current thinking in relation to waste and sewage disposal, that if not adequately dealt with, must ultimately cause serious health problems.

Perhaps the worst environmental contamination that can occur is that which is directly attributable to the operation of some industrial complex and its discharges into its immediate surroundings. Fundamentally the defence of any local discharge is the contention that the waste will be so diluted that it will be harmless. There are many examples, particularly with regard to metals and pesticides where this was manifestly untrue, for instance the mercury discharge at Minimata or the Kepone discharge into the James River in the USA [37]. A greater concern as the dilution concept becomes increasingly discredited is that if local discharge is prohibited, centralized facilities are required and these may not be available. Collection and disposal of toxic wastes has been in operation for decades because some wastes are clearly not disposable locally because the amounts or nature of the waste prevent effective local dilution. Unfortunately, the procedures adopted in previous decades resulted in the dumping of such materials in some isolated site without any regard to the geological properties of the site or any appreciation of the possibilities of leaching to important water sources such as ground water or, more particularly, because of long term implications, aquifers. The quantities of such potentially toxic waste disposal were already astonishing in the 1970s. For example, in the USA it was reported that the toxic waste dumped from one particularly large pesticide factory totalled 300,000 barrels over a period of about 8 years, that is some 6000 gallons each working day. The annual rate of production of hazardous waste in the USA has been estimated to be some 40 million wet metric tons in a total of some 100s of millions of tons of waste from all sources [38]. Although domestic rubbish is not considered to be hazardous waste, its accumulation and disposal, particularly by incineration, may generate chemical hazards, particularly from heavy metals such as lead, cadmium and mercury, solvents or complex hydrocarbons such as dioxins and furans [39].

Whyte and Burton [40] have suggested that there are 2 general stages in the establishment of priorities in relation to the general problem of environmental contamination:

i) It is necessary to define the boundaries of the problem. A threat to human health may be sufficient to justify action but threats to important groups of animals or plants may reinforce initial reason for concern. In the context of human health, a hierarchy of effects has been identified [41] and is as follows, from most serious to least serious:

- Premature death of many individuals
- Premature death of any individual
- Severe acute illness or major disability
- Chronic debilitating disease
- Minor disability
- Temporary minor illness
- Discomfort
- Behavioural changes
- Temporary emotional effects
- Minor physiological change; and

ii) The problem should be considered in the context of related risks and benefits. Risks must be evaluated in terms of the additional probability of harm compared to:

- Those associated with the natural environment;
- Those which have been tolerated over a long period of time without detectable ill effects; and,
- Those associated with levels of the relevant chemical that have been accepted as beneficial, *eg*, the case of pesticides.

Once a chemical has been associated with potential or actual environmental health problems, the next step is to try to establish the extent of the problem. The World Health Organization [42] has proposed 5 criteria for this purpose:

i) Severity and frequency of observed or suspected adverse effects on human health. Particular attention is drawn to irreversible and chronic effects, *eg*, netic, neurotoxic,carcinogenic, teratogenic and embryotoxic effects; continuous and repeated exposure should generally be given higher priority than isolated or accidental exposure;

ii) Ubiquity and abundance of the potentially toxic chemical in the environment. Particular attention should be paid to chemicals that may add to an already occurring natural hazard;

iii) Persistence of the potentially toxic chemical in the environment;

iv) Possibilities of environmental transformation of the potentially toxic chemical to more toxic derivatives; and,

v) Nature of the population exposed. Particular attention should be given to problems that may affect a large proportion of the general population or specific occupational groups, and to very vulnerable groups such as pregnant women, new born children, the infirm and the elderly.

Having thus delineated a suspected environmental problem, some confirmation will usually be required. An approach that may be adopted is that chosen by the USA's Centre for Disease Control in considering possible environmental problems associated with polychlorinated biphenyls (PCBs), as described in Andelman and Underhill's book [43]. This multistage approach was designed to detect significant human exposures with the least expenditure of resources. There are 4 stages:

i) Ecological assessment (Level I effort) to identify sites with PCB exposures;

ii) Pilot exposure study (Level II effort) to document body burdens of PCBs among the 'most exposed' persons at each site;

iii) Community survey (Level II effort) to identify cohorts of PCB-exposed persons with little or no levels of other toxic chemicals which would confound the health effects of PCBs; and,

iv) Cohort study (Level III effort) to design and conduct registries of PCB-exposed cohorts detected in the 3rd stage in order to examine the long term effects of low-level PCB exposure. Although Level III studies are expensive, complex, and time consuming, they provide a practical approach to determining the long-term effects of low-level exposures.

In order to apply approaches and criteria of the kind described above, it is essential to have ready access to all the relevant information. This means that it is necessary to develop centralized data banks integrating data from environmental field studies with information from the literature in readily retrievable form to facilitate its use. It is also necessary to develop state and local registries of morbid events, especially in relation to sentinel diseases which are relatively rare and may be associated with exposure to potentially toxic chemicals in the environment. In addition, it is necessary to develop exposure-specific and site-specific registries of exposed populations and suitable control populations with provision for short-term monitoring and long-term follow up. This should be part of the general development of computerized data systems of births, deaths and diseases. Much of this information is common to that required in connection with occupational diseases.

Examples of existing large-scale databases which can be used as models are the US National Priority List databases at the Centers for Disease Control in Atlanta and at the Mitre Corporation in McLean, Virginia. Other examples are the SEEDIS and UPGRADE computer systems that integrate mortality and morbidity statistics with various sources of environmental data. Reference may also be made to the chemical substances information network developed jointly by the US EPA and the Council on Environmental Quality in accordance with the Toxic Substances Control Act, linking together many computer data systems providing information on chemicals, toxicity production, and environmental effects.

## 30.12 Summary

This chapter has reviewed the historical development of our awareness of the health problems associated with exposure to chemicals and current approaches to identifying adverse health effects of chemicals in use. From the review, we have attempted to extract the elements of a systematic approach.

History shows that the crucial element in identifying adverse effects of chemicals in use is the alert physician who can spot the association between a specific illness and exposure to a potentially toxic chemical. Such physicians must have available proper support in the form of responsive facilities for epidemiological and toxicological studies to test their hypotheses. Epidemiological studies require adequate information on health records of those at risk and on possible occupational and environmental exposures. Since the patient may not realize the possible chemical causation of his illness and thus fail to give the physician all relevant information, it is important to ensure that the possibilities of chemical etiology are more widely known to the lay public.

The second crucial element in addition to the alert physician is relevant information available in a manageable form. Nowadays, this means in a form which can be readily analyzed by the application of well designed computer programmes. The use of 'smart cards' by patients to carry their records in a portable form instantly available to the physician offers great possibilities. Thought should be given to the possibility of incorporating work records and other information which might indicate exposure to potentially toxic chemicals. Sentinel health events might be emphasized in such records. Computer analysis would be greatly facilitated if the WHO International Classification of Diseases were used and specific chemicals always designated with Chemical Abstracts Service (CAS) registry numbers.

Availability of information on individual patients in 'smart card' form is a new development but information on general mortality and morbidity has been available for some time. Unfortunately, the quality of the information has often left something to be desired and, in the case of morbidities, the information has rarely been collated at all. Clearly, these records need to be upgraded and examples of increasing morbidities, such as asthmas and eczemas in the United Kingdom, looked at more closely for possible chemical causation. National and international sentinel networks could be further developed. Further information would come from the integration of the needs of chemical safety into the growing networks of primary health care. All these developments should be undertaken in co-operation with the existing poison information and control centres.

The workplace is clearly an area of high risk where potential chemical exposure will always be a matter of concern. Identification of adverse effects of chemicals in use in the workplace may proceed either from the periphery, that is from knowledge of the nature of industries, of the chemicals in use and of the levels of use as a surrogate for potential exposure, or from worker-centred considerations. The approach from the periphery may involve the use of indices and classifications of various kinds discussed in this chapter. Worker-centred assessment looks at individual factories and groups of workers. It is based essentially on monitoring the workplace and of the workers at risk and is aimed at primary prevention. Medical screening for well-defined health effects and associated epidemiology may contribute to secondary prevention. In both cases, there is a clear need to support more research in occupational medicine if resources are to be used wisely.

Effective identification of adverse health effects of chemicals in use in industry requires that management and safety personnel have a good awareness of chemical hazards, something which many lack at the present time. There is thus an educational need to be satisfied. Such education must include instruction in the maintenance of adequate factory records for both patterns of sickness and patterns of work. Statutory national or state safety bodies must have sufficient resources for this as well as their other responsibilities.

More thought should be given to the problems of the small factory, which is often not well covered by existing regulation and control, and of the home, where many chemical hazards lurk unsuspected. Monitoring for primary prevention is very difficult in these situations. Use of mobile laboratories may be valuable to small industries which cannot afford their own fixed facilities but the only solution in the home would seem to be increased public awareness.

Ultimately, identification of adverse health effects arising from chemicals already in use depends upon the availability of sufficient reliable information to analyze according to chosen criteria. The collection of information must be structured to defined objectives and data recording systems. The human input must be right and this depends upon effective education and training. The input must relate to the data handling and analysis to be carried out. This requires careful design of databases and their subsequent manipulation by various levels of computer facility. The challenge for the future is to optimize the collection and analysis of data relating to health and relevant chemical exposures so that health problems and causes can be identified and brought under control with a minimum of delay and hence with a minimum of human suffering.

## 30.13 References


[1] Carson, R., *Silent Spring*, Boston, Horton Miflin, 1962.

[2] OECD, *Guidelines for Testing Chemicals (including supplements)*. 1981, Paris, OECD.

[3] European Commission, *Off. J. Eur. Comm.*, 1990. **33**, Annex C146A.

[4] OECD, *Existing Chemicals: Systematic Investigation, Priority Setting, and Chemicals Reviews*, Paris, OECD, 1986.

[5] US National Academy of Sciences, *Strategies to Determine Needs and Priorities for Toxicity Testing*, Washington, National Academy Press, 1981.
[6] Selikoff, I.J. and Hammond E.C., (Ed.), *Brain Tumors in the Chemical Industry*, New York Academy of Sciences, New York, 1982, pp. 363.
[7] Rehn, L., *Arch. Klin. Chirurg.*, 1895. **50**, 588-600.
[8] Samuels, S.W., *J. Occup. Med.*, 1986. **28**, 572-577.
[9] Case, R.A.M., Hosker, M.E., McDonald, D.B.and Pearson, J.T., *Br. J. ind. Med.*, 1954. **11**, 75-104.
[10] Hueper, W.C., Wiley, F.H. and Wolfe, H.D., *J. Ind. Hyg. Toxicol.*, 1938. **20**, 46-84.
[11] Walpole, A.L., Williams, M.H.C., and Roberts, D.C., *Br. J. Ind. Med.*, 1954. **11**, 105-109.
[12] Melick, W.F., Escue, H.M., Naryka, J.J., Mezera, R.A, and Wheeler, E.P. *J. Urol.*, 1955. **74**, 760-766.
[13] Williamson, R.C.N., *Br. Med. J.*, 1988. **296**, 445-446.
[14] Rosenman, K.D., *Arch. Environ. Health*, 1984, **39**, 218-224.
[15] Goldman, R.H. and Peters, J.M., *J. Am. Med. Assoc.*, 1981. **246**, 2831-2836.
[16] Lindup, W.E. and Nowell, P.T., *Food Cosmet. Toxicol.*, 1978. **16**, 59-62.
[17] Rutstein, D.D., Mullan, R.J., Frazier, T.M., Halperin, W.E., Melius, J.M. and Sestito, J.P., *Am. J. Publ. Health*, 1983. **73**, (9), 1054-1062.
[18] World Health Organization, *Manual of the international statistical classification of diseases, injuries and causes of death*, Ninth revision, Vol. 1., Geneva, World Health Organization, 1977, pp. 773.
[19] World Health Organization, International statistical classification of diseases and related health problems, Tenth revision, Vol. 1., Geneva, World Health Organization, 1992, pp. 1243.
[20] Van Casteren, V., *A descriptive study on sentinel health information systems with GPs in the countries of the European Community*, Brussels, Institute of Hygiene and Epidemiology, 1987, pp. 57.
[21] Lobet, M.P., Stroobant, A., Mertens, R., Van Casteren, V., Walckiers, D., Masuy-Stroobant, G., and Cornelis, R., *Int. J. Epidem.*, 1987. **16**, (4), 612-618.
[22] HMSO, *Morbidity Statistics from General Practice, Third National Study*, London, HMSO, 1986.
[23] Froines, J.R., Dellenbaugh, C.A. and Wegman, D.H. *Am. J. Publ. Health*, 1986. **76**, 1089-1096.
[24] Schilling, R.S., *J. occup. Med.*, 1986. **28**, (8), 553-557.
[25] Halperin, W.E., *et al.*, *J. occup. Med.*, 1986. **28**, (8), 547-552.
[26] Cockroft, A.E., *J. Roy. Soc. Med.*, 1988. **81**, 255-257.
[27] Bidstrup, P.L., *J. Roy. Soc. Med.*, 1988. **81**, 254-255.
[28] Burge, P.S., *J. Roy. Soc. Med.*, 1988. **81**, 252-254.
[29] World Health Organization, *Acrylonitrile*. IPCS Environmental Health Criteria, Vol. 28, Geneva, World Health Organization, 1983.
[30] Institute of Petroleum, *Health and Hazards in a Changing Oil Scene. Proceedings of the Institute of Petroleum 1982 Annual Conference*, Chichester, John Wiley and Sons, 1983, pp. 201.
[31] Harrington, J.M., *Am. J. Ind. Med.*, 1987. **12**, 475-497.
[32] Wong, O. and Raabe, G.K., *Am. J. Ind. Med.*, 1989. **15**, 283-310.

[33] LaDou, J., *Scand. J. Work Environ. Health*, 1983. **9**, 42-46.

[34] LaDou, J., *Technology Review*, 1984. (May/June), 23-26.

[35] McCurdy, S.A., Schencker, M.B., and Lassiter, D.V. *Am. J. Ind. Med.*, 1989. **15**, 499-510.

[36] Louw, S.J., Cowie, H.A., and Seaton, A., *Am. J. Ind. Med.*, 1986. **9**, (5), 423-432.

[37] Duffus, J.H., *Environmental Toxicology*, London, Edward Arnold, 1980.

[38] Upton, A.C., Kneip, T., and Toniolo, P., *Ann. Rev. Publ. Health*, 1989. **10**, 1-25.

[39] Landrigan, P.J., *Am. J. Ind. Med.*, 1989. **15**, 243-244.

[40] Whyte, A.V. and Burton, I., (Ed.), *Environmental Risk Assessment*. SCOPE Reports, Vol. 15, John Wiley and Sons, New York, 1980.

[41] World Health Organization, *Mercury*. IPCS Environmental Health Criteria, Vol. 1, Geneva, World Health Organization, 1976.

[42] World Health Organization, *Methods used in establishing permissible levels in occupational exposure to harmful agents. Report of a WHO Expert Committee with participation of ILO*. Technical Reports Series, Vol. 601, Geneva, World Health Organization, 1977.

[43] Andelman, J.B. and Underhill, D.B., (Ed.), *Health Effects from Hazardous Waste Sites*, Lewis Publishers, Chelsea, Michigan, 1987, pp. 294.

# 31. Liability for Dangerous Industrial Activities and Damage to the Environment; Where Do We Stand After the Council of Europe Convention and the Commission Green Paper?

Jean-Marie Devos and Marja Ekroos

*Domat: 'All losses and all damage caused by the deeds of any person, through negligence, thoughtlessness, ignorance of what one should know or similar shortcomings, however trivial they may be, must be compensated by the person whose fault or negligence has created the damage'* [1].

## 31.1 Introduction

Civil liability for damage to the environment is a topic of great importance and growing impact on industry, especially operators of dangerous activities. The chemical industry is in particular, due to its huge diversity, a sector on which the economic impact of civil liability law is remarkable. A significant number of research, production and processing activities are carried out and many diverse products are placed on the market which are subject to transport, packaging, labelling and storage operations. Products might have properties harmful or dangerous to the environment if not properly handled and several are manufactured involving the use of dangerous substances. Therefore, liability questions may be especially complicated and might be raised at several stages of the industrial and trade activities.

After having first concentrated on the establishment of administrative rules *ie*, environmental protection rules, the public interest has been focusing on civil law *ie*, liability schemes complementary to protection rules respectively. It is argued that (strict) liability rules are deemed not only to ensure compensation for the party who suffered the damage, but also ensure that the operators behave in most responsible manner in order to avoid possible liability.

The interest has been both national and international. As a result, on a European scale, there is now divergence in environmental liability regimes. The conceptual basis of those is partially similar, but differs considerably in terms of rules for liability exemptions, liability limits, compulsory financial security schemes or rules for proving causation or other important aspects.

Liability issues in general may be among the most crucial for industry in the near future. Unclear or ambiguous liabilities might affect investment decisions or location of certain operations, *ie*, international trade and industry.

This chapter reviews various major international legal instruments recently adopted or under discussion in the area of civil liability and describes the main features of those most important in context of industrial activities.

## 31.2 Review of New Trends

Traditionally speaking, civil liability for environmental damage means an obligation, under certain conditions, to compensate for damages caused to persons, property, or proprietary rights. It is for the plaintiff to prove the existence of the following factors:

i) That he has suffered damage to his person or property;

ii) That the damage was caused with an offence of negligence by the defending party (*ie*, was based on fault); and,

iii) There is a causal link between the damage and the incident.

These fundamental principles are now subject to evolution as will be explained below.

### 31.2.1 Foundation of Liability and Causation

In most European countries the existing civil liability laws are based on fault or on the *negligence* concepts (in *common law systems*). However, in some countries new laws with a *strict* liability regime as a basis for liability have been enacted. In others, the case law theoretically based on the fault concept has led in some cases to a similar result. The *duty of care* that is to be considered under fault-based liability is interpreted in such a stringent manner that the difference between these regimes has shrunk.

A strict liability regime has also been adopted by several international legal instruments, namely in the Council of Europe Convention (see 31.3.2.2), the UNIDROIT Convention (31.3.1.3) and the EC Directive for defective products (31.3.1.1). Such a regime is proposed to be adopted in the waste liability directive proposal (31.3.1.2) and in the draft HNS Convention (31.3.1.4). Also, the Commission Green Paper (31.3.3) clearly favors strict liability as a basis for liability on environmental damage.

Despite the theoretically remarkable development from the fault-based liability towards the system of strict liability (*ie*, non-fault based), the result at the end might not be that different since the case law already has evolved in the same direction and therefore a fault-based system when interpreted as said could lead to a similar conclusion. However, there are some essential requirements for any legislation on civil liability that need to be maintained, especially the establishment of causation. It is of utmost importance that the causal link between the incident and the damage suffered, is to be shown by the plaintiff. Likewise, in the context of damage caused by an industrial activity, causation is to be proved to exist between the operator in charge of the activity and the incident that led to the damage.

### 31.2.2 International Harmonization

There is a growing opinion that civil liability rules should be addressed at international level. International rules are necessary, it is claimed, since pollution is no respecter of national boundaries and Member States have been establishing different regulations in this field which could distort competition and hamper the smooth operation of the single market. Civil liability is also considered to belong to the domain of the Community legislation as it is a legal principle closely linked to general European environment policy principles, such as prevention of damages and the polluter pays principle.

These are the arguments the European Commission used when launching its communication on environmental liability. The Commission *Green Paper on Remedying Environmental Damage* (see 31.3.3) envisages harmonization of (strict) civil liability rules for environmental damage and secondly, the possibility of remedying environmental damage not met by the application of civil liability principles. The latter means creating compensation funds to be used when no liable party can be identified, or in case of insolvency of the liable party.

Another important international document is the *Council of Europe Convention on civil liability for damage resulting from activities dangerous to the environment* (see 31.3.2.2). The main aim of the Convention is to ensure prompt and effective compensation of damage to people, to property, and to the environment occurring during the exercise of dangerous activities carried out in a professional capacity in installations or on sites. It also provides for means of prevention and reinstatement. The aim is based on the belief that issues relating to civil liability and compensation for damage resulting from dangerous activities need to be addressed at an international level.

The Convention was opened for signatures on 21 June 1993 in Lugano and was signed by 7 Council of Europe Member States (Cyprus, Greece, Finland, Italy, Liechtenstein, Luxembourg and the Netherlands) whilst some Member States expressed the intention not to sign, since they already have legislation of their own. It is to be noted, that the Convention is open for all members and thus covers also Central European countries, such as Czech Republic, Hungary, Poland, Slovak Republic and Turkey.

Though harmonization of civil laws is conceptually attractive in the perspective of the internal market, it is effectively desirable only if it would bring simplification of existing systems and if new international instruments do not simply add a new layer of possible legal actions. Due to differences of administrative and legal structures, real harmonization is not easy to achieve by harmonizing a part of the system (for example, the basis of the liability as referred to) while leaving other (procedural) parts of the system as they are. Nevertheless, it has to be admitted that complete harmonization might be an impossible dream.

### 31.2.3 Towards Recognition of Ecological Damage

A significant aspect of current development in the international sphere is also the extension of the concept of damage (death, personal injury, damage to property) to *ecological damage* called environmental damage from hereon. Environmental damage concerns the community, not the individual since there is no direct right under threat. Environmental damage could therefore perhaps be defined as damage to *an unowned property*. There is a growing demand to internalize environmental costs fully in production costs. By doing so, all harmful impacts of industrial activities would be taken into account, this is an application of the 'Polluter Pays Principle' (PPP).

Historically, an economic and preventive principle, the 'Polluter Pays', is gradually recognized as having legal effects either in public and administrative law, or in civil law. The 'PPP' was adopted by the OECD in its 1972 ([C(72) 128], OECD 1972) and 1974 ([C(74) 223], OECD 1974 Recommendations. The 1991 OECD Recommendation ([C(90) 177(final)], OECD 1991) extended the 'PPP' to the 'cost of damages' generated by pollutions.

The Parliamentary Assembly of the Council of Europe summarized the extensions of the 'PPP' to compensation of damages as follows:

> 'Stages, industry and all persons shall be liable to pay for the environmentally harmful consequences of their actions and development programmes... The principle of the polluter's liability, or the 'polluter pays' principle as it is commonly known, shall be strictly applicable.' (Recommendation 1130(1990)).

The 'PPP' has been introduced in the EC Constitution via Article 130 r of the Single European Act [2].

Scientific literature on the 'PPP' is considerable. For a recent study on the extension of the 'PPP' as an (environmental) law principle, *qv* Henri Smets [3].

However, the introduction of the 'Polluter Pays' principle in civil liability law raises complex questions as for example, how to quantify the values of disappearing vegetal species as a consequence of the pollution of a river, how to quantify restoration costs, who should have a legal right claiming compensation or restoration.

The amended proposal for a Council directive on civil liability for damage caused by waste defines *impairment of the environment* as any significant physical, chemical or biological deterioration of the environment in so far as this is not considered to be damage within the meaning of *damage to property. Damage* in turn is traditionally defined meaning death or physical injury and damage to property. The directive would apply for both damage and impairment of the environment. This definition appears to be more restrictive than the one adopted in the Council of Europe Convention, which refers to '*loss or damage by impairment of the environment ... shall be limited to the costs of measures of reinstatement actually undertaken or to be undertaken*'. This definition includes the definition of the *UNIDROIT Convention* of 10 October 1989.

The word environment itself is defined very broadly in the Council of Europe Convention, as it covers natural abiotic and biotic resources, such as air, water, soil, fauna and flora, ans the interaction between the same factors, assets making up the cultural heritage and the characteristic aspects of the landscape. These last 2 elements of the definition serve to illustrate admirably the erosion of the traditional concept of damage, as it is now a matter of covering damage to collective property by civil liability mechanisms.

It is seriously questionable and debated that civil liability is suited as an instrument to remedy environmental damage. Remedial action should remain primarily within the domain of public law and it is up to the States to decide what public instruments they are going to use to restore damage to the environment. Civil liability is only seen to have a role in compensating damage suffered by a party to his person, property or proprietary rights. The extension of civil liability law mechanisms to compensation of pure environmental damage is by nature somewhat artificial and limited (as for example in the Council of Europe Convention).

### 31.2.4 Liability for Future and *Historic* Pollution?

One single topic of utmost importance is the question of *historic non-liability related pollution* versus future pollution. Most gradual pollution results from very slow and gradual accumulation of substances which at the time when put in the environment were not considered harmful. The owners of these kind of properties have inherited, apart from the site, a possible liability for the pollution. Clean up of all old polluted sites is a vast task that must be arranged if the pollution threatens health or the environment.

Civil liability rules are usually not suitable in these cases since the basic elements of liability do not exist. This being the case, problems should be dealt by means of administrative law and not by civil law. Given the absence of individual liability and the huge costs involved, the burden of clean-up should be shouldered by several parties or even society as a whole.

### 31.2.5 Actions of Interest Groups

The right to sue is normally given only to the party with a legal (*ie*, direct and certain) interest in recovering compensation for injuries or for damage to property. Where damage occurs to property that is not owned (*ie*, environmental damage), no injured party with the right to bring legal action can be identified. At European level the tendency — though limited — is to give such a right to (environmental) associations. In opposition to this tendency, it is argued that this right to protect *public interest* should better rest with public authorities which operate under public law and democratic institutions.

For example, according to Article 4(3) of the amended proposal for a Council Directive on civil liability for damage caused by waste, common interest groups or associations [2-4], which have as their object the protection of nature and the environment, are given the right either to seek remedy or join in legal proceedings that have already been brought.

Also, the Council of Europe Convention gives certain restricted rights to associations seeking to protect the environment, namely, the group may request:

i) The prohibition of an unlawful, dangerous activity, which poses a grave threat of damage to the environment;

ii) That the operator be ordered to take measures to prevent an incident, or after an incident to prevent damage; or,

iii) That the operator be ordered to take measures of reinstatement.

However, any party to the Convention may reserve the right not to apply this article.

## 31.3 Review of Some Major Recent Industrial Liability and Compensation Instruments

### 31.3.1 Development of International Instruments in Relation to Defective Products, Waste and Carriage of Dangerous Goods

#### 31.3.1.1 Product Liability

The EC Directive on liability for defective products [4] was adopted in 1985. According to the directive the producer is to be held liable for damage caused by a defect in his product. It is based on a strict liability regime, *ie*, one does not have to prove negligence or fault to be able to get compensation. What the injured party has to prove, is the existence of the damage, the defect of a product and the causal relationship between the damage and the defect (Art. 4).

There are certain exemptions from liability as stated in the Art. 7 of the Directive. In order not to be held liable, it is for the producer to prove that:

i) He did not put the product into circulation;

ii) The defect did not exist when the product was put into circulation, or that it came into being afterwards;

iii) The product was neither manufactured for sale or any other form of distribution, nor manufactured or distributed by him in the course of his business;

iv) The defect is due to compliance of the product with mandatory regulations issued by the public authorities;

v) The state of scientific an technical knowledge at the time when he put the product into circulation was not such as to enable the existence of the defect to be discovered; or,

vi) In the case of the manufacturer of a component, that the defect is attributable to the design of the product in which the component has been fitted or to the instructions given by the manufacturer of the product.

The area of product liability was the first to be covered by uniform legislation at the Community level. For the chemical industry, being a manufacturer of diverse range of product, it is of great importance. However, safety of products have to be — and is — even without any specific liability legislation under extremely strict control. Therefore, implementation of the 1985 Directive in the Member States has been relatively smooth and no major legal or economic negative impact has been detected so far.

#### 31.3.1.2 Liability for Damage Caused by Waste

At the EC level there also exists — though being shelved in 1991 — an amended proposal for a Council Directive on civil liability for damage caused by waste [5]. This proposal applies only to damage that is caused by *waste*. Due to difficulties in defining waste, the scope of the proposed directive is far from clear. The proposal also channels liability, contrary to international conventions to be described below, onto the waste producer regardless of whether or not the producer is in control of waste at the time of the incident. This solution is not deemed to match the polluter pays principle according which it should be for the operator actually in control of the activity to shoulder the possible liability.

The future of the proposal partly depends on results of the discussions launched by the Commission so-called 1993 'Green Paper' on remedying environmental damage.

#### 31.3.1.3 Liability for Damage Caused During the Carriage of Dangerous Goods

Transport damage is covered by an international Convention on civil liability for damage caused during the carriage of dangerous goods by road, rail and inland waterway [6]. The proposal was originally drafted by The International Institute for the Unification of Private Law and the United Nations Economic Commission for Europe together and finally adopted by the UN Economic Commission for Europe in October 1989.

This, so-called *UNIDROIT Convention*, is based on a strict liability regime and it channels liability on to the carrier from the time of loading to the time of unloading. The carrier is defined as being the person having use of the vehicle, and in the case of a rail carrier the person operating the railway. The Convention will apply only to *dangerous substances* with reference to the *ADR* list that also includes hazardous wastes. The system includes compulsory (insurance) covers up to defined financial ceilings.

Liability exemptions under the Convention are traditional; the intent to cause damage by a third party, the deliberate fault of the injured party, *force majeure* (*ie*, act of war, natural phenomenon of an exceptional and irresistible character) and finally, the lack of information by the shipper or any other person as to the nature of the goods.

#### 31.3.1.4 Liability for Damage Caused During the Carriage of Dangerous Substances by Sea (HNS)

Different from the *UNIDROIT Convention* described above, is a draft International Convention on liability and compensation that covers especially hazardous and noxious substances when carried by sea [7]. This work is carried out by the International Maritime Organization (IMO) and maintains as a priority for coming years.

The shipowner would be liable for damage caused by any hazardous and noxious substances in connection with their carriage by sea on board. Usual liability exemptions as in the context of the UNIDROIT Convention would apply. The feasibility of establishing *a second tier*, *ie*, an additional, non-liability, related special compensation scheme, was still under consideration in the 1993 sessions of the IMO Legal Committee.

Who should participate in collection of contributions to the scheme is one of complex questions to be solved.

### 31.3.2 Operator Liability in the Context of Dangerous Activities; Review of Some National Developments and the Council of Europe Convention

#### 31.3.2.1 Review of Some National Developments and Trends

##### 31.3.2.1.1 Germany

In Germany, the Civil Code forms a basis for civil liability rules. However, a special environmental liability act [8] was enacted in 1990. The act entered into force on 1.1.1991. It applies to installations subject to approval pursuant to the Federal emission control law and it is based on *a strict liability regime*. If such an installation impairs the environment, the operator has to compensate for death, bodily injuries and damages to property or individual rights.

In connection with fault-based liability pursuant to Art. 823 para. 1 of the German Civil Code, the burden of proof for the cause of damage has been reversed in German jurisdiction if the damage was caused by the operation of an industrial installation.

One of the provisions in the Environmental Liability Act relating to the proof for the cause of damage is new in German legislation. According to para 6. of the Act: '*Where, with regard to the circumstances of the individual case, an installation is (generally) capable of causing the respective damage, it shall be presumed that the (individual) damage has been caused by the installation. However, this 'shall not apply if the installation has been operated according to regular standards. Operational duties are in accordance with regular standards if the special operational duties have been complied with and if there has been no breakdowns or other interferences of the operations*'.

If the installation has been operated according to regular standards as quoted above, liability for property damage is excluded if the impairment of the property is insignificant or if the property has only been damaged to an extent reasonable and acceptable under the local conditions (para 5.)

The act imposes a maximum liability ceiling of DEM 160 million case$^{-1}$ and an obligation to have sufficient coverage of liability which may be provided through a liability insurance or by an indemnification guarantee or a warranty. Details of the form of insurance are to be laid down in a separate statutory provisions. *This has not been enacted owing to difficulties in stipulating the sum* in which the insurance should be taken out in order to be sufficient.

Also, the German Water Resources Act holds the author of an unauthorized pollution of water strictly liable for any damage caused.

##### 31.3.2.1.2 The United Kingdom

The UK legal system, *Common Law*, differs from systems in the other EC Member States. For the individual suffering damage to person or property, common law actions in negligence or nuisance are the main vehicle by which to seek redress. The complainant must show that there is a causal link between the incident and the damage, negligence or nuisance and that the perpetrator acted unreasonably. Though common law doctrine of *Rylands and Fletcher*, named after the case from which it developed, states that *'a person, who for his own purpose brings onto his land and collects there something which is likely to cause damage if it escapes, has a duty to prevent such escape'* and is strictly liable for damage caused as a natural consequence of any escape. For a claim of this type it is unnecessary to prove negligence.

The common law may take a new turn in the next 2 years when the *Cambridge Water Company v Eastern County Leather* case is heard by the House of Lords. The case involves alleged gradual pollution of a public water supply borehole due to the storage of organochlorines by companies involved in the tanning industry. If the House of Lords upholds the Court of Appeals ruling in favour of the water company, it could introduce a new element of strict and retrospective liability into United Kingdom common law.

The Environmental Protection Act (EPA) 1990 gives the authorities, under some circumstances, to clean up pollution and charge the work to the polluter or in many cases to the owner or occupier of the site. Although not being a liability act, this could be described, in a wide sense, as an *absolute* liability of a land owner.

#### 31.3.2.1.3 The Netherlands

In the Netherlands liability for damage to the environment is based on fault and covers, similarly to other countries, death and damage to person and property (Art. 6:162 of the Civil Code). However, in case of damage as resulting from a dangerous activity the existence of fault is more easily accepted by the courts. It should also be noted, that a proposal for an act [9] establishing strict liability for damage caused by dangerous activities, is submitted to the parliamentary proceedings and was still to be accepted by the First Chamber of the Parliament at the time of writing this section.

In the framework of the Soil Protection Act and the Interim Soil Cleanup Act, the Government may charge the costs of cleaning up soil pollution to the polluter designated by a civil law proceeding. These claims are also based on fault, but the courts have been interpreting the duty of care concept in an extremely stringent manner. Finally, from the Dutch Supreme Court ruling [10] it is deduced that generally speaking soil pollution predating 1 january 1975 is not tortious under existing legislation (but after that date that is the case). Thereafter the Government has submitted a bill [11] to the Parliament which contains extensive provisions according to which owners or users of land can be instructed to take protective measures or to clean up contaminated land irrespective of the time the incident causing the damage took place and irrespective of fault (Soil Protection Act, Art. 47). The draft is also to be accepted by the First Chamber of the Parliament.

It should be reminded here that the Netherlands has signed the Council of Europe Convention (see Section 31.3.2.2). This should bring new legislative adaptations.

#### 31.3.2.1.4 Other Countries

Strict liability has also been adopted at least partly in a large number of other European countries. For example the following laws are based on strict liability: Belgian Law on Toxic Waste (1974) and on the control of organisms harmful to plants and plant products (1981), French Law on Waste (1975), Greek Law on Environmental Protection (1986) and Portuguese Law on the Environment (1987). Special, generally applicable environmental damage compensation rules have been enacted also in Sweden (1986) and in Norway. Drafts for such an act exist in Denmark and in Finland.

### 31.3.2.2 The Council of Europe Convention on Civil Liability for Damage Resulting from Activities Dangerous to the Environment [12]

#### 31.3.2.2.1 Institutional Basis and Status

The Council of Europe is an international organization established by Western European countries in 1949. Since then it has expanded to include new members, *viz.* the Nordic countries, Turkey, and the Central European countries like the Republics of Czech and Slovak. The Council of Europe works for greater European unity; more specifically, it aims to achieve a greater unity between Members for the purpose of safeguarding and realizing the ideas and principles which are their common heritage and facilitating their economic and social progress. The principles of parliamentary democracy and human rights are important for all its work.

The main organs of the Council of Europe are Committee of the Ministers and Parliamentary Assembly. Conclusions of the Committee of the Ministers often take the form of conventions or agreements harmonizing national legislation. The Conventions bind Members which sign and ratify them in a given procedure.

#### 31.3.2.2.2 Origin and Importance of the Convention

In the 1986 Oslo Conference of European Ministers of Justice, the decision was taken to consider options to extend the reach of civil law into promoting environmental protection. Accordingly, the Committee of the Council of Ministers (of the Council of Europe) set up a Committee of experts in 1987, to propose measures for compensation for damage caused to the environment.

After its sixth meeting, the Committee of Experts instructed the Secretariat General and the Legal Affairs Directorate of the Council of Europe to prepare an interim activity report. This report was to be submitted to the European Committee on Legal Co-operation (CDCJ), a senior Council of Europe body in the legal field, and to Member States of the Council. The report enclosed preliminary draft rules on compensation for damage resulting from dangerous activities. At this stage, also the chemical industry was consulted and it presented its views on the draft.

The Convention was finally adopted by the Council of Ministers in March 1993 and opened for signature on 21 June 1993. It was immediately signed by 7 Member States, as already referred to. However, some EC Member States have clearly expressed their opposition to the Convention. Thus it is not to be awaited that all the EC countries would sign the Convention in the near future. The Convention naturally binds only the Members which will sign and ratify it.

The Convention will enter into force in 3 months after the date on which at least 3 Member States expressed their consent to be bound by the Convention, *ie*, have signed and ratified it as provided.

#### 31.3.2.2.3 Review of Main Characteristics of the Convention

##### 31.3.2.2.3.1 Objectives

The main aim of the Convention is to set rules to ensure prompt and effective compensation of damage to people, to property, and to the environment during the exercise of dangerous activities carried out in a professional capacity in installations or on sites. As stated in Article 1 of the Convention, it aims at providing for the possibility for adequate compensation for damage resulting from activities which are dangerous to the environment and it also provides for means of prevention and reinstatement. The aim is based on the belief that issues relating to civil liability and compensation for damage resulting from dangerous activities need to be addressed at international level as pollution does not stop at frontiers.

##### 31.3.2.2.3.2 Scope

**Dangerous activity** is defined as being — One or more of the following activities provided that it is performed professionally, including activities conducted by public authorities:

i) The production, handling, storage, use or discharge of one or more dangerous substances or any operation of a similar nature dealing with such substances;

ii) The production, culturing, handling, storage, use, destruction, disposal, release or any other operation dealing with one or more:

- Genetically modified organisms which as a result of the properties of the organism, the genetic modification and the conditions under which the operation is exercised, pose a significant risk for man, the environment or property; or,

- Micro-organisms which as a result of their properties and the conditions under which the operation is exercised pose a significant risk for man, the environment or property, such as those micro-organisms which are pathogenic or which produce toxins;

iii) The operation of an installation or site for the incineration, treatment, handling or recycling of waste, such as those installations or sites specified in Annex II, provided that the quantities involved pose a significant risk for man, the environment or property; or

iv) The operation of a site for the permanent deposit of waste.

**Dangerous substances**, in turn, are defined as follows:

i) Substances or preparations which have properties which constitute a significant risk for man, the environment or property. A substance or preparation which is explosive, oxidizing, extremely flammable, highly flammable, very toxic, toxic, harmful, corrosive, irritant, sensitizing, carcinogenic, mutagenic, toxic for reproduction or dangerous for the environment within the meaning of Annex I, Part A to the Convention shall in any event be deemed to constitute such a risk; or

ii) Substances specified in Annex I, Part B to the Convention. Without prejudice to the application of sub-paragraph a above, Annex I, Part B may restrict the specification of dangerous substances to certain quantities or concentrations, certain risks or certain situations.

Owing to its wide coverage of dangerous substances, the Convention applies to many industrial sectors. Also incinerators of waste and other similar installations are regarded as chemical industry. It should be noted that sites for permanent deposits of waste are explicitly subject to the system. However, specific transitional provisions and liability rules are to be applied in case of a permanent waste deposit.

### 31.3.2.2.3.3 Liability Regime

The Convention provides for a regime involving strict liability of *the operator of a dangerous activity*. The operator's responsibility is not based on the concept of fault, but on the causal link existing between the damage caused and the incident occurring at the time or during the period when the operator was in charge of a dangerous activity.

The operator is defined as being '*the person who exercises the control of a dangerous activity*'. Essential in determining the person who is in charge of a certain activity is to consider, who has the power to decide upon the way in which the activity is carried out. The Explanatory report to the Convention rightly points out major reasons for making the person in charge of the activity from which the damage resulted bear cost of damage; the activity of this person is the source of the damage and this person is best placed to prevent the damage and limit its extent.

According to Article 10, while maintaining the requirement of a causal relationship between the incident giving rise to damage and the activity of the operator, it is specified that the court '*shall take due account of the increased danger of causing such damage inherent in the dangerous activity*'.

#### 31.3.2.2.3.4 Concept of Damage

The concept of damage is defined as follows:

i) Loss of life or personal injury;

ii) Loss of or damage to property other than to the installation itself or property held under the control of the operator, at the site of the dangerous activity;

iii) Loss or damage by impairment of the environment in so far as this is not considered to be damage within the meaning of sub-paragraphs above provided that compensation for impairment of the environment, other than for loss of profit from such impairment, shall be limited to the costs of measures of reinstatement actually undertaken or to be undertaken; or

iv) The costs of preventive measures and any loss or damage caused by preventive measures, to the extent that the loss or damage referred to in sub-paragraphs i) to iii) arises out of or results from the hazardous properties of the dangerous substances, genetically modified organisms or arises or results from waste.

The Convention covers legal categories traditionally included under the concept of *damage* in civil law, *ie*, loss of life or personal injury. Additionally, the text introduces the concept of loss or damage by impairment of the environment provided that compensation shall be limited to the costs of measures of reinstatement actually undertaken or to be undertaken. Since *the environment* is defined in a remarkably broad manner as already previously noted, it seems obvious that the Convention goes clearly beyond the precedents established in the *UNIDROIT Convention* or in the EC draft Directive on liability for waste. As referred to, the environment means in the context of the Convention:

i) Natural resources both abiotic and biotic, such as air, water, soil, fauna and flora and the interaction between the same factors;

ii) Property which forms part of the cultural heritage; and,

iii) The characteristic aspects of the landscape

The first category already covers the unowned environment, for instance vegetal species not *belonging* to anyone, but the 2 latter classes extend the definition to something not regulated before. Such wide definition will raise difficult questions about what is to be protected, 'how clean is clean', and to which extent the Convention mechanisms apply.

#### 31.3.2.2.3.5 Joint and Several Liability

Where more than one party have been responsible for the damage, each liable party must usually pay compensation only for that amount of damage which can be actually attributed to his particular activity. The Convention introduces, among other novelties, a concept of joint and several liability. When damage results from incidents which have occurred in several installations or on several sites, the operators of the installations or sites concerned will be jointly and severally liable for all such damage (Art. 11). That means that each and every operator, against which causation is established, is liable for the entire amount of damage but may in turn seek contribution from other liable parties. A liable operator may demonstrate that he caused only part of the damage.

#### 31.3.2.2.3.6 Limitation of Liability

The Convention contains *usual defenses* such as *force majeure* or *Act of God*, intentional acts by a third party and necessary compliance with an order of a public authority. A significant new exemption concerns damage which was caused by pollution at tolerable levels under local relevant circumstances that establishes a threshold for claiming damages. Convention enshrines an obligation to tolerate certain disturbances usual in that specific area taking into account local circumstances.

Additionally, any Member State may reserve the right to provide in its internal law that the operator will not be liable if he proves that the state of scientific and technical knowledge at the time of the incident was not such as to enable the risk involved to be discovered. This right does not, however, apply to the damage caused by a permanent deposit of waste or an installation for handling of waste.

#### 31.3.2.2.3.7 Financial Guarantee

According to Article 12 of the Convention it is to be ensured that where appropriate, taking due account of the risks of the activity, operators conducting a dangerous activity on its territory be required to participate in a financial security scheme or to have and maintain a financial guarantee up to a certain limit, of such type and terms as specified by internal law, to cover the liability under this Convention.

The Article leaves some freedom for national legislators, and allows the choice between several technical arrangements including insurance or fund arrangements.

#### 31.3.2.2.3.8 Right of Action for Private Groups

Article 18 of the Convention to some extent authorizes actions by private associations which according to their statutes aim at the protection of the environment whilst restricting the scope of such actions before the courts and jurisdictions:

i) Requests for prohibition of any unlawful dangerous activity posing a grave threat of damage to the environment;

ii) Requests for an order to the operator to prevent an incident or damage; or,

iii) Requests for an order to after an incident prevent damage or reinstate the environment.

Any party to the Convention may reserve the right not to apply this Article.

#### 31.3.2.2.3.9 Future Role of the Convention

As said earlier (Section 31.2.3), the Convention was signed in Lugano on 21 June 1993 and is expected to influence considerably, whether directly or directly, any future legislative activities in the area of civil liability in the context of dangerous activities. It has introduced major **conceptual** clarification on the liability regime ('operational responsibility equals legal liability').

## 31.4 Liability, and Behind Liability, the Debate on Collective Compensation Mechanisms; the Commission Green Paper

In addition to international organizations, new civil liability regimes have been enacted by various EC Member States. In its 1993 'Green Paper' on 'Remedying Environmental Damage', the European Commission assumed that different approaches adopted may lead to distortion of competition and hamper the smooth operation of the single market. It is for this reason that the Commission suggested that a Community system of civil liability in relation to activities dangerous to the environment was necessary. Civil liability is also considered to belong to the domain of the Community legislation as it presents many interfaces with EC environment policy (refer to previous developments on the 'Polluter Pays' principle).

Thus, in March 1993 the Commission adopted a Green Paper on Remedying Environmental Damage [13]. The purpose of the Green Paper is to inspire discussion on whether and how requirements to remedy environmental damage might be introduced appropriately and effectively within the Community to recover the costs of such restoration. As its name envisages, the communication is a discussion document which does not formally propose a certain regime on the matter. Instead, it presents alternatives for the legislator and summarizes different arguments for and against different solutions. Nonetheless, the document does outline the main principles as follows:

i) The Commission aims at harmonization of civil liability systems for environmental damage in cases when a liable party can be identified and it expresses a clear preference for strict (objective) liability, for example, as defined in the Council of Europe Convention; and,

ii) Civil liability is not seen as a means for compensating damages when no liable party can be found, and therefore, the Green Paper looks for another kind of compensation mechanism, such as a collective compensation fund.

Therefore, the Commission aims at a strict liability regime combined with a non-liability related system, *ie*, the cost of repair could be shared among several economic sectors.

The Green Paper suggests that such a joint compensation mechanism is needed in the cases where:

i) The damage is unbounded or latent;

ii) There are cumulative acts or incidents in question;

iii) It is not possible to identify liable parties;

iv) There is no basis for liability;

v) There is no causal link determinable; or,

vi) There is no party with legal interest to bring action.

Upon whom should the burden to contribute to such funds rest, and are such funds at all necessary in addition to existing mechanisms, are questions to be answered. The Green Paper does not provide the answer, but is asking whether one should not respect the *polluter pays* principle to the greatest degree possible, and therefore, request the contributions from '*the economic sectors most closely linked to the type damage needing restoration*'. However, there are a number of difficulties in interpretation of the principle and in the identification of those sectors. For example, should the 'sector' which is today *most closely linked to the damage* pay for damage caused by the operators of the past? In addition, the identification of sectors that are most closely linked to the damage, raises serious principle and technical objections. It can be argued that post pollutions, unrelated to faulty or illegal pollutions are the result of a *given stage of development of society*. Therefore, collective and public law answers and compensation are more suitable for such 'historic' pollution.

Apart from the US Superfund [14] and the funds established by the oil industry [15], such compensation schemes are still unusual and of minor significance. In the Netherlands a fund on damage from air pollution was created already in 1972 and in France, a fund for noise, which compensates persons living around Paris airports, in 1973. The US Superfund, as is widely agreed, has proved inefficient and unfair, and therefore, should not serve as a model. The solutions for the oil industry, in turn, serve only for purposes characteristic to that industry, *ie*, are created in case of major transport accidents.

The Green Paper considers a number of issues related to civil liability and aims at stimulating discussions with all interested circles. Therefore, it has a major role as an opener of discussions on fundamental principles in the Community environmental policy and also on the Community's role and need of harmonization in this area. It is to be noted that the Council of Europe Convention recently adopted will without no doubt have a great influence on the discussions since, although being a convention binding only a few States so far, it is the first existing international legal instrument covering civil liability in the context of dangerous activities for environmental damages but also for damages to persons and property.

It is to be added, that the communication does not suggest any definition of environmental damage but only refers to definitions contained in the Council of Europe Convention and in the amended proposal for a Council directive for damage caused by waste. However, the fundamental importance of and the difficulties related to the definition are emphasized.

## 31.5 Conclusions

The US liability and insurance crisis have demonstrated clearly that the dilution of basic legal requirements related for example to causation and evidence can lead to a complete economic and legal failure. The question of need, justification and possible creation of non-liability related compensation mechanisms will have to be carefully addressed in the coming years, especially in relation to compensation of damage for 'historic' gradual non-attributable pollution damage and *old dumping sites*. Public authorities, the Industry and the Insurance world and the public at large have a joint interest in finding consensus based solutions in a most important societal issue of the end of the century.

## 31.6 Authors' Note

The opinions expressed in this chapter are the authors' own and do not engage private or public institutions.

## 31.7 References

[1] Domat (Jean) 1625-1695 - Lois Civiles, II. Domat was the most important representative of the French classic liberal school of law in the 17th Century and exercised a determining influence on modern civil liability law.

[2] EC Constitution via Article 130 r of the Single European Act, *Off. J. Eur. Commun.*, L169, 23-08-87.

[3] Smets, Henri, 'Le principe pollueur payeur, un principe de l'environnement', in: *Revue Générale de Droit International Public*, numéro 2, Avril-Juin 1993.

[4] *Off. J. Eur. Comm.*, No. L 210, 07-08-1985.

[5] COM(91) 219 final - SYN 217, *Off. J. Eur. Comm.*, No. c 192, 23-07-1991.

[6] Convention on Civil Liability for Damage Caused During the Carriage of Dangerous Goods by Road, Rail and Inland Waterway (CRTD), Geneva, ECE/TRANS/79, 10 October 1989.

[7] Draft International Convention on Liability and Compensation for Damage in Connection with the Carriage of Hazardous and Noxious Substances by Sea (HNS), International Maritime Organization.

[8] Umwelthaftungsgesetz, 1990.

[9] Aanvullig van de Boeken 3, 6 en 8 nieuw Burgerlijk Wetboek met regels betreffende de aansprakelijkheid voor gevaarlijke stoffen en verontreiniging van lucht, water of bodem, Eerste Kamer 1992-1993, **21**, 202, No. 283.

[10] Case No. 14.746, 24 April 1992.

[11] Eerste Kamer 1992-1993, **21**, 556, No. 266.

[12] Council of Europe, Convention on Civil Liability for Damage Resulting from Activities Dangerous to the Environment, 24 March 1993.

[13] Communication to Council and Parliament: Green Paper on Remedying Environmental Damage, COM(93), 47, March 1993.

[14] Comprehensive Environmental Response Compensation Liability Act 1980, (CERCLA).

[15] Brussels Convention on the Establishment of an International Fund for Compensation for Oil Pollution Damage (1971) and parallel financial structures, such as TOVALOP (Tankers Owners Voluntary Agreement Concerning Liability for Oil Pollution), CHRISTAL (Contract Regarding Interim Supplement to Tanker Liability for Oil Pollution), and OPOL (The Offshore Pollution Liability Agreement).

# 32. Safety and Environmental Stewardship in the Single Market

William G. Seddon-Brown

## 32.1 Introduction

The subject of safety may be viewed as a logical part of the modern business scene. The pursuit of excellence in this domain, however, requires not only scientific and management expertise, but also in many cases serious investment and apparent cost increases. Drawing the lines between requirements dictated by economics, legislation, regulatory frameworks and environmental stewardship policy, is a complex and delicate matter which can have a major effect on corporate performance.

This book has concentrated on explaining and defining many aspects of safety, it is therefore perhaps logical to conclude with some thoughts on the other parts of the equation.

## 32.2 Issues and Legislation

Issues are the cradle of legislation, and indeed the fundamental nature of issues is naturally linked to responsibility and stewardship. Three important factors should be noted with respect to issues.

i) Issues arise from broad trends;

ii) Issues have stake holders, opponents, advocates and bystanders; and,

iii) Issues are transient, have a life cycle and can disappear.

### 32.2.1 Life Cycle

It is interesting to look at the life cycle of an issue in terms of its impact (Figure 32.1).

**ISSUES LIFE CYCLE**

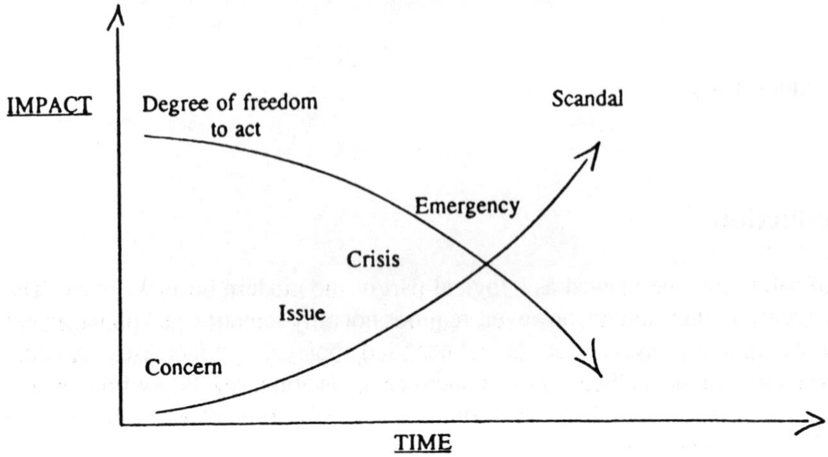


**Figure 32.1** Issues life cycle

### 32.2.2 Legislation Life Cycle

Similarly, the life cycle for legislation can also be charted. An example shown below, sets this in the context of the approval route for EC legislation.

**LEGISLATION LIFE CYCLE**

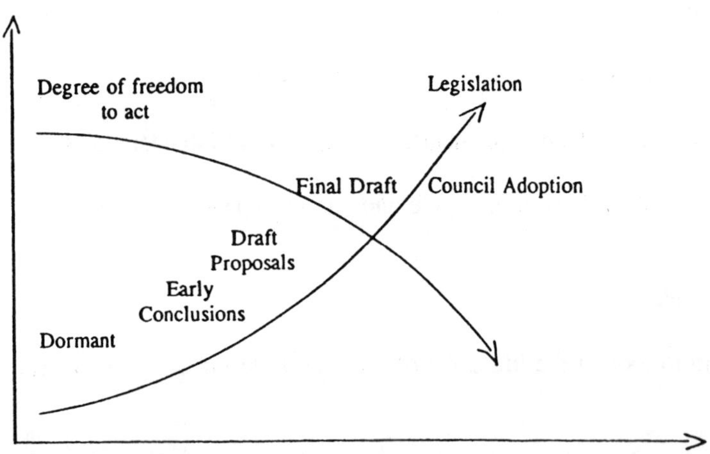


**Figure 32.2** Legislation life cycle

It will be noted that there is a limited window of opportunity to influence both issues and subsequent legislation.

## 32.3 Perception

An important factor which influences both the legislators and corporate management is public opinion. Today, the perception of how well legislation protects the environment, whilst enabling a competitive and responsible business climate, varies widely across Europe.

A recent poll undertaken by Harris Research for United Parcels Services covered 1,500 interviews with Directors of companies selected from Europe's top 15,000 by revenue [1]. The result was as follows.

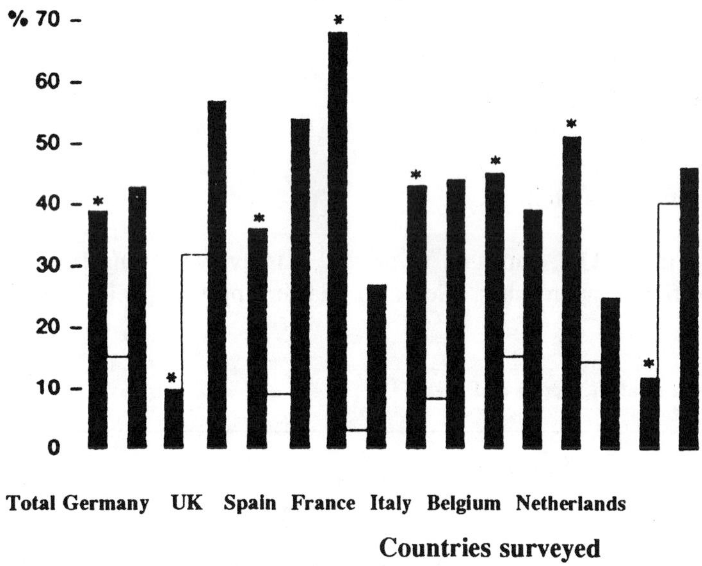


**Figure 32.3** **Does everyone agree on environmental legislation? Respondents' opinion of their country's environmental legislation [1].** Reproduced with permission of the Copyright holders.

*■ Does not go far enough to protect environment
□ Goes too far and puts company at a disadvantage
■ Is about right

It will be noted that countries such as Spain and Belgium feel strongly that legislation is inadequate, whereas Germany and the Netherlands are more satisfied that laws are adequate.

## 32.4 Compliance Policy and Stewardship

So what can environmental policies and good stewardship hope to achieve and where are the limits? Why should a company do more than just comply? Two quotations are particularly appropriate.

- 'Environmental policies are of limited significance in measuring environmental progress. Environmental 'practice' is the only relevant measure of the effectiveness of environmental policy' (Dean L. Buntrock, Chairman Waste Management Inc.).
- 'Environmental law should be a framework for action, not the spur or catalyst'. (Lord Nathan, International Environment Conference, Wembley 1992).

## 32.5 An Integrated Approach and Shared Responsibility

To respond to the above dilemma, let us take 2 practical examples:

i) The evolution of waste management legislation; and,

ii) Recycling as an example of shared responsibility.

### 32.5.1 Waste Management Legislation

Environmental legislation in the US, compared to the EC, has evolved from different origins and resulted in different approaches. (See also chapters by Campbell, Knight, Kulkarni and Nangle.)

**Table 32.1** **Environmental legislation 'Apples and Pears'**

| USA | Europe |
|---|---|
| Federal legislation based on regulations with direct applicability on the action of industry | EC framework approach<br>Sets limit values, (*eg*, emissions waste)<br>Permitting Member States<br>Scope to enforce and apply |
| Numerous derogations | |
| Liability enforced by massive litigation | Struggling with liability concept<br>Weak enforcement<br>Environment Agency delay |
| Economic consequences of legislation (Superfund) | EC examining lead use of economic and fiscal initiatives |
| Some Federal/State issues (*eg*, shipment of waste) | Maastricht — 'subsidiarity' |

This is reflected specifically in the development of waste management legislation.

**Table 32.2** **Waste legislation**

| USA | | EC |
|---|---|---|
| **SWDA**<br>(Solid Waste Disposal Act) | 1972 | |
| | 1973 | First EC **Environment Program** |
| **RCRA**<br>(Resource, conservation and recovery) | 1976 | |
| Subtitle C. | | |
| Superfund (CERCLA)<br>+ SWDA Amendment | 1980 | |
| | 1981 | Formation of **DG XI** |
| **HSWA**<br>(Hazardous and Solid Waste Amendments) | 1984 | |
| Superfund (SARA) | 1986 | |
| | 1987 | **Single European Act**<br>Incorporating Environmental Policy |
| | 1989 | **Basel** Convention<br>Signed but not ratified |
| Senate Resolution adapted<br>on **Basel** | 1992 | **Basel** into force |
| | | **OECD** transfrontier movement of waste for recovery |
| | | **Fifth** E.C. Environmental Program |
| **RCRA** | 1993 | Major waste legislation under way |
| Subtitle D. | | |

The EC has developed action plans for the management of waste and has defined a basic hierarchy or 'ladder'.

**Table 32.3** **5th EC Environment action plan 'Policy on Waste'**

| | The Principles | |
|---|---|---|
| **Prevention** | **Recovery** | **Disposal** |
| **Technologies** | Segregation/sorting | |
| — Clean | | Reduction of volume |
| **Products** | Separate collection | |
| — Ecolabel/criteria | | |
| **Avoidance** | Material recycling | |
| — Reuse | | Stricter standards |
| **Behavioural change** | Energy recovery | |
| — Producer/consumer | | |

During a recent international exhibition and congress of solid wastes, the CEO of the US National Solid Waste Management Association stated that effective waste management must reflect the following:

i) Demographics of waste generation and populations served;

ii) Technologies for effective environmental solutions;

iii) The political realities of countries served; and,

iv) Active public participation.

At the same time, the European Community has been moving in parallel towards a similar analysis which leads to an integrated approach. This integration is leading more and more to the concept of the need for shared responsibility. Again, an interesting view point in this area is:

— 'Government and society, as a whole, should set objectives, business should decide routes and how to achieve'. (Ken Collins, Member of European Parliament/Chairman Environment, Health and Consumer Protection Committee) [2].

### 32.5.2 Shared Responsibility

As an example of how this may work, take recycling as an example. Firstly, recycling means different things to different people:

| | |
|---|---|
| **Consumer:** | Bottles/cans etc for collection |
| **Manufacturer:** | Reformulating goods to include recycled materials |
| **Recycling Service Providers:** | — Providing cost-efficient collection<br>— Waste-to-Energy |
| **Policy Makers** | Establishing collection and utilization regulations and<br>Encouraging recovery, re-use, resale |

In fact, the whole process is a balanced cycle, with multiple players and a number of key influence factors.

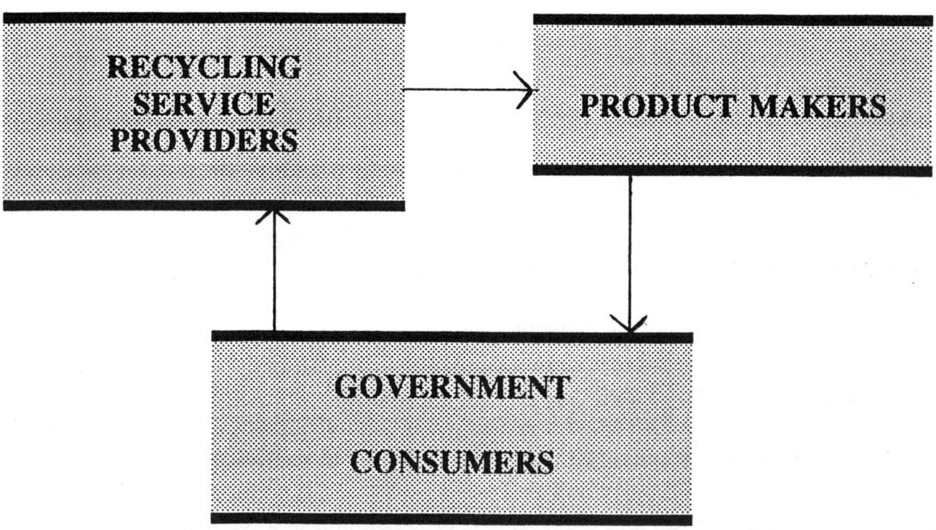


**Figure 32.4** **Balanced cycle with multiple players**

**Table 32.4** Some key factors affecting recycling

| | |
|---|---|
| **Cost** | Collection |
| | Sorting |
| | Saving in cost of disposal |
| **Technology** | EC and National incentives |
| | Quality of recycled products |
| | Limitations (contamination, mixtures, new end uses) |
| **Markets** | End uses |
| | Pricing |
| | Realism/Limits to volume |
| **Behavioural changes** | Consumer |
| | Manufacturer |
| | Service industries |

So what does this mean to each of the players or 'stake holders'.

#### 32.5.2.1 Government

i) Redefine recycling for the consumer;

ii) Foster use of recycled materials through incentives;

iii) Establish utilization policies to match diversion goals; and,

iv) Drive implementation and enforcement of legislation and regulation.

#### 32.5.2.2 Product Makers

i) Improve efficiencies in use of recycled materials;

ii) Commit to using or finding outlets for collected materials; and,

iii) Work with government to change policies that inhibit market-oriented solutions.

#### 32.5.2.3 Recycling Service Providers

i) Maximize efficiencies and productivity;

ii) Break down barriers on cost, technology and quality; and,

iii) Share knowledge of recycling with all constituents.

#### 32.5.2.4 Consumers

i) Balance demand for recycling with willingness to pay;

ii) Understand value of recycling; and,

iii) Purchase products containing recycled content.

## 32.6 Conclusion

'Environmental stewardship' is no longer the isolated policy or domain of any one stake holder. Improved consultation is vital, both sectorially and between national and EC level interests. Shared responsibilities, particularly in areas such as safety and other environmental issues will require reaching out to create even greater links between the worlds of industry, academia and government.

Two final thoughts:

i) 'High public awareness of environmental issues and increasingly stringent regulatory and legislative standards should be viewed by industry and the business community as an opportunity, not a burden'; and,

ii) 'If you are not part of the solution, you may be part of the problem'.

(Edwin G. Falkman, Chief Executive Waste Management International)

## 32.7 References

[1] United Parcel Service Europa Business Monitor (Table 10), April 1992.
[2] Collins, K., Speach at American Chamber of Commerce, Brussels, EC Committee Dinner 1992.

# 33. Chemical Regulation in Europe and the United States: International Implications

Marlissa Campbell

## 33.1 Introduction

Legislation regulating chemical substances falls into 4 basic categories:

i) General identification of hazard;

ii) Workplace safety;

iii) Pesticides; and,

iv) Environmental protection.

The European Community and the Federal Government of the United States of America are both actively concerned with regulating in these 4 areas. Not surprisingly, there are both similarities and differences between the 2 systems. The United Kingdom can be used to exemplify how various EC directives have been implemented, in the light of previously existing national legislation. The US approach is then compared to that taken in Europe. This chapter cannot be taken as an exhaustive treatment of chemical regulation, but rather as a highlighting of some significant efforts in this area.

EC efforts to harmonize regulatory requirements of Member States are well advanced. Nonetheless, other international harmonization programs also merit discussion. In particular (see also chapter by Kilkarni and Nangle), the Organization for Economic Cooperation and Development (OECD) is evaluating risks to health and the environment posed by chemicals produced in large quantities. Several EC countries as well as the US, Canada, Switzerland, Finland and Japan are all participating in the program. Such coordinated efforts increase the number of chemicals receiving full evaluations, and minimize unnecessary duplication of testing and data assessment.

## 33.2 General Hazard Identification

### 33.2.1 European Community — 67/548/EEC and 88/379/EEC

The stated purpose of Directive 67/548/EEC is twofold:

i) To reduce non-tariff barriers to trade between Member States; and,

ii) To provide a high level of protection for human health and the environment [1].

Achieving this goal requires all Member States to have the same data requirements and assessment criteria. There must also be complete and efficient exchange of information on chemical products between Member States.

Apart from specific exceptions, all chemical substances or preparations manufactured in, or imported into, the Community are included within the scope of the Directive, Preparations or mixtures of chemical substances are covered by a sister Directive, 88/379/EEC [2]. Specifically excluded are: human or veterinary medicines, waste streams, food and animal feedstuffs, pesticides, radioactive materials, and any other products which are covered by equivalent Community requirements.

Since its original introduction, amendments have expanded and updated the provisions of the Directive. Procedures for notification of new substances were introduced with the 6th Amendment to the Directive in 1979. In order to define 'new substances', it was necessary to establish an inventory of chemicals then on the Community market. EINECS, the European Inventory of Existing Commercial Substances, was compiled as of 18th September 1981. New chemicals, notified within the European Community after that date, are added to the European List of Notified (New) Chemical Substances (ELINCS).

#### 33.2.1.1 Data Requirements

Data requirements for new chemicals are tied to the quantity of chemical actually placed on the market. The 'Base Set' consists of chemistry, production details, proposed uses and handling precautions, acute toxicity, skin and eye irritation, *in vitro* mutagenicity, and environmental fate [3]. Base Set data are required for chemicals sold in quantities of $\leq 1$ tonne $a^{-1}$; chemicals used in small quantities, for research and development purposes only, may be excused. Further tests are added to the base set requirements as the quantity sold increases up to the highest level of 1000 tonnes $a^{-1}$/manufacturer, or 5000 tonnes total.

#### 33.2.1.2 Data Evaluation

The Directive defines a system for the classification and categorization of substances according to their hazard potential. Risk assessment, evaluating hazard in the context of quantitative exposure information, is not carried out [3]. Generally, the classification and categorization procedure is conducted by a committee of 'National Experts' who represent Member States. If necessary, a committee of 'Specialized Experts' in a particular field may be convened to review the scientific evidence and attempt to reach a consensus.

### 33.2.2 Council Directive 76/769/EEC

Council Directive (76/769/EEC) empowers the EC to restrict the marketing and use of certain dangerous substances and preparations [4].

## 33.3 United Kingdom Regulation of New and Existing Chemicals in Commerce

Under the Classification and Labelling Directive, manufacturers or importers of a new chemical must notify the 'competent authority' of the relevant Member State. In the United Kingdom, the competent authority is the Health and Safety Executive along with the Department of the Environment. As of 1993, EC Directives on dangerous substances and preparations will be implemented in the United Kingdom by means of the Chemicals (Hazard Information and Packaging) Regulations (CHIP) [5].

Industry must generate data on their own chemicals, and assign appropriate hazard and safety classifications in accordance with guidelines laid out in the Directive. Summaries of the information must be provided to the Commission, and subsequently to other Member States. The United Kingdom currently receives approximately 70 full notifications each year [6]. About 40% of these have been classified as dangerous to health in some way.

Chemicals on the EINECS list, but not yet formally categorized by EC procedures, are subject to a new EC regulation on the 'Evaluation and the Control of Environmental Risks of Existing Substances.' Provisions of EC regulations come into force automatically in each Member State, hence no national implementation legislation is necessary. The intent of this regulation is to bring the information available on existing chemicals up to the standard required of a new chemical produced in the same quantities. As there are over 100,000 chemicals on EINECS, simply prioritizing chemicals for review will be a tremendous task [7]. A priority list for review of data on existing chemicals will be agreed by the Commission, and Member States will be assigned a set of chemicals for review [8].

## 33.4 United States Regulation of Chemical Hazard

### 33.4.1 Toxic Substances Control Act, 1976 (TSCA)

EC activities in the areas of marketing, use, classification and labelling can be compared in scope to US Toxic Substances Control Act of 1976 (TSCA). TSCA gives the US Environmental Protection Agency (EPA) authority to regulate the production, distribution, use and disposal of chemicals. Certain product categories are specifically excluded from TSCA. Pesticides, for example, are regulated by EPA under the Federal Insecticide, Fungicide and Rodenticide Act (FIFRA). There is some overlap, however, as chemicals which are intermediates in pesticide production are regulated under TSCA.

The 3 principle regulatory arms of TSCA are:

i) The new chemicals program;

ii) EPA-directed review of existing chemicals; and,

iii) The obligation of industry to notify the Agency of any evidence for deleterious effects of existing chemicals.

When TSCA became law, there was no list of chemicals then used in the United States. Thus a vital first step was compilation of a comprehensive inventory of chemical substances in commercial production. As chemicals pass through the new chemicals program, they are added to the TSCA inventory. As of 1991, there were about 70,000 chemicals on the inventory [9].

### 33.4.2 New Chemicals

Manufacturers or importers of a chemical not currently on the TSCA inventory are required to notify EPA at least 90 days prior to manufacture or importation. This premanufacture notice (PMN) must contain information on:

i) The nature of the chemical;

ii) Its intended uses;

iii) The expected exposure of people and the environment; and,

iii) Available data on the chemical's health and environmental effects.

If the agency fails to act within the 90 day period, the chemical can be freely manufactured thereafter.

EPA makes a decision about a chemical based upon:

i) Any data submitted with the PMN;

ii) Predicted health and environmental toxicity of the chemical based upon its chemical properties; and,

iii) Its structural or functional resemblance to other chemicals for which toxicity data are available.

The toxicity of a new chemical relative to chemicals currently in use for the same purpose is also considered, as is intended production volume. Several possible courses of action are available to the Agency:

i) The chemical may be banned or its use restricted;

ii) Further testing or a special label may be required; or,

iii) The chemical may be judged unlikely to cause harm and allowed to pass into commerce with no restrictions.

If a testing program is required for a new chemical, it may be designed to take effect in stages, according to production volume. Production volume is presumed to reflect both exposure to, and profit accruing from, that chemical. More expensive tests, such as a multigeneration-reproductive-toxicity study, may be deferred until it is deemed that profits from the chemical could support testing costs.

More than 18,000 PMNs have gone through EPA's new chemicals program [10]. Between 1979 and 1991, >10% of PMN chemicals were banned or restricted, pending receipt of additional data, or were voluntarily withdrawn by the submitter because of Agency concerns.

### 33.4.3 Existing Chemicals Program

TSCA gives EPA authority to require that industry conduct toxicity testing of chemicals already in the marketplace. In order to require testing, the Agency must demonstrate:

i) That existing data are insufficient to perform a reasonable risk assessment;

ii) That only testing can provide the necessary data;

iii) That there is an 'unreasonable risk' of harm to human health or the environment; or,

iv) That the quantities of chemical produced result in significant human or environmental exposure [11]

Industry is encouraged to voluntarily provide test data desired by EPA in lieu of a formal rulemaking. Where statutory imposition of testing requirements is necessary, the rulemaking procedure includes a public hearing as well as opportunity for submission of written comments to the Agency.

### 33.4.4 8(e) and FYI

Any manufacturer, processor, or distributer of a chemical must notify EPA of any information demonstrating a substantial risk to human health or the environment. This report, or '8(e)' notification, must be made within 15 working days of learning that such information exists. EPA evaluates 8(e) notices and decides upon any action. Industry is also encouraged to submit health and environmental toxicity data on a voluntary, or 'For Your Information' (FYI) basis.

### 33.4.5 Data Disclosure and Freedom of Information

All health and safety information submitted under TSCA is subject to public disclosure. A submitter may claim other types of data, such as information pertaining to a manufacturing or purification process, as 'confidential business information' (CBI). This may include the chemical name. The Agency may disclose CBI if it determines that such protection is not warranted or that disclosure is necessary to protect human health or the environment [11].

### 33.4.6 Enforcement and Citizen Action

The EPA has the authority to investigate possible TSCA violations. Failure to comply with regulations made under TSCA may incur imprisonment, as well as severe financial penalties. Conversely, EPA can be sued by any individual in order to compel the Agency to carry out its obligations under TSCA. The testing, reporting and restriction sections of TSCA may be subject to petitioning on the part of any member of the public. EPA must respond to such a petition within 90 days, or the petitioner has the right to request judicial review by a US District Court.

## 33.5 Workplace Safety

### 33.5.1 EC Directives Impacting on Chemicals in the Workplace

#### 33.5.1.1 'The Framework Directive' 89/391/EEC

The Directive was adopted by the Council of Ministers on 12 June 1989, and was to be implemented by Member States by 31 December, 1992 [12]. It is intended to provide a 'framework' for other current and future EC directives on health and safety at work.

This Directive is concerned with all aspects of worker safety, including exposure to chemical substances. The primary responsibility for health and safety of employees at work is assigned to the employer. Employers are required to:

i) Assess risks and introduce appropriate measures to prevent or reduce risk;

ii) Develop an overall policy for prevention or reduction of risk;

iii) Consider health and safety requirements with regards to individual workers;

iv) Have competent personnel in charge of health and safety matters;

v) Have suitable arrangements for first aid and emergencies; and,

vi) Provide suitable information and training for employees and to consult employee representatives.

For their part, employees are required to cooperate with their employer's efforts to promote health and safety. Employees are expected to actively protect their own health and safety, as well as that of their fellow workers.

#### 33.5.1.2 Directive on the Protection of Workers from the Risks Related to Exposure to Carcinogens at Work [13]

This is one of the 'daughter directives' of the Framework Directive discussed above [12]. It applies to substances and processes specified in Annex 1 of the Directive, as well as to substances labelled R-45, 'may cause cancer' (under the Classification and Labelling Directive, [1]. It was adopted in June 1990, and scheduled for implementation by Member States by 31 December 1992.

Compliance with the Carcinogens Directive requires the employer to assess the risk of exposure, and the nature and degree of that risk. The hierarchy of control mechanisms, in descending order of preference, is:

i) Replacement with a less hazardous substance;

ii) Use in a closed system;

iii) If closed system not possible, then worker exposure must be reduced as far as possible.

Emergency procedures must be established, and suitable monitoring and health surveillance procedures adopted. Employers must provide employees with results of employee-health surveillance, as well as with training about risks to health and appropriate precautions.

### 33.5.2 Pregnant Workers Directive (92/85/EEC) [14]

This Directive is another daughter of the Framework Directive. Agents and working conditions are listed to which pregnant or breast feeding mothers must not be exposed. These include:

i) Underground mining;

ii) Underwater diving; and,

iii) Exposure to lead or rubella virus.

Pregnant or breast feeding women are to be moved to employment not requiring these exposures, or placed on paid leave until the need to avoid these risks has ended. A second list names agents and working conditions which are to be the subject of risk assessments by employers, with regards to special risks for pregnant, newly delivered, or lactating women. In the case of chemical agents, employers are obliged to assess the nature, degree, and duration of exposure. The employer must decide on what measures should be taken and inform employees accordingly. Duties of pregnant/breast feeding women will be adjusted if necessary and possible, or paid leave given [15].

### 33.5.3 Protection of Workers from Risks Related to Exposure to Chemical, Physical and Biological Agents at Work, Directive 88/642/EEC [16].

This Directive instructs Member States to take account of indicative limit values set by the Commission when determining national exposure limits. A Scientific Experts Group (SEG) advises on indicative criteria documents, and assists the Commission in proposing indicative limit values. The intent is to harmonize the data used for limit setting, allowing possible exchange of criteria documents between Member States [17]. The first Directive on Indicative Limit Values was adopted in May 1991 [18]. It covers 27 substances, including: acetic acid, bromine, methanol, nicotine, pyrethrum, and inorganic tin compounds.

## 33.6 United Kingdom Workplace Safety

**Control of Substances Hazardous to Health Regulations 1988 (COSHH) [19]**

These regulations were made under the authority of the Health and Safety at Work etc. Act 1974, and came into force from October 1989. They set up a basic framework allowing the United Kingdom to comply with EC health and safety directives. COSHH requires employers to assess risks from hazardous substances used in the workplace. A written risk assessment is required which is specific to each workplace; this written assessment must be available to employees. These assessments are subject to examination by Health and Safety Executive inspectors.

Suitable risk control measures must be developed and used. The hierarchy of control measures, from most to least preferred is:

i) Eliminate exposure by, *eg*, substituting a safer alternative method or chemical;

ii) Control exposure by engineering methods, such as enclosing the system, or by changing procedures or processes;

iii) Reduce exposure by use of personal protective equipment (PPE). PPE is to be used only in combination with other methods, not in place of other methods.

Health surveillance of workers may be necessary, if there is doubt about exposure being successfully controlled. Surveillance can range from a simple register of incidents to periodic medical examinations.

Under the COSHH Regulations there are 2 categories of limits on exposure to substances in the workplace:

i) A Maximum Exposure Limit (MEL); or,

ii) An Occupational Exposure Standard (OES).

The alternative designations place different obligations on employers. With an MEL, exposure to the substance should be reduced as far as is 'reasonably practicable', and should in no case exceed the MEL. For an OES, it is sufficient for employers to ensure that exposure is no higher than the OES. 'Excursions' above an OES may be allowed, providing the employer identifies the reasons for exceeding the standard, and takes steps to reduce exposure as soon as is reasonably practicable [20].

Exposure limits are set by the Health and Safety Commission, on the advice of its Advisory Committee on Toxic Substances (ACTS) and Working Group on the Assessment of Toxic Chemicals (WATCH). ACTS has begun publishing the full rationale for establishing exposure limits as 'Criteria Documents'. The format of these documents is modelled on that adopted by the EC [17].

## 33.7 United States Workplace Safety

### The US Occupational Safety and Health Act of 1970

The Act regulates workplace safety at the Federal level. Responsibilities under the Act are distributed between the Department of Labor and the Department of Health and Human Services. The National Advisory Committee on Occupational Safety and Health was created to coordinate activities between the 2 departments. The 12 members of this committee represent employees, employers, the public, and health and safety professionals. A 3-member Occupational Safety and Health Review Commission, comprised of presidential appointees, is empowered to settle disputes arising from enforcement of the Act.

In order to carry out the provisions of the Act, the National Institute for Occupational Safety and Health (NIOSH) and the Occupational Safety and Health Administration (OSHA) were created. OSHA is in the US Department of Labor, and is responsible for regulating health and safety. NIOSH is part of the Department of Health and Human Services, and is a research agency.

OSHA develops new, and improves existing, statutory workplace health and safety standards. Setting and enforcing occupational exposure limits for hazardous substances is part of this mandate. OSHA also regulates the employee-health records kept by employers. This includes documentation of exposure to hazardous chemicals. In conjunction with NIOSH, OSHA collects and analyzes employee health statistics, providing the means to evaluate possible adverse effects of workplace exposures.

NIOSH conducts research aimed at improving health and safety in the workplace. A major goal of NIOSH research is to provide the scientific basis for setting exposure standards. The *Registry of toxic effects of chemical substances* (RTECS), is published and regularly updated by NIOSH. RTECS lists all known toxic substances, the types of toxicity seen at different concentrations, and current US regulatory standards. At the request of an employer, employee or employee representative, NIOSH will conduct a site investigation into possible health effects from exposure to hazardous substances.

## 33.8 Pesticides

### 33.8.1 EC Pesticides

#### 33.8.1.1 Directive Concerning the Placing of Plant Protection Products on the Market (91/414/EEC) [21]

The intention of this Directive is to harmonize registration standards for agricultural pesticides throughout the Community. A sister Directive covering nonagricultural pesticides is in draft stages. An EC agreed list of pesticide active ingredients, 'the EC-positive list', is to be established. Individual Member States will then register products having active ingredients from that list. To facilitate mutual recognition, 'Uniform Principles' for the decision-making process are being developed.

EC Regulation 3600/92 [22] details the program by which Member States will review existing active ingredients. Member States will review data supplied by pesticide producers, or generated by themselves, and forward their recommendations to the Commission. Final decisions concerning additions to the EC-positive list will be made by the EC's Standing Committee on Plant Health.

#### 33.8.1.2 Framework Directive for Fixing Maximum Residue Levels (90/642/EEC) [23]

This Directive was to be implemented in all Member States as of 31st December, 1992. Its purpose is to fix Community-wide Maximum Residue Levels (MRLs) for pesticides in a wide spectrum of produce. The intent is to facilitate free movement of produce between Member States, while assuring consumers of consistent approaches to regulation of pesticide residues in food.

Member States are not allowed to set MRLs lower than the agreed EC MRLs. Additionally, produce from other Member States cannot be refused for containing pesticide residues not exceeding EC adopted MRLs. MRLs based on Codex, or other requirements, are to be reviewed and agreed or adjusted by the Standing Committee on Plant Health.

### 33.8.2 United Kingdom Pesticide Legislation

#### The Food and Environment Protection Act of 1985 (FEPA)

FEPA has the avowed aim of protecting human health and the environment, at the same time as ensuring effective methods of pest control. Under the authority of FEPA, the Control of Pesticides Regulations 1986 (COPR) [24] were enacted. Pesticide residues in food are controlled by the Maximum Residue Level Regulations of 1988. Together, these regulations impose statutory requirements on everyone involved with pesticides, from the manufacturer to the user.

FEPA specified the establishment of an independent committee, the Advisory Committee on Pesticides (ACP), to advise Government Ministers on pesticide issues. Members of the ACP are generally academic scientists having expertise in various aspects of toxicology or crop protection; Government and industry are not represented. The ACP is assisted and advised by civil servants, as well as by other independent committees, expert panels, and working parties. For example, the Working Party on Pesticide Residues (WPPR) prepares an annual report on pesticide residues in food. Membership of the panels and working parties is broader than that of the ACP itself. Government scientists may participate, as well as representatives from industry and trade unions. More recently, consumer groups have been invited to nominate participants.

The ACP assesses hazard and risk, and makes a set of specific recommendations as to what uses, if any, should be approved for the pesticide in question. Formal approval of a pesticide application comes from the relevant Minister. The Ministry of Agriculture, Fisheries and Food (MAFF) is responsible for agricultural pesticides; the Health and Safety Executive (HSE) regulates non-agricultural pesticides.

COPR states that all pesticide approvals will be subject to review every 10 years following the date of initial approval. Any approval, however, is subject to review at any time if new information becomes available. Approval holders must submit any new data indicating adverse effects to the regulatory authority. The general goal of the rolling review program is to bring the dockets on older pesticides up to the standard currently required for new approvals. The order of review is prioritized, although appearance on the list does not necessarily imply a suspected safety problem. The priority list is published, but the number and type of outstanding studies are not included. Approval holders may decide that meeting new data requirements is too expensive, and withdraw a product for commercial reasons.

### 33.8.3 The United States Pesticide Legislation

#### Federal Insecticide, Fungicide and Rodenticide Act (FIFRA), 1972

FIFRA stipulates that all pesticides, agricultural and nonagricultural, must be registered by the US Environmental Protection Agency. Approximately 1,200 active ingredients are registered for use in the US, in roughly 20,000 different products [10]. Approval is granted if the Agency determines that health and environmental toxicity data reveal no 'unreasonable risk'. Approval may be granted for some, but not all, proposed uses. Restrictions may be placed on approval, such as 'for use only by certified pesticide applicators'; other specific labelling requirements may be designated.

Pesticides which were registered prior to the enactment of FIFRA are subject to re-registration by EPA. Additional testing may be required by the Agency. EPA's Office of Pesticide Programs publishes regular updates of its pesticide review program. These include details of studies requested, studies completed, references to contents of the docket, and summaries of Agency actions.

If a pesticide is found to pose 'unreasonable risk to health or the environment', uses of that pesticide may be restricted, or the registration cancelled. Since 1985, over 30 pesticides have been restricted or cancelled [10]. Aldrin, carbon tetrachloride, dinoseb, and ethylene dibromide have had their registrations cancelled for all uses. As the cancellation process can be lengthy, EPA has the discretion to declare an emergency and suspend use of the pesticide pending a cancellation. This discretionary power was used in the case of dinoseb.

## 33.9 Environmental Legislation

### 33.9.1 EC Environmental Legislation

EC directives such as the Labelling and Classification Directive and the Pesticides Acceptance Directive, include environmental toxicity in their regulatory framework. Two directives specifically addressing water pollution are the 'Dangerous Substances in Water Directive' [25], and the 'Drinking Water Directive' [26]. The goal of the former Directive is to eliminate or substantially reduce water pollution by banning or restricting discharges to groundwater of certain chemicals. The latter Directive establishes Maximum Admissible Concentrations (MACs) of certain chemicals, such as pesticides, in drinking water.

### 33.9.2 The United Kingdom Environmental Legislation

#### 33.9.2.1 Environmental Protection Act, 1990

The broad aim of the Act is to prevent pollution by regulating emissions at source. Environmental emission limits are expected to be met according to the principle of BATNEEC (best available technology not entailing excessive cost), also see reference [27].

#### 33.9.2.2 The Water Industry Act, 1991

The Act empowers the Secretary of State, through HM Inspectorate of Pollution, to control consents for discharge of industrial effluent to water. Discharge of any chemicals on the Department of Environment's (DoE) 'red list' is controlled under the principle of BATNEEC. The red list consists of chemicals considered likely to be present in water, and which are toxic to health or the environment. High priority is given to chemicals which bioaccumulate or which are persistent in the environment.

The National Rivers Authority (NRA) enforces quality standards in surface waters. In order to ensure water quality, the NRA may prohibit the use of certain chemicals. The NRA can also establish 'Water Protection Zones', where certain activities are prohibited.

### 33.9.3 The United States Environmental Legislation

**Comprehensive Environmental Response Compensation and Liability Act of 1980 ('Superfund')**

This Act gives EPA authority to deal with major toxic chemical emergencies, such as spills or leaching from disused disposal sites.

#### 33.9.3.1 The Superfund Amendments and Reauthorization Act of 1986 (Emergency Planning and Community Right-to-Know Act)

Under provisions of this act, qualifying industrial facilities are required to report certain information to EPA. These annual reports must contain details of environmental releases and other movements of specified chemicals above a minimum amount. EPA makes this information publicly available as the Toxic Release Inventory (TRI).

Any interested party may petition EPA requesting that specific chemicals be removed from, or added to, the list of reportable chemicals. The Agency evaluates evidence submitted with such petitions and grants or denies the request. Partly as a result of this petitioning process, specified chemicals and the reporting threshold have changed for each reporting year. In 1989, reporting was required for 322 chemicals produced, imported, or processed in amounts of ≥25,000 pounds [10].

#### 33.9.3.2 Pollution Prevention Act, 1990

This Act formally declares 'the national policy of the United States that pollution should be prevented or reduced at the source' [10]. Previous environmental programs were considered to emphasize clean-up, rather than technology which would abate pollution in the first place. In contrast, much of the substance of the Pollution Prevention Act concerns development and dissemination of pollution-reduction technology.

The Pollution Prevention Act also adds to the reporting requirements already established under the Superfund Amendments and Reauthorization Act. Previously voluntary reporting of recycling or pollution-reduction activities is now mandatory. The intent is to make TRI data useful for assessing industry's progress in pollution prevention.

#### 33.9.3.3 Resource Conservation and Recovery Act (RCRA)

The Act which authorizes EPA to regulate waste treatment and disposal. Waste streams, containing any number of chemicals, are generally covered by RCRA. In contrast, disposal of an individual chemical is regulated with the rest of that chemical's life-cycle under TSCA.

#### 33.9.3.4 Hazardous and Solid Waste Amendments to the Resource Conservation and Recovery Act, 1984

These Amendments set a priority for pollution prevention with respect to land disposal of hazardous waste. Industries generating hazardous waste were required to establish a hazardous-waste reduction program, as distinct from recycling. Reporting requirements have been established in order to assess the success of pollution-reduction strategies.

#### 33.9.3.5 Clean Air Act; Clean Air Act Amendments, 1990

The Clean Air Act authorizes EPA to enact regulations and establish programs with the aim of enhancing air quality. The amendments emphasize pollution-prevention strategies as a means of improving air quality. Previous programs are considered to have relied too heavily upon meeting emission standards, resulting in secondary clean up of hazardous air pollutants.

Strategies for reducing emissions of sulfur dioxide and nitrogen oxide, the components of acid rain, are specifically outlined in the amendments. Other specific programs are aimed at reducing air pollution from vehicles.

#### 33.9.3.6 Clean Water Act, 1977; Safe Drinking Water Act, amended 1977; Marine Protection, Research and Sanctuaries Act, 1972

Between them, these acts authorize EPA to regulate water pollution in order to protect drinking water, inland recreational waters, and coastal waters.

## 33.10 International Programs in Chemical Risk Assessment: Organization for Economic Cooperation and Development (OECD)

### 33.10.1 The High-volume Chemicals Project [28]

In 1987, OECD member countries agreed to undertake a systematic investigation of chemicals currently in commerce in large quantities. The following countries are involved: United States, Germany, Canada, Denmark, the Netherlands, Switzerland, Sweden, Belgium, United Kingdom, France, Finland, Japan, Austria, and Italy. Sharing the task of data compilation, review and assessment should result in a greater number of chemicals receiving a detailed review than could be accomplished by any one country alone. As a step towards more general international harmonization, the project is expected to reduce duplication of testing to fill requirements of diverse regulatory authorities.

### 33.10.2 Collaborators

This effort by the OECD is actively supported by other international organizations concerned with chemical safety, as well as by the chemical industry. The Commission of the European Community (CEC), the United Nations International Program on Chemical Safety (IPCS), and the International Register of Potentially Toxic Chemicals (IRPTC) of the United Nations Environment Program (UNEP) all send observers to chemical review meetings. The UN organizations intend to disseminate the final conclusions and recommendations for specific chemicals internationally, beyond OECD member countries.

Industry has agreed to assist the OECD by supplying existing data, as well as by undertaking any necessary additional testing in a timely manner. Chemical review meetings are attended by observers from the OECD Business and Industry Advisory Committee (BIAC), and by chemical manufacturers.

### 33.10.3 Identification of Candidate Chemicals

Production volume was assumed to provide a crude indication of potential human and environmental exposure. Thus high-production-volume chemicals were considered to be associated with the highest potential risk, and were flagged for priority attention. High-production-volume chemicals were defined as those produced in one OECD member country at quantities above 10,000 tonnes $a^{-1}$, or by ≥2 member countries at quantities above 1000 tonnes $a^{-1}$.

The 'OECD Representative List', as revised in 1991, contained 1592 entries. Highest priority was given to those chemicals for which little or no information was currently available. A working list of approximately 600 chemicals was derived.

### 33.10.4 The SIDS Data Set [28,29]

The 'Screening Information Data Set' (SIDS) was developed concurrently with the Representative List. SIDS was designed to encompass the minimum information needed to allow a decision to be made as to whether or not a chemical should be considered:

i) Of low current concern;

ii) A candidate for further information gathering, testing, or review; or,

iii) A possible candidate for risk-reduction activities.

The basic components of SIDS are:

i) Chemical identity and physical-chemical data;

ii) Production and use information;

iii) Environmental fate;

iv) Ecotoxicity; and,

v) A minimum set of toxicological data.

### 33.10.5 Guidance for Data Reporting, Assessment, and Testing

To facilitate consistency in the quality of data, data assessment, and reporting, the OECD has published reporting forms and guidance documents. The EC has agreed to adopt an identical reporting form, using computer diskettes, for their existing chemicals program [8,28]. Previously promulgated OECD guidelines for 'Good Laboratory Practice' and for specific toxicity tests already provide a widely-used international standard.

### 33.10.6 Steps in the Process

Each OECD member country sponsors a set of chemicals throughout various phases of the SIDS project. Existing data are collected, reviewed, and assessed. The review is not restricted to SIDS elements; any relevant information is included. Chemical companies are asked to provide any unpublished data which they hold.

A SIDS dossier is prepared and, if appropriate, a testing program is developed. Dossiers and test programs are agreed by a SIDS review meeting which includes experts from all member countries, as well as observers from UN organizations and from industry. Any necessary testing is conducted by the sponsoring country, and the results evaluated. Recommendations are considered at the OECD SIDS Initial Assessment Meeting. Participation in this meeting is similar to that for the SIDS review meeting described above. An initial hazard assessment is agreed. Chemicals are categorized as:

i) Of no immediate concern;

ii) A candidate for further testing/review; or,

iii) A potential candidate for risk-reduction activities.

### 33.10.7 Public Availability of Information

Sponsoring countries are responsible for making information on 'their' chemicals publicly available. All health and safety information will be shared with IRPTC, who will make it available worldwide. If sufficient information is available, a Health and Safety Guide or an Environmental Health Criteria document will be prepared in conjunction the IPCS.

### 33.10.8 Status of the Program

Testing on 38 chemicals in Phase 1 of the program is nearly completed [29]. About 60 additional chemicals are scheduled for testing in Phase 2. Testing programs for 61 Phase 3 chemicals are expected to be agreed during 1993.

## 33.11 Conclusions

All the regulatory programs discussed in this chapter are directed towards protecting human health and the environment, while at the same time not unduly hampering industrial developments or trade. International efforts are being made to share data and research costs, as well as to harmonize data requirements and risk assessment standards. The OECD high-volume-chemicals program is one such effort, but there are other examples of projects which are well under way or in initial stages. (See also chapter by Duffus and Draper.)

The Codex Committee on Pesticide Residues is sponsored jointly by the World Health Organization (WHO) and the Food and Agriculture Organization (FAO) of the United Nations. Codex sets Maximum Residues Levels (MRLs) for pesticides and foodstuffs, with the intention of protecting consumers as well as facilitating international trade in food. A major topic at the United Nations Conference on Environment and Development, held in Rio de Janeiro in June 1992 was the need for an international toxic emissions inventory [30]. A follow-up meeting which considered this topic included participants from the UN International Program on Chemical Safety, the UN Institute for Training and Research, the World Health Organization, the OECD, the United States, Australia, the Netherlands, the Slovak Republic, and Canada. Cooperative research on chemical toxicity can be exemplified by a joint project of the United States Environmental Protection Agency and scientists for the Czech Republic [31]. Studies are underway to determine the effects on health of exposure to extremely high amounts of certain pollutants. The purpose of this research is to improve the scientific basis for helping exposed populations in the Czech Republic, as well as to increase general understanding of the relationship between pollution and adverse effects on health.

If they are to be successful, international programs in chemical regulation require open communication concerning emission and toxicity data. Sharing expertise and working towards consensus standards for data requirements and risk assessment procedures are also vital. Active, voluntary participation by the chemical industry should be encouraged. In this way, the goals of minimizing risks to health and the environment, while avoiding unnecessary duplication of testing, can be advanced.

## 33.12 References

[1] 67/548/EEC. Council Directive on the approximation of laws, regulations and administrative provisions relating to the classification, packaging and labelling of dangerous substances, *Off. J. Eur. Commiss.*, 196/1 16-08-88

[2] 88/379/EEC. Council Directive on the approximation of the laws, regulations and administrative provision of the Member States relating to the classification, packaging and labelling of dangerous preparations, *Off. J. Eur. Commiss.*, L.187/14, 16-07-88.

[3] Sullivan, F.M., *Toxicology Letts*, 1992, **64/65**, 183-189.

[4] 76/769/EEC. Council Directive on the approximation of the laws, regulations and administrative provisions of the Member States relating to restrictions of the marketing and use of certain substances and preparations, *Off. J. Eur. Commiss.*, L.262, 27-09-76, amended by Directives 89/677/EEC, *Off. J. Eur. Commiss.*, L.398, 30.12.89, and 91/173/EEC, *Off. J. Eur. Commiss.*, L.85, 05-04-91.

[5] Brown, B., *Toxic Substances Bull.*, Health and Safety Executive, 1993, **20**, 1-2.

[6] Davis, J., *Toxic Substances Bull.*, Health and Safety Executive, 1991, **16**, 6.

[7] Rea, J., Shillaker, R., and Smith, P., *Toxic Substances Bull.*, Health and Safety Executive, 1991, **15**, 2-3.

[8] Roswell, F., *Toxic Substances Bull.*, Health and Safety Executive, 1992, **20**, 1-2.

[9] Office of Toxic Substances, United States Environmental Protection Agency, new chemicals program: intervention to prevent risk is program's basis. *Chemicals in Progress Bull.*, 1991, **12**, (4), 6-7 and 30.

[10] United States Environmental Protection Agency, Pollution Prevention 1991: Progress on Reducing Industrial Pollutants. United States Government Printing Office, 1991.

[11] United States Environmental Protection Agency. Office of Toxic Substances, The layman's guide to the toxic substances control act. TSCA Assistance Office, 1987.

[12] 8391/EEC. Council Directive on the introduction of measures to encourage improvements in the safety of workers at work (Framework Directive), *Off. J. Eur. Commiss.*, L.183, 29-06-89.

[13] 90/394/EEC. Council Directive on the protection of workers from the risks related to exposure to carcinogens at work (Carcinogens Directive), *Off. J. Eur. Commiss.*, L.196, 26-07-90.

[14] 92/85/EEC. Council Directive on the introduction of measures to encourage improvements in the safety and health at work of pregnant workers and workers who have recently given birth or are breast feeding, (Pregnant Workers Directive), *Off. J. Eur. Commiss.*, L.348, 28-11-92.

[15] *Reproductive Toxicology*, Richardson, M.L. (Ed.), VCH Publishers, Weinheim, 1993, pp. 286.

[16] 88/642/EEC. Council Directive amending directive 80/1107/EEC on the protection of workers from the risks related to chemical, physical and biological agents at work, *Off. J. Eur. Commiss.*, L.256, 24-12-88.

[17] Topping, M., Criteria documents, *Toxic Substances Bull.*, Health and Safety Executive, 1992, **19**, 5.

[18] 91/322. Commission Directive on establishing indicative limit values to protect workers from the risks related to exposure to chemical, physical and biological agents at work, *Off. J. Eur. Commiss.*, L.177, 05-07-91.

[19] Control of Substances Hazardous to Health Regulations 1988. Statutory Instruments 1988 No. 1657, and as amended by 1990 No. 2026, 1991 No. 2431, 1992 No. 2382, and 1992 No. 2966., HMSO, London.

[20] West, N., Revised indicative criteria for occupational exposure limits, *Toxic Substances Bull.*, Health and Safety Executive, 1991, **16**, 4-5.

[21] 91/414/EEC. Council Directive concerning the policy of placing plant protection products on the market, *Off. J. Eur. Commiss.*, L.230, 19-08-91.

[22] 3600/92/EEC. Commission regulation laying down the detailed rules for the implementation of the first stage of the program of work referred to in article 8, (2) of Directive 91/414/EEC concerning the placing of plant protection products on the market, *Off. J. Eur. Commiss.*, L.366, 15-12-92.

[23] 90/642/EEC. Council Directive on the fixing of maximum levels for pesticide residues in and on certain products of plant origin including fruit and vegetables, *Off. J. Eur. Commiss.*, L.350, 14-12-90

[24] Control of Pesticides Regulations. Statutory Instrument, 1986, No. 1510, HMSO, London.

[25] 76/464/EEC. Council Directive on pollution caused by certain dangerous substances discharged into the aquatic environment of the community, *Off. J. Eur. Commiss.*, L.129, 18-05-86.

[26] 80/778/EEC. Council Directive relating to the quality of water intended for human consumption, *Off. J. Eur. Commiss.*, L.229, 30-08-80.

[27] Environmental Protection (Prescribed Process and Substances) Regulations 1991. Statutory Instrument 1991, No. 472, HMSO, London.

[28] United States Environmental Protection Agency. Office of Pesticides and Toxic Substances, Existing Chemicals Assessment Division. Information packet on the OECD Screening Information Data Set (SIDS) Program for high production volume (HPV) chemicals, 1992.

[29] United States Environmental Protection Agency. Office of Pollution Prevention and Toxics, SIDS Phase 1 Chemicals Test Data Almost Completed, *Chemicals in Progress Bull.*, 1993, **14**, (2), 18.

[30] United States Environmental Protection Agency, Office of Pollution Prevention and Toxics, 'Nations begin groundwork for toxics emissions inventory', *Chemicals in Progress Bulletin*, 1993, **14**, (2), 19.

[31] Balter, M., *Science*, 1993, **261**, 24-25.

# 34. Worldwide Regulatory Controls to Ensure Safety of Chemicals

Derek Knight

## 34.1 Introduction

Progressing of a new chemical, from its invention or discovery to eventual placing on the market, involves many individuals and bodies with different functions.

Before marketing a new product, the manufacturer, for both product liability reasons and in order to meet various national and international legal requirements, has to establish not only the efficiency of the product to perform as required but also its hazardous properties, to ensure it can be used safely.

Chemical manufacturers often supply their products in many markets, and consequently various national chemical control systems have to be complied with. It is prudent to obtain advice on these requirements early in the development stage, to enable informed business decisions to be made and to ensure full regulatory compliance. For a new chemical substance, notifications in different countries may be necessary, and it is essential to design the testing programme to fulfil all the various requirements to ensure timely regulatory approvals, and also to minimise the total cost of the studies and the use of animals.

This chapter begins with an overview of the general aspects of chemical control which may have to be considered to enable a product to be marketed. Specific national requirements are then highlighted, with a view to supply worldwide. Regional and national chemical control legislation is summarised in more detail, with the emphasis on the testing and notification requirements for new chemical substances to ensure adequate information is available to evaluate whether they can be used safely. Finally, certain general conclusions are drawn, and the role of the regulatory affairs professional in maintaining quality for registration projects is discussed briefly.

## 34.2 General Aspects of Chemical Control

Chemical control legislation, including the degree of its practical enforcement, varies between countries, as does the associated official advice and voluntary industry codes of practice. These systems for chemical control are being developed and improved, sometimes with a view to international harmonisation. In practice the supply, use and disposal of chemicals throughout their full life cycle is regulated in most of the developed world, and these general aspects of chemical control are highlighted below.

Chemicals have to be classified, packaged and labelled according to the United Nations (UN) scheme for safe transport, *ie*, by ship, inland waterways, air, rail and road. Advice on action to take following accidental spillage has to be available, *eg*, from

Transport and Emergency (TREM) cards, poison centres or other information sources. Safe transport of marine pollutants is ensured by MARPOL 73/78 [1], which is in effect a supplement to the International Maritime Dangerous Goods Code of the International Maritime Organization.

The intrinsic chemical, health and environmental hazards of chemical substances and preparations have to be communicated to the user, to enable the material to be used and stored safely. This is achieved by standardised classification and labelling of 'dangerous' chemicals, and by providing Material Safety Data Sheets (MSDSs). Management can use this information to ensure chemical workers are operating under safe conditions, with appropriate engineering controls to minimize chemical release, and are using adequate protective equipment conforming to suitable national or international standards to minimize exposure to released chemicals. Relevant worker exposure limits must be complied with, and the employer may be obliged to undertake health surveillance.

The disposal of waste chemicals, including absorbed spillages and contaminated containers, will also be regulated to ensure pollution is minimised. Recycling and the use of safer or less polluting chemicals may be encouraged. The annual environmental release of certain chemicals has to be reported to the Toxic Release Inventory in the USA, and other countries could follow this example, following the initiative of the UN Conference on the Environment and Development (UNCED) held in Rio de Janeiro, June 1992.

Discharge of pollutants to air and water are controlled by suitable means, to enforce the appropriate national environmental quality standards or internationally-agreed pollution control targets, such as the release of ozone-depleting chemicals according to the Montreal Protocol [2]. The original polluter may be responsible for restoring contaminated land to a state suitable for alternative use, as under the US 'superfund' legislation [3].

The necessary emergency measures to be taken following accidental spillage or poisoning have to be assessed, and national fire control legislation will also apply. Exceptional risks to the community surrounding a chemical plant may have to be evaluated under major accidents hazards legislation, such as the European Community (EC) 'Seveso' Directive [4].

The information used to classify a chemical substance as 'dangerous', either to health or the environment, can be used for hazard assessment, which can be combined with chemical exposure data to produce a risk assessment. Further information on toxicity or exposure may be needed to refine the risk assessment, before any necessary risk management action is taken to ban or restrict the use of the chemical. (See also chapter by Cowie and Richardson.) Defined hazard and risk assessment procedures may be used by regulators, or informal assessments based on practical experience can be undertaken by chemical users, either voluntarily or to fulfil statutory obligations.

Some countries, such as Finland, Norway and Sweden, require chemicals to be reported to commercial product inventories. (See also chapter by Kulkarni and Nangle.) Furthermore, the appropriate national Customs requirements have to be fulfilled before chemicals can be imported. There may also be restrictions on the export of substances banned or restricted in the country of manufacture, because of the UN Prior Informed Consent programme [5].

Chemical products have to be fit for their intended purpose and may be covered by mandatory or advisory product standards. They will certainly be subject to civil legislation on product liability. Industry association voluntary codes of practice may apply, or alternatively a manufacturer may decide it is commercially undesirable to sell a product containing chemicals with certain properties (*eg*, which are Ames positive) even though there is no legal or ethical restriction. The choice of chemicals to use in the manufacturing process may be governed by the desire to have an environmental (ECO) label for the finished product, to obtain a competitive advantage in retail sales. Finally, the packaging of the finished product might be chosen with a consideration of packaging waste legislation, such as the scheme already in operation in the Federal Republic of Germany [6].

The EC, most of the countries of the European Free Trade Association (EFTA), the USA, Australia and Japan, and certain developing countries require new chemical substances to be notified before they are imported or either manufactured or marketed. 'Existing' chemicals, which can be supplied without notification, are listed in an inventory, *eg*, the EC in the European Inventory of Existing Chemical Substances (EINECS). Notified new chemicals are either listed in a separate inventory, *eg*, in the EC in ELINCS (see also chapter by Campbell), or added to the inventory of existing substances, often in a confidential section which can only be retrieved by those with a proven genuine intention to supply the particular substance. Notification schemes vary in the provisions for protecting confidential information from public disclosure, and the rights of second suppliers to use the original data to fulfil regulatory obligations.

Chemicals supplied only for uses regulated separately are exempt from new chemicals legislation, because in principle they have been tested and evaluated to a standard at least equivalent to that for notification as a new chemical substance. Exemption from full notification often also applies to other categories of new chemical substances, such as polymers, non-isolated intermediates, and perhaps, also pharmaceutical or other chemical intermediates, and to chemicals supplied only for 'research' or for 'commercial development', although a reduced notification may be necessary. The content of a full notification varies between schemes, as does that for reduced notification for low volume supply (usually at <1 tonne $a^{-1}$). The studies for notification are conducted in compliance with Good Laboratory Practice (GLP) following the Organization for Economic Co-operation and Development (OECD) or national guidelines. The official notification acceptance procedure and the duration of the waiting period required for review of the submission depends on the particular country. The purpose of the review might be simply to ensure regulatory compliance, but an initial hazard and risk assessment may be conducted which could trigger a request for further information and/or result in risk management. Further testing may also be necessary when the supply level of the notified substance reaches defined threshold values.

Existing chemical substances, especially those supplied in high volume, may be subject to review in one of the national or international evaluation programs, such as the OECD Screening Information Data Set (SIDS) scheme [7]. Existing data are reported initially, but new studies may be required subsequently to fill data gaps, especially if necessary for adequate assessment of the substance. The hazard and risk assessment could lead to risk management.

Risk management measures for new and existing chemicals, which may be taken after a risk/benefit evaluation, can be in the form of recommendations for safe use, labelling or occupational exposure limits. Most developed countries also have legal provisions for banning chemicals, or restricting their use to safe conditions.

Many countries have regulatory authorities with responsibilities for assessing the acceptability of chemicals. This assessment is often made prior to marketing approval. There are normally separate authorities to deal with each type of chemical: *eg*, pesticides, pharmaceutical products, industrial chemicals or food additives. It is normal for each of these authorities to have individual legal requirements for the information which must be provided in the regulatory submission. Some international co-ordination in this area has been developed through the OECD, and the basic data requirements for most authorities can be similar.

Some chemicals may be used in such a way that they are regulated not only by general chemical control legislation for household and industrial chemicals, but also as other chemical products, such as detergents, biocides/slimicides (*ie*, non-agricultural pesticides) or offshore chemicals (*eg*, guidelines of the Group on Oil Pollution of the Paris Commission) [8]. The regulation of such chemical products varies considerably between countries, and it is not uncommon for the same chemical to be defined as an industrial chemical in one country, as a biocide in another, and to be covered by both use categories in a third.

Regulatory authorities rely for their safety assessment of chemicals entirely upon data provided to them by the registrant. Generally, they can have confidence in the companies and laboratories providing and generating the data for the assessments. The consequences of false data could be extremely serious, however, and hence most regulatory authorities require the studies submitted for the purposes of safety assessment of chemicals to be conducted in compliance with Good Laboratory Practice (GLP). The regulatory submission can consist of many separate studies, which may have been carried out by a number of laboratories, perhaps in different countries, and hence the authorities need assurance of the quality of the studies submitted and that the study reports are a true reflection of the results obtained during the studies. The principles of GLP were first developed in the early to mid 1970s by the US Food and Drug Administration (FDA). However, as part of a parallel initiative, the OECD were considering ways in which the amount of testing required to register new chemicals in the various OECD member countries could be reduced. Hence the OECD study guidelines were developed. It was also acknowledged that adoption of a harmonised set of GLP principles by the OECD would ensure that studies undertaken in different member countries were carried out to the same minimum standards. Completion of this work led to the 'Mutual Acceptance of Data' [9]. Fortunately the OECD Principles of GLP have served as the basis for most of the various national and European GLP regulations, and hence there are only minor differences between the GLP principles currently in use throughout the world.

## 34.3 Chemical Control Schemes

Various international organizations are involved in the testing, safety evaluation and regulation of chemicals: UN agencies, the OECD, the Council of Europe, the EC and EFTA. The national regulatory authorities co-operate with each other, often under the auspices of these international organizations, and hold joint meetings which include industry and academia, with a view to harmonizing chemical control. Repeat testing of the same chemical to meet different regulatory requirements is undesirable commercially, and from an animal welfare viewpoint. The EC intend to co-ordinate their existing chemicals review programme with that of the OECD, and the associated hazard and risk assessment procedures are currently being developed, although it may be difficult to harmonize these at OECD level. The OECD is also an important forum for developing standard test guidelines, and an example of this is the agreement between the EC and the US Environmental Protection Agency (EPA) on the option of using the new OECD fixed-dose procedure to test acute oral toxicity, instead of determining the $LD_{50}$ [10]. Another example of co-operation between national authorities is the recent study, in which the US EPA use structure activity relationships (SAR) to evaluate new chemical substances already notified in the EC, so that these results can be compared with the actual test data [11].

New chemical notification schemes vary considerably between countries, but many base the studies for full notification on the OECD minimum pre-marketing set of data (MPD): the EC, certain EFTA countries, Australia and the imminent Canadian scheme (See Table 34.1). Only a few studies additional to the EC Base Set are needed for full notification in Austria and Switzerland. Chemical control legislation in Scandinavia is in the process of being changed, in order to achieve the intended harmonization by 1 January 1995 of chemical control legislation between the EC and 6 of the EFTA countries under the new European Economic Area (EEA). The EC notification scheme will have been updated by then, under the 'Seventh Amendment' Council Directive 92/32/EEC [12], which was brought into force by 31 October 1993. Thus the current Finnish new chemicals notification scheme will be modified to conform exactly to that of Council Directive 92/32/EEC as from 31 October 1993, and the proposed notification schemes for Norway and Sweden will also have to be in harmony with the EC.

**Table 34.1** **Testing programmes for worldwide full notification of a new chemical substance**

| Study | Requirement for supply in: | | | | | |
|---|---|---|---|---|---|---|
| | OECD (a) | EC (b) | CH (c) | A (d) | Can. (e) | Aus. (f) |
| Spectra | √ | √ | √ | √ | √ | √ |
| Melting point | √}(g) | √ | √ | √ | √ | √}(g) |
| Boiling point | √} | √ | √ | √ | √ | √} |
| Relative density | √ | √ | √ | √ | √ | √ |
| Vapour pressure | √ | √ | √ | √ | √ | √ |
| Surface tension | | √ | √ | √ | | |
| Water solubility | √ | √ | √ | √ | √ | √ |
| Partition coefficient | √ | √ | √ | √ | √ | √ |
| Fat solubility | √ | | √(h) | √ | √ | |
| Dissociation constant | √ | | √ | | √ | √ |
| Granulometry | √ | √ | (i) | | √ | √ |
| Henry's Law constant | | | (i) | | | |
| Volatility from water | | | (i) | | | |

| Study | Requirement for supply in: | | | | | |
|---|---|---|---|---|---|---|
| | OECD (a) | EC (b) | CH (c) | A (d) | Can. (e) | Aus. (f) |
| Complex formation constants | | | (i) | | | |
| Stability | | | (i) | | | |
| Viscosity | | | (i) | | | |
| Permeability | | | (i) | | | |
| Flash point (liquids) | | √ | | √ | | √ |
| Flammability tests | | √ | | √ | | √ |
| Explosivity | | √ | | √ | | √ |
| Oxidising properties | | √ | | √ | | √ |
| Autoflammability | | √ | | √ | | √ |
| Acute oral toxicity | √ | √ | (j) | √ | √ | √ |
| Acute dermal toxicity | √ | √}(k) | (j) | √}(k) | √}(k) | √}(k) |
| Acute inhalation toxicity | √ | √} | (j) | √} | √} | √} |
| Skin irritation | √ | √ | (j) | √ | √ | √ |
| Eye irritation | √ | √ | (j) | √ | | √ |
| Skin sensitisation | √ | √ | (j) | √ | √ | √ |
| Subacute toxicity | √ | √ | (j) | √ | √ | √ |
| Ames test | } | √ | √ | √ | √ | √ |
| *In vitro* chromosome aberration test | }<br>}(l) | √ | √ | √}(m) | √ | √ |
| Mouse micronucleus test | } | (n) | (j) | } | √(o) | √(p) |
| Mouse lymphoma assay | } | (q) | (j) | | | |
| Acute fish toxicity | √ | √ | √ | √ | √ | √ |
| Acute *Daphnia* toxicity | | √ | √ | √ | √ | √ |
| Algal growth inhibition | √ | √ | (i) | | | √ |
| *Daphnia* reproduction study | √ | | √ | | | √ |
| Fish bioaccumulation | | | (i) | | | (r) |
| Earthworm toxicity | | | | √ | | |
| Ready biodegradability | √ | √ | √ | √ | √ | √ |
| Activated sludge respiration inhibition | | √(s) | | | | |
| Abiotic degradation by hydrolysis | √ | √(t) | √ | √ | √ | √ |
| Soil adsorption/desorption screening test | √ | √(u) | (i) | | √ | √ |
| Anaerobic biodegradation | | | (i) | | | |
| Soil biodegradation | | | (i) | | | |
| Photolysis | | | (i) | | | |

Notes

a. The MPD is recommended by the OECD for adequate hazard assessment of new chemical substances.
b. Full notification for supply in the EC at 1 tonne $a^{-1}$ (or 5 tonnes cumulative) under the 'Seventh Amendment' Council Directive 92/32/EEC [12]. Note that a screening test for toxicity to reproduction will also be required as part of the Base Set when a suitable method has been developed.
c. These are the minimum data requirements for notification under the Swiss Ordinance on Environmentally Hazardous Substances.
d. Full notification for supply in Austria at 1 tonne $a^{-1}$.
e. These are the data of Schedule III of the Canadian New Substances Notification Regulations to permit supply >10 tonnes $a^{-1}$ (>50 tonnes cumulative).
f. Full notification for supply in Australia at 1 tonne $a^{-1}$.
g. It is adequate to determine either the melting point or boiling point, whichever is most appropriate.
h. Solubility in an organic solvent is adequate as an alternative to fat solubility.
i. These additional studies may be required if the minimum data are inadequate for full environmental assessment.
j. Available toxicity studies are evaluated for notification under the Swiss Ordinance on Environmentally Hazardous Substances and also under the Order relating to Toxic Substances.
k. The choice of exposure route for the second acute toxicity study depends on the respirability of the substance evaluated from the granulometry test and the likely human exposure route.
l. The OECD MPD specifies that mutagenicity should be evaluated.
m. The second mutagenicity test for notification in Austria can be either the *in vitro* chromosome aberration test or an *in vivo* study such as the mouse micronucleus test, although the former may be preferred from an animal welfare viewpoint and to be consistent with other notification schemes.
n. The mouse micronucleus test or an *in vivo* chromosome aberration test will normally be required immediately after notification in the EC if any of the *in vitro* Base Set mutagenicity tests are positive.
o. The third mutagenicity study required for notification in Canada can be either the mouse micronucleus test or the *in vivo* chromosome aberration test.
p. The mouse micronucleus test has been agreed with the Australian regulatory authorities as an alternative to the dominant lethal assay suggested in the official guidelines.
q. The mouse lymphoma assay or HPRT locus test is required as part of the EC Base Set if the Ames test is positive.
r. A fish bioaccumulation study may be needed if the substance is not 'readily biodegradable'and has a high partition coefficient.
s. The activated sludge respiration inhibition test is conducted on non-biodegradable substances to establish whether the lack of biodegradation is caused by toxicity to micro-organisms, and also to predict if adverse effects on sewage treatment plants could occur.
t. Required for substances which are not 'readily biodegradable'.
u. A soil adsorption/desorption screening test is part of the Base Set, but notifications will be accepted without this until the proposed reverse-phase high performance liquid chromatography method is finalised, as an alternative to the OECD screening test.

Notification of new chemical substances in the USA under the Toxic Substances Control Act (TSCA) [13] differs from other notification schemes based on the OECD MPD, in that a Premanufacture Notice (PMN) can be submitted incorporating only the existing data on the substance. However, the EPA can require studies to be conducted if necessary for adequate evaluation of the safety of the substance.

The philosophical approach of Japanese chemical control seems to be somewhat different to the rest of the developed world. For example, the fundamental aim of the MITI/MHW notification scheme [14] is to evaluate the potential human hazard from exposure to new chemicals through the environment. Therefore a stepwise testing procedure is adopted, and the ecotoxicity and toxicity studies may have to be conducted on the environmental degradants, instead of on the parent compound. Another significant difference to other notification schemes is that the properties of the pure chemical compound are considered in Japan, whereas the standard technical-grade substance with its associated impurities is of concern elsewhere. Therefore, it may be necessary to test a purified sample of the substance for Japanese notification, and any impurities are in principle subject to separate notification.

In principle there are also notification schemes for new chemicals in Turkey and the former Yugoslavia. The South Korean scheme is now in operation, after being revised to take account of US and EC petitions regarding confidentiality of commercially-sensitive information and other issues. A notification scheme for new chemicals is scheduled to come into force in the Philippines as from 31 December 1993. Chemical control legislation in New Zealand and South Africa is also in a state of development.

## 34.4 Chemical Control in Europe

### 34.4.1 European Community

#### 34.4.1.1 Hazard Communication and Classification, Packaging and Labelling of Dangerous Chemicals

All 'dangerous' substances have to be classified, packaged and labelled according to the requirements of Council Directive 67/548/EEC [15], and it is the responsibility of EC suppliers to ensure that these requirements are met. Substances officially classified as dangerous are listed in Annex 1 of Council Directive 67/548/EEC, after they have been evaluated by the Labelling Group of the Commission of the European Communities (CEC).

The criteria to enable substances to be classified and labelled are given in Annex VI of Council Directive 67/548/EEC, and this labelling guide has recently been updated as Commission Directive 91/325/EEC [16], which is the 12th Adaptation to Technical Progress. The new provisions for classification of substances as 'dangerous for the environment' were scheduled to be brought into force by 1 July 1992, but the rest of the Directive was supposed to be implemented nationally by 8 June 1991. Although many EC Member States did not meet these target dates, classification and labelling in accordance with Commission Directive 91/325/EEC can be used throughout the EC. The labelling guide has been updated again as Commission Directive 93/21/EEC [17], which is the 18th Adaptation to Technical Progress of Council Directive 67/548/EEC. The aim is to improve the criteria for classifying and labelling substances which are 'toxic to reproduction' [18], to clarify the criteria for 'dangerous for the environment', especially the safety phrases, and to clarify how the results of the 'fixed-dose' procedure for acute oral toxicity are to be used for classification as an alternative to the $LD_{50}$. Most of the provisions of this Directive are to be brought into force by 1 July 1994.

Substances are classified for labelling by evaluation of their physical, toxicological and ecotoxicological properties. Existing data (*eg*, from non-GLP and/or non-EC/OECD studies), can be used to classify 'existing' chemical substances and there is no obligation for new testing. For full classification, the Base Set of tests for notification of a new substance is effectively the minimum requirement, and some 'existing' substances which have not been officially classified and listed on Annex I of Council Directive 67/548/EEC are tested voluntarily to enable adequate classification to be made.

There are 14 'dangerous' classifications: explosive, oxidising, flammable, highly flammable, extremely flammable, harmful, toxic, very toxic, irritant, corrosive, carcinogenic, mutagenic, toxic for reproduction and dangerous for the environment. Labelling consists of appropriate hazard symbols and information on risks in the form of standard Risk Phrases and safety advice as Safety Phrases. Packaging of dangerous substances is also regulated.

The classification of a substance as 'dangerous for the environment', and the accompanying appropriate labelling, is based primarily on the acute toxic effects determined in standard laboratory studies to fish, *Daphnia* and algae, as representative of 3 taxonomic groups in the aquatic environment, and its biodegradability and bioaccumulation potential. Chronic effects in aquatic organisms and abiotic degradation are also of concern and can be taken into account in evaluating the substance. The hazard symbol may be required. The Risk and Safety Phrases are listed in Table 34.2.

**Table 34.2 Risk and Safety Phrases for Substances Classified as 'Dangerous for the Environment' in the EC(a)**

| | |
|---|---|
| R50 | Very toxic to aquatic organisms. |
| R51 | Toxic to aquatic organisms. |
| R52 | Harmful to aquatic organisms. |
| R53 | May cause long-term adverse effects in the aquatic environment. |
| R54 | Toxic to flora. |
| R55 | Toxic to fauna. |
| R56 | Toxic to soil organisms. |
| R57 | Toxic to bees. |
| R58 | May cause long-term adverse effects in the environment. |
| R59 | Dangerous for the ozone layer. |
| S56 | Dispose of this material and its container to hazardous or special waste collection point. |
| S57 | Use appropriate containment to avoid environmental contamination. |
| S59 | Refer to manufacturer/supplier for information on recovery/recycling. |
| S60 | This material and its container must be disposed of as hazardous waste. |
| S61 | Avoid release to the environment. Refer to special instructions/safety data sheet. |

a. According to the updated labelling guide of Commission Directive 93/21/EEC [17].

The EC scheme for classification and labelling of dangerous 'preparations' (*ie*, formulated products consisting of a mixture of substances) is specified in Council Directive 88/379/EEC [19]. This scheme can now be used in all EC Member States, even though some have not yet officially adopted it. Alternatively, national provisions can continue to be used until Council Directive 88/379/EEC is incorporated into the national legislation. Council Directive 88/379/EEC was adopted on 7 June 1988, and was scheduled to be brought into force by 7 June 1991.

The classification and labelling of both new preparations and those currently supplied has to be determined by the manufacturer or importer, and a record kept of the evaluation for inspection by the regulatory authorities if requested. There are provisions for keeping confidential the identity of substances present in a preparation.

A single assessment is adequate for similar preparations. The physico-chemical properties of the preparation are determined using the standard EC test methods. General health hazards of preparations can be assessed either by studies using EC methods or by evaluation from the dangerous components using the procedure given in Council Directive 88/379/EEC. The required concentration limits for individual dangerous substances already classified by the CEC are given in Annex I of Council Directive 67/548/EEC. For dangerous substances not yet listed in Annex I, general limits for individual properties (Annex I of Council Directive 88/379/EEC, as amended by Commission Directive 90/492/EEC for gaseous preparations [20]) can be used for the estimation of health hazard. No account is taken of 'very toxic' or 'toxic' substances contained in preparations at <0.1% or 'harmful', 'corrosive' or 'irritant' substances at <1%, unless lower limits are specified for individual substances. Preparations containing substances which are carcinogenic, mutagenic or toxic for reproduction are classified only by the calculation method, and studies on the preparation are not appropriate.

Packaging of preparations is regulated by this scheme. Certain categories of preparation sold to the public have to be fitted with child-resistant fastenings and a tactile warning of danger.

Classification and labelling as 'dangerous for the environment' does not yet apply to chemical preparations, although criteria are being developed.

The provision of information on dangerous preparations to industrial users is covered by Council Directive 88/379/EEC, which requires the introduction of an MSDS information scheme. This MSDS scheme is implemented by Commission Directive 91/155/EEC [21]. The provisions of the Directive were scheduled to take effect from 8 June 1991.

Industrial users of a dangerous preparation must be supplied with a free MSDS, but sheets need not be supplied when dangerous preparations are sold to the general public with other sufficient health and safety information. Revised versions must be provided free to all those users who received the preparation within the preceding 12-month period. Individual EC Member States may specify the acceptable languages in which information must be supplied.

MSDSs have to contain the headings listed in Table 34.3, although the sequence in which the information is given is permitted to vary. A guide to what information to include under each heading is given in Commission Directive 91/155/EEC as the Annex.

The EC format for MSDSs for substances will correspond with that required under Commission Directive 91/155/EEC for preparations. However, until this measure is brought into force, in principle the requirements for MSDSs for substances will continue to be controlled by national legislation.

**Table 34.3** Information to be included in an EC Material Safety Data Sheet

1. Identification of the substance/preparation and of the company/undertaking
2. Composition/information on ingredients
3. Hazards identification
4. First-aid measures
5. Fire-fighting measures
6. Accidental release measures
7. Handling and storage
8. Exposure controls/personal protection
9. Physical and chemical properties
10. Stability and reactivity
11. Toxicological information
12. Ecological information
13. Disposal considerations
14. Transport information
15. Regulatory information
16. Other information.

### 34.4.1.2 Notification of New Chemical Substances

Council Directive 79/831/EEC [22] (which is the 'Sixth Amendment' of Council Directive 67/548/EEC) requires pre-marketing notification of new substances, and classification, packaging and labelling according to the degree of hazard. Thus sufficient information on new substances is available to enable the hazard to be assessed and any necessary control measures to be taken. The EC notification scheme has been updated by Council Directive 92/32/EEC [12] (*ie*, the 'Seventh Amendment' of Council Directive 67/548/EEC), which is to be brought into force by 31 October 1993, and hence the revised scheme is discussed.

Full notification is required 60 days before a substance is to be supplied to the EC at an amount of one tonne $a^{-1}$ (or 5 tonnes cumulative). The information required for the notification (the 'Base Set') is specified in Annex VII of the Directive (see Table 34.1). It consists of the identity of the substance, commercial information, recommendations for safe handling and use, physico-chemical properties, animal toxicology, mutagenicity studies, ecotoxicology, recommendations for disposal, the proposed classification and labelling and a draft MSDS for 'dangerous' substances.

Further information must be submitted when the amount of substance supplied to the EC reaches the Level 1 and Level 2 trigger points. The possible studies are given in Annex VIII of the Directive (see Tables 34.4 and 34.5) although those required will depend on the particular substance. Level 1 testing may be required at 10 tonnes $a^{-1}$ (or 50 tonnes cumulative), but will definitely be required (if not already done) at 100 tonnes annually (or 500 tonnes cumulative). Level 2 testing will be required at 1000 tonnes $a^{-1}$ (or 5000 tonnes cumulative).

**Table 34.4** Level 1 Testing Programme for a New Chemical Substance Notified in the EC(a)

| |
|---|
| Analysis of the substance and its transformation products |
| Identification of thermal decomposition products |
| |
| Fertility study |
| Teratology study |
| Sub-chronic and/or chronic toxicity study |
| Additional mutagenicity screening studies |
| Basic toxicokinetic information |
| |
| 21-d *Daphnia* reproduction study |
| Test on higher plants |
| Test on earthworms |
| Further fish toxicity study |
| Fish bioaccumulation study |
| Further biodegradation studies |
| Further soil adsorption/desorption studies |

a. The detailed testing programme will depend on the results of the Base Set studies and the use pattern of the substance. However, studies on all these aspects must be included in the Level 1 testing programme, unless it is technically impossible or scientifically unnecessary.

**Table 34.5** Level 2 Testing Programme for a New Chemical Substance Notified in the EC(a)

| |
|---|
| Chronic toxicity study |
| Carcinogenicity study |
| Fertility study |
| Developmental toxicity study for peri- and postnatal effects |
| Teratology study in a second species |
| Additional toxicokinetic study for biotransformation and pharmacokinetics |
| Studies on organ or systemic toxicity |
| |
| Additional accumulation study |
| Additional degradation studies |
| Investigation of environmental mobility |
| Further adsorption/desorption study |
| Further fish toxicity studies |
| Bird toxicity studies |
| Additional toxicity studies with other organisms |

a. The Level 2 testing programme will depend on the particular substance, but all these aspects will be covered unless it is justified to omit any.

The EC study methods are given in Annex V of the Directive. The Base Set tests are published as Commission Directive 92/69/EEC [23], which is the update to the methods of Commission Directive 84/449/EEC [24] used for 'Sixth Amendment' notifications. Some of the methods for Level 1 studies are contained in Commission Directive 87/302/EEC [25]. The EC methods closely parallel the OECD Guidelines [26]. The Annex V methods must be followed unless deviation is scientifically justified. Omission of a Base Set test for technical reasons must also be justified. Tests must be performed in compliance with GLP. In view of Council Directive 86/609/EEC [27] on the protection of experimental animals, tests on animals are to be performed as humanely as possible, and limit tests are acceptable for substances only toxic under extreme conditions.

Tests should be carried out on the commercial grade substance (including additives and impurities, but excluding any gross amounts of water, solvents or oil). If a chemical consists of a mixture of compounds which cannot be separated, the mixture can be tested and notified as a 'substance'.

A harmonised system of limited notification of new substances for supply in the EC at below 1 tonne $a^{-1}$ has replaced the 'Sixth Amendment' system of national 'Limited Announcements'. As with a Base Set notification for supply of a substance in the EC at 1 tonne $a^{-1}$ and above, a limited notification permits the notifier to supply the substance in all EC Member States without multiple regulatory submissions. The studies required for limited notification depend on whether the substance is to be supplied at a 100 kg $a^{-1}$ (or 500 kg cumulative) threshold, as shown in Table 34.6. The waiting period is 30 d after submission of satisfactory documents, or 15 d after official acceptance of the limited notification by the authorities if no additional information is required.

Chemicals controlled under separate EC legislation are exempt from notification, as are 'existing' chemical substances, which are defined as those listed in the European Inventory of Existing Commercial Chemical Substances (EINECS). This is an inventory of substances supplied within the EC from 1 January 1971 to 18 September 1981, which were reported for inclusion by the suppliers. EINECS is a closed inventory, and any substances omitted in error cannot now be included.

'New' substances, which are those not listed in EINECS, have to be notified before being placed on the EC market, which includes import into the EC from non-EC manufacturers. Substances used only in the establishment in which they are manufactured, such as chemical intermediates, are not considered to be supplied and therefore do not have to be notified. However, intermediates must be notified if they are imported from outside the EC, or otherwise legally supplied. Also, intermediates involved in the manufacture of exempted substances such as pesticides and pharmaceuticals are notifiable.

Substances supplied at <10 kg $a^{-1}$ are exempt from notification, but individual Member States may choose to require appropriate technical and commercial data to be submitted. Substances supplied at <100 kg $a^{-1}$ for 'scientific research and development' are exempt from notification, but records of supply to customers must be available for inspection by the national Competent Authority. Substances can be supplied for 'process-orientated research and development' to a limited number of registered customers without tonnage limit for up to 1 year (extended to 2 years if justifiable). Individual Member States can decide what information is required, up to the maximum requirement for 'limited notification'. If substances supplied under these three exemption categories are provisionally classified as 'very toxic', 'toxic', 'carcinogenic', 'toxic for reproduction' or 'mutagenic', recommendations for safe handling and use have to be provided to the authorities.

**Table 34.6** **Studies required for EC Limited Notification of a New Chemical Substance**

| Study | Requirement for supply in the EC at: | |
|---|---|---|
| | below 100 kg per annum (a) | 100 kg per annum and above (a and b) |
| Melting point | | √ |
| Boiling point | | √ |
| Vapour pressure | | √(c) |
| Water solubility | | √ |
| Partition coefficient | | √ |
| Flash point (liquids) | √ | √ |
| Flammability (solids) | √ | √ |
| Acute toxicity (d) | √ | √ |
| Skin irritation | | √ |
| Eye irritation | | √ |
| Skin sensitisation | | √ |
| Ames test | | √ |
| Ready biodegradability | | √ |
| Acute toxicity to *Daphnia* | | √(c) |

Notes

a. The threshold for testing applies at 500 kg cumulative as well as at 100 kg $a^{-1}$.
b. Full notification is required at 1 tonne $a^{-1}$ (or 5 tonnes cumulative), with the Base Set studies listed in Table 34.1.
c. Individual EC Member States may require these studies.
d. A single acute toxicity study using the most appropriate exposure route, which is normally oral, is required.

Notified new chemical substances are listed in the European List of New Commercial Chemical Substances (ELINCS). Annual supplements are published listing substances notified during the previous year. If a notified substance is to be supplied by a different supplier, it must be renotified. Potential notifiers will be able to use ELINCS to find out if the substance they are developing has already been notified. The original Base Set studies can be used to support the repeat notification, providing the first notifier gives permission to cross-refer to their original information, and also that the 2 substances are essentially equivalent, with similar purity, impurities and additives. However, the Base Set studies are protected from unauthorised use by a second notifier only for 10 years. Such studies thus need not be submitted with a repeat 'notification' or 'limited notification' of a substance previously notified 10 or more years ago. In the interests of animal welfare, notifiers are encouraged to come to a commercial agreement to share data on animal studies. Thus, before testing begins, a potential notifier must find out from the Competent Authority if the substance has been notified previously. If it has, the Competent Authority will disclose the identity of the first notifier (who can request an exemption from this for up to 1 year from the date of notification). There is the option for particular EC Member States to oblige the parties to share data on animal studies.

New substances manufactured in the EC are notified by the manufacturer. Substances manufactured outside the EC can be notified by the EC importer, which may require a series of repeat notifications because there could be several importers. The trigger quantities for Level 1 and 2 testing would be based on the aggregated totals for all importers, with all notifiers jointly responsible for testing. Alternatively, a non-EC manufacturer is permitted to choose a sole EC representative to make one notification; the manufacturer is to include all importers in all countries. The notifier can supply the notified new substance throughout the EC.

A Competent Authority will not accept a notification until all the required information has been provided and is to the necessary standard. The substance can be supplied 60 d after the notification is officially accepted (or 15 or 30 d for a limited notification, as described previously). Hazard and risk assessment has to be done using the CEC guidelines. The Competent Authority will carry out the detailed assessment, but a preliminary evaluation is encouraged to be included in the notification. The Competent Authority sends a summary of the notification and risk assessment to the CEC for distribution to the Competent Authorities of the other EC Member States. It may be necessary to refine the risk assessment by improving the exposure assessment and requesting additional studies to evaluate the hazard further. If necessary, risk management measures can be taken using existing EC provisions.

Polymers are exempt from notification, unless they contain ≥2% in combined form of any non-EINECS listed new substance. The EC definition of 'polymer' is the same as that agreed by the OECD. Basically a polymer must have molecular weight (MW) spread and consist of at least 50% by weight of molecules which are a chain of 3 (or more) monomer units linked to at least one other unit (which may be a monomer or another moiety). This essentially means that at least 50% of a polymer must be of 4 units or more. It does not matter how many types of monomer are present.

Polymers are not listed in EINECS, but the criteria used for excluding materials from EINECS reporting do not correspond to the definition of 'polymer' under the 'Seventh Amendment'. Therefore, certain substances, mainly oligomers, but also including monodispersed polymers with low MW spread, were excluded from listing on EINECS, but will no longer be defined as polymers. Therefore, the CEC is to compile a list of such substances supplied in the EC between the beginning of the EINECS-reporting period (1 January 1971) and the entry into force of the 'Seventh Amendment' (31 October 1993). The deadline for this voluntary reporting of such materials for inclusion in this 'List of no longer polymers' was 31 December 1992. The list will be published in the *Off. J. Eur. Comm.*, and can be used by suppliers of these materials to establish if they are exempt from notification. The list will certainly not be exhaustive and apparently will not be updated. However, suppliers can argue on a case-by-case basis with Competent Authorities that non-listed materials also qualify for exemption from notification.

It is widely recognised that polymers are a special category of chemical substance which can be considered as posing less risk to health and the environment than other substances, providing they are inert and have certain properties such as high MW. Also, special analytical techniques are required for adequate characterisation of polymers. Hence, the 'Seventh Amendment' provides for specific data requirements for notification and limited notification of polymers in Annex VIID. For all polymers, additional data will be required for the identification, such as MW distribution, starting materials and reactive groups. A 'family' concept has been developed to avoid unnecessary notifications and testing. This consists of testing representative members of a family of polymers instead of requesting notification for each member of the family. Furthermore, polymers which can be regarded as inert and non-bioavailable will be subject to a reduced testing package (RTP). Such polymers are likely to have to be non-biodegradable, have a high number-average MW (Mn) with a low oligomer content, have a low water extractivity and be of low lipophilicity. Some of the RTP studies are to determine whether these criteria are met. Less stringent criteria apply to permit a limited notification for supply at below 1 tonne $a^{-1}$ using a RTP. Normally no toxicology or ecotoxicology studies will be required, although this will depend on the results of the RTP physico-chemical studies.

### 34.4.1.3 Evaluation of Existing Chemical Substances

The EC Council Regulation Number 793/93 on the evaluation and control of the risks of existing substances was adopted on the 23 March 1993, and was published in the *Off. J. Eur. Comm.* on 5 April 1993 [28]. Its provisions enter into force directly in all EC countries 60 d after publication, *ie*, on 4 June 1993.

The Regulation applies to all EC manufacturers or importers of existing chemical substances listed in EINECS. Each manufacturer or importer must report the available data specified in Annex III (identity, technical and commercial information and available physico-chemical, toxicological and ecotoxicological data, including environmental fate) to the CEC by 4 June 1994 for substances listed in Annex I which they supply at above 1000 tonnes $a^{-1}$. Data are to be reported on non-Annex I substances supplied at above 1000 tonnes $a^{-1}$ by 4 June 1995, and the more limited data specified in Annex IV (identity, technical and commercial information) on all substances supplied at 10 to 1000 tonnes $a^{-1}$ are to be reported between 4 June 1996 and 4 June 1998. There is an Annex II which lists high-volume substances which are obviously non-hazardous to health or the environment and which are hence not reportable unless separately requested by the CEC. All manufacturers or importers who manufacture or import EINECS-listed substances at the relevant tonnages must report at the appropriate time, including for substances not 'supplied', such as site-limited intermediates and export-only substances. The submitted information has to be updated when appropriate.

Data must be reported in summarised format using Harmonised Electronic Data Set (HEDSET) computer diskettes. To avoid language problems all text is codified. HEDSET is available free of charge from national EC offices. The EC's Joint Research Centre at Ispra will collate all the HEDSET data into an EC database called EUCLID. There will be a public version and a confidential version, because notifiers can claim certain HEDSET data as secret. Data reporters are encouraged to cooperate in HEDSET submissions of general data, but separate submissions are needed for the information unique to the manufacturer or importer. The same HEDSET computer diskettes are also used for the OECD SIDS programme for evaluation of existing chemicals.

It has been estimated that 1,500 to 2,000 chemicals could be reported in Phase 1, perhaps 400 to 800 in Phase 2 and up to 6,000 in Phase 3. However, in practice only about 50 chemicals can be subjected to full risk assessment each year. Therefore, reported chemicals are to be selected for full assessment in a priority setting scheme using criteria which are currently being developed. Lists of priority chemicals will be published annually in the *Off. J. Eur. Comm.* The first list will be selected on an *ad hoc* basis from Member States individual nominations, and has to be published by 4 June 1994.

A rapporteur Competent Authority will be selected to conduct the risk assessment on each priority chemical. A Commission Directive has to be adopted by 4 June 1994 to set out the principles for risk assessment. The CEC will publish detailed guidelines on how to conduct the assessment, which can be updated and revised as necessary. This risk assessment scheme will correspond closely with that for notified new chemical substances required under the 'Seventh Amendment' (Council Directive 92/32/EEC [12]).

The HEDSET summary data for the selected priority chemicals must be supplemented with full reports and other existing data within 6 months of listing. A full EC 'Seventh Amendment' Base Set (see Table 34.1) must be made available for risk assessment, and any necessary new studies to fill 'data gaps' have to be provided within 12 months of listing, unless the notifier applies for an extension of the time limits or derogations for data requirements on the grounds that the test is technically impossible or it is unnecessary for risk assessment. The rapporteur then evaluates this data package, and decides on whether any non-GLP or non-standard studies are adequate. The rapporteur may request repeat testing or additional GLP-compliant studies if these are necessary for risk assessment, but this has to be approved at EC level first. The manufacturers and importers who originally reported the substance are jointly responsible for providing these new studies, but data sharing by consortia formation is encouraged to prevent repeat animal testing.

The rapporteur then produces a draft risk assessment regarding human health and the environment, and proposes any necessary risk limitation strategies. Such measures are for adoption at EC level using existing provisions (such as classification and labelling, occupational exposure limits or very occasionally, by restrictions on marketing and use under the provisions of the 'marketing and use directive', *ie*, Council Directive 76/769/EEC [29] as amended), and can be undertaken only after a risk/benefit evaluation on the chemical.

### 34.4.2 European Free Trade Association

#### 34.4.2.1 Switzerland

There are 2 important laws controlling chemical substances in Switzerland.

The 1969 Federal Law on Trade in Toxic Substances, which is implemented by the 1983 Order relating to Toxic Substances (OTS), is concerned with protection of human health. It gives requirements for classification, labelling, listing and sale of 'toxic' substances and preparations (for public and commercial use). These are listed in the Toxic Substances Lists 1 to 3 respectively.

The Federal Office of Public Health (FOPH) classifies chemical substances in terms of acute oral toxicity in the rat, and other available data such as skin and/or inhalation toxicity, skin and eye irritation/corrosive effects, subacute/subchronic/chronic toxicity, carcinogenicity/mutagenicity/teratogenicity and human exposure. Substances are placed in one of 5 classes ranging from Category 1 (most hazardous) to Category 5 (least hazardous).

The Swiss manufacturer or importer of a substance which might be 'toxic' and hence have to be entered onto the Toxic Substances List has to register the substance with FOPH, who consider the data on the substance and decide whether it is to be so listed. In case of doubt, the FOPH is to be consulted. The notification must include chemical identity and composition, appearance, pH, intended uses, any test results required for classification and a description of the container and packaging, directions for use and product literature.

'Toxic' substances can only be 'traded', which includes manufacture and import, if they are on the appropriate Toxic Substances List. Furthermore, such regulated toxic substances can only be traded by 'authorised' persons who hold the appropriate permit. However, there is no obligation to register a toxic substance which is to be traded exclusively for research or as an intermediate for chemical production. Also, 'toxic' substances contained in articles are not regulated. Appropriate protective measures must be taken to protect human health when trading in toxic substances, which includes suitable packaging, labelling and user instructions.

The 1983 Federal Law on Environmental Protection deals mainly with the effect of chemicals on the environment and on humans via the environment. The Law is implemented through various Ordinances dealing with specific aspects of environmental protection, such as air and soil pollution, waste disposal, noise and radiation. The 1986 Ordinance on Environmentally Hazardous Substances (OEHS) requires the measures discussed below.

An importer or manufacturer may only supply a 'substance', 'product' (*ie*, formulated preparation) or 'article' if its environmental impact has been assessed, and it can justifiably be assumed that handling in accordance with the information on the label and the instructions for use cannot present a hazard to the environment or to persons indirectly through the environment. Furthermore, the customer must receive appropriate information, in the form of labelling, instructions for use and MSDSs, if there will be environmentally hazardous applications or methods of disposal. The format of MSDSs and the information content is defined in OEHS (Annex 2.2 for 'substances' and Annex 2.3 for 'products'). The hazards for the environment and the protective measures must be indicated on the label and may also be shown by symbols (pictograms), which are specified in Annex 1 of the OEHS.

New substances must be notified to the Federal Office of Environment, Forests and Landscape (FOEFL) before they can be supplied in Switzerland by manufacture or import in any quantity. Existing substances are defined as ones on EINECS, included on the 1985 Toxic Substances List 1 or marketed in Switzerland between 1975 and 1984 in a total quantity of at least 0.5 tonnes. Notification of an existing substance can be requested by the authorities. The categories of substances exempt from notification are as follows:

i) Products regulated by separate legislation, such as pharmaceuticals, food additives, pesticides and wood preservatives;

ii) Substances used exclusively as chemical intermediates;

iii) Substances supplied for research and development to a small number of customers over a limited period in small quantities; and,

iv) Polymers containing <2% of a new monomer substance in bound form, or which contain only carbon, hydrogen, oxygen and nitrogen.

The information required for a notification is the chemical identity, amount manufactured or imported, use, physico-chemical properties, ecotoxicity studies, available mutagenicity studies and animal toxicity, indirect long-term effects on humans and recommendations for disposal and labelling. The data requirements for the notification of new substances are based on the OECD MPD and are very similar to those in the EC. The minimum information required is listed in Table 34.1. There are no official reduced data requirements for notification of substances to be supplied only in low amounts, although FOEFL will negotiate on a case-by-case basis for certain of the standard tests to be omitted, especially if the substance is to be used in special applications or has special disposal methods which minimise environmental contamination. Studies are to be conducted in compliance with GLP to OECD guidelines or their equivalent.

There is no official review period, and the new substance can be imported or manufactured by the notifier as soon as FOEFL has received the notification. However, FOEFL can request further information necessary for full environmental assessment of the substance, or take regulatory action at any time after notification.

An Environmental Impact Report is also required for a notification. This is an assessment of the environmental compatibility made by the notifier, and is based on an evaluation of degradation, accumulation and mobility in the environment, effects on micro-organisms, plants, animals and ecosystems and long-term indirect effects on humans via the environment.

For existing substances, manufacturers and importers must, if possible, perform a similar evaluation to that for new substances. The authorities can demand a detailed environmental assessment for existing substances which are produced in large quantities, are poorly degradable, accumulate in the food chain, are harmful to plants or animals at low levels, or potentiate the environmental effects of other chemicals. For products and articles, manufacturers and importers must base their evaluation on the data provided by suppliers for each constituent (labels, user instructions and MSDSs) and any other relevant information in their possession. The environmental impact of a substance, product or article must be re-evaluated when new uses or significantly larger volumes are introduced or the impurity profile changes.

There are currently no official Swiss criteria for classification of substances as 'dangerous for the environment', although in due course the EC scheme is likely to be adopted. Hence the EC classification and labelling can be used for Switzerland, except for the EC hazard symbol. There are also no criteria for classification and labelling of chemical products containing substances which are 'dangerous for the environment', although their evaluation will take account of the content of such environmentally hazardous substances.

The OEHS requires detergents, dishwasher products and new fertilisers and soil additives to be registered with the appropriate Swiss authority. Also, wood preservatives and plant treatment products can only be supplied when a marketing permit is granted.

#### 34.4.2.2 Austria

The Austrian Chemicals Law of 1987, which does not apply to products regulated by other legislation, requires notification of new chemical substances, and regulations implementing this were issued in 1989. The notification system is similar to the former 'Sixth Amendment' EC scheme of Council Directive 79/831/EEC. [22]. In due course the Austrian notification scheme will in principle become harmonized with the updated 'Seventh Amendment' EC scheme of Council Directive 92/32/EEC [12], because Austria is one of the 6 EFTA countries participating in the agreement with the EC to form the EEA.

The Austrian inventory of existing substances will consist of EINECS and *ca.* 1,500 additional substances reported by suppliers which were marketed in Austria between 1 February 1982 and 31 January 1989.

Substances not included in the final inventory are defined as 'new' and must be notified to the Federal Ministry of the Environment, Youth and the Family before they are manufactured or imported, unless notified more than 10 years previously. The authorities will publish an annual list of those substances which were notified 10 years earlier. New substances supplied exclusively for testing purposes are exempt from notification. Also exempt are those exported to specified countries where there are equivalent regulations for the notification or safety assessment of new substances, although the Austrian authorities must be notified in writing of the substance's identity and the expected production and export quantities, as well as the classification, labelling and proposed uses of hazardous substances. Finally, polymers are not notifiable, unless they contain >2% (by weight) in chemically-bound form of a new substance monomer.

Full notification is required for substances supplied ≥1 tonne $a^{-1}$. The review period is 3 months, which may be stopped by the authorities for a deficient notification and begun again at day 1 only when the omitted data are provided. Notification may also be required if the total annual amount of a substance supplied by several manufacturers or importers exceeds 1.5 tonnes, even though each supplies <1 tonne. The information required consists of the 'Sixth Amendment' EC Base Set, a description of the manufacturing process and raw materials and a 14-d earthworm toxicity test (see Table 34.1). Tests must be performed to OECD methods in compliance with GLP.

Further information corresponding to EC Level 1 is required when a substance is supplied at 10 tonnes $a^{-1}$ (or 50 tonnes cumulative), and may be required when supply from several manufacturers or importers combined is 15 tonnes annually. EC Level 2 testing is required at 100 tonnes annually (500 tonnes cumulative), or may be required at 150 tonnes annually from several suppliers.

A Limited Announcement can be made for a new substance supplied at <1 tonne $a^{-1}$, or to a restricted number of specified users for commercial development at above this amount for 1 year only. Less information is required for Limited Announcement for supply at <10 kg $a^{-1}$, and even less for <1 kg $a^{-1}$. Comparatively few new substances reach the 1 tonne $a^{-1}$ supply level, so most are authorised under the Limited Announcement scheme, although sometimes the full EC Base Set data are available to enable definitive and complete hazard classification and labelling and avoid having to label the substance as 'Caution - Substance not yet fully tested'.

The classification, packaging and labelling of 'dangerous' substances in Austria essentially corresponds to the EC requirements of Council Directive 67/548/EEC [15], as adapted to technical progress by Commission Directive 91/325/EEC [16]. However, the criteria to classify as 'dangerous for the environment' have not yet been officially included in the Austrian legislation, although in practice the EC system of classification and labelling is followed.

All existing and notified new substances which are 'very toxic', 'toxic' or 'harmful' are listed in the List of Toxic Substances, which is in principle updated annually with those new hazardous substances which have been notified or for which a Limited Announcement has been made.

Classification, packaging and labelling of 'preparations' in Austria corresponds with the EC requirements of Council Directive 88/379/EEC [19]. The criteria for classification of preparations as 'dangerous for the environment' have not been developed, but the proposed EC scheme can be followed based on taking account of the concentration and aquatic toxicity of substances in the preparation.

An Ordinance will be produced in due course for testing of existing substances.

#### 34.4.2.3 Scandinavia

##### 34.4.2.3.1 Finland

The Finnish Chemicals Act of 14 August 1989 came into force on 1 September 1990, and is implemented by various decrees.

Classification, packaging and labelling requirements are similar to the EC and other Scandinavian countries. The category of 'dangerous for the environment' is in effect for substances from 1 August 1993, according to the requirements of the EC scheme. Finland is involved in the joint Nordic project to evaluate different approaches to classification of preparations which contain environmentally hazardous substances, which will be considered by the EC in developing criteria for environmental classification of preparations. There is an official list of 'dangerous' chemicals, which defines the labelling of these. Preparations must be labelled with the amounts of dangerous ingredients. MSDSs are required for all 'dangerous' substances and preparations, and the National Board of Labour Protection has to ensure they conform to the specified format, which will be fully harmonised with that of the EC. These data sheets have to be in both the official languages of Finnish and Swedish. Before a chemical classified as 'toxic' or 'very toxic' can be supplied to the public, the National Board of Health has to be informed, to enable such distribution to be prohibited if necessary. Also, a chemical which has been banned for use in Finland can be exported only after informing the National Board of Waters and the Environment.

The Chemicals Act requires new chemical substances to be notified by the Finnish manufacturer or importer 45 days before they are supplied in Finland. Existing non-notifiable substances are those listed in EINECS or supplied in Finland before 1 September 1990. The Finnish notification scheme closely follows the revised EC system under the 'Seventh Amendment' Council Directive 92/32/EEC [12], but differs in certain details because it was based on the proposed 'Seventh Amendment' not the final version. However, as from 31 October 1993 when Council Directive 92/32/EEC comes into force in the EC, the Finnish notification scheme will be amended to be fully harmonised.

Medicinal products, cosmetics, explosives, protective chemicals (slimicides and wood preservatives), pesticides, foodstuffs, food additives, animal feed and feed additives, fertilisers, wastes and chemicals in transit are exempt from the notification provisions of the Chemicals Act. Substances supplied at $<10$ kg $a^{-1}$ and polymers which contain $<2\%$ of a new substance monomer are also exempt from notification, but are subject to the standard reporting to the National Board of Labour Protection if they are classified as 'toxic' or 'very toxic'. Finally, substances supplied at $<100$ kg $a^{-1}$ for scientific research or for commercial development to a limited number of customers without tonnage restriction for one year only (which may be extended to 2 years) do not have to be notified, but certain relevant information is required by the National Board of Health.

The information required for notification of a new chemical substance in Finland corresponds with that of the EC 'Seventh Amendment'. There are limited notifications with different data requirements at below and above 100 kg $a^{-1}$ (see Table 34.6), full notification at above 1 tonne $a^{-1}$ (see Table 34.1) and Level 1 and 2 testing (see Tables 34.4 and 34.5 respectively). A new substance already notified in the EC or in an EFTA country can be notified in Finland using a simplified administrative procedure.

'Protective chemicals' (*ie*, wood preservatives and slimicides) require advance approval from the National Board of Waters and the Environment, and wood preservatives for use by painting have to be notified to this authority 45 d before being supplied.

A Chemicals Register is maintained by the appropriate regulatory authorities consisting of MSDSs of 'dangerous' substances, information on notified new substances, notified and approved protective chemicals and 'toxic' and 'very toxic' chemicals supplied to the public.

### 34.4.2.3.2 Iceland

General provisions for controlling poisonous and dangerous chemical substances are given in the Icelandic Poisons Act, and various Regulations have been made to implement the Act.

Classification, packaging and labelling requirements for dangerous chemical substances and preparations are similar to the EC and other Scandinavian countries, but labelling has to be in Icelandic. There is currently no legal requirement for MSDSs, but a Regulation to make these mandatory is being developed. The EC format defined in Commission Directive 91/155/EEC [21] will form the basis of the Icelandic data sheets, but it is likely that the more extensive Norwegian requirements will also be included. The information will have to be in Icelandic.

There is no scheme for notification of new chemical substances, and no formal registration requirements for wood preservatives, surface biocides and anti-fouling paints, although some of these chemicals may be banned or have their use restricted on an *ad hoc* basis.

### 34.4.2.3.3 Norway

The Norwegian Labelling Regulations for Health Hazard and Fire and Explosion Hazard specify classification, packaging and labelling requirements for dangerous chemical substances and preparations which are broadly similar to those of the EC. The category of 'dangerous for the environment' is not yet included, and the proposed scheme extends that of the EC for 'substances' to include chemical 'preparations'. There is an official list of 'dangerous' chemicals, which defines the labelling of these. Labelling has to be in Norwegian, and chemicals not classified as dangerous can be labelled as 'evaluated as not required to be labelled'. Occupational Air Requirement (OAR) labelling applies to organic solvents, including preparations containing them, in order to warn users of the need for an adequate supply of fresh air to minimise the potential health hazard from such materials which are not necessarily classified as 'dangerous' under the Health Hazard Labelling Regulations.

An MSDS has to accompany a chemical supplied to a new user. There is a recommended format for Norwegian data sheets.

The Norwegian Product Register contains information on all 'dangerous' chemical substances and preparations, and those subject to OAR labelling. Information has to be reported for chemicals supplied at 100 kg $a^{-1}$. Confidential data, such as the composition of preparations, can be reported directly by foreign manufacturers, but the Norwegian importer is still responsible for declaring the administrative information and for the MSDS. All significant changes in a product declaration have to be reported to the Product Register.

'Very toxic' and 'toxic' substances and preparations can normally only be sold to the public by holders of a permit from the State Pollution Control Authority.

An original proposal for a Norwegian notification scheme for new chemical substances was based on the 'Sixth Amendment' EC scheme of Council Directive 79/831/EEC [22], with corresponding notification requirements and EINECS to define existing substances. However, the final scheme will have to be completely harmonised with that of the updated EC system under the 'Seventh Amendment' of Council Directive 92/32/EEC [12].

#### 34.4.2.3.4 Sweden

The 1986 Act on Chemical Products enables chemical substances and preparations to be controlled by specific Ordinances. The National Chemicals Inspectorate (KEMI) is responsible for supervising this chemical control legislation.

The 1985 Ordinance on Chemical Products, and the implementing KEMI Regulations, specify classification, packaging and labelling requirements for dangerous chemical substances and preparations which are broadly similar to those of the EC. The category of 'dangerous for the environment' came into effect on 1 January 1993 for substances, and corresponds with the EC scheme. Labelling has to be in Swedish. There is a fourth Danger Class for substances categorised as 'moderately harmful', which includes some solvents with irritant or central nervous system effects and substances with acute oral toxicities of 2000 mg $kg^{-1} < LD_{50} <$ *ca.* 5000 mg $kg^{-1}$, and these are labelled with the phrase 'May be harmful' but not with a danger symbol. There are also differences in the way Sweden and the EC determine whether a product is a sensitiser. Sweden has an extended system for classifying carcinogens, employing the phrase R340, 'Some risk of cancer cannot be excluded after frequently repeated exposure'.

The Act on Chemical Products requires the manufacturer or importer of a chemical to assess its health and environmental hazards. This process involves evaluating the 'dangerous' classification for health and chemical effects, and in order to help the supplier, KEMI have produced an advisory, non-mandatory Swedish Substance List of classifications for common substances. The hazard assessment is of value to the user of the chemical for risk assessment to ensure safe use.

The Ordinance on Chemical Products requires that a MSDS in Swedish is supplied with all chemicals which are hazardous to health. The information content is specified in the KEMI Regulations, and a detailed format recommended by Swedish industry associations is often used.

All chemical substances or preparations manufactured or imported at ≥100 kg $a^{-1}$ must be notified annually to the Swedish Products Register with administrative and commercial information. A full declaration containing chemical information is required for all products hazardous to health and certain petroleum products. Confidential information can be reported by a foreign manufacturer.

A notification scheme for new chemical substances is scheduled to be in force on 1 January 1994. This Swedish scheme will be fully harmonized with the 'Seventh Amendment' EC scheme of Council Directive 92/32/EEC [12], and use EINECS to define existing substances.

Biocides have to be registered under the Swedish pesticide approval scheme.

## 34.5 Chemical Control in North America

### 34.5.1 United States of America

There are many legal and administrative provisions controlling chemicals in the USA. Compliance with the various measures is often strictly monitored and enforced, and penalties for non-compliance can be severe. The chemical control measures of the Toxic Substances Control Act [13,30] are highlighted below.

TSCA, which came into force on 1 January 1977, provides control over chemical hazards to human health and the environment which are not regulated by other Federal legislation. The Act requires pre-manufacturing notification of new chemical substances, testing of existing substances and regulation of substances which pose an unreasonable risk. Substances controlled by other legislation, such as pesticides, food additives, pharmaceuticals and cosmetics, are exempt from the provisions of TSCA. The Act is administered by the Environmental Protection Agency.

Section 4 of TSCA gives the EPA authority to require testing of existing substances which pose an unreasonable risk to health or the environment or which are produced in substantial amounts and have substantial human or environmental exposure. An Interagency Testing Committee advises the EPA on the priority for testing. The EPA issues Test Rules specifying the extra information required. A company subject to a Test Rule can perform the required tests, perhaps under joint sponsorship with other companies subject to the Test Rule, or apply for exemption for tests already performed and reimburse the owners of the data. Voluntary agreements to test existing chemicals, the Consent Order Process, are encouraged by the EPA.

A PMN must be made to the EPA, under Section 5 of TSCA, 90 d before a new chemical substance is manufactured or imported into the USA. A new substance is one not on the Chemical Substances Inventory, which is the list of existing and previously-notified substances. A notification is also required for a new use of a listed substance which is subject to a Significant New Use Rule (SNUR). Notified substances are listed in the TSCA inventory only after being supplied and the mandatory Notice of Commencement of Manufacture or Import is filed with the EPA. Notified substances can be placed in the confidential section of the TSCA inventory, on justified request. However, potential suppliers can establish from the EPA whether the substance of concern is listed and hence is not notifiable by filing a *bona fide* intent to manufacture or import.

The EPA may require extra data to be provided before manufacture or import begins if the information already provided is inadequate for risk assessment, or (under Section 5e of TSCA) if the substance is produced in substantial amounts with substantial human or environmental exposure.

TSCA does not specify what toxicity and ecotoxicity testing should be performed for a PMN, but the EPA have recommended the OECD MPD as the basis. The EPA guidelines [31] should normally be used for the tests, but others such as those of the OECD [26] may be accepted.

The EPA has adopted the 'exposure-based new chemicals testing strategy' to enable sufficient data to be obtained for adequate risk assessment using the existing legislation (Section 5e of TSCA). Core testing is required if the production volume is >300 tonnes $a^{-1}$ and there is either substantial or significant human exposure or substantial environmental release according to any one of the defined criteria. The core tests are mutagenicity (Ames and mouse micronucleus), acute oral toxicity in the rat, 28-d oral toxicity in the rat, acute toxicity to *Daphnia*, acute toxicity to fish and algal growth inhibition.

The EPA use SARs, including Quantitative Structure Activity Relationships (QSAR), in the PMN review process, to help with risk assessment in the absence of test data.

Small volume chemicals for research and development and non-isolated chemical intermediates are automatically exempt from notification. The EPA may also grant exemption by 'rule' for substances not presenting unreasonable risk to health or the environment or used only for test marketing. PMN exemption is available for low volume chemicals which are supplied at ≤1 tonne $a^{-1}$, but an exemption notice must be submitted 21 d before manufacture or import begins. Certain polymers are exempt from full PMN, and instead a limited PMN is submitted 21 d before manufacture or import begins.

Section 6 of TSCA empowers the EPA to regulate any substance posing an unreasonable risk to health or the environment. This applies to both existing chemicals and to new ones following PMN review. Restrictions are imposed by regulation. They must be the least burdensome for adequate protection, and they range from labelling requirements to banning. The EPA may also take action under Section 7 of TSCA against substances presenting an imminent and unreasonable risk.

### 34.5.2 Canada

The Canadian Environmental Protection Act (CEPA) of 30 June 1988 requires new chemical substances to be notified before manufacture or import. The Canadian notification scheme is scheduled to come into effect in January 1994. Until then, chemicals can be manufactured or imported into Canada without notification. The New Substances Notification Regulations have been published in the *Canada Gazette* for final public consultation before being finalised and brought into force. 'Guidelines for the Notification and Testing of New Substances: Chemicals and Polymers' are also now available [32].

New chemical substances are all those not on the Domestic Substances List (DSL), which is a list of substances in commerce in Canada at ≥100 kg $a^{-1}$ from 1 January 1984 to 31 December 1986. If a new substance is on the Non-Domestic Substances List (NDSL), the information required for the notification is considerably less than for a standard notification. The NDSL, which is the 1985 US TSCA Inventory (as amended) minus the substances on the DSL, attempts to take account of established substances which did not happen to be sold in Canada during the period for inclusion in the DSL. The first DSL [33] and NDSL [34] were both published in the *Canada Gazette* on 26 January 1991, and these inventories will be updated and corrected periodically when necessary. Most polymers are represented on the inventories in terms of the starting materials from which they are manufactured, and 'products of biotechnology' will be included subsequently if necessary when their regulatory controls have been finalised. The DSL and NDSL contain confidential sections, which can be searched by Environment Canada if a *bona fide* intent to manufacture or import is established by submitting specified data.

The information required for notification of new substances is listed in Schedules to the Regulations, and Part I of the Regulations applies to chemicals. Schedule I testing is required for new chemical substances supplied at >20 kg and ≤1 tonne $a^{-1}$ (or ≤5 tonnes cumulative). Most of Schedule II testing applies to substances supplied at >1 tonne and ≤10 tonnes $a^{-1}$ (or >5 tonnes but ≤50 tonnes cumulative), and Schedule III (see Table 34.1) applies for supply >10 tonnes $a^{-1}$ (or >50 tonnes cumulative). This assumes that the substance is not on the NDSL. New substances on the NDSL require less testing: full Schedule II applies for supply >5 tonnes $a^{-1}$ (or >25 tonnes cumulative) and Schedule I for supply at >1 and ≤5 tonnes $a^{-1}$ (or >5 but ≤25 tonnes cumulative). Substances also have reduced data requirements if they are supplied only for 'product development' (*ie*, Schedule IV may apply), or they are 'site-limited intermediates' or 'export only' substances (*ie*, Schedule V may apply). The waiting period for review of the submission by Environment Canada varies between 5 and 90 d, depending on which Schedule the notification follows. New substances are exempt from notification in the following circumstances: when in transit, if not on the NDSL but only supplied at ≤20 kg $a^{-1}$, if supplied at ≤1 tonne $a^{-1}$ (or ≤5 tonnes cumulative) when on the NDSL or only used for 'research and development', or if a transient non-isolated reaction intermediate which is unlikely to be released. Also exempt from notification are products regulated under separate Canadian legislation, such as pharmaceuticals, pesticides, cosmetics, food and animal feedstuffs. Furthermore, certain special categories of chemical (such as those associated with cement manufacture) and also 'substances occurring in nature', whether or not they are specifically listed, are considered to be part of the DSL and hence are not notifiable.

Polymers are covered by Part II of the Regulations. The OECD definition of 'polymer' is used to decide if a product is to be notified as a chemical or a polymer. New polymers made by modifying an existing polymer specified on the DSL by adding extra reactants are exempt from notification, providing none of the new ingredients constitute more than 2% (by weight) of the polymer, either in combined form or measured by the amount charged to the reaction vessel. Polymers on the DSL or supplied at <1 tonne $a^{-1}$ (or <5 tonnes cumulative) are also not subject to notification. 'Low - concern polymers' include polymers of high Mn with a low oligomer content that are chemically stable and do not contain reactive or cationic moieties (as exemplified in Schedule IX), and most polyesters made solely from reactants on the DSL and specified in Schedule X. The information required for notification of a polymer depends on the amount supplied, whether the polymer is on the NDSL and/or meets the low-concern criteria and whether all the reactants are on the DSL and/or the NDSL. There are also reduced data requirements for 'research and development', 'product development', 'site limited' and 'export only' polymers. Schedules VI, VII, VIII, XI, XII, and XIII specify the data requirements.

Studies for notification of new chemical substances are to be conducted to OECD guidelines or their equivalent. They must be conducted by a laboratory whose practices are consistent with the principles of OECD GLP, and Canadian GLP is to be developed. Pre-notification consultations with Environment Canada may be useful, to establish whether specific existing non-standard or non-GLP studies are acceptable, if surrogate data (*ie*, SAR, QSAR or other calculation methods) would be adequate instead of actual tests, or if requests for waivers for specific data requirements will be likely to be accepted.

'Transitional substances' are those supplied in Canada at >20 kg $a^{-1}$ between 1 January 1987 (and hence which cannot be included in the DSL) and the date on which the New Substances Notification Regulations come into force. These substances have to be notified within 90 d with Schedule I data. If specified trigger supply quantities are exceeded during the transition period or the subsequent 5 years, the maximum additional supplement is with Schedule II data for chemicals, with deadlines dependent on the year in which the trigger quantity was exceeded. However, when a trigger quantity for a transitional chemical is exceeded after this 5-year period, the standard provisions for non-transitional chemicals apply.

Biotechnology products are micro-organisms, parts of micro-organisms and substances produced by micro-organisms and cell cultures. Regulations and accompanying guidelines are being developed for notification of biotechnology products (*ie*, biochemicals and biopolymers).

Information submitted in a notification can be claimed as confidential business information (CBI), and the degree of protection given to such data will be consistent with the provisions of the Access to Information Act. Hence confidentiality claims have to be substantiated with the supplementary information prescribed in the Confidential Information Disclosure Regulations. If the substance identity is claimed as confidential, a masked name has to be chosen for use in official publications such as the DSL. The masking procedures correspond with those used in the USA with TSCA.

The notification scheme is administered by Environment Canada and National Health and Welfare. Evaluators from these agencies assess notification packages to ensure they are adequate, and deficiencies may result in the notification being rejected. The substance is then assessed to determine whether it is 'toxic', or is suspected of being so. The definition of a 'toxic' substance in this regard is one which has or may have an immediate or long-term harmful effect on the environment or it constitutes or may constitute a danger to the environment on which human life depends or to human life or health. Consequently, such assessment of likely 'toxicity' involves comparison of the predicted exposure with the anticipated hazardous effects of such exposure, both these properties being estimated from the submitted data and covering human health and the environment. The purpose of the assessment and control process is to ensure that the commercial use of the substance in Canada will pose only minimal risk to human health and the environment, either because of its inherent properties or because of the control measures taken to reduce exposure to the substance. Therefore, if a notified substance is assessed as suspected of being 'toxic', control measures may be taken before the review period expires.

Notified substances are listed in the DSL, as a supplement published in the *Canada Gazette* as necessary. After listing they can be manufactured or imported by other suppliers for unrestricted use. Hence substances notified with a reduced data set, because of limited use or exposure or with data waivers, are not listed in the DSL. Also, substances suspected of being 'toxic' can only be listed in the DSL after they are regulated under CEPA to ensure their safe use.

The Workplace Hazardous Materials Information System (WHMIS), which was established in 1988, aims to protect workers using chemicals by improved communication of hazards. This involves labelling and MSDSs, in English and French, and employee information and training programmes.

## 34.6 Pacific Rim Countries

### 34.6.1 Australia

The Australian Industrial Chemicals (Notification and Assessment) Act 1989, as amended, provides for a national scheme for the notification and assessment of industrial chemicals in order to protect people and the environment from the harmful effects of industrial chemicals. The scheme, known as the National Industrial Chemicals Notification and Assessment Scheme (NICNAS), began operating in July 1990 and is administered by the National Occupational Health and Safety Commission (Worksafe Australia), who also perform the primary toxicological assessment and the occupational health and safety assessment. The Department of Arts, Sport, the Environment, Tourism and Territories undertake the environmental hazard assessment, and the Department of Community Services and Health carry out the public health assessment. A 'Handbook for Notifiers' is available from Worksafe Australia [35].

The Australian Inventory of Chemical Substances (AICS) distinguishes between 'new' and 'existing' industrial chemicals. Therefore manufacturers and importers of an industrial chemical must firstly refer to AICS when determining whether a notification is required. Under the Eligible Chemicals Category, a 2-year amnesty period commencing on 1 March 1993 has been allowed for listing of eligible chemicals in AICS. An eligible chemical is one which was in use in Australia during the period 1 December 1977 to 16 July 1990. If a chemical is listed in AICS, a notification is not required. AICS consists of a confidential section and a non-confidential section. A potential notifier can request Worksafe Australia to search the confidential section of AICS, providing he can establish a *bona fide* intent to manufacture or import the substance. Notified new substances will be added to AICS after 5 years, although they can be kept in the confidential section for up to 6 years thereafter.

Articles, formulated preparations of notified or existing substances and radioactive chemicals are not notifiable. Furthermore, agricultural chemicals, food additives, animal feed additives and veterinary and pharmaceutical products are exempt from the notification scheme, because they are controlled under separate legislation. Any other new industrial chemical substance has to be notified before manufacture or import, unless it is a confined reaction intermediate of transient existence, a non-commercially produced byproduct or impurity in another material, or for research and development or analysis for supply at ≤50 kg $a^{-1}$. Biopolymers and new synthetic polymers also have to be notified, but not existing synthetic polymers. A new synthetic polymer is defined as one containing a new combination of existing monomers (*ie*, different from any polymer already listed on the polymer section of AICS) or a polymer derived from a new monomer (*ie*, a substance not listed on AICS) at ≥2% (by weight) in the product. Finally, the original notifier of a substance already assessed under the voluntary Interim Notification Scheme (INS), which began operating in 1981 but has now closed, is exempt from notification under NICNAS, but a new supplier is not and would have to make a notification.

The information required for a full notification essentially corresponds to the OECD MPD, and is detailed in the Schedule to the Act (Table 34.1). The review period is 90 d. OECD Guidelines are recommended, but equivalent methods are accepted. Tests must be performed in compliance with GLP, and Australian Codes of Practice on GLP are to be in harmony with OECD GLP principles. Further information may be required when the substance is supplied at 10, 100, 1000 or 10,000 tonnes annually, or before the 90-d assessment period can begin if this is essential for adequate evaluation of the hazard of the substance. NICNAS provides for confidentiality and flexibility of data requirements in a notification; for example, it may be agreed that certain matters required in a notification are irrelevant, unnecessary or economically prohibitive for the assessment of the chemical. There are also special provisions for substances new to Australia but already notified in other countries, or listed on foreign inventories.

Limited notification is available for small volume chemicals (*ie*, <1 tonne $a^{-1}$), site-limited chemicals (*ie*, not confined and transient reaction intermediates) ≤10 tonnes $a^{-1}$ and substances used only for research and development for supply at 50 kg to 1 tonne $a^{-1}$ (no notification being required for a level of <50 kg). The toxicological and ecotoxicological studies are not required for a limited notification. As from 4 August 1992, a Commercial Evaluation Category has been introduced, with reduced notification requirements, consisting mainly of administrative information, for new chemical substances to be imported or manufactured solely for commercial evaluation. The maximum quantity permitted is 2 tonnes for 2 years, but amounts >1 tonne and times longer than 1 year have to be justified. The review period is only 20 d. The NICNAS scheme was amended with effect from 1 March 1993 to introduce the Low Volume Chemicals Category for chemicals which will be introduced in quantities of ≤100 kg $a^{-1}$. The application consists mainly of administrative information and is processed within 20 d. The maximum period during which the permit will be valid is 3 years.

Polymers which meet the definition of a polymer of low concern are eligible for the new Synthetic Polymers of Low Concern Category. A synthetic polymer of low concern is one which has a Mn >1000, low charge density, low residual monomer content, does not dissociate readily, has low water solubility, if solid has a particle-size distribution such that <1% of particles have a diameter of <70 μm, is stable under conditions of use, and does not contain reactive functional groups. For these polymers less information is required and applications will be processed within 50 d.

NICNAS provides a mechanism for evaluating AICS-listed existing chemicals which are declared as priority existing chemicals (PECs). Declared PECs are assessed for the risks they represent to human health or the environment, and appropriate recommendations made on their use.

Road and rail transport of chemicals in Australia is covered by the Australian Dangerous Goods Code (ADG Code) which corresponds with the UN transportation recommendations. The criteria used for the Australian user classification and labelling scheme closely parallel those of the EC, except for corrosives and physico-chemical hazards which are in accordance with the ADG Code. However, there is as yet no classification of 'dangerous for the environment'.

### 34.6.2 New Zealand

The 1979 Toxic Substances Act and the 1983 Toxic Substances Regulations require new 'toxic' substances to be notified before manufacture or import. The information required is only the name, composition and uses, although more can be requested. The definition of 'toxic' in the Act is broad and in practice virtually all chemical substances and preparations are notifiable. However, substances covered by other legislation, such as pesticides, food additives and human and veterinary pharmaceuticals, are not notifiable.

A voluntary notification and assessment for new industrial chemicals, the Interim Notification Scheme (INS), operated until 17 July 1990, under the auspices of the Australian and New Zealand Environment Council.

The Resource Management Act [36] came into force on 1 October 1991. It consolidates over 50 existing statutes governing air, land and water resources and includes measures on coastal issues, town and country planning, mining, pollution, water and soil management. One of the key aspects of this Act is the provision for establishing an Environmental Risk Management Authority (ERMA) for the management and control of hazardous substances and new organisms. 'Hazardous substances' would include all materials (solid, liquid and gas) which are toxic, corrosive, explosive, radioactive, flammable, oxidising or otherwise have the potential to damage human, plant or animal health, or have an adverse effect on the environment. Policy development and planning for the establishment or ERMA is still under development.

### 34.6.3 Japan

The following laws control the production, import, handling and processing of chemicals in Japan:

i) Law concerning the Examination and Regulation of Manufacture etc. of Chemical Substances, which is administered by the Ministry of International Trade and Industry (MITI) and the Ministry of Health and Welfare (MHW);

ii) Labour Safety and Health Law, which is administered by the Ministry of Labour (MOL);

iii) Poisonous and Deleterious Materials Control Law;

iv) Fire Service Law;

v) High-pressure Gases Control Law; and,

vi) Law concerning the Protection of the Ozone Layer through the Regulation of Specified Substances and other Measures.

The MITI/MHW [14] and MOL laws are of primary concern to non-Japanese manufacturers who export chemicals to Japan, and the former will be discussed here.

Japanese labelling requirements are not as comprehensive as in the EC and the USA, and there is currently no legal requirement for MSDSs. 'Specified' and 'designated' chemical substances under the MITI/MHW scheme have to be labelled appropriately, as do dangerous substances under the MOL law and other legislation.

For MITI/MHW notification, the Japanese test methods are based on those of the OECD, although in many cases they are more stringent and the standard EC studies have to be enlarged. Many of the studies have to be reported in a prescribed format, with the data interpreted in a specific way. There is mutual acceptance of GLP between the EC Member States and Japan. Consequently, the Japanese regulatory authorities will accept foreign studies. In principle, existing GLP-compliant studies conducted to OECD/EC methods for non-Japanese notifiers are acceptable, but the results have to be 'suitable for interpretation' by the Japanese authorities, which in practice may mean only a positive test result is accepted.

Impurities contained at >1% in a new chemical substance are regarded as components of a mixture. In principle, each such impurity should be tested separately for notification. Hence, the technical-grade substance is considered to be a mixture of notified/existing substances, and consequently its composition can be varied as required. It may be necessary to use purified substance as the test material. Alternatively, the doses used for the three toxicity screening tests may have to be corrected to 100% if the purity of the test material is below 99%. Poorly defined reaction mixtures consisting of isomers and congeners can be tested and notified as the mixture.

The first stage in the testing programme is to evaluate the biodegradation potential of the substance. To pass the MITI ready biodegradability test, and hence be classified as a 'safe' chemical substance under the MITI/MHW scheme without further testing, virtually complete biodegradation is necessary. Furthermore, safe degradation products must be produced, so stable degradants may have to be further tested for biodegradability, bioaccumulation and toxicity, following discussion with the authorities.

Non-biodegradable substances are assessed for bioaccumulation potential. This may be done by measuring the n-octanol/water partition coefficient ($P_{ow}$). The pKa and a preliminary hydrolysis test are also required as part of the evaluation of bioaccumulation potential. If log $P_{ow}$ <3, the substance can be considered unlikely to bioaccumulate. A non-readily-biodegradable substance with a log $P_{ow}$ >3 is tested for bioaccumulation in carp. Alternatively, bioaccumulation can be assessed by analogy with chemically similar compounds which have already been tested.

Screening toxicity tests are conducted on a non-biodegradable but non-bioaccumulative substance. These are a 28-d subacute oral toxicity study, an Ames test and an *in vitro* chromosome aberration test in cell lines. The 28-d subacute toxicity study must include a 'satellite' group (dosed at the maximum level of the main study) with a 14-d recovery period, and consequently a corresponding control group is normally used. Certain parameters additional to the standard OECD requirements are investigated. The minimum testing requirement for the Ames test differs between the EC and Japan, but an 'expanded protocol' can be used so that the study complies with both methods. In particular, an *Escherichia coli* strain is included (for Japan) with plating in triplicate (for the EC). The exposure conditions for the Japanese *in vitro* chromosome aberration test differ from those required for the EC.

Full toxicity testing would be required on a substance shown to bioaccumulate, to establish whether it is a 'Class 1 specified' or a 'safe' substance. A full toxicity testing programme covers chronic toxicity, mutagenicity, carcinogenicity, reproduction toxicity, teratogenicity, toxicokinetics and pharmacology.

The physico-chemical tests required for Japanese MITI/MHW notification depend on the results of the ecotoxicological and toxicological studies, *ie*, in which class the substance is categorised.

### 34.6.4 South Korea

The Toxic Chemicals Control Law (TCCL) was enacted on 1 August 1990 to control chemical substances which are hazardous to human health or the environment, and in principle it has been enforced since 8 February 1991. All new chemical substances have to be notified to the Ministry of Environment (MoE) before being imported or manufactured, to enable the Chemical Substances Examination Committee (CSEC) to conduct a 'toxicity examination' to decide if action is needed to prevent harmful effects from this substance. Existing chemical substances can also be re-evaluated to decide if their use should be controlled as a Toxic Chemical. 'A Guide for Chemical Manufacturers/Importers' is available for the TCCL [37].

The TCCL applies to all chemical substances except those regulated by other legislation: *ie*, radioactive materials, pharmaceuticals, cosmetics, agrochemicals and fertilisers and additives for food and animal feed. However, naturally occurring substances and articles are excluded from the provisions of the TCCL. Also, substances manufactured or imported at <100 kg $a^{-1}$ or solely for testing and research are exempt from notification.

Existing Chemicals are substances manufactured or imported before 8 February 1991. The list was first published in June 1992, for substances nominated by manufacturers and importers, and with the first supplement of March 1993, approximately 17,000 substances are included. Any substance supplied before 8 February 1991 but not yet included in the Existing Chemicals List has to be registered for inclusion on the list by 31 December 1993.

A New Chemical has to be notified to the MoE 90 d before it is first manufactured or imported at ≥100 kg $a^{-1}$, but the MoE can extend the review period by 3 months. Technical and commercial information is included in the notification, including details of the proposed use and disposal. The studies required for the toxicity examination are an acute toxicity study, Ames test, *in vitro* chromosome aberration test and a ready biodegradability test. If either of the *in vitro* mutagenicity tests is positive, an *in vivo* study such as the mouse micronucleus test is needed to confirm the mutagenic potential. Data on abiotic degradation by hydrolysis or photolysis can be included as supporting information. The MoE can request additional studies necessary for the toxicity examination. The notification requirements are simplified for substances which have been established as safe by prolonged use in developed countries. Thus only an acute toxicity study and the Ames test are required if the substance is on three foreign inventories published by 1985. The notification requirements are also simplified for stable polymers which have a low potential for toxicity.

The CSEC use the information in the notification for the 'toxicity examination' of the new substance. If the substance has a high probability of human or environmental exposure and is also hazardous, the risk assessment could establish there is a potential to cause serious harm and hence the MoE may restrict its use, require annual reporting of the amount supplied or designate it as a Toxic Chemical or Specified Toxic Chemical.

Exposure is assessed from the use pattern, quantity to be supplied and physico-chemical properties. A substance is considered hazardous to health if the rodent oral $LD_{50}$ <300 mg $kg^{-1}$ or it is suspected of being mutagenic or carcinogenic. A substance is considered to be hazardous to the environment either if it is not biodegradable and the abiotic degradation data and physico-chemical properties indicate it will remain in the environment, or if the information on ecotoxicity and bioaccumulation suggest special control measures are needed.

Toxic Chemicals are existing or new substances designated as being harmful to public health or the environment. Specified Toxic Chemicals may be banned or have their use restricted. By March 1993 there were 432 chemicals designated as Toxic Chemicals and over 94 as Specified Toxic Chemicals either in single chemical substances, or in chemical classes. Importers of Toxic Chemicals have to register them annually, with administrative and commercial information, together with an environmental control plan. Any organization engaged in the manufacture, import, sale, storage, transport or use above a specified amount of Toxic Chemicals has to be registered as a Toxic Chemical Business. The MoE can order such a business to be relocated if there is considered to be a high risk to local residents from accidents involving Toxic Chemicals.

### 34.6.5 The Philippines

Chemical control in the Philippines is covered by the 1990 Toxic Substances and Hazardous Wastes Control Act (TSHWCA). The rules and regulations of this Act cover import, manufacture, processing, handling, storage, transport, sale, distribution, use and disposal of chemical substances and mixtures that present an unreasonable risk to human health or the environment. However, chemicals controlled by other Philippine legislation are not covered by TSHWCA. The Act is administered by the Department of Environment and Natural Resources (DENR).

The Philippine Inventory of Chemicals and Chemical Substances (PICCS) is currently in preparation, and is scheduled to be available from DENR in January 1994. Chemicals already supplied in the Philippines can be nominated for inclusion in the Inventory until 31 December 1993. Chemicals on PICCS are 'existing chemicals' and are not notifiable.

As from 31 December 1993, any 'new chemical' not on PICCS has to be notified 180 d before it is imported or manufactured. Technical and commercial information is required, together with studies on flash point of liquids, physico-chemical properties (melting point, boiling point, specific gravity, vapour pressure, partition coefficient and solubility in water and organic solvents), applicable toxicological studies (acute oral and inhalation toxicity, skin and eye irritation and subacute toxicity) and an evaluation of the carcinogenic, mutagenic and teratogenic potential. Technical dossiers are considered to be public documents, but some information can be claimed as confidential.

Within 90 d of receipt of the notification, DENR assess the new chemical and inform the notifier whether it can be added to the PICCS or if further information is needed to evaluate the risk. If necessary a Chemical Control Order is issued to ensure safe use of the chemical.

## 34.7 Conclusions

National chemical control systems vary considerably, in spite of attempts at harmonization, and the situation is made more complex by frequent regulatory changes. Furthermore, chemicals are generally regulated throughout their entire life cycle, with controls at each separate stage. Consequently it can be difficult to ensure that all the regulatory requirements are met for worldwide supply of a chemical. The cost of not satisfactorily accomplishing this complex task could be considerable delay in marketing the product, or even legal penalties for non-compliance with regulatory requirements, with the associated bad publicity.

Planning to fulfil the various registration obligations is highly desirable early in the development of a new chemical product. Advice from the regulatory authorities or an experienced consultant may be needed to ensure the proposed testing programme is both adequate to meet the regulatory requirements and also does not include unnecessary studies, which are clearly undesirable in terms of cost and in the interests of animal welfare. There will almost invariably be ambiguities in such a major project, but appropriate and timely expert advice provides the basis for rational business decisions to be taken. The authorities will also almost certainly ask questions on the regulatory submissions, but hopefully at least some of these may have been anticipated and hence can be answered promptly to ensure minimum delay in regulatory approval and subsequent marketing of the product.

GLP has had a big impact in ensuring the quality of regulatory submissions, and the authorities can now rely on the accuracy and integrity of the data presented. Regulatory affairs professionals also aim to ensure another aspect of this quality by providing the full set of information required, in the specified format and in a manner which is 'reviewer friendly'.

The overall aim of the manufacturer of the new product is to receive regulatory approval to begin marketing in the chosen countries as soon as possible, and with the minimum of unanticipated delay. The cost of the registration project, and concerns for animal welfare, will also be important. Hence the manufacturer will not want any tests conducted which are additional to the minimum requirements for regulatory approval and to establish the safety of the product.

Bearing in mind this background, regulatory affairs professionals have the important function of ensuring the testing programmes conducted on chemicals meet the appropriate regulatory and scientific requirements, after consulting the authorities for advice if necessary. This involves establishing and keeping up-to-date with the requirements of the regulatory authorities in the various countries in which the product is to be marketed. It is also essential to evaluate and summarise the information on new chemicals necessary for the regulatory submission, and to deal with any subsequent questions from the authorities. Part of this process involves evaluating the safety of the new chemical, to workers and the general public and to the environment, advising on hazard communication (labelling and MSDSs) and risk assessment.

## 34.8 References


[1] 'International Convention for the Prevention of Pollution from Ships, as modified by the Protocol of 1978 relating thereto', MARPOL 73/78, March 1992, consolidated edition, IMO, London.

[2] 'Montreal Protocol on Substances that Deplete the Ozone Layer', 1987, United Nations Environment Programme, New York.

[3] 'Comprehensive Environmental Response, Compensation, and Liability Act', Public Law 96-510, 1980, USA.

[4] EC Council Directive of 8 July 1982 on the major accident hazards of certain industrial activities (82/501/EEC), *Off.J.Eur. Comm.*, No. L230 of 05-08-82.

[5] 'London Guidelines for the Exchange of Information on Chemicals in International Trade', 1987, United Nations Environment Programme.

[6] 'Verordnung uber die Vermeidung von Verpackungsabfallen' (Regulation on the Avoidance of Packaging Waste), 12-06-91.

[7] 'Decision and Recommendation on the Systematic Investigation of Existing Chemicals', 1987, Organization for Economic Cooperation and Development.

[8] 'Paris Commission Guidelines Regarding Harmonisation of Procedures of Approval, Evaluation and Testing of Offshore Chemicals and Drilling Muds', September 1990.

[9] 'Decision concerning the Mutual Acceptance of Data in the Assessment of Chemicals', 1981, C(81)30 (Final) and 'Recommendation concerning the Mutual Recognition of Compliance with Good Laboratory Practice', 1983, C(83)95 (Final), Organization for Economic Cooperation and Development.

[10] *Laboratory Animal Science Newsletter*, 1992, **5**, 12-13.

[11] *Chemicals-in-Progress Bulletin*, 1992, **13**, (2), 27.

[12] EC Council Directive of 30 April 1992 amending for the seventh time Directive 67/548/EEC on the approximation of the Laws, regulations and administrative provisions relating to the classification, packaging and labelling of dangerous substances (92/32/EEC), *Off.J. Eur. Comm.*. No. L154 of 05-06-92.

[13] Toxic Substances Control Act, Public Law 94-469, 1976, USA.

[14] Law Concerning the Examination and Regulation of Manufacture etc., of Chemical Substances, Law No. 117, 1973, Japan.

[15] EC Council Directive of 27 June 1967 on the approximation of laws, regulations and administrative provisions relating to the classification, packaging and labelling of dangerous substances (67/548/EEC), *Off.J. Eur. Comm.*, No.196/1 of 16-08-67.

[16] EC Commission Directive of 1 March 1991 adapting to technical progress for the twelfth time Council Directive 67/548/EEC on the approximation of the laws, regulations and administrative provisions relating to the classification, packaging and labelling of dangerous substances (91/325/EEC), *Off.J. Eur. Comm.*, No. L180 of 08-07-91.

[17] EC Commission Directive of 27 April 1993 adapting to technical progress for the 18th time Council Directive 67/548/EEC on the approximation of the laws, regulations and administrative provisions relating to the classification, packaging and labelling of dangerous substances (93/21/EEC), *Off.J. Eur. Comm.*, No. L110 and L110A of 04-05-93.

[18] *Reproductive Toxicology*, Richardson, M.L., (Ed.), VCH Publishers, Weinheim, 1993. pp.286.
[19] EC Council Directive of 7 June 1988 on the approximation of the laws, regulations and administrative provisions of the Member States relating to the classification, packaging and labelling of dangerous preparations (88/379/EEC), *Off.J. Eur. Comm.* No. L187/14 of 16-07-88.
[20] EC Commission Directive of 5 September 1990 adapting to technical progress for the second time Council Directive 88/379/EEC on the approximation of the laws, regulations and administrative provisions of the Member States relating to the classification, packaging and labelling of dangerous preparations (90/492/EEC), *Off.J. Eur. Comm.*, No. L275 of 05-10-90.
[21] EC Commission Directive of 5 March 1991 defining and laying down the detailed arrangements for the system of specific information relating to dangerous preparations in implementation of Article 10 of Directive 88/379/EEC (91/155/EEC), *Off.J. Eur. Comm.*, No. L76 of 22-03-91.
[22] EC Council Directive of 18 September 1979, amending for the sixth time Directive 67/548/EEC on the approximation of the laws, regulations and administrative provisions relating to the classification, packaging and labelling of dangerous substances (79/831/EEC), *Off.J. Eur. Comm.*, No. L259 of 15-10-79.
[23] EC Commission Directive of 31 July 1992 adapting to technical progress for the seventeenth time Council Directive 67/548/EEC on the approximation of laws, regulations and administrative provisions relating to the classification, packaging and labelling of dangerous substances (92/69/EEC), *Off.J. Eur. Comm.*, No. L383 and L383A of 29-12-92.
[24] EC Commission Directive of 25 April 1984 adapting to technical progress for the sixth time Council Directive 67/548/EEC on the approximation of laws, regulations and administrative provisions relating to the classification, packaging and labelling of dangerous substances (84/449/EEC), *Off.J. Eur. Comm.*, No. L251 of 19-09-84.
[25] EC Commission Directive of 18 November 1987 adapting to technical progress for the ninth time Council Directive 67/548/EEC on the approximation of laws, regulations and administrative provisions relating to the classification, packaging and labelling of dangerous substances (87/302/EEC), *Off.J. Eur. Comm.*, No. L133 of 30-05-88.
[26] 'OECD Guidelines for Testing of Chemicals', 1993, OECD, Paris, pp.1 to end.
[27] EC Council Directive of 24 November 1986, on the approximation of laws, regulations and administrative provisions of the Member States regarding the protection of animals used for experimental and other scientific purposes (86/609/EEC), *Off.J. Eur. Comm.*, No. L358 of 18-12-86.
[28] EC Council Regulation of 23 March 1993 on the evaluation and control of the risks of existing substances (No.793/93), *Off.J. Eur. Comm.*, No. L84 of 05-04-93.
[29] EC Council Directive of 27 July 1976 on the approximation of the laws, regulations and administrative provisions of the Member States relating to restrictions on the marketing and use of certain dangerous substances and preparations (76/769/EEC), *Off.J. Eur. Comm.*, No. L262 of 27-09-76.
[30] Toxic Substances Control Act [13], 40 CFR 700 to 799.
[31] Toxic Substances Control Act [13], 40 CFR 795 to 798.

[32] 'Guidelines for the notification and testing of new substances: chemicals and polymers: pursuant to the new substances notification regulations of the Canadian Environmental Protection Act', 1993, Ministry of Supply and Services, Canada.
[33] *Canada Gazette Extract*, 26 January 1991, 'Domestic Substances List' and *Canada Gazette Part I*, 5 September, 1992, pp.2735-2737.
[34] *Canada Gazette Extract*, 26 January 1991, 'Non-Domestic Substances List' Volumes I and II.
[35] 'Handbook for Notifiers: National Industrial Chemicals Notification and Assessment Scheme (NICNAS)', 1990, Commonwealth of Australia.
[36] Resource Management Act, No. 69, 1991, New Zealand.
[37] 'The Toxic Chemicals Control Law: A Guide for Chemical Manufacturers/ Importers', 1993, Ministry of Environment, Republic of Korea.

# 35. Epilogue

Mervyn Richardson

## 35.1 Introduction

The safety of chemicals, on which mankind now depends totally, is of paramount importance. However, in assessing chemical safety it is equally vital that pragmatic assessments are undertaken.

Total safety, *ie*, no risk, is not a reality. As stated by Mercier [1] 'a zero-risk concept has the appearance of supporting a generation's unreasonable wish to live forever'. Even an essential chemical such as water in hazardous situations, *eg*, drowning, is not safe, and if ingested in excessive quantities, *ie*, 30+ l $d^{-1}$, will cause kidney failure. Oxygen, essential to all mammals, if inhaled at excessive concentrations can result in injury caused via free radical mechanisms.

To adopt a sustainable strategy for an environment containing some 11 million chemicals, it is vital that professionals have a comprehensive reference manual which gives them instant access to current developments in information retrieval, hazard assessment, risk assessment and management, safety evaluation and legal aspects. Up to now, this information has been dispersed in texts covering particular aspects of safety, or in original research publications (some being in journals, technical reports, gray literature, etc., which prove difficult to obtain). This dispersal of information makes it increasingly difficult for the busy professional to form a balanced view of the present state of knowledge and practice, and thus to arrive at rapid, informed decisions on how best to tackle a real-life chemical safety problem.

Only by drawing on a wide range of technical expertise, from workers in different disciplines and in different countries throughout the world, is it possible to produce a really practical reference manual which answers this pressing need. In planning the contributions to this book, paramount importance was given to 2 criteria:

i) Coverage should be as broad as possible, both interdisciplinary and international; and,

ii) The data presented should be timely, representing a genuine picture of chemical safety in the 1990s.

Satisfying both these criteria is no simple matter and, inevitably, compromises had to be made, but the general, level of cooperation in response to invitations to contributors was truly outstanding. The book which has resulted from this cooperation makes a unique contribution to the reference literature on chemical safety with over 1000 cited references. Within a single volume it gathers together data which are vital for all whose day-to-day work involves taking decisions on chemical safety, be they industrial managers, health and safety advisors, or consultants to government and international agencies.

This book takes the reader through the various and essential stages of chemical safety, *viz:*

i) Information retrieval;

ii) Hazard assessment;

iii) Risk assessment, including the essential requirements of pragmatic monitoring;

iv) Risk management;

v) Safety; and finally,

vi) Legal aspects.

There are enormous differences in chemical safety as currently practised. Within the Western European countries, United States of America, Japan, etc., there is a profusion of excellent legislation (*qv*, chapters by Campbell, Knight, Kulkarni and Nangle, etc.) which provides an overview of the legislation in force by these countries. The European Community is to be congratulated on moving increasingly to a single market, which in turn will mean one set of environmental, health and safety regulations for 12 countries, a number which will increase during the next decade. The United Nations, as a result of its recommendations from UNCED held in Rio de Janeiro in June 1992, has made a number of recommendations which are now being enacted by many governments in an endeavour for greatly increased sustainability.

Regrettably, this healthy picture is not the case in Central and Eastern Europe. For example, where the dogma from the former Communist regimes has left an inheritance of old, inefficient, ineffective, costly, and beyond all, highly polluting chemical industry. A number of countries in Central Europe, by taking advantage of World Aid from in particular the EC — Poland, Hungary, Assistance for Reconstruction and Economy (PHARE) programme, coupled with loans from the European Bank for Reconstruction and Development (EBRD) are moving rapidly to accept the criteria now required in Western Europe and elsewhere.

Taking the view that some good always arises from harm, the devastation seen at first hand by the editor in January 1993 when surveying the damage caused to the environment by the destruction of the Croatian chemical industry is relevant [2]. In many countries, replacement of old and outmoded chemical processes means depriving the workforce from their only means of income; and, then demolishing the factory prior to considering reconstruction. The war in Croatia, and even more so in Bosnia, has achieved these stages; admittedly to be followed in many cases by a requirement for remediation and decontamination. What is vital is that countries which have suffered the ravages of war do not indulge in 'blind rebuilding'; and, further, have workable management schemes for waste disposal or better recycling; leading to sustainable development.

It is regrettable that the mediators, politicians, and in particular the media, whilst giving unceasing coverage to human misery and hostilities, pay little heed to the health and environmental consequences of such actions and destruction.

Since prehistoric times pollution to both air and water have known no boundaries. Whilst species have had $10^9$ years to become acclimatized to certain known noxious and carcinogenic substances such as the polyaromatic hydrocarbons, the time interval for the vast majority of new chemicals is 2 or 3 decades and, in many, cases much less.

The destruction to the Croatian and Bosnian chemical industry is predicted to be causing long-term effects to water resources from their boundaries to the Black and Mediterranean Seas, water used for drinking, fish breeding, watering of cattle, and not least, irrigation of crops. Nowadays, cereals, fruits, vegetables, milk, meat, and fish products, are transported over long distances to provide the vast array of foodstuffs now available to all; but little heed is given to the chemical contamination of such everyday products — is this a matter to be pursued more avidly in considering chemical safety.

## 35.2 Chemical Safety — The Essential Stages

The sections of this book indicate the essential stages.

### 35.2.1 Information Retrieval, Validation and Interpretation

There is now a wealth of good data available on the chemical properties of many of the 11 million substances listed in Chemical Abstracts. However, of the 100,000+ substances listed in various inventories, *eg*, EINECS, the available toxicological and ecotoxicological data which is freely and publicly available is often limited. Whilst many of the sources of these data are outlined in the chapters by Cowie and Richardson, Deschamps, Pantry, Pembleton, etc., it is regrettable that much of these important data remain solely locked away in the filing systems of some of the multinational chemical companies. Whilst it may neither be pragmatic nor in their interests to make these data totally available to all, they should at least be made available freely to the United Nations programmes.

Similarly, the matter in which these data are validated and interpreted should be made publicly available. It is unfortunate that as we approach the end of this millennium that public relations hype increases out of all proportion to public participation.

### 35.2.2 Hazard Assessment

Data, once retrieved has to be assessed for its hazard. That is, the effect of a chemical on biological species. It is interesting to note that in clinical toxicology, data are being extrapolated from many species to assess the effects to one species — human; whereas in ecotoxicology, data from relatively few species are being extrapolated to whole ecosystems. Again, the early chapters in this volume indicate the stages and sources available.

### 35.2.3 Risk Assessment

Until the last few years many regulators and chemical companies alike have been satisfied to undertake hazard assessment and pay little attention to risk.

Risk is the integration of hazard with dose, or rather, exposure. This means that an acknowledged hazard has to be quantified, semi-quantified, or at the very least, consideration needs to be given to the magnitude of the effects, even if the latter can only be achieved by professional judgement. The authors in this section have outlined a number of risks which indicates the wide range of events which need to be addressed in order to achieve chemical safety.

For many decades analytical chemists have produced increasingly sophisticated and expensive techniques for the determination of both inorganic and organic chemicals in every substrate imaginable. Whilst their success in the pharmaceutical industry has been notable, measurement of pesticides, for example, in water samples to a concentration of $<0.1\ \mu g\ l^{-1}$, has only achieved a success range of perhaps at the best 20%.

Over the past 10 years it has been appreciated increasingly that assessment of the biological effects of chemicals in order to ascertain the safety of chemicals is of paramount necessity. This has been achieved by various animal and bacterial tests, *eg*, the Ames test, and for monitoring, immunoassay techniques, have much to offer. However, in the future a much greater requirement will need to be made of techniques currently under development, *eg*, DNA probes, EROD, and cytochrome P-450 activities (see also chapter by Isenberg and Bulich). As described in *Ecotoxicology Monitoring*, generic techniques such as the Microtox® test based on the luciferase mechanisms in *Photobacterium phosphoreum* NRRL B-11177; or the Mutatox® test, based on a lux gene activation in *Vibrio fischeri* M169, are surely the way forward as an alternative to developing even more costly and sophisticated techniques in analytical chemistry [2]. After all, chemicals affect biological systems and hence it is appropriate to assess chemical safety by means of biological effects [3].

There are now increasing requirements to measure other effects, including immuno response, neurotoxic actions, psychological effects, but with a decrease in human sperm counts, reproductive toxicology is a matter of increasing importance, especially so in the industrial areas of Central and Eastern Europe, South America, Far East, etc. [4]. It is for this reason that only 2 specialist techniques are outlined in this manual.

### 35.2.4 Risk Management

This is the action that should be undertaken resulting from risk assessment.

In basic terms, it is the action that can be applied to take corrective action to diminish risks and hence increase **chemical safety**. It should be remembered, as mentioned in the first paragraph of this Epilogue, that zero-risk is unobtainable, but that we should make every attempt to manage risk in the most pragmatic manner.

Safety should never involve such high costs that the benefit of a product becomes unacceptable. It is the management of risks in the circumstances of use that is of importance which involves the assessment of 'how safe is safe enough?'

In today's complex international lifestyle, is it more appropriate for a transnational company to expend significant sums of money to decrease the operational risks of a sophisticated modern process by a factor of 10, or for that money to be used, perhaps via the World Aid agencies, to decrease the risks of a chemical process in a developing country?

A fundamental factor in many organizations is the difficulty that managers have had in relating to risk issues. The probabilities concerned with risk are viewed as being too remote; the language used in assessing risk is too conceptual; and, many of the options for the required action are often too impracticable. However, very few can argue that we live in a more risky world as continuing series of events involving terrorism, warfare and climate extremes, natural and artificial disasters are demonstrated only too frequently.

The requirement for risk management leading to safety (of chemicals) has to be seen to be a more relevant and vital part of the wider management process within any type of organization.

Consideration must be given to:

i) The importance of risk quantification to receive management attention;

ii) Methods to provide credence to intangible and nebulous exposures such as third party liabilities (see chapter by Devos and Ekroos);

iii) The growing interest and significance in corporate governance in defining organization's risk profile; and,

iv) The psychological barriers for managers understanding risk and means to overcome such barriers.

Currently, we are able to inherit only one planet, the Earth, and we continue to stretch our environmental hazard sustainable limits. Hence, our future must rest on good and pragmatic assessments of chemical safety.

## 35.3 Sustainability

Safety in the use of chemicals will lead to sustainable development. In communities of all sizes in all countries, the question 'is the way we are living today sustainable?' is being asked. Communities have to ensure that they meet today's needs without compromising the ability of the environment to sustain life in the future. Toxic chemicals do have an important place in a sustainable environment, and 'toxic' does not mean 'unacceptable', otherwise biocides would not be used — and in today's societal requirements, preservation of foods, paper, textiles, adhesives, paints, and many other commodities, is vital.

Simultaneously, the crucial issues of health and welfare have to be addressed. Resources have to be used effectively, efficiently, and safely, taking into account conservation and recycling. This entails new approaches to safety in energy, transport, housing, agriculture, human resources, and not least, biological diversity. Maintenance of cultural identities is important but will necessitate a partnership of change to ensure a full regard for chemical safety.

Above all, practical aspects need to be taken into account and whilst total safety requires to be viewed as the ultimate goal, the sub-title of this book '*how safe is safe enough*' has to be the formula for the future.

Different circumstances demand different approaches in the highly developed chemical industries of the West. Much emphasis is placed rightfully on attempting to achieve ultimate safety. In the developing countries this goal seems to be somewhat distant and in war zones the safety of chemicals, or otherwise, is not a high priority.

However, for the future, a sustainable enterprise can be generated by the will to change by both national and international business. Business has the power to innovate, to invest, to employ, and to provide solutions to problems. The role of financial institutions has also to be considered for a partnership in change, as these too often set the conditions in which development may take place. Sadly, too many current technologies are unsustainable and unsafe, especially in the less developed countries, hence business will need to modify its operating practices to provide new techniques involving best available technologies, coupled with management, education, training, and supervision, to ensure that new products are safe. This will provide a challenge to both the employer and employees.

In considering our future and sustainable development, in turn leading to chemical safety, a number of topics can be highlighted:

i) There is no universally acceptable manner of prioritizing environmental concerns;

ii) Management decisions relating to environmental matters cannot be considered in isolation from legislative responsibility or economic criteria;

iii) Organizations may specify targets to be met in their environmental policies, and use these to justify selection of practices or products on environmental grounds;

iv) Transportation considerations are vital when addressing environmental impacts;

v) Waste minimization has to be recognized as a requirement to be considered at source together with full life cycle analyses;

vi) Currently, there is widespread recognition that environmental protection must be among the highest priority of every business, especially small and medium enterprises;

vii) There needs to be a commitment to educate, train and motivate employees to conduct their activities in an environmentally responsible manner;

viii) We need to undertake environmental impact studies prior to commencing a new activity or project, and before decommissioning a facility or leaving a site;

ix) We must develop, design, and operate facilities taking into account efficient use of energy and materials, especially chemicals, the sustainable use of renewable resources, with minimization of adverse environmental impact, waste generation, together with the safe and responsible disposal of residual wastes;

x) We have to continue to improve the manufacture, marketing, use, transport and disposal of products, together with relevant services or activities, with emphasis on scientific and technical understanding and research to prevent serious or irreversible environmental degradation;

xi) There is a need to intensify international cooperation in environmental protection in Europe (and elsewhere) to assume responsibility at a global level and thus offer partnerships on a worldwide basis. This will ensure that actions, including industrial disasters and warfare, within one country will not have adverse environmental effects in other countries.

xii) There needs to be a convergence of environmental quality and policies within Europe, as we aim for peace, stability and sustainable development, and for these to be developed globally;

xiii) It is vital to enact an economic transformation in Central and Eastern Europe which has a positive impact on environmental quality, especially where ecosystems are at risk of suffering irreversible changes, or where the economic costs of environmental damage are very high, *eg*, in Bosnia and Croatia;

xiv) There is a requirement for expanding investments and promotion of projects, concerted action to improve the environmental situation in Central and Eastern Europe and elsewhere; and;

xv) Great stress will be need to be placed on transboundary pollution.

Sustainable development cannot be achieved without broad public participation in decision-making, a process which must overtake the publicity hype promulgated only too often by major corporations and indeed governments. Every citizen has a role to play in the creation of a sustainable future, and hence the means have to be found to allow people to voice their views, especially the growing number outside the current debating process. This needs to span the entire spectrum of institutions at international, national, and local levels. Knowledge and awareness are powerful components of active citizenship, and in order to achieve the fullest appreciation of chemical safety, there will need to be a partnership between teachers, communicators and scientists.

## 35.4 Conclusions

In the future, the pragmatic establishment of methodologies for the assessment of chemical safety is a matter of concern for all.

The United Nations programmes are and will be taking a major role. It is vital that, as a minimum requirement, innovators and regulators on an international basis provide the programmes with all relevant toxicological and ecotoxicological data.

As far as possible, regimes should include aims to:

i) Avoid complexity — not an easy task when attempting to extrapolate data from species to species, or to whole ecosystems;

ii) Be non-confrontational;

iii) Provide a means wherever possible for decisions to be taken locally; and,

iv) Include transparent and revealing reporting systems and procedures.

In doing so this will encourage various parties to cooperate in environmental and safety conventions within respective governing bodies and thus take steps to:

i) Improve knowledge, especially of objectives and obligations;

ii) Assist governments in providing and constructing pragmatic administrative, legal infrastructures, including enforcement and implementing mechanisms, via the exchange of legal and technical experts;

iii) Enhance opportunities for regular participation in meetings by representatives of countries, especially those in transition;

iv) Encourage free exchange of all relevant information on chemical safety; and,

v) In the case of natural or artificial disasters, including warfare, ensure that 'blind rebuilding' of outmoded, dirty and in some cases totally unnecessary chemical installations which were often built in undesirable locations is not repeated [2].

We need to remember that the scale of environmental changes now faced is far greater than ever before; these effect the biosphere as a whole and are a threat to the life-support systems on which human society as we now know it relies.

Chemical safety goes hand in glove with sustainable development, which has to meet the needs of the present without compromising the ability of future generations to meet their own needs, or even exist [4].

Chemical safety, with the ability to judge 'how safe is safe enough', is a pathway of deliberate change and improvement, which maintains or preferably enhances improvements of systems and enacts the ability of human, natural, or mixed systems to withstand or adapt to endogenous or exogenous changes in the future.

## 35.5 References


[1] Mercier, M., 'Risk Assessment of Chemicals: A Global Approach', in: *Risk Assessment of Chemicals in the Environment*, Richardson, M.L., (Ed.), The Royal Society of Chemistry, London, 1988, pp. 73-91.

[2] Richardson, M.L. and Sugavanam, B., 'Effects of War on the Environment', United Nations Industrial Development Organization, Report US/CRO/92/164, (10/R.263), Vienna, January 1993, pp. 111.

[3] *Ecotoxicology Monitoring*, Richardson, M.L., (Ed.), VCH Publishers, Weinheim, 1993, pp. 384.

[4] *Reproductive Toxicology*, Richardson, M.L., (Ed.), VCH Publishers, Weinheim, 1993, pp. 286.


*'There has never been a more important time for us to ensure that proper attention is paid to environmental issues ... we are seeking solutions that will work in the long term and take full account of the need to protect and safeguard the natural resources on which we all depend.'*

The Rt. Hon. The Baroness Chalker of Wallasey, May 1992.

# Annex 1

**Complete Record from Dictionary of Substances and Their Effects (DOSE), Richardson, M.L., (Ed.).**

**A5 Acetaldehyde**

$CH_3CHO$

**CAS Registry No.** 75-07-0
**Synonyms** acetic aldehyde; ethanal; ethylaldehyde
**Mol. Formula** $C_2H_4O$ **Mol. Wt.** 44.05
**Uses** In the manufacture of aniline dyestuffs, perfumes, flavours, plastics, synthetic rubbers and for silvering mirrors and hardening gelatin fibres.

**Physical properties**
**M. Pt.** -123/5°C; **B.Pt.** 20.2°C; **Flash point** 38°C; **Specific gravity** $d^{20}$0.783; **Partition coefficient** log $P_{ow}$-0.40 (calc.) (1).; **Volatility** v.p. 740 mm Hg.

**Solubility**
**Water:** miscible. Organic solvent: ethanol, diethyl ether

**Occupational exposure**
**US TLV (TWA)** 100 ppm (180 mg $m^{-3}$); **US TLV (STEL)** 150 ppm (2780 mg $m^{-3}$); **UK Long-term limit** 100 ppm (180 mg $m^{-3}$) under review; **UK Short-term limit** 150 ppm (270 mg $m^{-3}$) under review; **UN No.** 1089;
**HAZCHEM Code** 2YE; **Conveyance classification** flammable liquid; **Supply classification** extremely flammable and harmful.

**Risk phrases**
Extremely flammable — Irritating to eyes and respiratory system — Possible risk of irreversible effects (R12, R36/37,R40).

**Safety phrases**
Keep away from sources of ignition — No Smoking — Take precautionary measures against static discharges — Wear protective clothing and gloves (S16,S33,S36/37)

**Ecotoxicity**
**Fish toxicity**
$LC_{50}$ (25 hr) pinperch 70 mg $l^{-1}$ (2).
$LC_{50}$ (96 hr) bluegill sunfish 53 mg $l^{-1}$ (3).

**Invertebrate toxicity**
Cell multiplication inhibition test *Uronema parduczi* 57 mg $l^{-1}$ (4).
$EC_{50}$ (48 hr) *Daphnia magna* 9-14 g $l^{-1}$ (5).

**Environmental fate**
**Anaerobic effects**
67-97% degradation occurred in an anaerobic system (6,7).

**Degradation studies**
Biodegradable (8).
A number of studies confirm the degradability of acetaldehyde by acclimated sludge. Some loss may be attributed to volatilization (9-13).

**Abiotic removal**
Photolytic $t_{½}$ 8-16 hr (calc.) (14).

**Mammalian and avian toxicity**
**Acute data**
$LD_{50}$ oral rat 1930 mg $kg^{-1}$ (15).
$LD_{50}$ intravenous mouse 212 mg $kg^{-1}$ (16).

**Carcinogenicity and long-term effects**
Inadequate evidence for carcinogenicity to humans, sufficient evidence for carcinogenicity to animals, IARC classification group 2B (17).
Inhalation ♂/♀ rat (≤28 month) 0, 1500 or 3000 ppm (6 hr $day^{-1}$ 5 day $wk^{-1}$) gradually reduced to 1000 ppm during the first 52 wk. Major compound related effects include increased mortality, growth retardation, nasal tumours, and non-neoplastic nasal changes in each of the test groups. The treatment related nasal changes comprised: degeneration, hyperplasia, metaplasia, and adenocarcinomas of the olfactory epithelium at all exposure levels; squamous metaplasia accompanied by slight to severe keratinization and squamous cell carcinomas of the respiratory epithelium at the two highest exposure levels; and slight to severe rhinitis and sinusitis in the highest concentration group of rats (18,19).
Long-term inhalation and intratracheal instillation studies of acetaldehyde were carried out in Syrian hamsters. Exposure to acetaldehyde vapour at a concentration of 1500 ppm resulted in epithelial hyperplasia and metaplasia accompanied by inflammation in the nasal cavity and trachea. Extensive peribronchiolar adenomatoid lesions often accompanied by inflammatory changes occurred in the lungs after intratracheal instillation of acetaldehyde. There was no evidence of acetaldehyde possessing carcinogenic activity (20).

**Teratogenicity and reproductive effects**
In mice caused decreased weight and abnormal closure of neural tube (16).
Rat malformations included microcephaly, micromelia and digital anomalies (21).

**Genotoxicity**

Acetaldehyde produced chromosomal aberrations including chromosomal fragments, achromatic lesions and chromatid breaks in metaphases at 12 hr and 24 hr in primary cultures of rat skin fibroblasts. Dose-related increases in aneuploidy were also observed (22).

**Any other adverse effects to man**

General narcotic. In humans large doses cause death by respiratory paralysis (23).

**Any other comments**

Toxicity and hazards reviewed (24).
Exposure data, experimental toxicology and human health effects reviewed (25,26).

**References**


1. Hansch, C; et al. *Med. Chem. Proj.* 1981, No. 19, Pomona College, Claremont, CA.
2. Garrett, J.T; et al, *Texas J. Sci*, 1951, **3**, 391.
3. McKee, J.E; et al. *Water Quality Criteria* 1963, California State Water Quality Board.
4. Bringmann, G; et al. *Z. Wasser/Abwasser Forsch.* 1980, **1**, 26.
5. Takahashi, I.T; et al. *Bull. Environ. Contamin. Toxicol.* 1987, **39**, 229-236.
6. Chou, W.L; et al. *Biotech. Bioeng. Symp.* 1979, **8**, 391-414.
7. *Selected Biodegradation Techniques for Treatment/Ultimate Disposal of Organic Materials* 1979, EPA 600/2-79-006.
8. *MITI Report* 1984, Ministry of International Trade and Industry, Tokyo.
9. Gerhold, R.M; et al. *J. Water Pollut. Control Fed.* 1957, **38**, 562-579.
10. Hatfield, R. *Ind. Eng. Chem.* 1957, **49**, 192-196.
11. Heukelekian, H; et al. *J. Water Pollut. Control Fed.* 1955, **29**, 1040-1053.
12. Rogovskaya, T; et al. *Inst. Vodosnakzh Kanaliz Gidrotekhn Sooruzhenii Inzh Gidrogeol* 1962, 178-213 (Russ.) (*Chem. Abstr.* **57**, 11659b).
13. Ludzach, J.R; et al. *J. Water Pollut. Control Fed.* 1960, **32**, 1173-2000.
14. Weaver, J. *Diss. Abstract. Int. B 1977*, 1976, **37**, 3427.
15. *Arch. Ind. Hyg. Occup. Med.* 1951, **4**, 199.
16. O'Shea, K.S; et al. *J. Anat.* 1979, **128** (1), 65.
17. *IARC Monograph* 1987, **Suppl.7**, 77.
18. Wouterson, R.A; et al. *Toxicology* 1986, **41** (2), 213-231.
19. *Eur. J. Cancer Clin. Oncol.* 1982, **18**, 13.
20. Feron, V.J. *Prog. Exp. Tumour Res.* 1977, 162.
21. Padmanabhan, R; et al. *Indian J. Pharmcol.* 1982, **14** (3), 247.
22. Bird, R.P; et al. *Mutat. Res.* 1982, **101** (3), 237-246.
23. *The Merck Index* 11th ed. 1989, Merck & Co. Inc., Rahway, NJ.
24. Izmerov, N.F. *Scientific Reviews of Soviet Literature of Toxicity & Hazards of Chemicals* 1991, **111**, Eng. Trans. Richardson, M.L. (Ed.), UNEP/IRPTC, Geneva.
25. *BIBRA Toxicity Profile* 1989, British Industrial Biological Research Association, Carshalton.
26. *ECETOC Technical Report No. 30(4)* 1991, European Chemical Industry Ecology and Toxicology Centre, B-1160 Brussels.

# Annex 2

## OECD GUIDELINES FOR TESTING OF CHEMICALS

### PHYSICAL-CHEMICAL PROPERTIES

| | |
|---|---|
| 101 | UV-VIS Absorption Spectra |
| 102 | Melting Point/Melting Range |
| 103 | Boiling Point/Boiling Range |
| 104 | Vapour Pressure Curve |
| 105 | Water Solubility |
| 106 | Adsorption/Desorption |
| 107 | Partition Coefficient (n-octanol/water) |
| 108 | Complex Formation Ability in Water |
| 109 | Density of Liquids and Solids |
| 110 | Particle Size Distribution/Fibre Length and Diameter Distributions |
| 111 | Hydrolysis as a Function of pH |
| 112 | Dissociation Constants in Water |
| 113 | Screening Test for Thermal Stability and Stability in Air |
| 114 | Viscosity of Liquids |
| 115 | Surface Tension of Aqueous Solutions |
| 116 | Fat Solubility of Solid and Liquid Substances |

### EFFECTS IN BIOTIC SYSTEMS

| | |
|---|---|
| 201 | Alga, Growth Inhibition Test |
| 202 | *Daphnia sp.* Acute Immobilization Test and Reproduction Test |
| 203 | Fish, Acute Toxicity Test |
| 204 | Fish, Prolonged Toxicity Test: 14-d Study |
| 205 | Avian Dietary Toxicity Test |
| 206 | Avian Reproduction Test |
| 207 | Earthworm, Acute Toxicity Tests |
| 208 | Terrestrial Plants, Growth Test |
| 109 | Activated Sludge, Respiration Inhibition Test |

### DEGRADATION AND ACCUMULATION

**Ready Biodegradability**

301 A Modified AFNOR Test
301 B Modified Sturm Test
301 C Closed Bottle Test
301 E Modified OECD Screening Test

**Inherent Biodegradability**

302 A Modified SCAS Test
302 B Modified Zahn-Wellens Test
302 C Modified MITI Test (II)

**Simulation Test**

303 A Aerobic Sewage Treatment: Coupled Units Test

**Biodegradability in Soil**

304 A Inherent Biodegradability in Soil

**Bioaccumulation**

305 A Sequential Static Fish Test
305 B Semi-Static Fish Test
305 C Degree of Bioconcentration in Fish
305 D Static Fish Test
305 E Flow-Through Fish Test

## HEALTH EFFECTS

**Short Term Toxicology**

401 Acute Oral Toxicity
402 Acute Dermal Toxicity
403 Acute Inhalation Toxicity
404 Acute Dermal Irritation/Corrosion
405 Acute Eye Irritation/Corrosion
406 Skin Sensitization
407 Repeated Dose Oral Toxicity — Rodent: 28/14-d
408 Subchronic Oral Toxicity — Rodent: 90-d
409 Subchronic Oral Toxicity — Non-rodent: 90-d
410 Repeated Dose Dermal Toxicity: 21/28-d
411 Subchronic Dermal Toxicity: 90-d
412 Repeated Dose Inhalation Toxicity: 28/14-d
413 Subchronic Inhalation Toxicity: 90-d
414 Teratogenicity
415 One-Generation Reproduction Toxicity
416 Two-Generation Reproduction Toxicity
417 Toxicokinetics
418 Acute Delayed Neurotoxicity of Organophosphorus Substances
419 Subchronic Delayed Neurotoxicity of Organophosphorus Substances: 90-d

**Long Term Toxicology**

451 Carcinogenicity Studies
452 Chronic Toxicity Studies
453 Combined Chronic Toxicity/Carcinogenicity Studies

## GENETIC TOXICOLOGY

471 *Salmonella typhimurium*, Reverse Mutation Assay
472 *Escherichia coli.*, Reverse Mutation Assay
473 *In vitro* Mammalian Cytogenetic Test
474 Micronucleus Test
475 *In vivo* Mammalian Bone Marrow Cytogenetic Test — Chromosomal Analysis
476 *In vitro* Mammalian Cell Gene Mutation Tests
477 Sex-Linked Recessive Lethal Test in *Drosophila malanogaster*
478 Rodent Dominant Lethal Test
479 *In vitro* Sister Chromatid Exchange Assay in Mammalian Cells
480 *Saccharomyces cerevisiae*, Gene Mutation Assay
481 *Saccharomyces cerevisiae*, Mitotic Recombination Assay
482 DNA Damage and Repair, Unscheduled DNA Synthesis in Mammalian Cells *in vitro*
483 Mammalian Germ Cell Cytogenetic Assay
484 Mouse Spot Test
485 Mouse Heritable Translocation Assay

Organization for Economic Cooperation and Development, OECD Guidelines for Testing of Chemicals, OECD, Paris, 1983.

# Index

TOXICOLOGY

# Reproductive Toxicology

**edited by Mervyn Richardson**

1993. IV, 306 pages with 37 figures and 36 tables.
Hardcover. DM 195.-/öS 1521.-/sFr 180.-
ISBN 3-527-28561-X

Reproductive toxicology is a subject of crucial importance to future generations. Toxic exposure of the developing embryo is a well-recognized problem, but it is also necessary to consider the effects of certain chemicals prior to conception, both in humans and in animals. The mechanisms and routes of the biological action need to be established.

The book surveys the effects of chemical substances on female and male reproductive systems.

Both the legislative and regulatory positions are summarized. Whilst the EC is currently preparing legislation to control exposures to pregnant and nursing mothers, equal attention is required for similar hazards to males.

More than 1000 references guide the reader to the current international literature. Physicians, epidemiologists, toxicologists, chemists, and biologists in academia, industry, government and UN agencies will find in this book an invaluable survey of modern thinking on reproductive toxicology.

**Date of Information:**
**February, 1994**

**VCH, P.O. Box 10 11 61,**
**D-69451 Weinheim,**
**Telefax +49 (0) 62 01 - 60 61 84**

VCH

# Ecotoxicology Monitoring

**edited by Mervyn Richardson**

1993. XXV, 384 pages with 66 figures and 63 tables.
Hardcover. DM 192.-/öS 1498.-/sFr 180.-.
ISBN 3-527-28560-1

A pragmatic sourcebook for everyone concerned with hazards to the aquatic environment.

Quick, robust techniques are needed to monitor factory effluent in sewers and rivers. This book compares and contrasts the techniques available - from the simple, rapid Microtox test, to tests based on fish, algae or sophisticated chemical analysis. It also discusses the biochemistry and mechanisms of the biological processes involved.

Moreover the book surveys the current regulatory and legislative positions in Europe and the United States. It is thus a vital reference work for consultants, particularly those involved in World Aid Projects.

Using the monitoring techniques described in this book, readers will be able to identify hazards quickly and undertake pragmatic risk assessments to develop safety measures.

**Date of Information:**
**February, 1994**

**VCH, P.O. Box 10 11 61,**
**D-69451 Weinheim,**
**Telefax +49 (0) 62 01 - 60 61 84**